Dislocations and Mechanical Properties of Crystals

An International Conference held at Lake Placid

SEPTEMBER 6–8, 1956

Sponsored by

AIR FORCE OFFICE OF SCIENTIFIC RESEARCH
AIR RESEARCH AND DEVELOPMENT COMMAND

and

THE GENERAL ELECTRIC RESEARCH LABORATORY

New York · John Wiley & Sons, Inc.
London · Chapman & Hall, Limited

Library of Congress Catalog Card Number: 57-13441
Printed in the United States of America

Foreword

A small international conference on Dislocations and Mechanical Properties of Crystals was held September 6–8, 1956, at the Mirror Lake Inn, Lake Placid, New York. It was initiated during the summer of 1955 at the Bristol Conference on Dislocations in Solids by N. F. Mott and J. H. Hollomon, who recognized the need for a conference on the mechanical aspects of dislocations. I was asked to make the arrangements, and proceeded to do so with the considerable help of several groups of people whose joint efforts have made the conference a success.

The U. S. Air Force Office of Scientific Research, Air Research and Development Command, who wish to encourage the exchange of scientific knowledge of this type, provided valuable and welcome sponsorship. They made available travel and living expenses for all conferees, without which assistance many overseas conferees could not have attended. This organization and its representative, C. F. Yost, have the hearty thanks of all who participated in the conference. The General Electric Research Laboratory also provided valuable sponsorship, supplying personnel and facilities for the mechanics of conducting and recording the proceedings, and funds for entertainment and for preparing the conference records.

A small closed conference was settled upon to insure the maximum degree of informality, even though it was recognized that not all qualified men could receive invitations. The difficult task of selecting conference participants was undertaken by J. H. Hollomon, N. F. Mott, and W. Shockley. I am grateful for their efforts, and for the wide acceptance of their judgment.

Most of the work of editing the conference report has been done by W. G. Johnston, R. Thomson, and T. Vreeland, Jr. Of these three, W. G. Johnston has carried a major portion of this work in assembling the manuscript and working with the publisher.

The conferees themselves, of course, had most of all to do with the success of the conference. The editors appreciate their co-operation in processing manuscripts and discussion.

The work schedule of the conference was patterned after that of the A.A.A.S. Gordon Research Conferences. A three-hour session was held each morning and each evening; the afternoon was free for recreation and informal discussions. Although the general theme of the conference was set in advance, each conferee tended to emphasize his own most interesting work. As a result, the conference covered much of the recent work on dislocations in crystals, some of which was only tenuously related to mechanical properties.

The entire conference proceedings were recorded. If a man provided a manuscript, it is included in this book. If he did not, a summary of his remarks, prepared by the editors and corrected by him, is included. The printed discussion that follows most of the contributions is, with few exceptions, an edited version of the oral discussion that took place at the conference. Some of these discussions make additional contributions to the subject matter of the papers; others point to a lack of understanding in the field, or a lack of agreement among the conferees. In all instances it was considered worthwhile to report the discussion in some detail. A few comments were submitted in writing upon reflection after the conference, and these are presented in the discussions as *written* comments, to distinguish them from the oral discussions which took place in the heat of battle.

Perhaps the most striking contribution to the conference dealt with the *observation* of dislocations, which formed the subject of the first morning's discussion. Photographs of dislocations, slip-band formation, Frank-Read sources, prismatic dislocations, and even motion pictures of dislocation motion, were shown. Here was remarkable and breath-taking confirmation of much previous theoretical work, and a wealth of new experimental material which has given the experimentalist a period of supremacy.

As a final word, I should point out that the impact of the conference already has reached far beyond the small group that was present at Lake Placid. The average overseas conferee remained in this country several months, visiting friends and colleagues in many laboratories. Through the hundreds of personal contacts thus formed or renewed, important results of the conference received prompt and widespread dissemination as a part of more general exchanges of information that were of great value to all concerned.

JOHN C. FISHER

Schenectady, N. Y.
October 7, 1957

List of Conferees

S. Amelinckx	*University of Ghent, Ghent, Belgium*
C. S. Barrett	*Institute for the Study of Metals, University of Chicago, Chicago, Illinois*
F. E. Binns	*U. S. Air Force, Office of Scientific Research, Washington, D. C.*
T. H. Blewitt	*Oak Ridge National Laboratory, Oak Ridge, Tennessee*
W. Boas	*University of Melbourne, Melbourne, Australia*
B. Chalmers	*Harvard University, Cambridge, Massachusetts*
A. H. Cottrell	*Atomic Energy Research Establishment, Harwell, England*
P. H. Egli	*U. S. Naval Research Laboratory, Washington, D. C.*
J. D. Eshelby	*University of Birmingham, Birmingham, England*
J. C. Fisher	*General Electric Research Laboratory, Schenectady, New York*
F. C. Frank	*University of Bristol, Bristol, England*
J. Friedel	*Centre de Recherches Métallurgiques de L'École Nationale Superieure des Mines, Paris, France*
J. J. Gilman	*General Electric Research Laboratory, Schenectady, New York*

W. R. Gruner	*U. S. Office of Naval Research, Washington, D. C.*
E. W. Hart	*General Electric Research Laboratory, Schenectady, New York*
P. B. Hirsch	*University of Cambridge, Cambridge, England*
J. H. Hollomon	*General Electric Research Laboratory, Schenectady, New York*
R. W. K. Honeycombe	*University of Sheffield, Sheffield, England*
W. G. Johnston	*General Electric Research Laboratory, Schenectady, New York*
J. S. Koehler	*University of Illinois, Urbana, Illinois*
G. Leibfried	*University of Göttingen, Göttingen, Germany*
W. M. Lomer	*Atomic Energy Research Establishment, Harwell, England*
J. R. Low, Jr.	*General Electric Research Laboratory, Schenectady, New York*
K. Lücke	*Brown University, Providence, Rhode Island*
E. S. Machlin	*Columbia University, New York, New York*
J. W. Mitchell	*University of Bristol, Bristol, England*
N. F. Mott	*University of Cambridge, Cambridge, England*
F. R. N. Nabarro	*University of the Witwatersrand, Johannesburg, South Africa*
E. R. Parker	*University of California, Berkeley, California*
W. T. Read, Jr.	*Bell Telephone Laboratories, Murray Hill, New Jersey*
A. Seeger	*Max Planck Institut für Metallforschung, Stuttgart, Germany*
F. Seitz	*University of Illinois, Urbana, Illinois*
W. Shockley	*Shockley Semiconductor Laboratory, Beckman Instruments, Inc., Mountain View, California*
H. Suzuki	*Research Institute for Iron, Steel, and Other Metals, Tohoku University, Sendai, Japan*
T. Suzuki *	*University of Illinois, Urbana, Illinois*
R. Thomson	*University of Illinois, Urbana, Illinois*
T. Vreeland, Jr.	*California Institute of Technology, Pasadena, California*
N. J. Wadsworth	*Royal Aircraft Establishment, Farnborough, England*
J. Washburn	*University of California, Berkeley, California*
D. S. Wood	*California Institute of Technology, Pasadena, California*
C. F. Yost	*U. S. Air Force Office of Scientific Research, Washington, D. C.*

* On leave from the Research Institute for Iron, Steel, and Other Metals, Tohoku University, Sendai, Japan.

Contents

I Direct Observations of Dislocations

THE DIRECT OBSERVATION OF DISLOCATION PATTERNS IN TRANSPARENT CRYSTALS
S. Amelinckx 3

A SLIP SOURCE IN KCl
S. Amelinckx and W. Maenhout-Van der Vorst 55

THE OBSERVATION OF DISLOCATIONS IN SILICON
W. C. Dash 57

DISLOCATIONS IN CRYSTALS OF SILVER HALIDES
J. W. Mitchell 69

DIRECT OBSERVATIONS OF THE ARRANGEMENT AND MOTION OF DISLOCATIONS IN ALUMINUM
P. B. Hirsch, R. W. Horne, and M. J. Whelan 92

THE ORIGIN AND GROWTH OF GLIDE BANDS IN LITHIUM FLUORIDE CRYSTALS
John J. Gilman and William G. Johnston 116

Thermal Etching of Dislocations in Silver
E. S. Machlin 164

The Thermal Etching of Dislocations
Hideji Suzuki 172

II Deformation of Pure Single Crystals

Low-Temperature Deformation of Copper Single Crystals
T. H. Blewitt, R. R. Coltman, and J. K. Redman 179

Observations on Slip in Aluminum
T. S. Noggle and J. S. Koehler 208

Surface Sources and Plastic Flow in KCl Crystals
Taira Suzuki 215

Experimental Indications of Surface Sources
B. Chalmers and R. S. Davis 232

Deformation of NaCl Crystals
F. R. N. Nabarro 235

The Effect of Pressure on the Plastic Deformation of Ni and Al
C. S. Barrett 238

III Work Hardening and Recovery

The Mechanism of Glide and Work Hardening in Face-Centered Cubic and Hexagonal Close-Packed Metals
Alfred Seeger 243

Regarding Seeger's Paper on Work Hardening
Jacques Friedel 330

Lattice Defects in Plastically Deformed Metals
W. Boas 333

Stored Energy and Resistivity Changes in Cold-Worked Metals
Alfred Seeger 347

Effect of Impurities on Dislocation Climb
N. F. Mott 350

The Nature and Effect of Substructure in Polycrystalline Aluminum
C. J. Ball 353

IV Alloy Crystals, Impurities, Yield Point Phenomena

The Yield Strength of Binary Alloys
Hideji Suzuki 361

The Deformation of Alloy Single Crystals
J. Garstone and R. W. K. Honeycombe 391

Color Change in Metals upon Plastic Deformation
W. Boas 406

The Diffusion of Copper in Germanium
F. C. Frank 408

A Comparison of Preyield Microstrain in Steel with Dislocation Theory
D. S. Wood 413

Yield Points in Al and Ni Single Crystals
C. S. Barrett 419

V Dislocation Damping and Fatigue

Internal Friction Phenomena due to Dislocations
Kurt Lücke and Andrew Granato 425

The Behavior of Metals Under Reversed Stresses
N. F. Mott 458

Energy Dissipation During Fatigue Tests
N. J. Wadsworth 479

VI Theory of Dislocations

Thermal Motion of Dislocation Lines
G. Leibfried 495

Some Effects of the Nonlinearity of Elastic Laws in the Environment of a Dislocation Line
Alfred Seeger 504

The Intersection of Gliding Screw Dislocations
A. H. Cottrell 509

PRISMATIC LOOPS AS FRANK-READ SOURCES
J. C. Fisher 513

VII Whiskers and Thin Crystals

THE THEORY OF WHISKER DEKINKING
F. R. N. Nabarro 521

DEFORMATION AND FRACTURE OF SILICON
W. T. Read, Jr., and G. L. Pearson 537

X-RAY EXPERIMENTS ON TIN WHISKERS
Peter B. Hirsch 545

DEFORMATION OF THIN METAL CRYSTALS
H. Suzuki, S. Ikeda, and S. Takeuchi 548

VIII Radiation Damage

ON THE FORMATION OF CAVITIES ALONG DISLOCATIONS
P. Coulomb and J. Friedel 555

ON RADIATION AND QUENCH HARDENING IN METALS
A. H. Cottrell 577

LOCALIZED RADIATION DAMAGE AS A MEANS OF STUDYING VACANCIES AND INTERSTITIALS
William Shockley 581

THE THERMAL ANNEALING OF IMPERFECTIONS IN THE NOBLE METALS
J. S. Koehler, J. W. Henderson, and J. H. Bredt 587

MECHANISM OF ANNEALING IN NEUTRON-IRRADIATED METALS
T. H. Blewitt, R. R. Coltman, D. K. Holmes, and T. S. Noggle 603

Index of Contributors 625

Subject Index 627

I DIRECT OBSERVATIONS OF DISLOCATIONS

The Direct Observation of Dislocation Patterns in Transparent Crystals

S. AMELINCKX

Laboratorium voor Kristalkunde
Geologisch Instituut
Rijks Universiteit
Ghent, Belgium

ABSTRACT

Methods which allow the direct microscopic observation of dislocation lines are described and the "decoration" mechanism is discussed in this paper. The crystallography of the precipitated particles is considered. The method is applied to the study of the geometry of dislocation patterns in deformed and annealed sodium chloride single crystals. Attention is focused on dislocation nets and singularities in the patterns are analyzed in terms of Burgers vectors. Direct evidence for the climb of single dislocations and of networks is presented. Visual illustration for the pinning of dislocations by precipitates as well as by immobile dislocations is obtained.

---

1. INTRODUCTION

The procedure which consists in making dislocation lines directly accessible to microscopic observation by some decoration process is evidently a powerful method for the study of their geometry. It is clearly necessary to make use of some phenomenon which produces visible particles along the dislocation lines. Hedges and Mitchell (1953) utilized the photographic print-out effect in silver bromide, as a consequence of which colloidal silver segregates along the dislocation lines. This method, however, is restricted to silver bromide or in any case to the silver halides. In a previous paper (Amelinckx, 1956) we described a method of decorating dislocations in sodium chloride, based on additive coloration by means of sodium metal. This method has since been extended to other crystals. We will summarize further some other procedures which were used in this laboratory.

Precipitation of impurities ($CaCl_2$ and $BaCl_2$) as a consequence of Cottrell interaction was tried for NaCl too but proved to be inferior in resolving power to the other methods (Amelinckx, Van der Vorst, Gevers, and Dekeyser, 1955). The same principle has, however, recently been used with considerable success to make visible dislocation lines in silicon by the precipitation of copper (Dash, 1956).

The geometry of dislocation nets in crystals of the NaCl type has been discussed from a theoretical point of view by Frank (1955) and for face-centered cubic crystals by Suzuki and Suzuki (1954). A detailed discussion of observable complexities in dislocation nets has been given by the author (1956).

This paper will be concerned with the decoration mechanism as well as with the observations concerning the geometry of dislocations. Some of the results discussed here have already been reported earlier (Amelinckx, 1956).

2. DECORATION METHODS

The method used in the present investigation is a slightly modified form of the method employed earlier by Rexer (1932) to produce additive coloration. A stock of metallic sodium is enclosed in a cavity made in the crystal. The cavity is closed with the initially cleaved-off part so that cleavage steps on both parts match exactly in order to assure the maximum of tightness. The whole is mounted in a steel jig (see Fig. 1) and heated to about 750°C until a sufficiently well-developed zone of coloration is visible. In the case of "pure" NaCl, it is necessary to cool rapidly to room temperature (in about 15 min) in order to obtain decoration by means of colloidal particles. When decoration is optimum the crystals are blue in transmission; the decoration is satisfactory in the whole diffusion zone, but best near to the sodium stock.

In crystals containing small amounts of silver (0.01% to 0.001% addition to the melt) one can cool very slowly to room temperature. The color of the diffusion zone differs slightly from crystal to crystal; it goes from yellow to ruby red. Decoration is now optimum along the surface of the diffusion zone; in front of this surface needle-shaped precipitates are usually observed. These are oriented with respect to the matrix in the [110] directions.

A simpler decoration method has since been found by Van der Vorst and Dekeyser (1956). They use NaCl which is heavily doped in AgCl (1% to 3% addition to the melt) and anneal in a stream of hydrogen at a temperature between 600 and 700°C during some 12 hr. Decoration is then obtained in the region immediately under the surface; the depth of this region depends on the annealing time. It was found that annealing in sodium vapor also produces decoration in these heavily doped specimens. These methods can also be applied in the case of KCl, and it is to be expected that they are of general application to all the alkali halides.

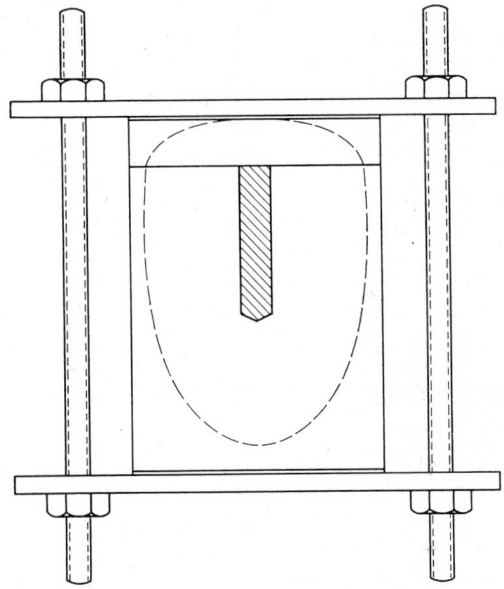

Fig. 1. Specimen in specimen holder.

Bontinck and Dekeyser (1956) have found that all the methods mentioned here are also successful in decorating dislocation lines in natural and synthetic CaF_2 (obtained from the Harshaw Chemical Co.). They used additive coloration by means of calcium and sodium in the way described here for NaCl, as well as annealing in hydrogen. The decoration mechanism has been discussed in more detail by Amelinckx, Bontinck, Dekeyser, and Seitz (1957).

3. NATURE OF THE DECORATING PARTICLES

In our previous paper (1956) we discussed the nature of the decorating particles and we considered several possibilities. Since Boesman,

Remaut, and Dekeyser (1956) found that the formation of a colored diffusion zone and visible specks was strongly dependent upon the presence of impurities, we re-examined the matter. We shall now summarize the results of these additional experiments.

1. In pure crystals which were air-quenched when a diffusion zone had developed, it was found that the decoration of the dislocation lines is due to colloidal sodium. This was verified in a simple way by dissolving the crystal in water under the microscope. The colloidal particles dissolve, react with water, and produce small bubbles, evidently hydrogen.

2. In crystals containing small amounts of silver ions (0.01% to 0.001% addition of AgCl to the melt) the described procedure will produce visible colloidal particles in the neighborhood of the diffusion surface, which are not soluble in water. They are soluble in dilute nitric acid, and are most probably metallic silver. It was found that in very heavily colored specimens the region in the neighborhood of the sodium stock contained sodium particles too. The needle-shaped precipitates formed in front of the diffusion surface were also found to be silver. The size of the silver particles diminishes gradually as one goes from the diffusion surface inward into the diffusion zone; there is as a consequence a zone where decoration is optimum. The silver colloids are very stable. Whereas colloidal sodium "evaporates" above 400°C, the silver colloids withstand heating to near the melting point of NaCl. Most of the photographs used to illustrate dislocation patterns were obtained from specimens treated in this way.

4. MECHANISM OF PRECIPITATION

We will now discuss in somewhat more detail than in our 1956 paper the mechanism whereby specks of metal are formed along the dislocation lines. We will conveniently distinguish two cases: (1) the formation of sodium specks in pure crystals; (2) the precipitation of silver in AgCl doped crystals.

A. Sodium Specks in Pure Crystals

One could consider the decoration process as a simple diffusion of sodium along dislocation lines. As shown by Seitz (1954), an edge dislocation in crystals of the type considered here contains two supplementary half planes, and one has to expect a fairly wide open core (Huntington, Dickey, and Thomson, 1955) along which diffusion could proceed rapidly. Against this explanation is the well-known fact that when cooling very rapidly, dispersed F-centers can be obtained which will coagulate to larger units on subsequent annealing at moderate temperature and which will finally grow to colloids. Also, the fact that pure screws decorate much less well or sometimes not at all would be difficult to explain on this basis (see § 6.I). We therefore feel that the diffusion of the excess sodium takes place as F-center diffusion.

The sequence of events during warming up and cooling down the specimen is then probably as follows: When heating the crystal to a sufficiently high temperature, vacancies of both kinds are produced at the dislocation (and eventually at voids or surfaces of any kind), making it climb by addition. The two extra half planes of the edge dislocation have to lengthen simultaneously to maintain the charge balance. Vacancies of both kinds will then be produced in equal numbers. During cooling, on the other hand, vacancies condense again at dislocations and the phenomenon is reversible in the sense that the same amount of material which was deposited at the dislocations will evaporate again. The material may, however, be distributed in a different way and as a consequence the dislocation pattern may change.

During additive coloring this sequence of events is somewhat modified. The sodium vacancies diffusing most rapidly will move to the sodium stock, where they die. The halogen vacancies, being less mobile, will remain in the crystal, eventually in the neighborhood of the dislocations; moreover, they are not accepted by the sodium stock, which on the contrary will try to send in Cl-vacancies. The latter will be converted at least partly to F-centers by capturing electrons sent in by the sodium metal every time a sodium vacancy dies, maintaining in such a way equal numbers of vacancies of both kinds as well as charge equilibrium. F-centers will thus be formed continuously at the expense of Cl-vacancies as long as the temperature of the sodium stock is sufficiently high to ionize sodium. At the same time F-centers will die and become halogen vacancies by loss of their electron or by going to a dislocation line. At a given pressure of sodium vapor a given concentration of F-centers is in equilibrium. This is the situation at high temperature. When quenching sufficiently rapidly this state of affairs can be frozen in, and dispersed F-centers will be found.

Cooling less rapidly will allow the formation of aggregates, e.g., M-centers (Seitz, 1954). We will reason on F-centers only, although the formation of small aggregates may be of importance to explain the mobility of the F-centers incorporated in these units.

During cooling the crystal becomes supersaturated in F-centers (and vacancies); these will have to condense, and in principle they can do this either by formation of a sodium speck in the bulk of the crystal or by going to a dislocation line. As the first procedure is evidently more difficult than the second, the latter will happen preferentially. The *F*-centers are, moreover, attracted to the dislocation by elastic interaction.

The arrival at a jog of an *F*-center will convert a sodium ion into a sodium atom, will make a halogen place vacant, and will move the jog two ions sideways. The condensation of *F*-centers (and also of vacancies of both kinds) will thus make the dislocation climb again, but in the reverse sense. The climbing process should be reversible if no sodium vacancies have been lost at the sodium stock.

The sequence of events becomes simpler if one considers the arrival of the constituents of the *F*-center separately, the anion vacancy and the electron. Suppose we have a jog consisting of a Na ion; this jog has an effective positive charge of half the electron charge (Seitz, 1954). It will attract an electron and convert, as we said above, the Na ion into a sodium atom. The jog will hereby change sign and be displaced sideways over one ion distance. It will now attract the anion vacancy, which has an effective positive charge. The same sequence of events can repeat indefinitely as new jogs are generated thermally from time to time.

The result will be the formation of a plane lattice of sodium atoms, each sodium atom being separated from its neighbors by vacancies (Cl-vacancies). It is evident that this situation will in fact never be produced. The vacancies in the plane lattice have effectively "lost their name" and they will as a consequence allow an easy rearrangement of Na-atoms, so that these can agglomerate and form colloidal particles; this will occur gradually. The precipitation of the decorating material, i.e., sodium, is as a consequence associated with climb; and, at least in the initial stage, the precipitated material simply constitutes the prolongation of the supplementary half planes of the dislocations. The elastic forces attracting the vacancies or *F*-centers toward the dislocations are not annihilated as a consequence of climb because of the difference in lattice parameter of the host crystal and the precipitated material. The climbed dislocation will continue to attract the precipitating entity toward its new position.

Figure 2 shows the situation schematically. The difference in lattice parameter will be responsible for the existence of a stress field around the edges of the precipitate, similar to the one existing at the end of a supplementary half plane. As a consequence, the precipitating entity will also be attracted toward the edges of the particle, facilitating growth. The process described here implies that a climbed dislocation should leave a trail of particles lying in the climb plane and that pure screw dislocations should not be decorated.

Seitz (private communication) suggested that the process just described could be generalized to other kinds of precipitations.

The foregoing reasoning presupposes that the number of jogs in the dislocation line is sufficiently large at every moment so that the flux of vacancies and F-centers toward the dislocation line can always be absorbed by the jogs. Quantitative estimates by Coulomb and Friedel (see their paper in Part VIII of this volume) present evidence that this may not be the case in a rapid quench. Coulomb and Friedel have

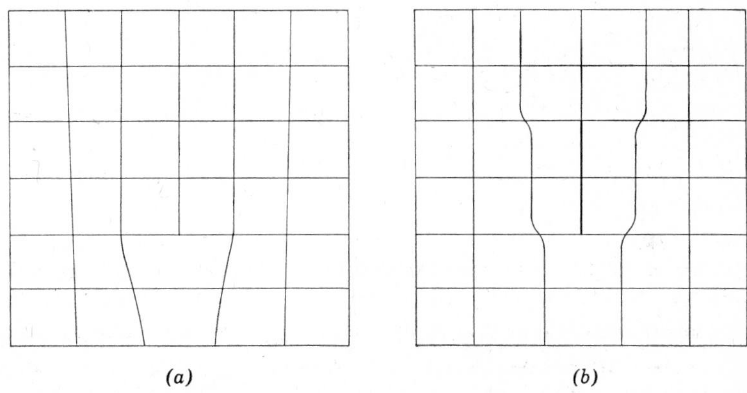

Fig. 2. The precipitation of sodium or silver along an edge dislocation. The precipitate "eats" away part of the supplementary half plane.

shown that in such a case the vacancies will condense into spherical cavities along, or centered on, the dislocation line. It is possible that in view of this evidence the foregoing reasoning has to be modified. One can then consider the precipitation mechanism as follows. The elastic interaction with vacancies being more pronounced than for F-centers, the first stage in the precipitation is probably the formation of cavities, mainly from the condensation of divacancies. Further condensation of F-centers at these cavities will make them grow, and will effectively result in the formation of sodium atoms, which will agglomerate inside the cavity to produce a sodium speck. This last mechanism could evidently also produce precipitation along screw dislocations.

B. Silver Precipitations in Silver Doped Sodium Chloride

The diffusion mechanism of the silver ion in NaCl is not known at present. We can thus only make guesses as to the decoration mechanism.

It is possible, although not very probable, that Ag^+ presents Frenkel disorder at higher temperatures in NaCl, as it does in AgCl. The decoration could then be considered, for simplicity, as proceeding in the following steps.

1. Migration of the interstitial silver toward the dislocations. Both interstitial and vacancy interact elastically with the dislocation, and they do not need another point defect for their migration.
2. Recombination of the interstitial ion and the vacancy at the dislocation, making the silver ion again substitutional.
3. Reduction of Ag^+ to metallic silver by the arrival of F-centers, or separated electrons and vacancies (or more complex centers involving F-centers).
4. Agglomeration of silver to form a speck. The growth of the speck can be considered as the successive attraction of F-centers (or electrons) and Ag^+ towards the speck.

We think, however, that it is more likely that Ag^+ occupies normal Na^+ sites, and presents the same kind of disorder as Na^+ in NaCl, i.e., of the Schottky type. In this case an alternative description can be given in terms of the B-center, described by Etzel and Schulman (1954). The B-center is a unit consisting of a silver ion with an F-center attached to it. When such units condense at the edge dislocation, the result is the formation of a silver atom and a vacant anion place. There is one important point: the presence of cation vacancies is necessary for the diffusion of the B-center. Moreover, the precipitation of silver also needs the arrival of cation vacancies to make room for the silver. It is now evident that in the presence of the sodium stock, which absorbs sodium vacancies, there will be a concentration gradient of sodium vacancies. The largest precipitates would be found at the edge of the diffusion zone where the supply of cation vacancies is largest and the particle size would decrease towards the sodium stock as observed. The condensation of a more complex center, consisting of an F-center, a silver ion, and a cation vacancy would also account for the observed decoration. The process is further quite similar to the one outlined for sodium, and it is also accompanied by climb by subtraction. As the specimens containing silver are cooled very slowly, we may assume that a high supersaturation of vacancies has not been built up near the dislocations, so that it is unlikely that cavities will be formed in this case. When more F-centers are present than can be bound to a silver ion (to form a B-center), these can coagulate separately and form sodium. This is most likely to occur near the sodium stock because the concentration of F-centers is largest there. This explains the presence of sodium particles in that region. It is not clear at present why sodium particles can be stabilized in the presence of silver, after a heat treatment which would evaporate them in the pure crystal.

C. Crystallography of the Silver Precipitation

In some regions in the neighborhood of the diffusion zone the precipitates are larger and they sometimes have a different habit; instead of needles they become truncated square platelets, either trapezoidal or pseudohexagonal. The orientation is such that (111) of NaCl coincides

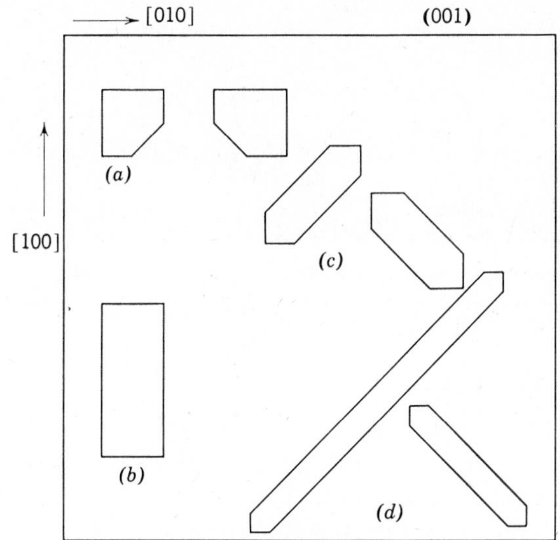

Fig. 3. Crystallography of the precipitation of silver in NaCl. The (111) plane of silver is parallel to the (111) plane of NaCl and the [001] directions are also parallel in both crystals (see also Fig. 4). The plane of the platelets is (111); the drawing shows the projection on (001).

with (111) of silver and that [001] of silver and NaCl are also parallel (Figs. 3 and 4). This is exactly one of the conditions under which oriented overgrowth of silver on sodium chloride takes place (Van der Merwe, 1949). This suggests that the rules governing oriented overgrowth and oriented precipitation should be similar. The needles, Fig. 3*d*, are probably a very elongated form of the pseudohexagons, Fig. 3*c*. It is clear that there is good reason to suppose that the colloidal precipitates have similar orientations and shape, when sufficiently large.

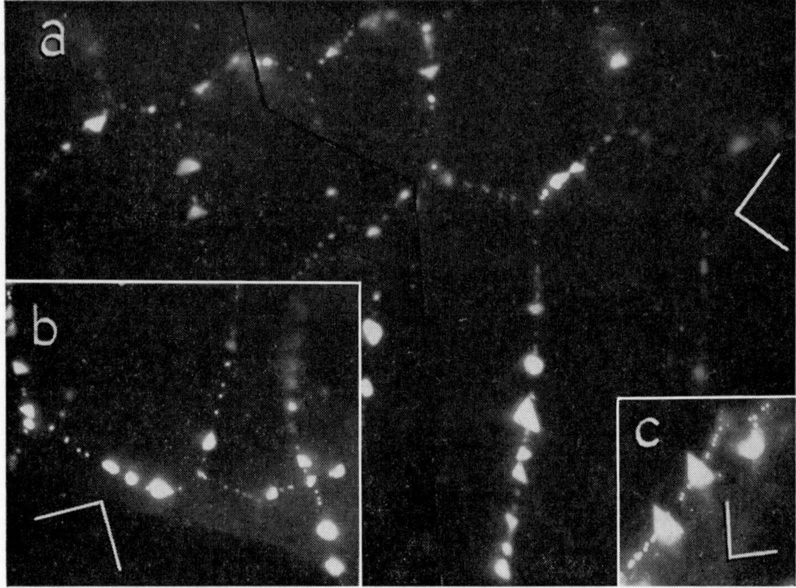

Fig. 4. Large precipitates along coarse network; the shape of the crystals is represented schematically in Fig. 3*a*. The drawn lines are parallel to the cube edge of the host crystal. 1050×.

D. Possible Extension

We would like to point out that, in principle, *V*-centers in additively colored alkali iodides could precipitate much like *F*-centers and could produce, for example, colloidal iodine particles at dislocations. The formation of colloidal iodine in KI, observed by Mollwo (1935, 1937), is probably to be explained in this way.

5. METHODS OF OBSERVATION

The patterns of particles were observed in ultramicroscopic illumination. Unfiltered light from a small mercury arc was focused by means of a suitable set of condenser lenses on the specimen, the direction of incidence being roughly perpendicular of the optical axis of the microscope.

Very thin slices were cleaved from the treated crystals; they were further reduced in thickness by dissolving in water; the ultimate thickness was of the order of $\frac{1}{5}$ mm or less. It is necessary to make such thin slices because otherwise the light diffused by particles which are not in focus is so intense that all contrast is lost. To avoid scattering by surface irregularities, the specimen is imbedded in a liquid having the same index of refraction as NaCl and covered with a thin microscope cover slide. It proved not practical to attempt to bring the plane of a net in the focal plane of the objective, as in general the nets are not even plane. As a consequence we photographed the nets at different depths in such a way that the patterns slightly overlapped. The inclination of a net with respect to the plane of observation [i.e., the cleavage plane (001)] was estimated from the "in-focus" width in the manner described previously (Amelinckx, 1956).

6. RESULTS OF THE OBSERVATIONS

We will now describe some of the patterns formed by the decorating particles. There is, at present, little doubt that they represent dislocation lines. In principle the whole geometry of dislocations can be observed by means of the described methods. There is, however, a practical limitation in the fact that a certain amount of anneal cannot be avoided in order to obtain decoration at all. This delayed up to the present time the study of the Frank-Read sources.

A. Dislocation Nodes

In the NaCl structure three types of nodes are geometrically possible. Assuming the stable dislocations to have a Burgers vector $a/2$ [110] (Frank and Nicholas, 1953), one can have threefold, fourfold, and sixfold nodes. Threefold nodes result when the Burgers vectors enclose angles of 60° or 120°, whereas fourfold nodes can result at the intersection of dislocations having mutually perpendicular Burgers vectors. Sixfold nodes result when three dislocations having coplanar Burgers vectors intersect in one point.

From energy considerations there is some doubt whether the fourfold node will dissociate into two threefold nodes or not. As we actually observed fourfold nodes, even networks containing nearly exclusively fourfold nodes, there seems to be no reason to doubt the stability of fourfold nodes. Sixfold nodes are occasionally observed as singularities in nets; the majority of nodes, however, are threefold. This is to be expected, as for a given dislocation there is but one chance to meet a dislocation having a Burgers vector perpendicular to its own one, whereas there are four chances to find one that forms an angle of 60° or 120°. As far as could be seen, all nodes are very nearly planar. In analyzing nets we accepted the occurrence of a fourfold node as an indication that the Burgers vectors of the intersecting lines are mutually perpendicular.

B. Dislocation Nets

Theory predicts three kinds of regular nets, consisting respectively of threefold, fourfold, and sixfold nodes. The first possibility leads to a hexagonal net, the second to a square one, and the third to a triangular one. In practice, only the two first possibilities will occur because these can be formed from two basic sets of dislocations, whereas the third needs three sets. Subboundaries in as-grown crystals have usually too large orientation differences to give well-resolved nets.

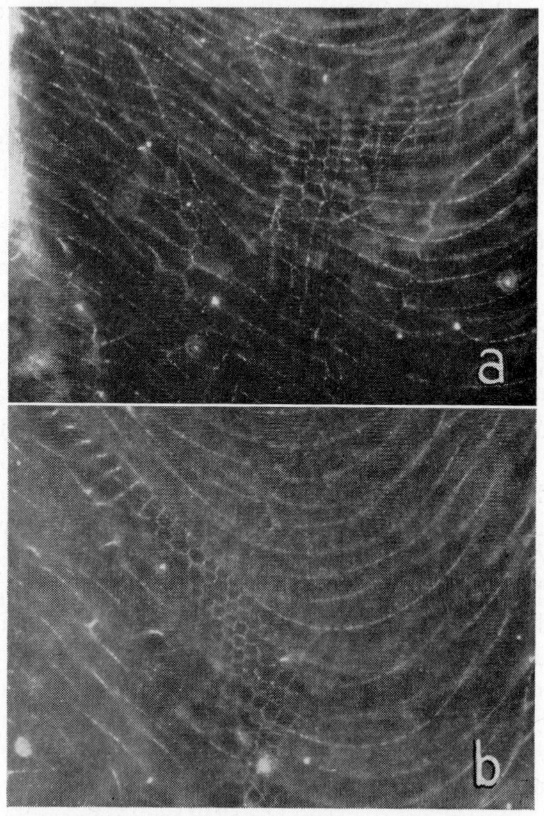

Fig. 5. Dislocation lines in crystals which were not annealed before decoration. The building up of nets out of curved dislocations from slip sources is visible. 500×.

The nets we studied were induced in the crystal by deformation under compression followed by anneal. In some cases the generating sets of dislocations can be recognized, as the net clearly consists of two intersecting sets of parallel curves, evidently dislocation loops from different sources (see, e.g., Figs. 5*a*, *b*, 6*a*, 7*a*). To obtain singularities in nets, the crystals were compressed following two directions to insure deformation on several glide systems; this was checked in polarized light. It was found that in the neighborhood of the free surface the network coarsens, evidently by the loss of dislocations at the surface.

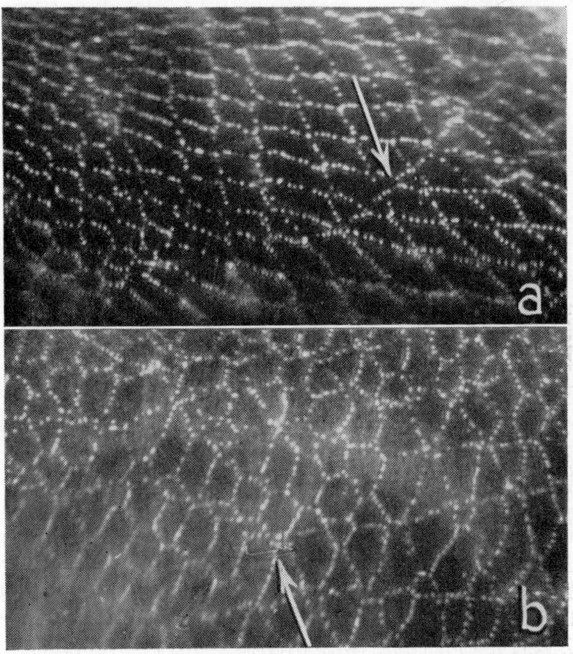

Fig. 6. (*a*) Singularity analyzed in Fig. 14*d*. 630×. (*b*) Singularity referred to in Fig. 14*a*. 800×.

Hexagonal nets. According to theory (Frank, 1955), the plane in which the perfectly hexagonal net should lie is the (111) plane and the rotation axis the [111] axis, all dislocations being pure screws. A change of the contact plane would change the shape of the meshes. We observed networks consisting of meshes of all possible shapes, ranging from the perfectly hexagonal shape to a very elongated and a very flattened one. Figure 8 gives examples of these different possibilities. There did not seem to be an evident relation between the shape of the meshes and the plane of the net. Not all the meshes of the same net were of the same shape, even though all were hexagonal. The reason for this apparent contradiction with theory is the fact that the dislocations, while building up the net during anneal, are subject to so many constraints that these become primary factors determining the shape of the individual meshes. The nets are not free to adopt the shape and position of minimum energy because they are bound to others building up the cellular structure of the polygonized crystal.

The perfectly hexagonal nets extending over an appreciable area are relatively rare. Most of them contain foreign dislocations; this intro-

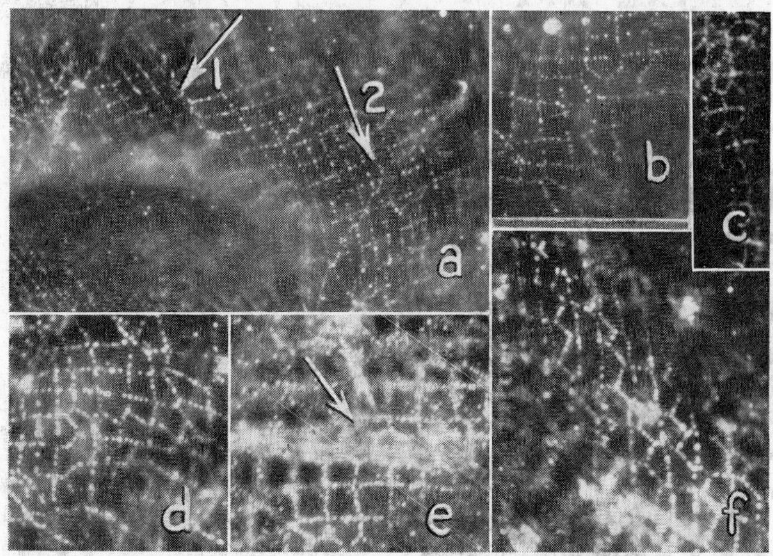

Fig. 7. Complexities in square nets. (*a*) Zigzag lines which result from the introduction of a singular line according to the scheme of Figs. 19 and 21. 500×. (*b*) Zigzag line bending over 90°. 650×. (*c*) Regular succession of zigzag lines. 650×. (*d*) Zigzag lines bending twice over 90°. 700×. (*e*) Two adjacent zigzag lines building a row of hexagons. 600×. (*f*) Zigzag lines jogging from one row of squares to the next. 700×.

duces certain singularities into the perfectly hexagonal pattern. By "foreign" dislocation we understand a dislocation with a Burgers vector which is different from the Burgers vector of the generating set of dislocations, or which had initially a different orientation so that it played a singular role in the formation of the net. The frequency with which such singular dislocations are found shows that a dislocation net exerts a pull on dislocations in its neighborhood, trying to build up a net with a higher angle of misorientation.

The same consideration that was used by Dunn and Daniels (1951) to explain the growth of domains during polygonization applies. The energy of a boundary with an angle of twist $\theta_1 + \theta_2$ is smaller than the sum of the energies of two twist boundaries respectively with angle θ_1 and θ_2.

We will now describe some of the observed patterns with special attention to these singularities. Previously (Amelinckx, 1956) we discussed from a theoretical point of view examples of complexities which were to be expected. Some of them have since been observed and will

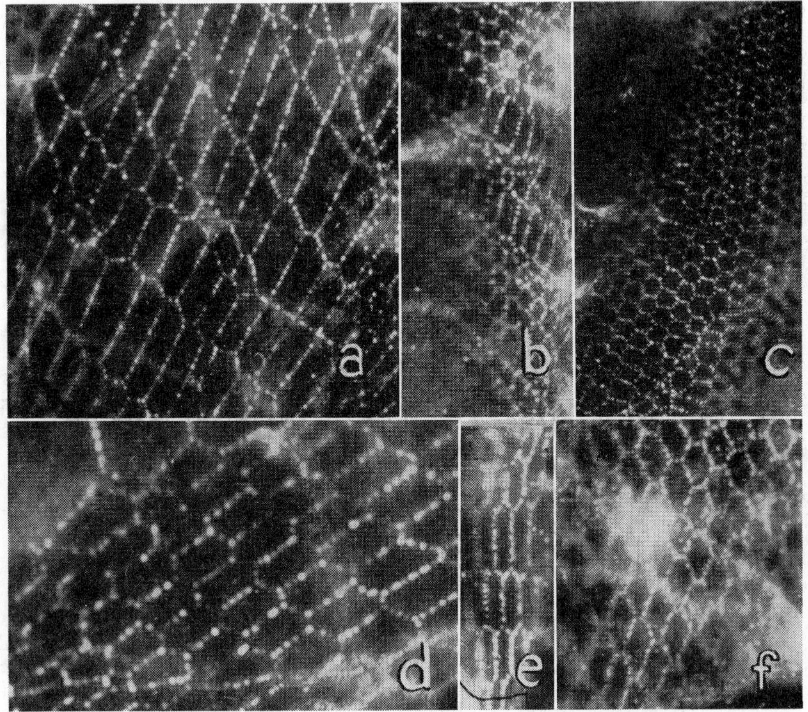

Fig. 8. Hexagonal networks exhibiting differently shaped meshes. (*a*) The network contains two singularities of which one is analyzed in Fig. 17. 600×. (*b*) Set of elongated hexagons in normal net. This is believed to be an example of the singularity described in Fig. 3*b* of the paper by Amelinckx (1956). 700×. (*c*) The nets contain a singularity of the same type as shown in Fig. 10. 600×. (*d*), (*e*), and (*f*) Differently shaped meshes (resp. 760×, 550×, 600×).

be discussed here; others require some further analysis. To summarize the result of the analysis we use the same procedure as Frank (1955) who adopted Thompson's notation (Thompson, 1953) for Burgers vectors in a face-centered cubic lattice.

The Singular Dislocation Cuts Only One Set of Lines. Figure 9 shows a hexagonal net; a singular line is indicated by means of an arrow. In its upper part this line cuts at right angles a number of dislocation lines of the same set, forming fourfold nodes with them. At some places the line is jogged as it jumps from one row of hexagons to the next (arrow 1). Finally at the point marked 2 it bends over about 60° and cuts another set of lines, but no longer at right angles. Oblique sections are formed, and a new row of hexagons results. When

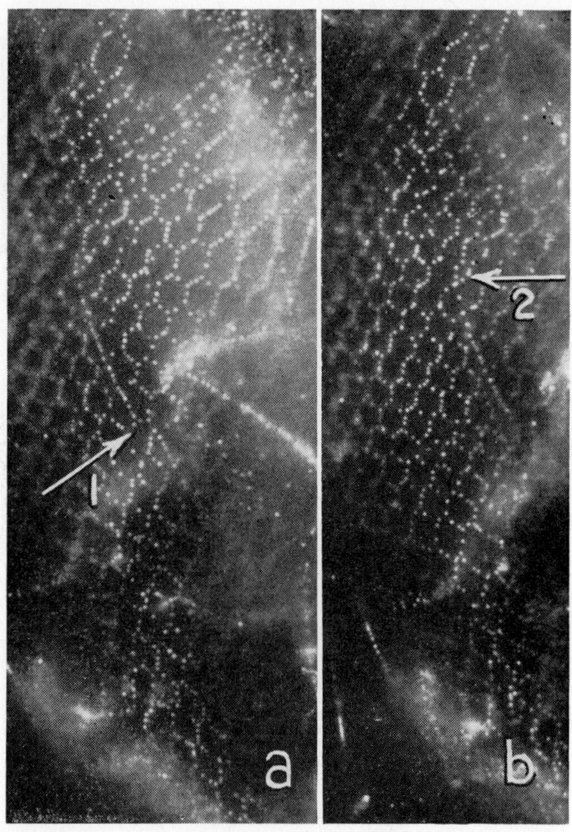

Fig. 9. Hexagonal net. Notice the singularities indicated by arrows 1 and 2 and analyzed in Fig. 10. The decoration is strongly dependent on the orientation of the lines. 800×.

we accept the fact that two dislocation lines cut at right angles without visible interaction, as a criterion that they have mutually perpendicular Burgers vector we get the lettering of Fig. 10. It is now evident that after being bent over 60° the singular line cuts dislocations of which the Burgers vector forms an angle of 60° (or 120°) with its own Burgers vector. Visible interaction and the formation of a row of meshes result. From the lettering it is evident that we have here an example of the first complication described by Frank (1955) (his Fig. 8), and

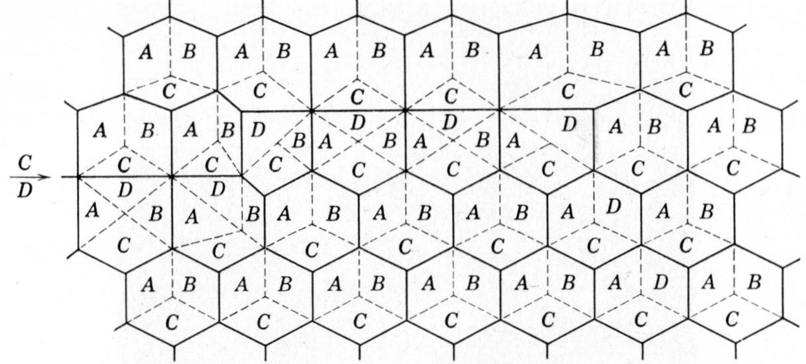

Fig. 10. Lettering pattern corresponding to the net of Fig. 9.

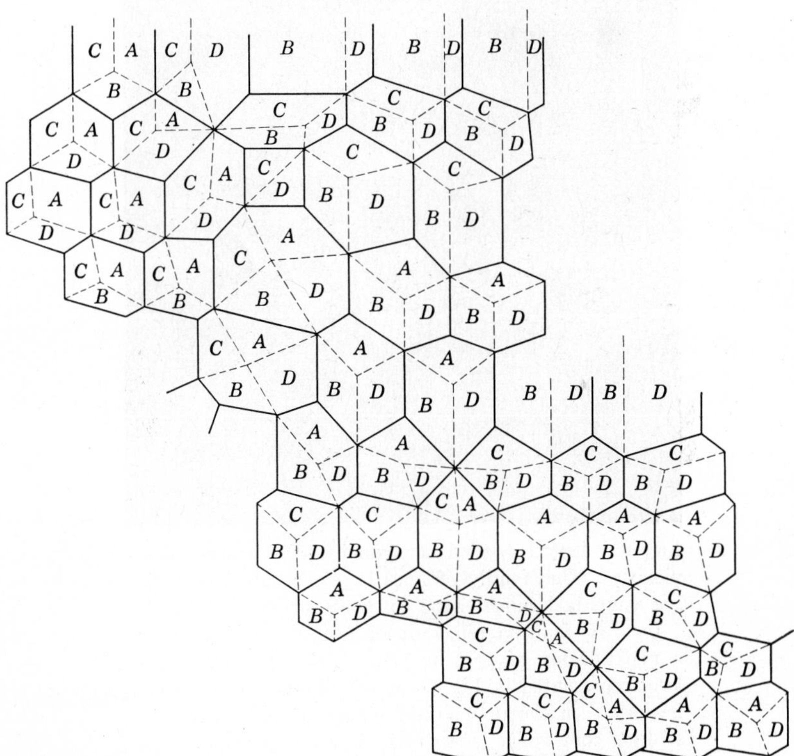

Fig. 11. Lettering pattern of part of the complicated net shown on the sequence of Fig. 12.

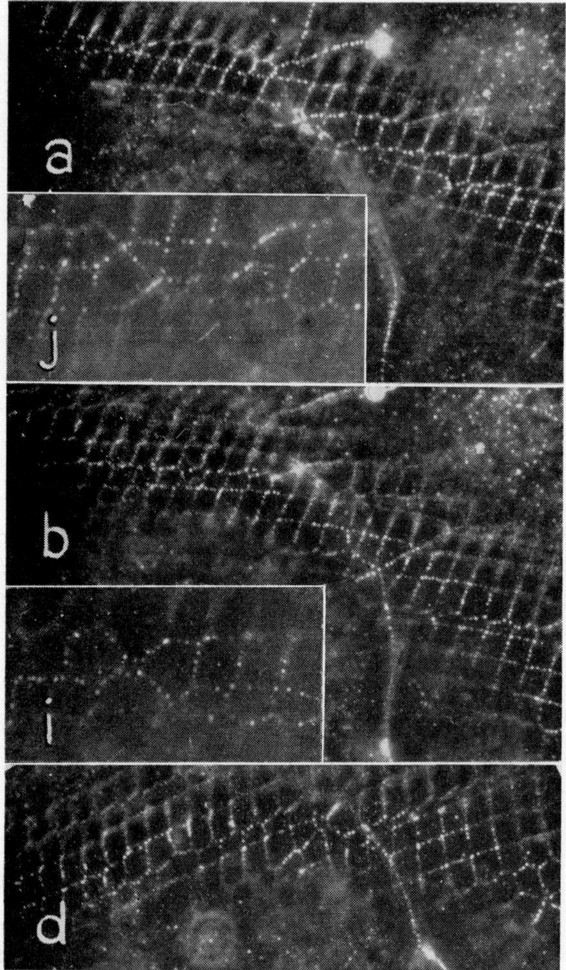

Fig. 12. Very extended hexagonal net with many complexities. One family of lines is poorly developed, giving a nearly lozenge shape to many meshes. 650×.

Inset (*i*) is a magnification of part of (*g*); inset (*j*) is a magnificaion of part of (*e*). A singular line of the kind represented in Fig. 3*c* of our previous work (1956) is present in the upper right corner of (*b*). The most striking complexity is the little square mesh of inset (*i*). The lettering for an important part of the net is given in Fig. 11.

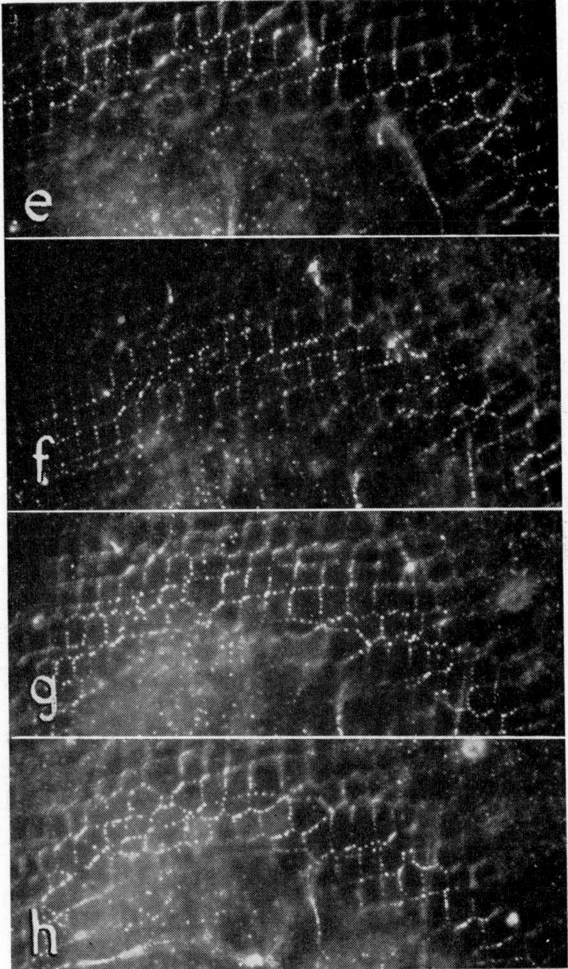

Fig. 12 (continued).

which consists in formally changing the lettering of one row of lozenge-shaped fields in a hexagonal network. This operation does not lead to an observable effect on the pattern, unless, as in the case just described, the dislocation changes its orientation.

When we introduce in one of the generating sets of dislocation lines of the net a dislocation with the same Burgers vector as the dislocations of the other set, it has been shown that a row of elongated hexagons should result (Amelinckx, 1956, Fig. 3*b*). Figure 8*b* gives an example illustrating this complexity.

The third kind of singularity which can result from the introduction of a foreign dislocation into the set of generating dislocations was discussed in our paper (1956) as Fig. 3*c*. Examples have now been observed: see Fig. 12*b* and *g* as well as the lettering of Fig. 11.

THE SINGULAR DISLOCATION CUTS TWO SETS OF LINES. Figure 6*b* shows a net consisting of three different sets of dislocations; the generating sets produced elongated hexagonal meshes. The singular lines are parallel to the short section of the hexagons and cut, as a consequence, both generating sets; at every intersection oblique sections are formed as shown more clearly in Fig. 13*a*. The lettering given corresponds to the generating sets *CA* and *BA* and a singular line *CB*. It will be clear that the lettering is the same in all meshes; the final equilibrium shape would as a consequence be again the perfectly hexagonal net. We can now generalize these considerations somewhat. We can assume all possible Burgers vectors for the singular dislocation. The case where the singular dislocation has vector *DA* is remarkable; it is shown in 13*b*: meshes with five and seven sides result. When the Burgers vector is perpendicular to the Burgers vector of one of the lines of the generating sets, fourfold nodes result. Two cases respectively assuming *DB* or *BD* as Burgers vectors for the singular dislocation are shown on Fig. 13*c* and *d*. Figure 13*d* can be compared directly with Fig. 6*a*. In this last case the analysis could be made unambiguously as a consequence of the fact that the singular dislocation bends over about 90° and it is taken up into the net in such a way that a new row of hexagons results. When the singular dislocation has *BC* as Burgers vector, the net remains completely hexagonal, apart from the fact that two rows of more elongated hexagons would result.

Coincidently the singular dislocation line may pass through the point of intersection of two dislocations of the generating sets: when it has a suitable Burgers vector a sixfold node (Fig. 13*a*) may result, as is visible in Fig. 14*c*. This sixfold node is not the same as the singularity termed "star" by Frank. The probability of observing this last kind of feature is small as it necessitates the intersection of three singular dislocation lines in one point.

SINGULAR LINE INTERSECTS ALL SIDES OF THE HEXAGONS. We will not consider this case as the analysis is a combination of results obtained in the two foregoing sections.

TWO INTERSECTING SINGULAR LINES. A number of possible cases were examined earlier (Amelinckx, 1956) from a theoretical point of view but no observed examples could be offered at that time. We have now obtained evidence for the cases shown in Figs. 4*c* and 5*a*

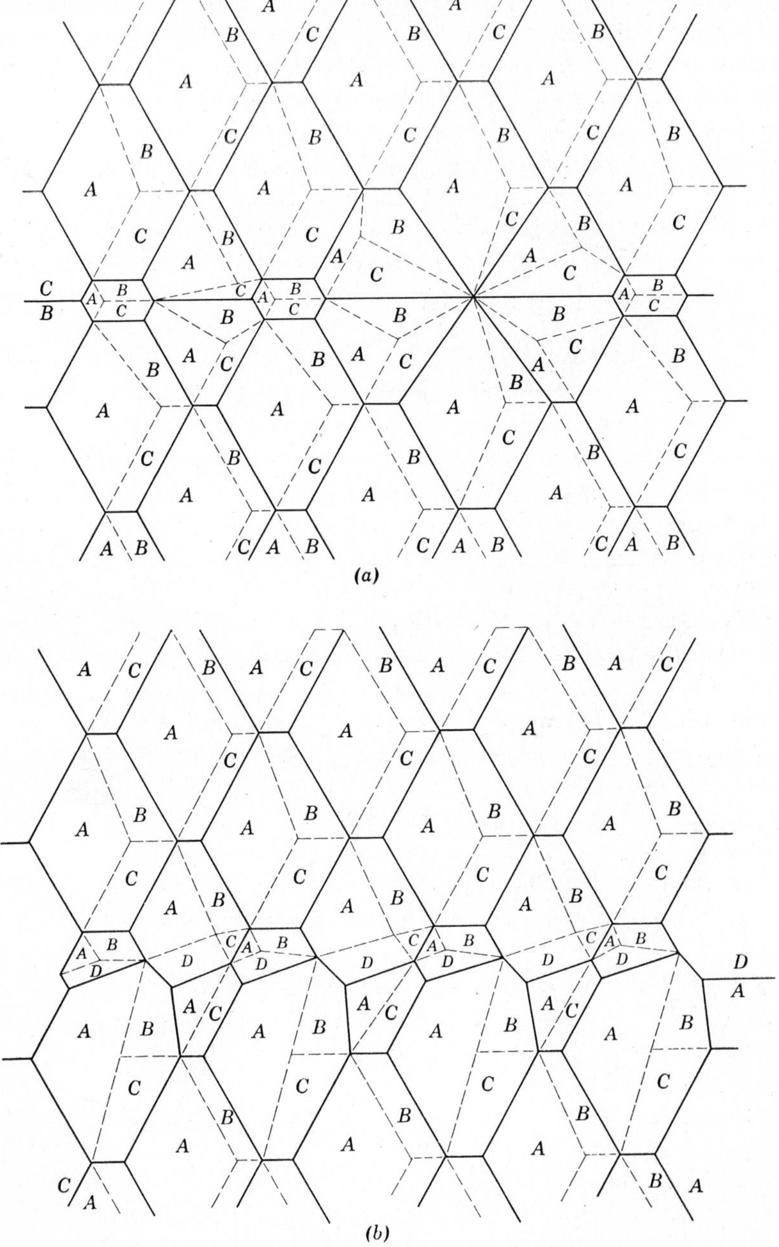

Fig. 13. (*a*) Lettering pattern of singularity visible on Figs. 6*b* and 14. The singular dislocation *CB* cuts the two generating sets *CA* and BA. (*b*) The singular dislocation *DA* cuts the two generating sets *CA* and *BA*.

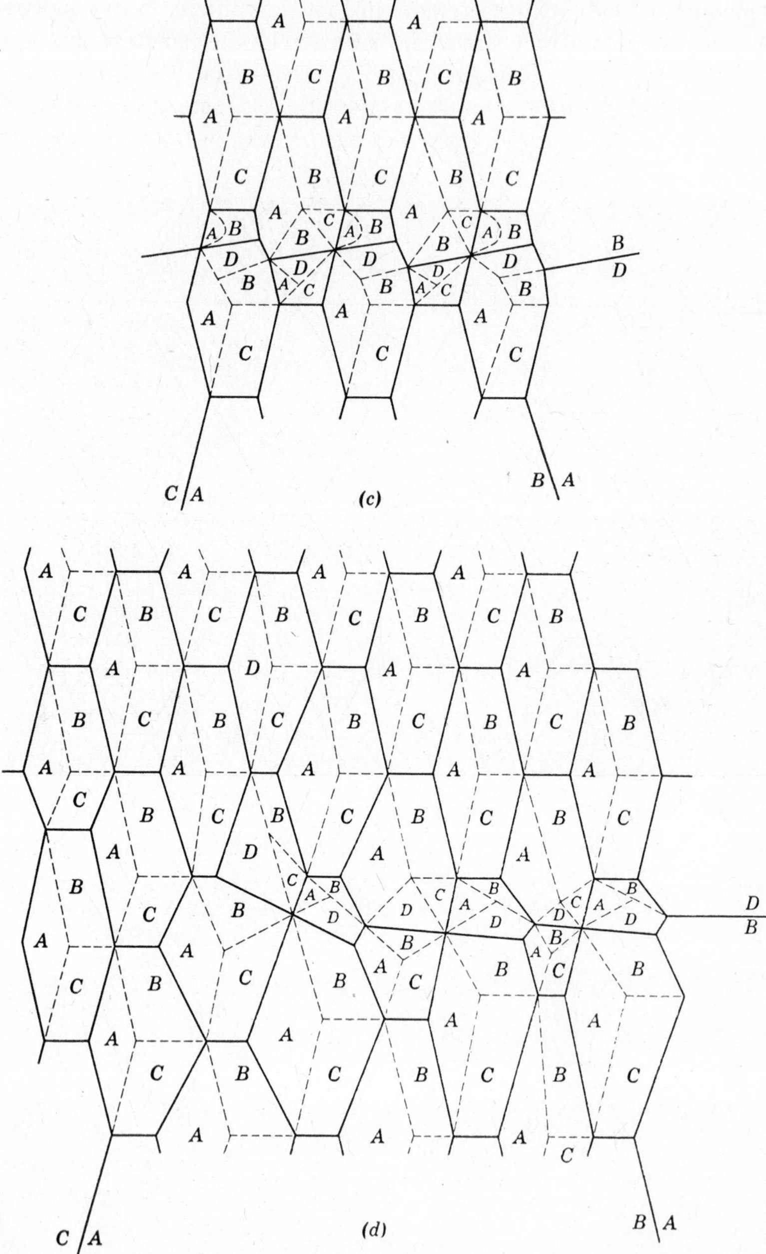

Fig. 13 (continued). (*c*) The singular dislocation *BD* cuts the two generating sets *CA* and *BA*. (*d*) Lettering pattern corresponding to Fig. 6*a*. The singular dislocation *DB* bends over 90° and cuts the two generating sets *CA* and *BA*.

(Amelinckx, 1956). Characteristic in Fig. 4*c* is the jog in the straight line with Burgers vector *BD* where it cuts the other singular line with Burgers vector *BC*. Such a jog can be observed on Fig. 12*f* and also on the lettering pattern of Fig. 11. The characteristic feature of Fig. 5*a* is the fourfold node formed between two pentagonal and two

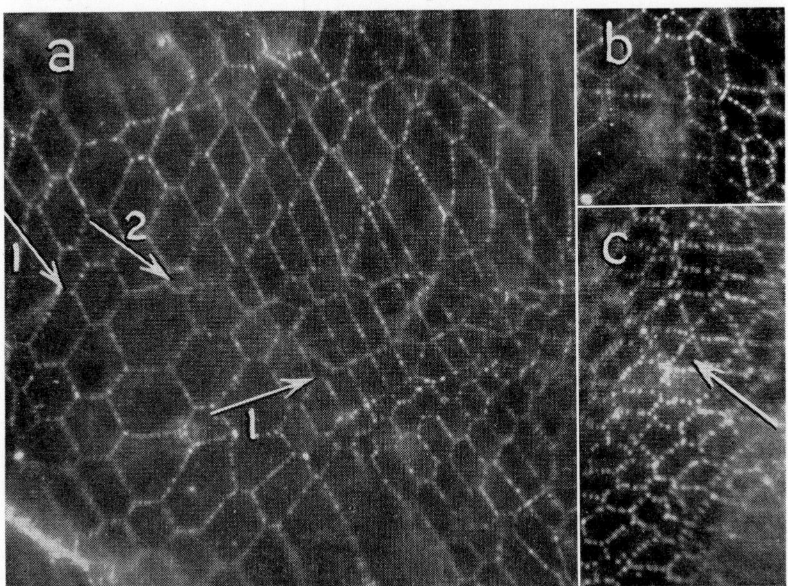

Fig. 14. Hexagonal nets containing many singularities. (*a*) Singular dislocation lines join the net in the points marked by arrows 1. At the point marked 2 a striking combination of two meshes: one with five, the other with seven sides. 600×. (*b*) Configuration of lines characteristic of the complexity described in our previous paper (1956) in Fig. 5*a*. 700×. (*c*) Singularities analyzed in Fig. 13*a*. 800×.

hexagonal meshes, in diametrically opposed position. Such nodes are visible in Figs. 14*a*, *b*, and 15 as well as in 12.

Analysis of Some Further Singularities in Hexagonal Nets. We consider now the net of Fig. 8*a*. It contains a supplementary row of hexagons. The lettering corresponding to this pattern is given in Fig. 16. It shows that the singularity simply results when a perfectly hexagonal net meets a node of three lines *DB*, *BC*, and *CD* in such a way that the line *DB* is perpendicular to the set *AC* of the net.

The net of Fig. 12 is of special interest as it contains a number of particularities. At a first glance one could consider the net as a square net with singularities; closer examination reveals that most of the meshes are hexagonal with two sides poorly developed. We therefore accept that the net is hexagonal. Under this assumption the lettering in the region of the small square mesh, shown in the inset, Fig. 12*i*, is unambiguously determined (not considering of course permutations of letters). It turns out further that the lettering of the rest of

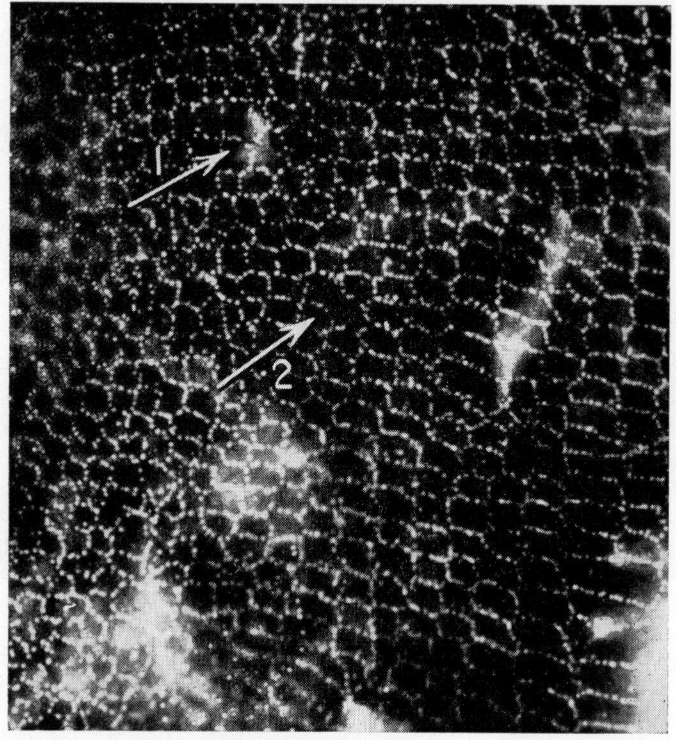

Fig. 15. Part of very extended hexagonal net. 600×. Singularities are marked by arrows. (1) corresponds to Fig. 5*a* of Amelinckx (1956) and (2) may well be the singularity of Fig. 9 of Frank's paper (1955).

the pattern follows from this without ambiguity. From Fig. 11 we can conclude that the net can be considered as built up from two sets of vertically oriented dislocations having Burgers vectors AC (left) and DB (right), the separation being at the small square. These sets are cut by a complicated sequence of horizontally oriented lines BA and DC. In the region of the small square these lines intersect.

Equilibrium Shape of Hexagonal Nets. In general it is difficult to attempt an unambiguous designation of Burgers vector to the dislocations of an observed net and to discuss its equilibrium condition. In one particular case, however, this was possible. We refer here to the net of Fig. 17. From the direction (parallel to [110]) and from the nondecorated character of one of the sets of dislocation lines, we conclude that these are pure screws (see § 6.I). We further find that the plane of the net is very near to the cube plane. We idealize the prob-

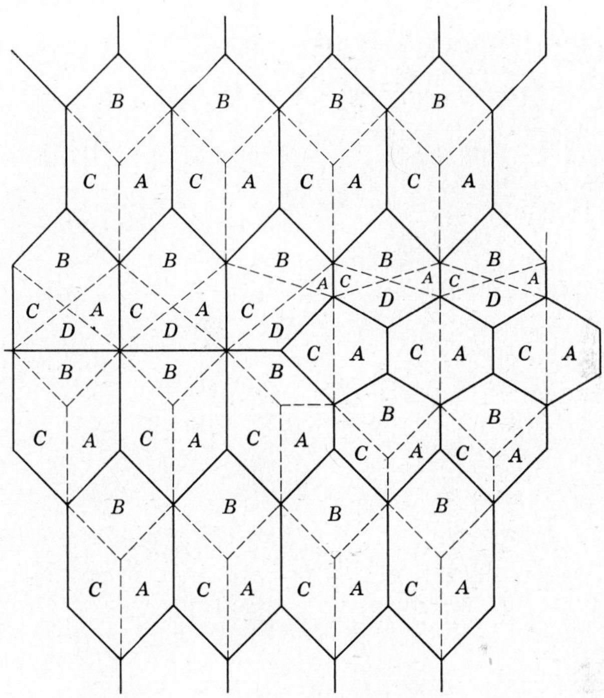

Fig. 16. Lettering pattern of the singularity shown on Fig. 8*a*.

lem somewhat and assume that the evolution towards equilibrium takes place in the way shown in Fig. 18*a*, and in such a manner that the net remains in the (001) plane. As a consequence of the symmetry of the problem the mid-points A, B, C, and D can be considered as fixed points and the problem reduces to minimizing the line energy of the configuration of dislocation lines shown in Fig. 18*b* with respect to the only parameter α. We assume hereby that the meshes are large enough so that the influence of the core energy as well as the elastic interaction of dislocations can be neglected.

Let us introduce the notation: $AE = x$; $EM = y$ $(EM = MF)$; $AB = 2l_1$; $AC = 2l_2$; it then follows that $x = l_2/\cos \alpha$ and $y = l_1 - l_2 \operatorname{tg} \alpha$.

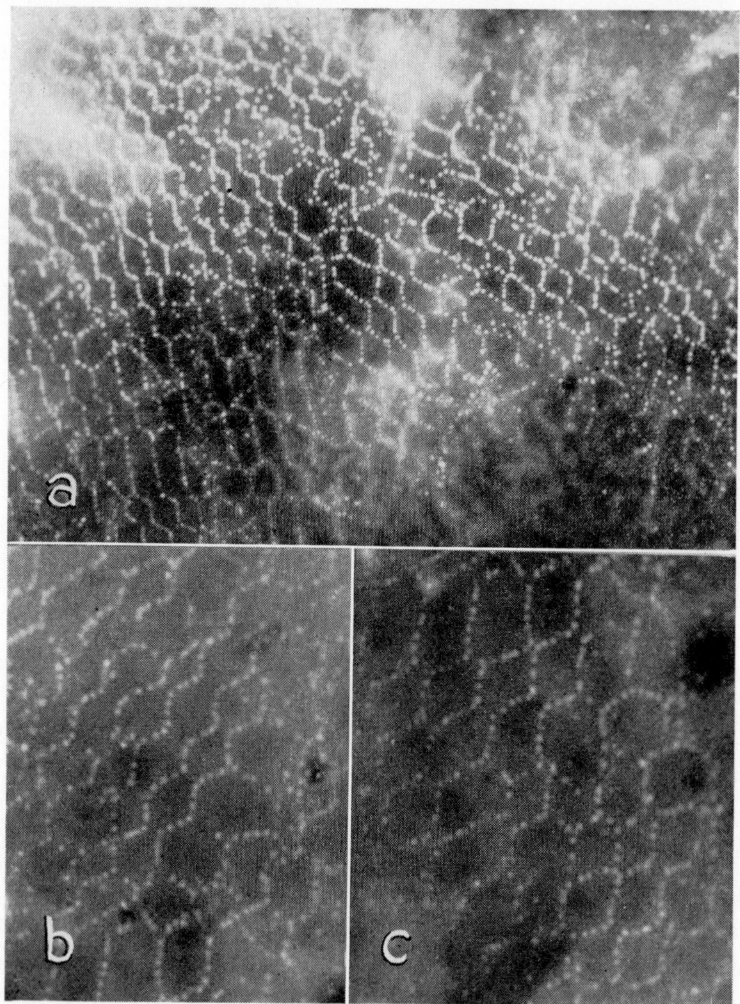

Fig. 17. Net of which one family of lines is not decorated. 600×. They are parallel to [110] and they are very probably pure screws. (*b*) and (*c*) are larger magnifications which were used to obtain the results discussed in § 6.B in "Analysis of Some Further Singularities in Hexagonal Nets." 1000×.

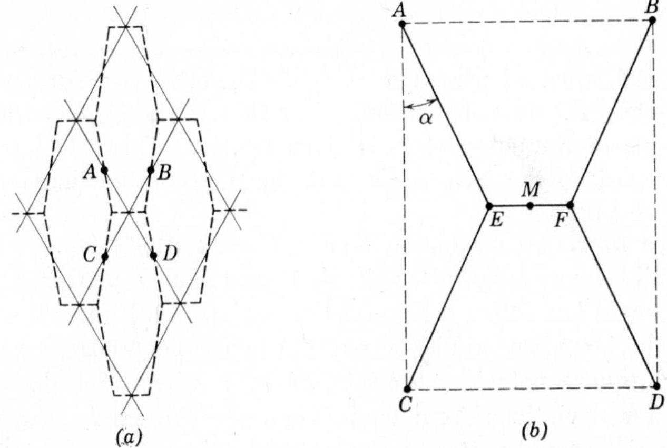

Fig. 18. (*a*) The net shown in dashed lines results from the set of generating dislocations. The points *ABCD* remain fixed during this operation. (*b*) Cell *ABCD;* to illustrate the calculation of § 6.B, "Equilibrium Shape of Hexagonal Nets."

The total line energy of half the cell *ABCD* is:

$$E_0 = x[E(\chi_2) + E(\chi_3)] + yE(\chi_1)$$

$E(\chi)$ is the expression

$$E(\chi) = \frac{\mu b^2}{4\pi(1-\nu)} \log\left(\frac{r_1}{r_0}\right)(1 - \nu\cos^2\chi) = A(1 - \nu\cos^2\chi)$$

where A may be regarded as a constant for our problem; χ is the angle between the dislocation line and the Burgers vector.

We now have to consider two possible sets of Burgers vectors satisfying the node conditions; one is

$$\bar{b}_1 = \frac{a}{2}[110]\cdot \qquad \bar{b}_2 = \frac{a}{2}[0\bar{1}\bar{1}]; \qquad \bar{b}_3 = [\bar{1}01]$$

the other results when indices 2 and 3 are interchanged. The total line energy reads

$$E_0 = 2Al_2 \sec\alpha[1 - \tfrac{1}{4}\nu(1 \mp \sin\alpha\cos\alpha)] + A(l_1 - l_2\,\mathrm{tg}\,\alpha)(1-\nu)$$

The sign $-$ corresponds to the set (1) and the $+$ sign to the other set. Minimizing with respect to α leads to the condition:

$$\nu(1 \pm \cos^3\alpha - \tfrac{1}{2}\sin\alpha) + (2\sin\alpha - 1) = 0$$

The observed value of α is between 30° and 31°. It is clear that $\alpha = 30°$ would lead to $\nu = 0$; for $\alpha = 31°$ one obtains a reasonable value for $\nu \simeq 0.25$, when adopting the $-$ sign. The other combination would lead to $\alpha \simeq 18°$. It thus becomes clear that in the observed case the distribution of Burgers vectors is given by (1). This calculation also lends support to the hypothesis that the undecorated lines are pure screws (see § 6.I).

Square nets. According to theory (Frank, 1955) square nets in their equilibrium configuration should lie in the cube plane. All dislocations would have the pure screw orientation [110] and the rotation axis of the boundary would be parallel to the cube edge. Again we observed square nets in a variety of orientations and shapes; the reasons for deviations from equilibrium are the same as discussed above for hexagonal patterns.

We did not find any visible development of oblique sections at the points of intersection of the constituent lines of the square nets as would result when a a [100] dislocation would form. Figure 12 shows a net which at a first glance could be interpreted as a square net with small oblique sections developed; this is particularly clearly visible in Fig. 12*d*. In an attempt to obtain a consistent lettering scheme, we found that this was not possible on the basis of this assumption. On the other hand, a lettering pattern (Fig. 11) satisfying the stability conditions could be found when assuming the net to be hexagonal with two sides poorly developed. As this lettering extended over an appreciable area containing a number of singularities, this can be considered as a critical test that the second interpretation is the correct one.

THE SINGULAR DISLOCATION LINE CUTS ONE SET OF BASIS DISLOCATIONS. When this singular dislocation has a Burgers vector which forms an angle of 60° (or 120°) with the one of the set which is cut, a zigzag line results as shown in the lettering pattern of Fig. 19 and visible in Fig. 7*a*. This zigzag line will often jog from one row of squares to the next; the corresponding lettering pattern is also shown in Fig. 19 and observed examples can be seen in Fig. 7*f*. Figure 7*d* and *b* shows cases where the zigzag line bends over 90°; the lettering can also be found on Fig. 19. Two adjacent singular dislocations can in some cases form a row of hexagons as represented in Fig. 20 and observed in Fig. 7*e*. In some boundaries zigzag lines alternate in a fairly regular way with straight lines (Fig. 7*c* and *f*). This leads of course to a change in rotation axis; the orientation deviates considerably from [001]; the more, the higher the density of zigzag lines.

THE SINGULAR LINE CUTS THE TWO SETS OF DISLOCATIONS. Figure 7*a* shows an example where the zigzag lines as described in the preceding section bend over and gradually cut the other set of basic dislocations. The lettering corresponding to this configuration is shown in Fig. 21.

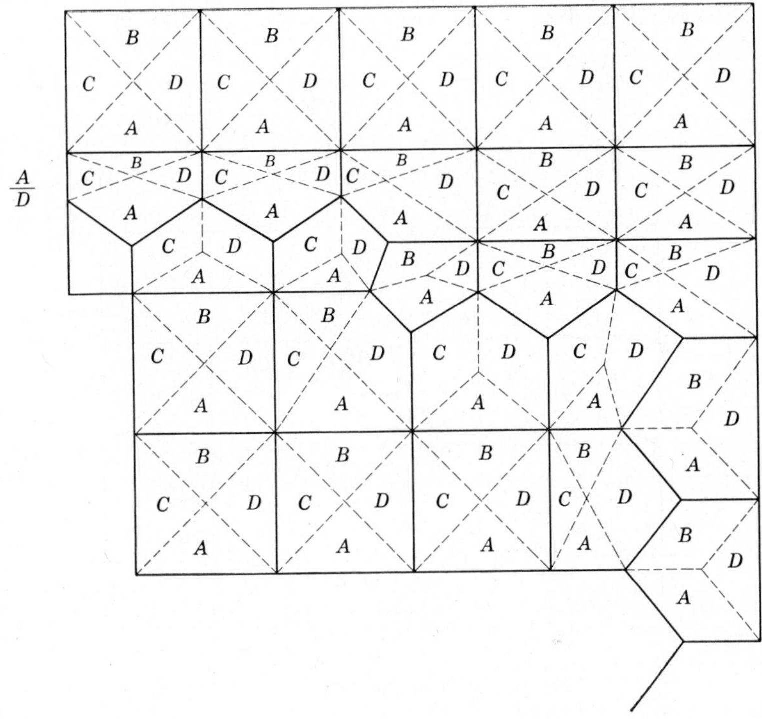

Fig. 19. Lettering pattern corresponding to several complexities to be seen on Fig. 7*a*, *b*, *f*, and *d*.

TWO INTERSECTING SINGULAR DISLOCATIONS. A number of possible cases have been discussed in our previous paper (1956).

Nets consisting of parallel lines: tilt boundaries. According to theory, boundaries consisting of parallel lines are tilt boundaries. In the ideal case the lines should be straight and parallel to the axis of rotation. In a simple case this could be verified directly. Figure 22 is a view parallel to the axis of bending of a bent and annealed, i.e., a polygonized, specimen. In such a case theory predicts that tilt boundaries perpendicular to the glide planes and consisting of edge dislocations parallel to the axis of bending should result. One actually observes rows of dots lying in (110) planes. When focusing deeper and deeper into the crystal, these dots hardly change place, proving that they mark dislocations perpendicular to the plane of observation or parallel to the axis of bending. This is further confirmed by observations in a plane (010) parallel to the axis of bending [001]; sets of parallel lines parallel to [001] are observed (Fig. 24*c*).

The geometry of polygonized specimens of sodium chloride is relatively complicated as a consequence of the fact that specimens are

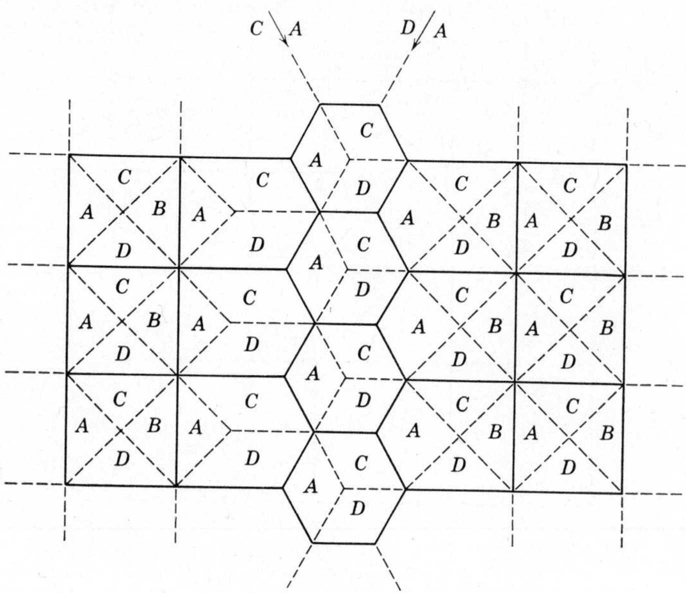

Fig. 20. Lettering of the singularity of Fig. 7*e*.

generally deformed on at least two mutually perpendicular planes, and also because glide planes and climb planes coincide. We are now in the process of analyzing this geometry in detail, but we shall discuss in a preliminary way some often found configurations of lines. In many cases deviations from the ideal model of a tilt boundary are observed; the lines are very often sets of parallel curves.

Tilt boundaries often contain singular dislocations which meander through them and interconnect successive lines. Figure 23 shows a typical lettering and Fig. 24*d* an observed example.

Tilt boundaries in polygonized specimens of NaCl show a marked preference in orientation, not only for (110) planes, as one would expect, but also for (100) planes. This is clearly visible in Fig. 25*b* and *c*; oblique boundaries are very often built up out of straight sections parallel to one of these directions. The boundaries parallel to the cube plane consist either of similar dislocations all having a [100] as Burgers vector; or they are boundaries consisting of equal numbers of dislocations $a/2$ [110] and $a/2$ [$1\bar{1}0$] placed in a regular succession. As (100) boundaries are also found at the intersection of two (110)

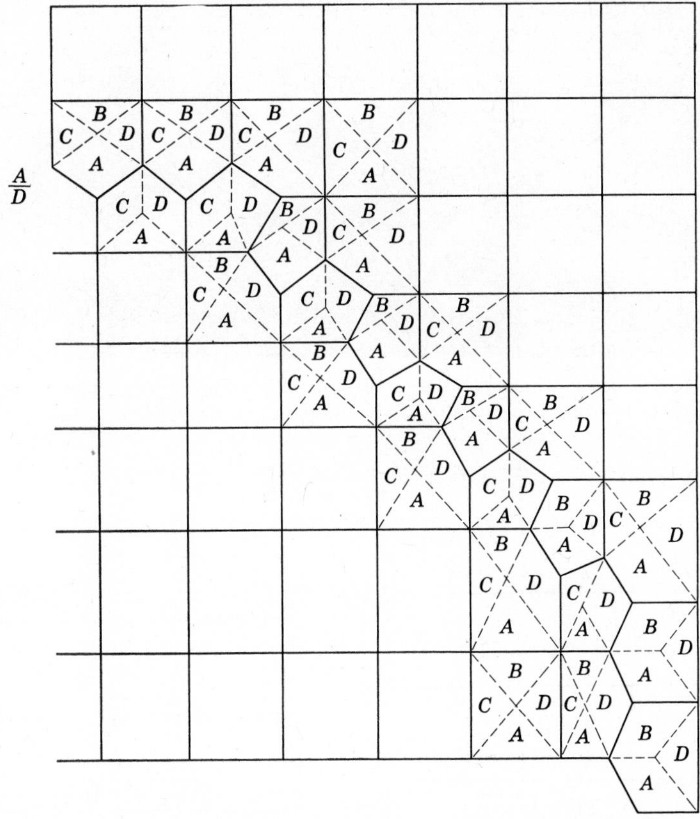

Fig. 21. Lettering corresponding to Fig. 7a, arrow 2.

boundaries, it is very probable that they are built up in the way suggested in the second place, and visualized in Fig. 26a. In the ideal case this needs only a conservative motion and lowers the energy because a single boundary with an orientation difference $\theta_1 + \theta_2$ replaces (at least partly) the two original boundaries with orientation differences θ_1 and θ_2. The same kind of rearrangement probably takes place when a set of tilt boundaries of the kind shown in Fig. 26b evolves towards final equilibrium. Orientations other than [100] seem to be particularly stable too; we very often observed remarkably plane

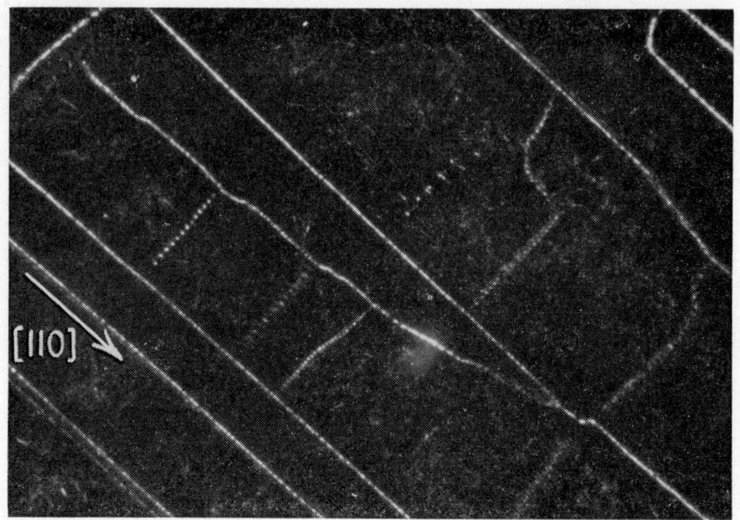

Fig. 22. Dislocation lines parallel to the axis of bending in polygonized specimen. The axis of bending is perpendicular to the plane of observation. 550×.

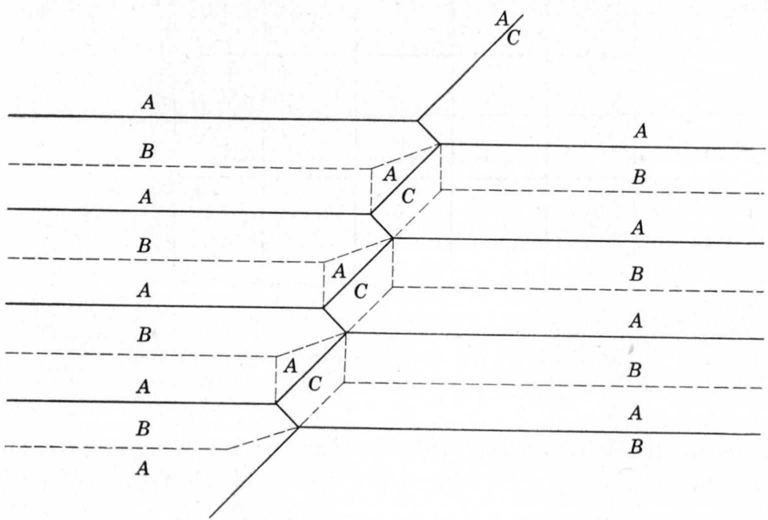

Fig. 23. Singular dislocation cutting a tilt boundary.

boundaries being parallel to (110) but jogging from one (110) plane to a parallel one (Fig. 24*a*). The jogs then frequently had a well-defined orientation; they were all parallel, often to (100) but sometimes also to other directions.

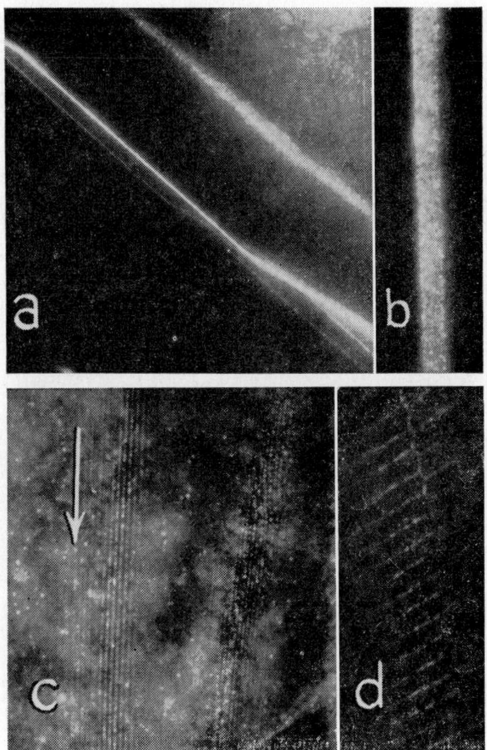

Fig. 24. (*a*) Tilt boundary in as-grown crystal. It consists of straight part jogging from one (110) plane to the next, interconnected by parts which are also parallel. 400×. (*b*) (110) boundary which is represented as a sheet of particles. 600×. (*c*) Polygonization walls seen parallel to the axis of bending which is indicated by an arrow. 550×. (*d*) Tilt boundary containing a singular dislocation.

Polygonized specimens are characterized by the great frequency of L- and T-shaped junctions (Fig. 25*a* and *b*). These junctions allow a simple verification of a relation between the dislocation densities in meeting tilt boundaries (Amelinckx, 1954; Vogel and Lovell, 1956).

In some cases relatively high angle boundaries (1° to 2°) were found which were decorated by a thick sheet of particles. The boundaries for which this could be established were those perpendicular to the plane of observation. It was found that they were marked by a ribbon of

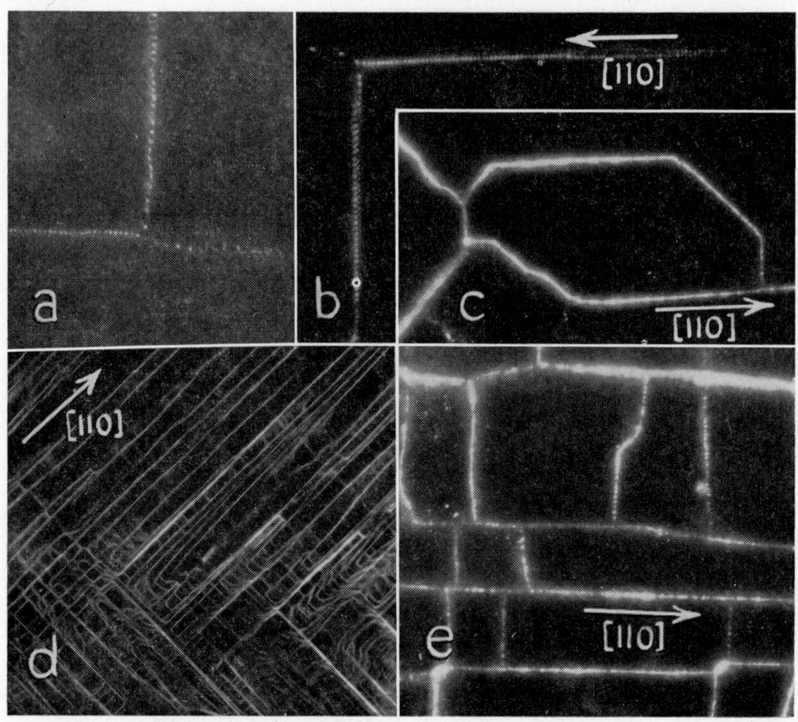

Fig. 25. (*a*) T-boundary in polygonized specimen. 600×. (*b*) L-boundary in polygonized specimen. 600×. (*c*) (110) and (100) boundaries in polygonized specimen. 550×. (*d*) General view of deformed and annealed specimen at small magnification. 150×. (*e*) (100) boundaries at the intersection of two (110) boundaries. 400×.

particles (Fig. 24*b*) which remained on the same spot whatever the position of the focus was in the crystal. These boundaries were present in the crystal as grown and were always remarkably straight, apart from jogging to parallel planes. By optical goniometry it was established that they had mainly tilt character. This observation seems to point to a somewhat modified model of boundary at relatively small angles.

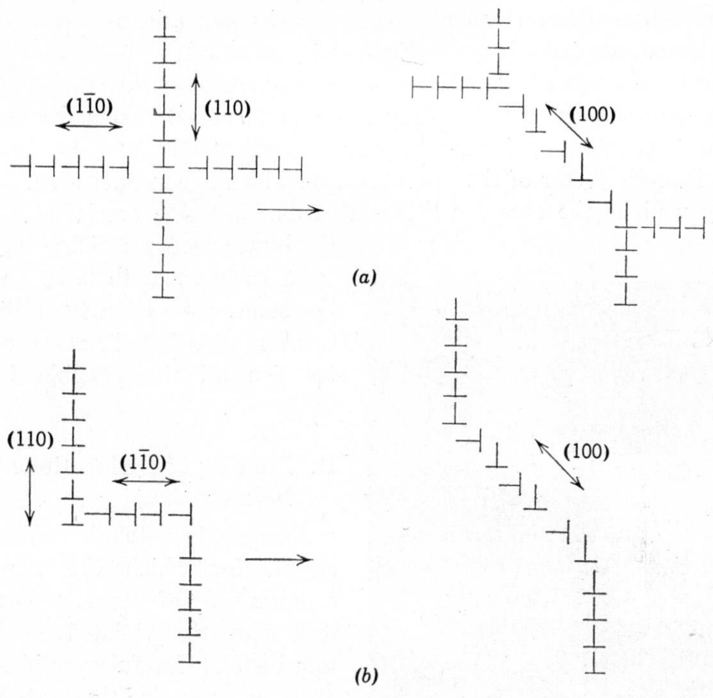

Fig. 26. The genesis of (100) boundaries in polygonized specimens of sodium chloride. Examples can be found in Fig. 25*b* and *c*.

C. Pinning of Dislocations by Precipitates

The theory of precipitation hardening makes use of the concept that dislocations can become pinned at certain points by impurity precipitations. We have obtained direct visual evidence that this is indeed the case. Figure 27*b* shows sections of a dislocation line which bulge out between points which are clearly marked by larger precipitates of silver. The curved shape is evidently not an equilibrium shape and the dislocation line would have straightened out if it were not that it was firmly pinned at the points which are now marked by larger precipitates. The genesis of this configuration of lines is presumably as follows. At a certain moment during cooling, precipitation started in a few isolated points of the dislocation. Soon after this the dislocation line was displaced, probably under the influence of thermal stresses developed during cooling. The dislocation, being pinned in certain points, developed bulges. The dislocation line was then decorated by further precipitation and fixed in its new position. As precipitation started at the pinning points, these are marked by larger precipitates.

These observations further prove that the larger precipitates are also nucleated at dislocations. Figure 30*b* illustrates this point more clearly. As this needle-shaped precipitate has a well-defined orientation with respect to the matrix, it was first hoped that a one-to-one correspondence might exist between the orientation of a needle and the Burgers vector of the dislocation on which it was nucleated. This may well be the case for the small submicroscopic precipitates, but the larger needles which grow out from them seem to have (along the same dislocation line) orientations distributed at random between all the possible [110] directions.

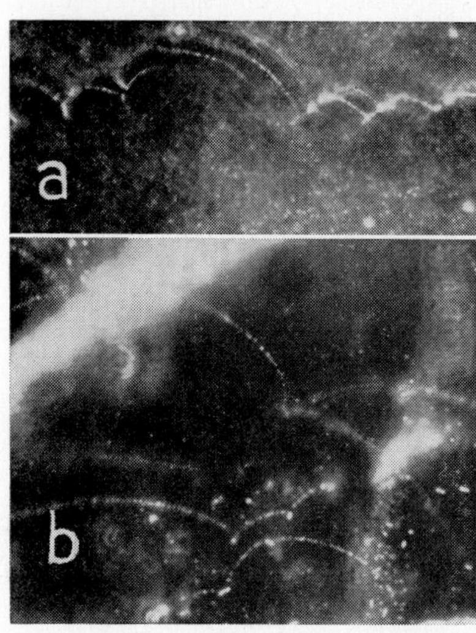

Fig. 27. (*a*) Pinning of dislocations at stationary dislocations of the networks (see Fig. 28*c*). 500×. (*b*) Pinning of dislocations at precipitates. 500×.

D. Pinning of Dislocations into Nets

Sometimes networks are observed for which the rule of conservation of Burgers vectors is apparently violated at certain nodes. Careful examination, however, reveals that at that point a dislocation leaves the net and joins at its other end another node or another net.

In this way long dislocation lines pinned at both ends result. They should be the internal slip sources which are most easily activated. Examples can be seen in Fig. 14*a*, where at the points marked by arrows 1 singular dislocations join the net.

That node points pin dislocations could also be verified directly. Figure 27*a* shows a number of dislocation lines all curved in the same sense, apparently under the influence of thermal stresses. They are all pinned at both ends to other stationary dislocations, in the manner shown schematically in Fig. 28*c*. They are in fact potential slip sources of the conical or spatial type (Bilby, 1955).

E. Intersection and Mutual Annihilation of Dislocations

The genesis of nets is a consequence of the intersection of dislocations from different slip sources. We will, however, discuss some characteristic patterns which are believed to be the result of the intersection and

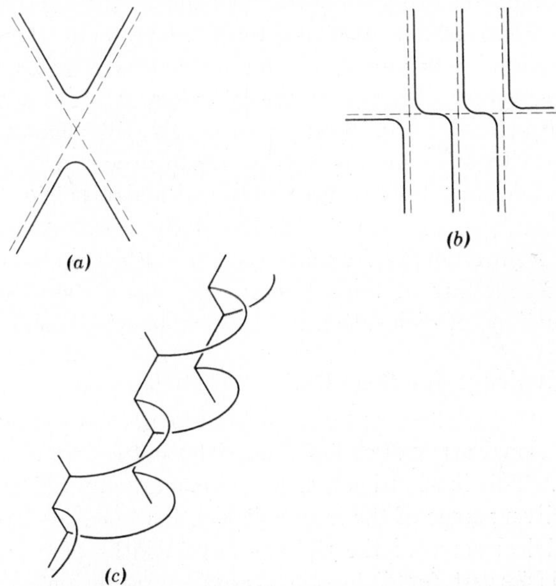

Fig. 28. (*a*) The intersection of two dislocations with the same Burgers vector produced two L-shaped dislocation lines. (*b*) When a tilt boundary is cut by a dislocation of the same Burgers vector the lines become jogged. (*c*) Pinning of dislocations at stationary dislocations of the network.

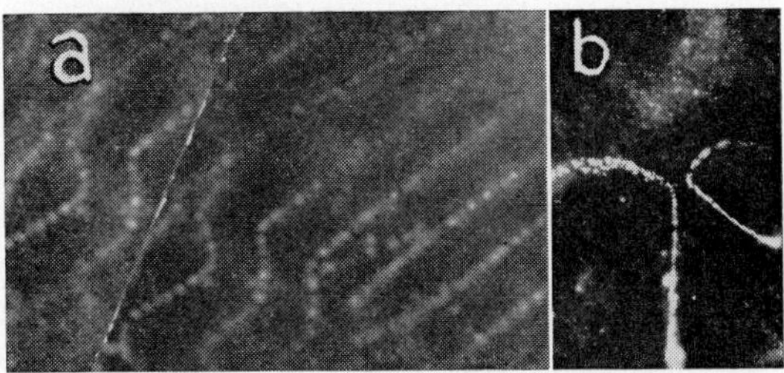

Fig. 29. (*a*) Intersection of tilt boundary with dislocation of the same Burgers vector (see Fig. 28*b*). 750×. (*b*) Intersection of two dislocations with the same Burgers vector (see Fig. 28*a*). 450×.

mutual annihilation of dislocations, either as a consequence of slip or of climb. When two dislocations of the same Burgers vector intersect, two L-shaped dislocations, pointing towards the point of intersection, result (Fig. 28*a*). When a tilt boundary is cut by a dislocation of the same Burgers vector, the lines of the boundary will become jogged in the way shown in Fig. 28*b*. Characteristically, the parts which originally belonged to the same dislocation are in prolongation of one another. Both phenomena have been observed and Fig. 29*a* and *b* gives examples. One has of course to take into account that during the decoration a certain amount of anneal occurred after intersection. This explains the rounding of the corners; they would be sharp if nondecorated sections of dislocation lines interconnected them.

F. Direct Evidence for the Climb of Dislocations

The decoration process, as we considered it, implies the formation of a two-dimensional array of colloidal particles in the trail of the climbed dislocations. This is what is observed most markedly in the specimens containing silver; some of the longer dislocation lines are seen as a ribbon of particles; some of the ribbons have widths of 5 μ and more. The width is largest for dislocations near the diffusion surface. Let us assume that the particles originate from a continuous monolayer of metal having the width of the ribbons. For a width of 1 μ, a density of dislocations of $10^6/\text{cm}^2$, and a distance between metal atoms of 1 A, we find that 10^{18} color centers have to condense per cm^3. This rough estimate shows that the assumption is not unreasonable, as a density of color centers of that order of magnitude was probably achieved during the intense additive coloration. It is not necessary to have this number of color centers present all at the same moment. Some may already have died at the dislocation while new ones were still formed. We conclude that it is not unreasonable to consider the ribbon of colloidal particles as direct evidence of climbing.

An alternative, but less probable, explanation would be to assume that the dislocation has moved by glide and has been decorated in its successive positions. We will, however, now consider some characteristic shapes of dislocation lines which will bring further evidence that climb has occurred.

The climb of individual dislocations. The climb of a pure edge dislocation gives rise to a parallel displacement, unless it is pinned at both ends. In this case it can either give rise to concentric closed loops (Bardeen and Herring, 1952) or to a spiral prismatic dislocation, depending upon the configuration of the pinning screws at the end points. Direct observation of a Bardeen-Herring source seems possible but has not yet been achieved, although some features observed in crystals of CaF_2 (Bontinck and Dekeyser, 1956) have been interpreted on this basis. Direct observation of a spiral prismatic dislocation, in the form originally described by Seitz (1952), seems difficult. A phenomenon which is closely related to it has been observed. It has been shown previously (Bontinck and Amelinckx, 1957; Amelinckx, Bontinck, Dekeyser, and Seitz, 1957) that the combined effect of climb and glide of a mixed dislocation will give rise to a helically wound dislocation line.

The phenomenon is especially striking in CaF_2 where very regular helices have been observed first (Bontinck and Amelinckx, 1957). Figure 30*e* shows an example. It has also been observed in NaCl and Fig. 30*a* and *f* shows several examples. The difference in development is probably due to the smaller supersaturation of the climb-inducing entity which can be achieved in the case of NaCl in comparison with CaF_2. As a consequence of the trail of particles the spiral dislocation lines are seen as helical surfaces (Fig. 30*f*).

Dislocation rings. Although no direct evidence has been obtained for a Bardeen-Herring source, isolated dislocation rings have been observed frequently. Bontinck (private communication) also observed them in CaF_2. They lie most frequently in a (110) plane, sometimes in (100), and they are usually seen as more or less circular ribbons lying in the same plane, suggesting that they climbed in their plane and consequently have predominantly prismatic character. Figure 31*a* is an example. We could conclude unambiguously that during their last step of formation they have climbed outward, increasing their diameter. This could be concluded from the coalescence of two such rings which were in the same plane. A configuration of specks as schematized on Fig. 32*b* was formed (Fig. 31*b*).

As during the last period of decoration climb was by substraction, this proves that the dislocation rings are of the kind that would be formed by the condensation of vacancies.

Another case leading to the same conclusion has been observed (Fig. 31*e*). Now rings lying in parallel planes have climbed to overlap slightly; at that stage glide has occurred, leading to the configuration of Fig. 33*b*. When two rings lying in intersecting (110) planes meet, they can intersect and a configuration as seen on Figs. 34*b* and 31*c* results.

In some cases rings were observed with some detail in the center. The rings lay approximately in the cube plane. No climb in the plane of the ring is visible; their character is therefore not necessarily prismatic (Fig. 31*d*).

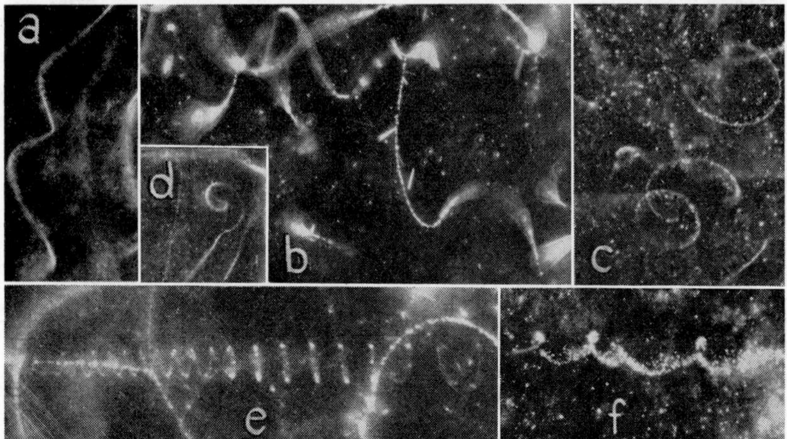

Fig. 30. Helically wound dislocations. 332×. In (*b*) needle-shaped precipitates are seen to nucleate on the dislocation line. 332×. (*d*) Represents a helix seen "head on." 375×. (*e*) Helix in CaF_2. The right end consists of isolated rings (after Bontinck and Amelinckx, 1957).

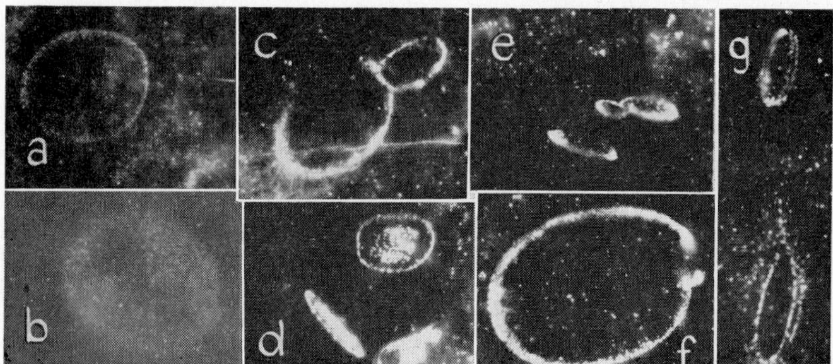

Fig. 31. Dislocation rings very probably of the prismatic type. (*a*) Ring lying in (100) plane. 425×. (*b*) Coalescence of two rings lying in the same plane (Fig. 32). 465×. (*c*) Intersection of two rings lying in intersecting planes (Fig. 34). 385×. (*d*) Rings showing some structure in the center, suggesting concentric rings. 385×. (*e*) Coalescence of rings lying in parallel planes (Fig. 33). 385×. (*f*) Nonclosed loop connected to two dislocations going down in the right part of the photograph. The geometry corresponds to the one responsible for a Bardeen-Herring source. 348×. (*g*) Rings consisting of parallel lines. Assuming the lines to represent the ring in two successive stages, the lower picture gives evidence for a rotation of the ring during climb. 425×.

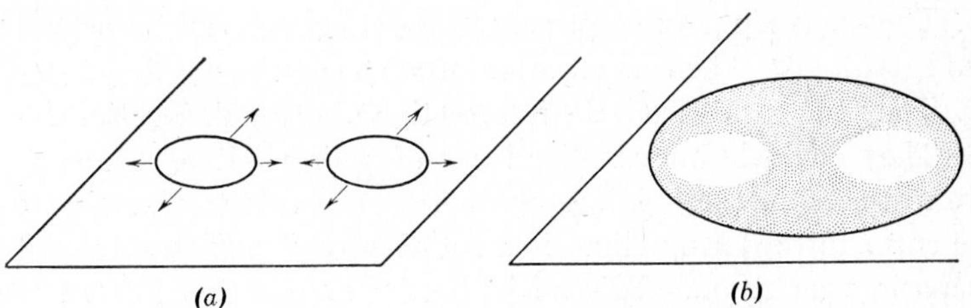

Fig. 32. The coalescence of two prismatic dislocation rings lying in the same plane.

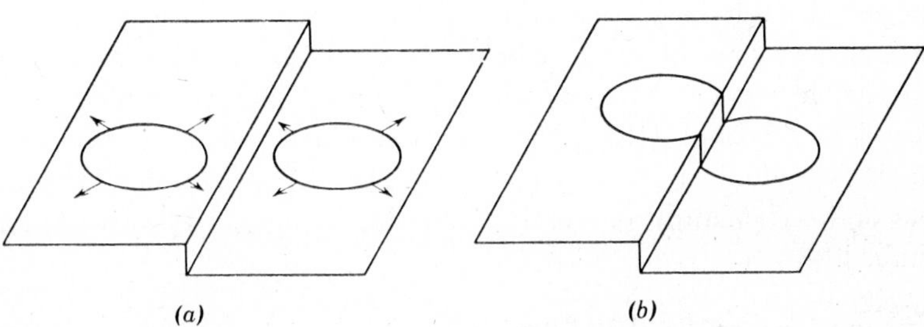

Fig. 33. Junction by glide of two prismatic dislocation rings lying in parallel planes.

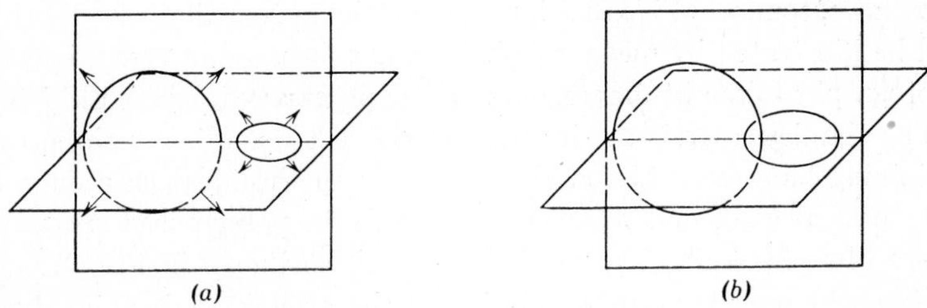

Fig. 34. Intersection of two prismatic dislocation rings lying in intersecting planes.

As to the origin of isolated dislocation rings, many possibilities can be considered:

1. They may already be present in the as-grown crystal, where they would result from the condensation of vacancies.
2. They can result from the intersection of other dislocations.
3. They could be the smaller loops of a Frank-Read source, which were not used in the building-up of nets. The first thing that would happen to them during climb is a rotation of their plane towards the prismatic orientation. This might be the explanation for the genesis of rings lying in random planes.

Many other possibilities necessitating a more complicated sequence of events can be imagined.

Climb of networks. Although the formation of ribbons is largely confined to the long dislocations of the three-dimensional network, some dislocations in plane networks show it also. This proves that dislocation networks are capable of climbing too, as pointed out by Suzuki and Suzuki (1954). Figure 35*b* and *c* shows tilt boundaries which have climbed as a whole whereas Fig. 35*a* and *d* shows hexagonal nets of which mainly one or two families of lines, respectively, have climbed.

G. Junctions of Subboundaries

It is clear that the detailed way in which boundaries join at a nodal line can in principle also be studied. In general, the junction takes place in a complicated way and we shall only sketch some well-defined examples. The simplest way of summarizing the results is to give a schematic, somewhat idealized, representation. Not all of the examples will be illustrated by means of photographs, because in general several photographs taken at different levels are necessary to show all details.

The simplest case is the junction of two tilt boundaries; three ways of joining have been observed (Fig. 36). In the ideal case only (*a*) is to be expected, and it occurs frequently in polygonized specimens. Cases like (*b*) and (*c*) were also observed, as shown in Fig. 37.

Case (*b*) may have some relation to the growth of domains during polygonization. Growth consists only of a lateral shift of the junction line; a situation like (*c*) may inhibit this shift.

The junction drawn in Fig. 38 can be derived from the set of three photographs, Fig. 39.

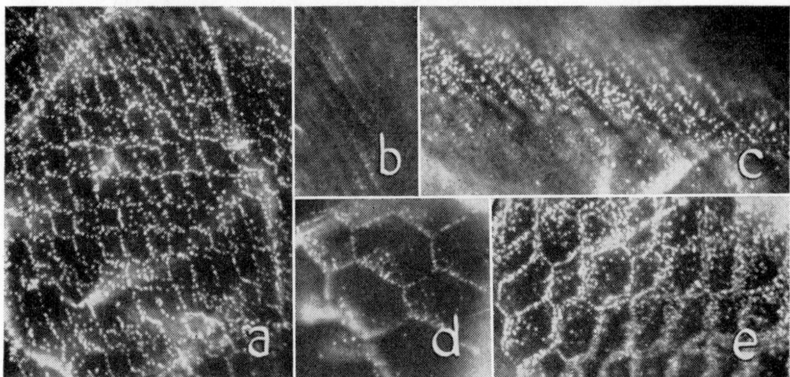

Fig. 35. The climb of networks. (*b*) and (*c*) Climb of tilt boundaries. As every dislocation climbs, the boundary climbs as a whole. 345×. (*a*), (*d*), and (*e*) Climb of hexagonal nets. 556×. Not all segments of dislocation climb over the same distance; all dislocations of the same family, however, behave in the same way. The singular dislocation in (*a*) behaves differently.

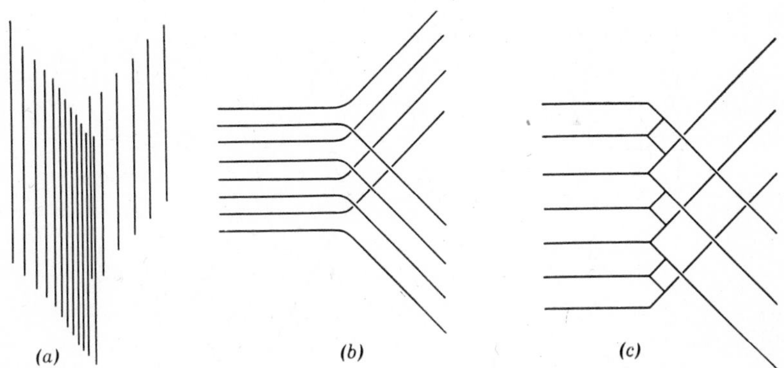

Fig. 36. (*a*) Junction of three tilt boundaries as observed in polygonized specimens (see, e.g., Figs. 22 and 25*a*). (*b*) Junction of three tilt boundaries as observed in polygonized specimens (see Fig. 37*a*, *b*, and *c*). (*c*) Junction of three tilt boundaries through the intermediance of a singular dislocation (cf. Fig. 23).

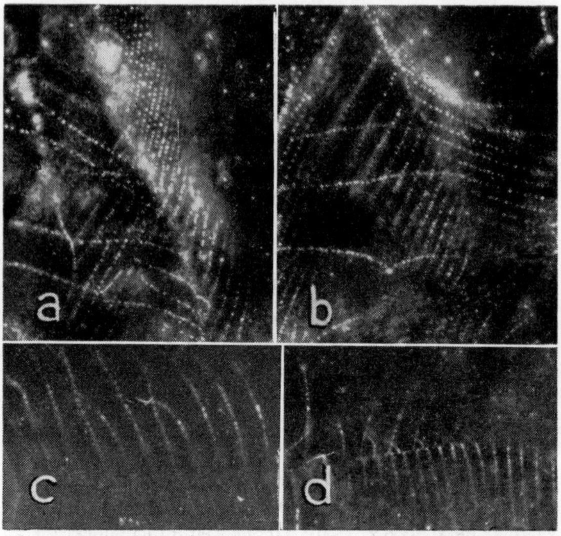

Fig. 37. The junction of tilt boundaries. (*a*) and (*b*) Two views of the same junction of the type of Fig. 36*b*. 500×. (*c*) Illustrating Fig. 36*b*. 500×. (*d*) Illustrating Fig. 36*c*. 500×.

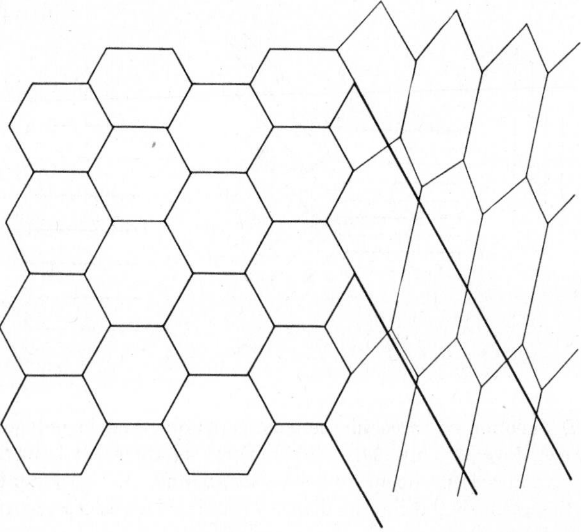

Fig. 38. Junction of two hexagonal nets and one tilt boundary (see Fig. 31*a*, *b*, and *c*).

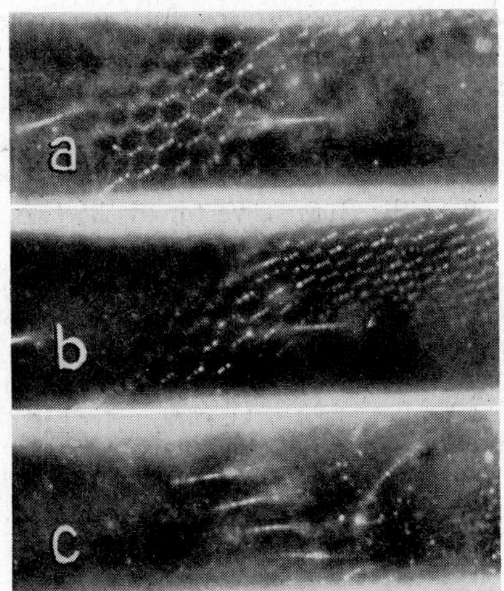

Fig. 39. Junction of two hexagonal nets and a set of parallel lines; (*a*), (*b*), and (*c*) are photographs of the same network made at different depths.

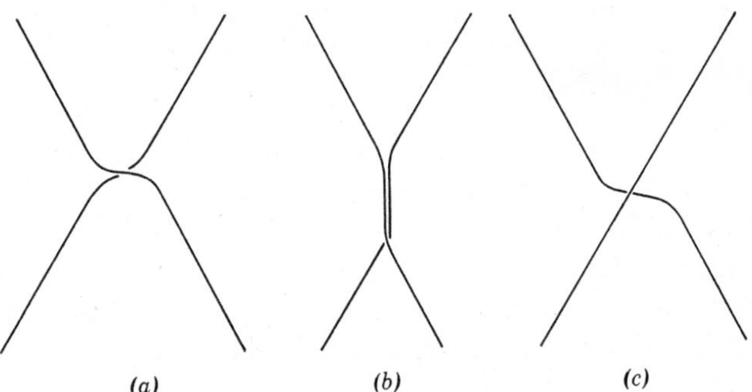

Fig. 40. Configurations of crossing dislocation lines. The twisted shapes result from the torque that the dislocations exert one on the other. (*a*) Symmetrical with bending towards the bisector of the obtuse angle. (*b*) Symmetrical with bending towards the bisector of the acute angle. (*c*) Asymmetrical twisting.

H. Forces Between Crossing Dislocations

Theory (Read, 1953) predicts that crossing dislocations exert high local stresses one on the other; in general they produce a torque that twists the dislocations into a curved shape. That is, in fact, the first stage in the formation of a hexagonal network starting from two sets of generating dislocations. Configurations of the kind shown in Fig. 40 are to be expected according to Read (1953). Depending upon the relative orientation of the Burgers vector of the two dislocations, the

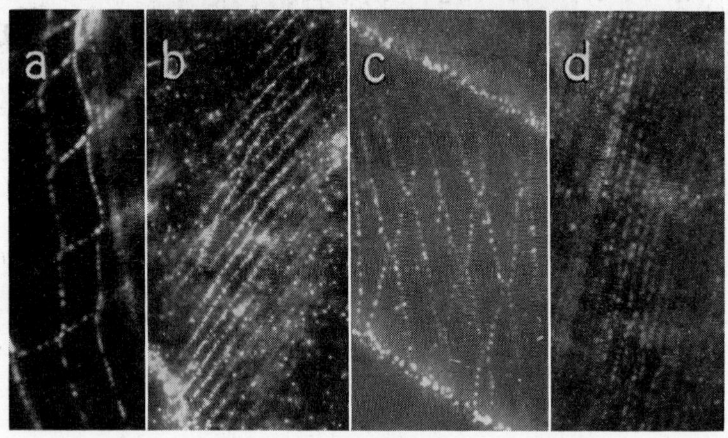

Fig. 41. The twisting of crossing dislocations. (*a*) and (*b*) Asymmetrical twisting (see Fig. 40*a, c*). 700×. (*c*) and (*d*) Symmetrical twisting (see Fig. 40*b*). 700×.

resulting configuration can be either symmetrical or asymmetrical. Fig. 41*b* shows a case where the configuration is asymmetrical. The set of parallel lines being a tilt boundary, it is reasonable to assign mainly edge character to them. Assuming the crossing dislocation to have mainly screw character, the asymmetry, as well as the fact that the twist is mainly on the edge, is in accordance with theory.

I. Density of Precipitates

On many photographs (e.g., Figs. 9, 17, and especially 42*a*) it is clearly visible that the density of precipitates depends on the orientation of the lines. Some lines of the set parallel to [110] are not decorated in Fig. 17*b, c*. In Fig. 17*a* sets of zigzag lines of the kind drawn in Fig. 43*a* are present. It is evident that this situation would not be stable unless segments of dislocation lines represented as dashed lines in Fig. 43*a* were present, although not decorated. From the orienta-

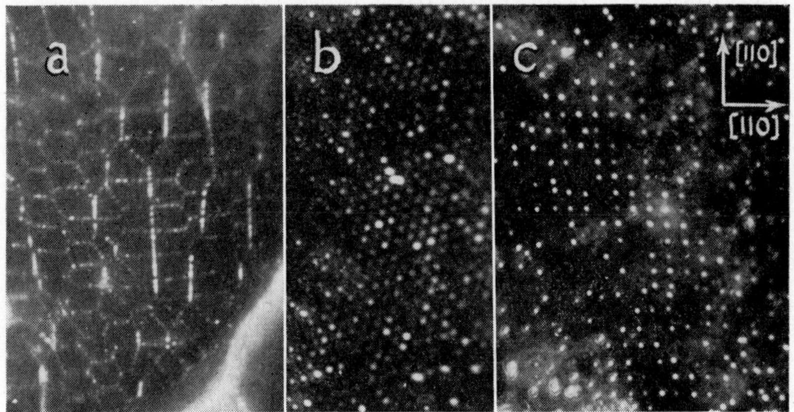

Fig. 42. (*a*) Difference in decoration along different families of lines of the network. 600×. (*b*) and (*c*) Arrays of dots. 750×.

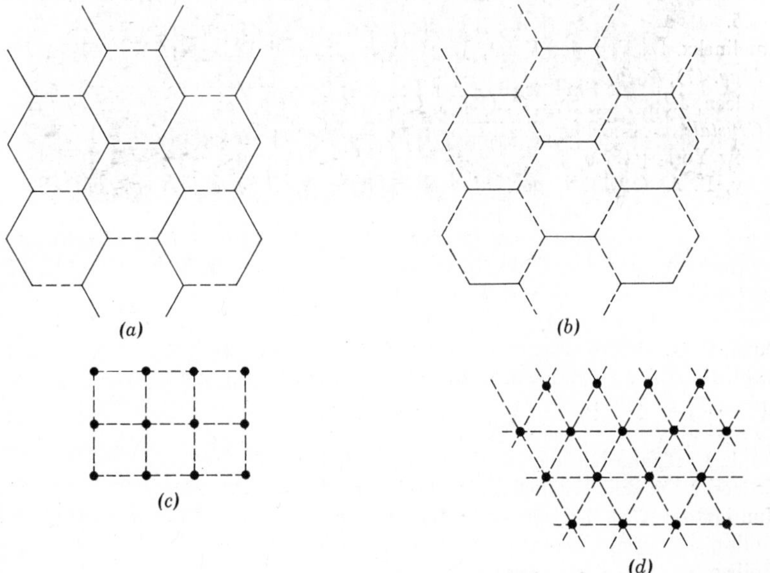

Fig. 43. Patterns which result when certain parts of nets are not decorated. (*a*) Zigzag lines which result when one family of lines is not decorated (see Fig. 17). (*b*) Set of parallel segments when two families of lines are not decorated (see Fig. 31). (*c*) and (*d*) Arrays of dots which result when only node points are decorated.

tion of these lines parallel to [110] it is concluded that they could be pure screws. The discussed decoration mechanism accounts for the absence of precipitates along such dislocations. The net of Fig. 31 is only represented as a set of parallel segments, the connecting zigzag lines not being decorated (Fig. 43*b*). When all constituents of the net are pure screws its representation is reduced to a plane array of dots (Fig. 43*c*), corresponding to the node points (Fig. 42*c*). It was also found sometimes that even when the orientation of the lines is such that they cannot be pure screws, node points are decorated only (Fig. 42*b*).

Some precipitates seem to be distributed at random; it is striking that such precipitates are rarely found in the neighborhood of nets.

REFERENCES

Amelinckx, S. (1954), *Acta Met.*, **2,** 848.

Amelinckx, S. (1956), *Phil. Mag.* (8), **1,** 269.

Amelinckx, S., Bontinck, W., Dekeyser, W., and Seitz, F. (1957), *Phil. Mag.*, **2,** 355.

Amelinckx, S., Van der Vorst, W., Gevers, R., and Dekeyser, W. (1955), *Phil. Mag.* (7), **46,** 450.

Bardeen, J., and Herring, C. (1952), Chap. 10 in *Imperfections in Nearly Perfect Crystals,* W. Shockley, J. H. Hollomon, R. Maurer, F. Seitz, John Wiley & Sons, New York, p. 279.

Bilby, B. A. (1955), *Report of a Conference on Defects in Crystalline Solids,* Physical Society, London, p. 124.

Boesman, E., Remaut, G., and Dekeyser, W. (1956), *J. Chem. Phys.*, **25,** 359.

Bontinck, W., and Amelinckx, S. (1957), *Phil. Mag.* (8), **2,** 94.

Bontinck, W., and Dekeyser, W. (1956), *Physica,* **22,** 595.

Dash, W. C. (1956), *J. Appl. Phys.*, **27,** 1153.

Dunn, C. G., and Daniels, F. W. (1951), *Trans. AIME,* **121,** 147.

Etzel, H. W., and Schulman, J. H. (1954), *J. Chem. Phys.*, **22,** 1549.

Frank, F. C. (1955), *Report of a Conference on Defects in Crystalline Solids,* Physical Society, London, p. 159.

Frank, F. C., and Nicholas, J. F. (1953), *Phil. Mag.*, **44,** 1213.

Hedges, J. N., and Mitchell, J. W. (1953), *Phil. Mag.*, **44,** 223.

Huntington, H. B., Dickey, J. E., and Thomson, R. (1955), *Phys. Rev.*, **100,** 1117.

Mollwo, E. (1935), *Nachr. Akad. Wiss. Göttingen,* 215.

Mollwo, E. (1937), *Ann. Physik,* **29,** 399.

Read, T. W. (1953), *Dislocations in Crystals,* McGraw Hill Book Co., New York.

Rexer, E. (1932), *Z. Physik,* **78,** 538.

Seitz, F. (1952), *Advances in Phys.*, **1,** 43.

Seitz, F. (1954), *Rev. Mod. Phys.*, **26,** 7.

Suzuki, T., and Suzuki, H. (1954), *Sci. Rep. Res. Inst. Tohoku Univ., A,* **6,** No. 6, 573.

Thompson, N. (1953), *Proc. Phys. Soc. (London), B,* **66,** 481.

Van der Merwe, J. H. (1949), *Discussions Faraday Soc.*, No. 5, 201.

Van der Vorst, W., and Dekeyser, W. (1956), *Phil. Mag.* (8), **1,** 882.
Vogel, F. L., Jr., and Lovell, L. Clarice (1956), *J. Appl. Phys.*, **27,** 1413.

ACKNOWLEDGMENTS

This work is part of a Research Scheme supported by I.R.S.I.A. (Brussels). I wish to thank Professor Dr. W. Dekeyser for his continuous interest, Professor Dr. F. Seitz and Mrs. Maenhout-Van der Vorst for discussion concerning some aspects of the decoration processes, and Dr. R. Thomson for correspondence on some problems of the dislocation aspect. I must also thank Mr. W. Bontinck for the use of Fig. 30*e*. I am indebted to Dr. Friedel for reading his manuscript before publication.

DISCUSSION

FRANK inquired as to the difference in treatment of the crystals that exhibited dislocation climb and those that did not exhibit climb. AMELINCKX explained that the treatment was the same in both cases, but the climb was more prominent in the region at the boundary of the diffusion zone.

KOEHLER suggested that the relative energies of the different types of dislocation might be determined from an analysis of the dislocation network; and AMELINCKX replied that such an analysis had been made, using the angles of the network to calculate the relative energy, and a reasonable value was obtained. AMELINCKX agreed with LEIBFRIED that the anisotropy of the crystal has to be taken into account in such a calculation.

HIRSCH pointed out that one could also investigate the possible arrangements of dislocations when three boundaries meet in a line. He added that there are a number of conditions that must be satisfied; for instance, the boundaries have to be stress-free, tensions have to balance at the nodes, and the Burgers vectors must be conserved. HIRSCH said that if this is studied for the case of a face-centered cubic crystal with a (111) [110] slip system, the possibilities for such junctions of three boundaries are extremely limited, if all the conditions are satisfied.

Written comment by AMELINCKX:

As a consequence of the remark by Hirsch, we devoted some attention to the geometry of boundary junctions in the NaCl lattice. The number of ways in which stable boundaries can be made to join along a node line is indeed rather limited when one considers only dislocations confined to their glide planes; we presume that this is the case to which Hirsch referred. However, when one allows climb, the number of possibilities increases very much even when only considering two dislocation boundaries. We are now in the process of analyzing all cases.

In reply to THOMSON's question as to whether dislocations with a [100] Burgers vector had been found, AMELINCKX said that the only evidence for such a dislocation is the existence of loops on the (100) plane which seem to be prismatic, and would, therefore, presumably have a [100] Burgers vector.

Written comment by AMELINCKX (added in press):

Recent observations of decorated dislocations in KCl crystals, as grown, have brought evidence for the occurrence of segments of dislocation with Burgers vector a [100].

They are formed at the intersection point of two dislocations with mutually perpendicular Burgers vectors, when some external influence catalyzes the reaction $a/2$ [110] + $a/2$ $[1\bar{1}0] \rightarrow a$ [100]. Such an external influence can be exerted, for example, by a third crossing dislocation which twists the first two dislocations into the antiparallel orientation.

The dislocations with a [100] Burgers vector also form at the node points of nets with a [100] rotation axis, when these nets are lying in planes oblique with respect to (100). The segments then form in the acute angles of the lozenge-shaped meshes.

JOHNSTON asked how much of the dislocation structure could be attributed to the presence of the excess sodium; and he mentioned that in lithium fluoride the dislocation density is greatly increased by the introduction of excess lithium. AMELINCKX replied that this effect had not been studied in the rock salt.

LEIBFRIED pointed out that the cooling down and the precipitation should cause stresses on the dislocation so that the dislocations are not in an equilibrium network. AMELINCKX agreed that there is not necessarily equilibrium; the dislocations are restricted in their evolution toward equilibrium shape, because they are pinned at other dislocations and probably at precipitates.

Written discussion by AMELINCKX and THOMSON:

One of the possibilities suggested by the experimental results of this paper is to check the observed angles of the dislocations at the nodal points with the values predicted on the basis of energy considerations. One of the observed networks is sketched in Fig. D1. The plane of the net is (100), and the direction of the horizontal screw is (110). Actually, in the observations, the screw dislocation is not seen—its existence is only inferred by the presence of what seem to be incomplete nodes at each end of the screw. Also, the direction between the two nodal points is that corresponding to the usual Burgers vector in the crystal, and it is entirely reasonable that the screws are not decorated so easily as the edges.

If one makes the assumption that the horizontal dislocation is a screw, then the Burgers vectors of the other dislocations are fixed to one of two possibilities. The Burgers vectors at a node, taken together, define one of the (111) planes, and a Burgers vector in the [110] direction can be

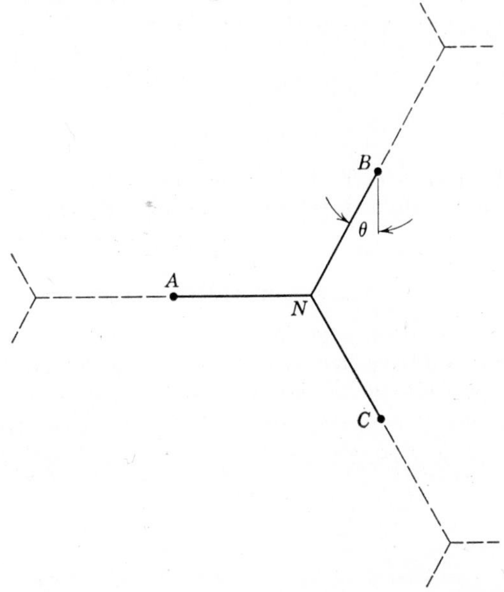

Fig. D1. Part of a dislocation network seen in rock salt. The horizontal line *AN* is a screw dislocation with orientation [110] which is split at the node *N* into two other dislocations. The network thus formed lies in a (100) plane. The two dislocations to the right of *N* are mixed screw-edge dislocations with complicated slip planes. In making the energy minimization, we have assumed that the dislocations are pinned down at points *A*, *B*, and *C*, which localizes the network, but allows it to change its shape.

either in a $(1\bar{1}1)$ or $(\bar{1}11)$ plane, which correspond to the two possible choices for the other Burgers vectors at the node. Let us now assume that the three points *A*, *B*, and *C* in the figure are fixed. The energy of the part of the network drawn with a solid line may be computed, and if the horizontal position of the node *N* is allowed to move so that the length of line *AN* is allowed to vary, the energy may be minimized, and the angle θ calculated. Corresponding to the two choices mentioned above, there will be two values of θ. One choice leads to a slip plane near (110), and the second to a slip plane near (100).

As a first approximation, one may take the value of the line energy of the dislocation to be that of an infinitely long dislocation, and neglect the interaction energy of one part of the network on another. We have used the energy as computed by Huntington, Dickey, and Thomson.* An inspection of the dislocations of this network shows that the slip plane is not a simple one, and that the dislocation is mixed screw-edge. One of the results of the energy calculations in ref. 1, however, is that when the dislocation density is 4×10^3 dislocations/cm^2, the energy of a dislocation is not a function of its slip plane. Also, in the vicinity of $N = 10^4$, the variation of energy on slip plane is very small. (This result is due to a cancellation of core and elastic effects.) We have thus assumed that $N = 10^4/\text{cm}^2$ leads to a reasonable cutoff radius in the elastic energy for this network. We have also assumed that the variation of the energy from edge to screw is sinusoidal, as suggested in ref. 1. The energy may then be written as

$$E = A(1 - 0.273 \cos^2 \chi)$$

where χ is the angle between the Burgers vector and the dislocation.

With the simplifications listed above, the angle θ is given below.

Slip plane near (110): $\theta = 29°$

Slip plane near (100): $\theta = 15°$

The observed value of the angle in the decorated crystal is $\theta = 30°$ in very close agreement with the first value. The value of 30°, however, is also the value one would expect if the energy of the dislocation line was a constant, independent of the screw-edge orientation.

* H. B. Huntington, J. E. Dickey, and R. Thomson, *Phys. Rev.*, **100,** 1117 (1955).

A Slip Source in KCl

S. AMELINCKX

W. MAENHOUT-VAN DER VORST

Laboratorium voor Kristalkunde
Geologisch Instituut
Rijks Universiteit
Ghent, Belgium

We would like to show one photograph of what we believe to be a slip source in KCl (Fig. 1). We used KCl doped by the addition of 2% AgCl to the melt. Decoration, after deformation by compression, was obtained by annealing in hydrogen.

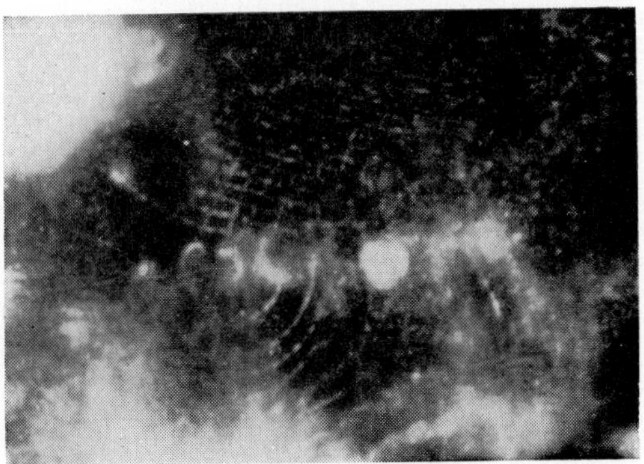

Fig. 1. Slip source in KCl.

When changing focus it was found that the source had the structure shown in Fig. 2. It may be worthwhile to point out that slip sources of this configuration (i.e., a sweeping dislocation pinned at both ends by nodes) in the NaCl-structure are of the "spatial" or "conical" type (Suzuki and Fujita, 1954; Bilby, 1955). This follows from the following argument. The condition for planity is that the plane of the Burgers vectors of the three dislocations meeting in the two nodes

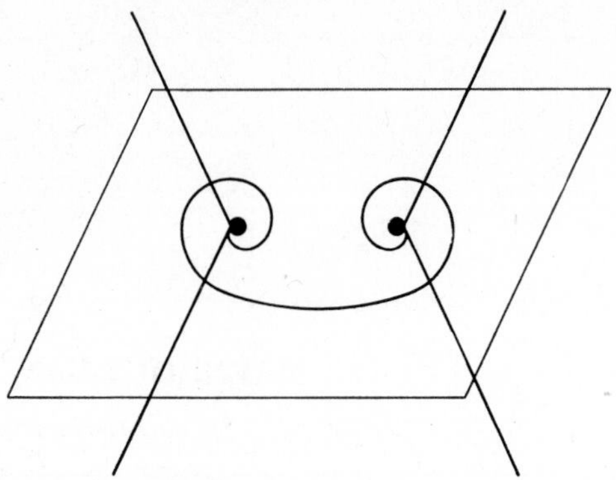

Fig. 2. Schematic structure of the slip source of Fig. 1.

[i.e., one of the (111) planes] should be parallel to the slip plane. This cannot be the case in KCl, where the slip planes are (110) planes.

REFERENCES

Bilby, B. A. (1955), *Report of a Conference on Defects in Crystalline Solids*, Physical Society, London, p. 124.

Suzuki, H., and Fujita, F. E. (1954), *J. Phys. Soc. Japan*, **9**, 428

The Observation of Dislocations in Silicon

W. C. DASH

General Electric Research Laboratory
Schenectady, New York

A technique has been developed to decorate dislocations in silicon so that they are visually observable with an infrared image tube in conjunction with a microscope.[1,2] This technique enables one to observe the dislocation structures that are produced by small deformations.

For the work presented here silicon single crystals were grown by drawing from the melt contained in a quartz crucible. The number of dislocations in the crystals studied ranged from fewer than 10/cm^2 to about 10^4/cm^2 as determined from etch pits and subsequent decoration.*

Bars of about 10-mm^2 cross-sectional area were deformed very slightly by twisting about a [111] axis or by bending about a suitable axis. These were then etched during a period of several hours or overnight in a mixture of nitric, hydrofluoric, and acetic acids to produce deep pits at the points of emergence of the dislocations. Etch-pit concentrations of a few hundred per cm^2 are readily obtainable

* The existence of small dislocation loops which are less than a few microns in diameter cannot be determined by the method used and therefore are not included in the quoted dislocation densities. In addition, it is not inconceivable that there exist dislocations so modified by impurities that they are not detectable by either etch pits or decoration.

upon deformation of specimens with a few grown-in dislocations.

After etching, the bars were cut into 1-mm thick slices parallel to (111) planes and the cut surfaces optically polished. A drop of copper nitrate solution with as little as 10^{-7} to 10^{-6} atom fraction of copper was dried on the edge of each slice. The specimens were then heated to about 900°C for 30 min and cooled to room temperature in a few seconds to a minute. They were then examined with transmitted

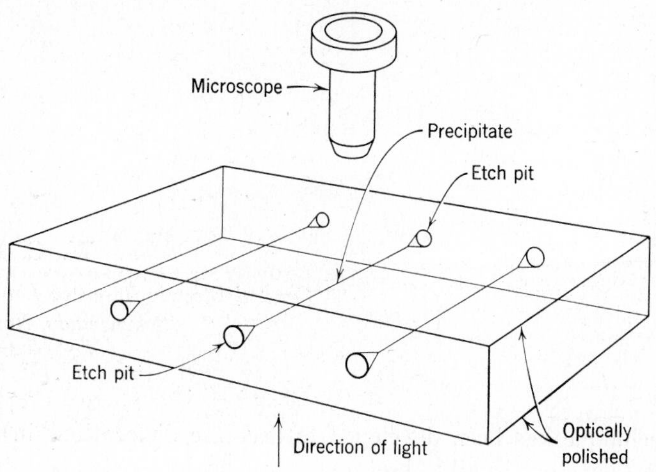

Fig. 1. Experimental arrangement for viewing decorated dislocations in silicon. Infrared light transmitted by the silicon is converted to visible light by an infrared image tube at the position of the microscope eyepiece.

infrared as illustrated schematically in Fig. 1. An infrared image tube at the position of the eyepiece in a Leitz Panphot microscope makes possible direct observations of the precipitates formed. Photographs of the precipitates are made with infrared sensitive plates.

Figure 2*a* shows a wedge-shaped portion of a bar bent about the [001] axis, and viewed along the axis of bending as illustrated in Fig. 2*b*. Deep etch pits enter from the two wedge faces. The copper has decorated the dislocations in a distinct manner, joining pairs of etch pits on opposite sides of the sample. The dislocations are generally straight lines lying in the [110] direction.

Figure 3 is a view along a [111] direction of a twisted bar, showing a series of dislocation half loops that intersect a surface with orientation approximating (112). The lower part of the figure shows the pits as they appear on the surface. All parts of the loops lie in [110] directions. The sections approximately parallel to the edge of the

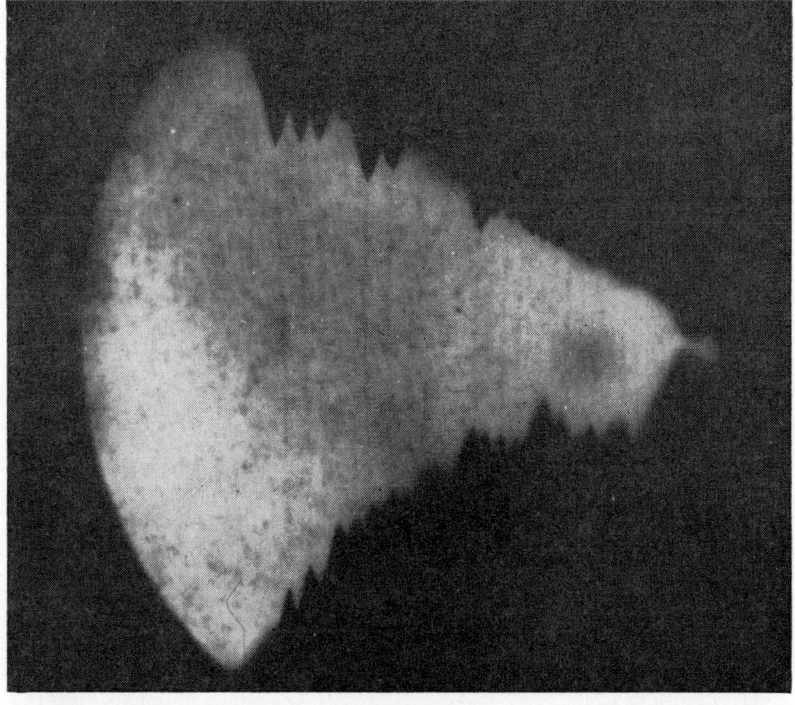

(*a*)

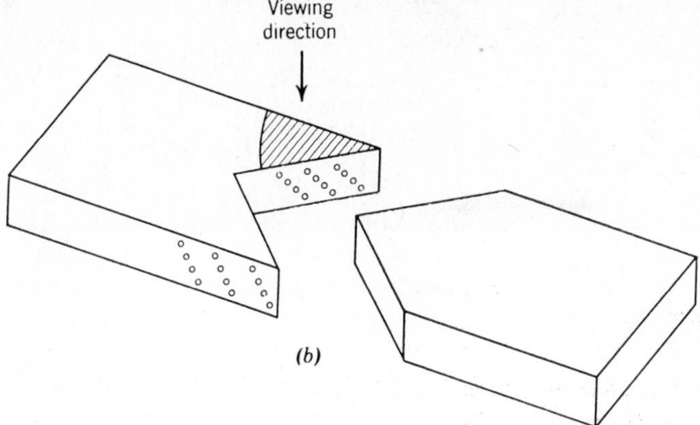

Fig. 2. (*a*) Decorated dislocations joining etch pits (seen in silhouette) on opposite sides of wedge-shaped specimen viewed along a [001] bend axis. (*b*) The crosshatched area shows the portion of broken bar in (*a*).

sample are screws; the inclined sections are composite edge and screw.* The etch pits make abrupt turns to follow the paths of the dislocations, indicating that screws and composites are etched at approximately the

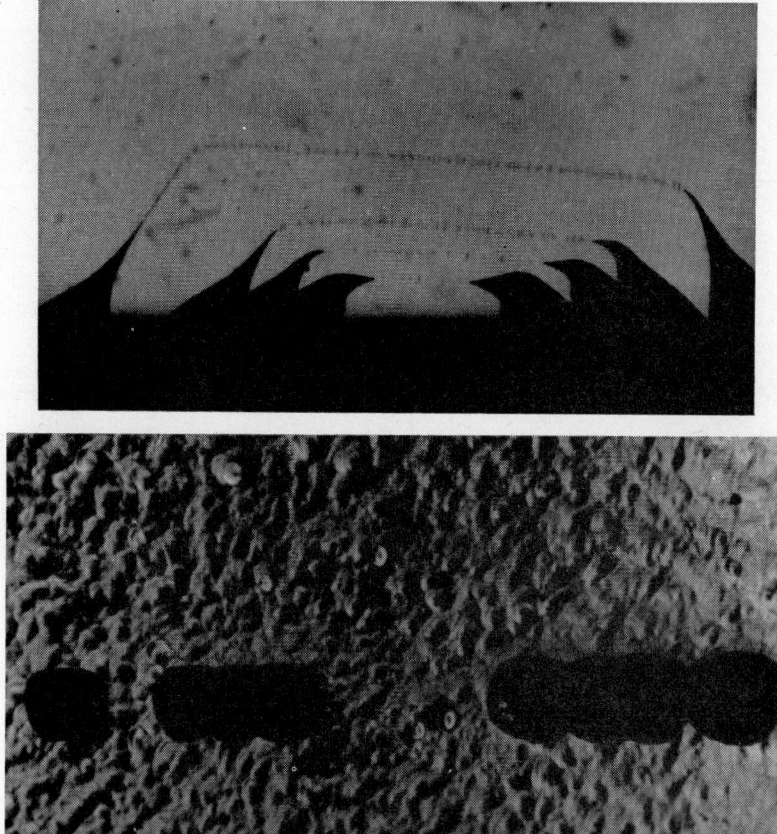

Fig. 3. Etch pits and dislocation loops entering from a (112) surface in a specimen twisted about [111] viewing direction. Lower photograph shows pits at the (112) surface.

same rate. It is of interest that neither within the specimen nor at its surface is there any evidence of a dislocation that could serve as a source for this sequence of loops.

Figure 4 shows another set of dislocation half loops entering from a (110) surface of the same specimen. In this case the Burgers vectors

* The nature of the various sections of loops such as these was determined from experiments in which the slip direction was controlled.

are inclined to the edge of the specimen. The lines in the array consist of two apparently non-coplanar sets since many of them cross each other and end on alternate pits.

The small loop in the center is best described in conjunction with

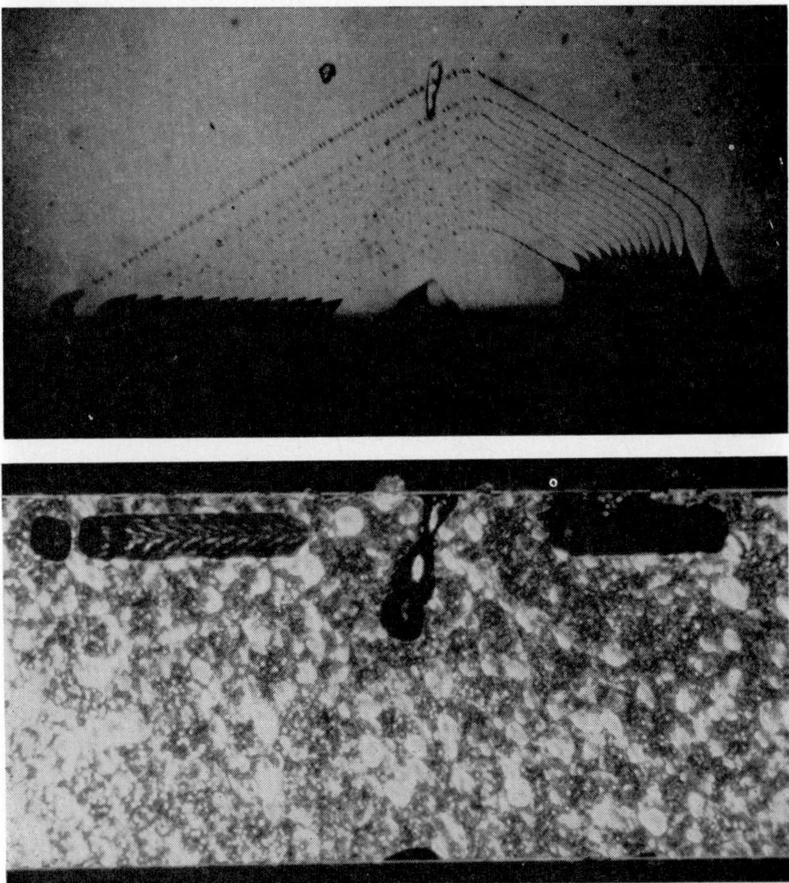

Fig. 4. Etch pits and dislocation loops entering from a (110) surface of the specimen shown in Fig. 3. Lower photograph shows pits at the (110) surface.

the lower part of Fig. 4 showing the pits at the surface. This line lies in a (111) plane which intersects the other array. The pit terminating the right-hand side in the upper picture was nearly removed in the polishing process, but a small part of it formed a hole in the polished surface. The pit on the left corresponds to the lowest one in the photograph of the surface. The other two pits resembling a bow tie

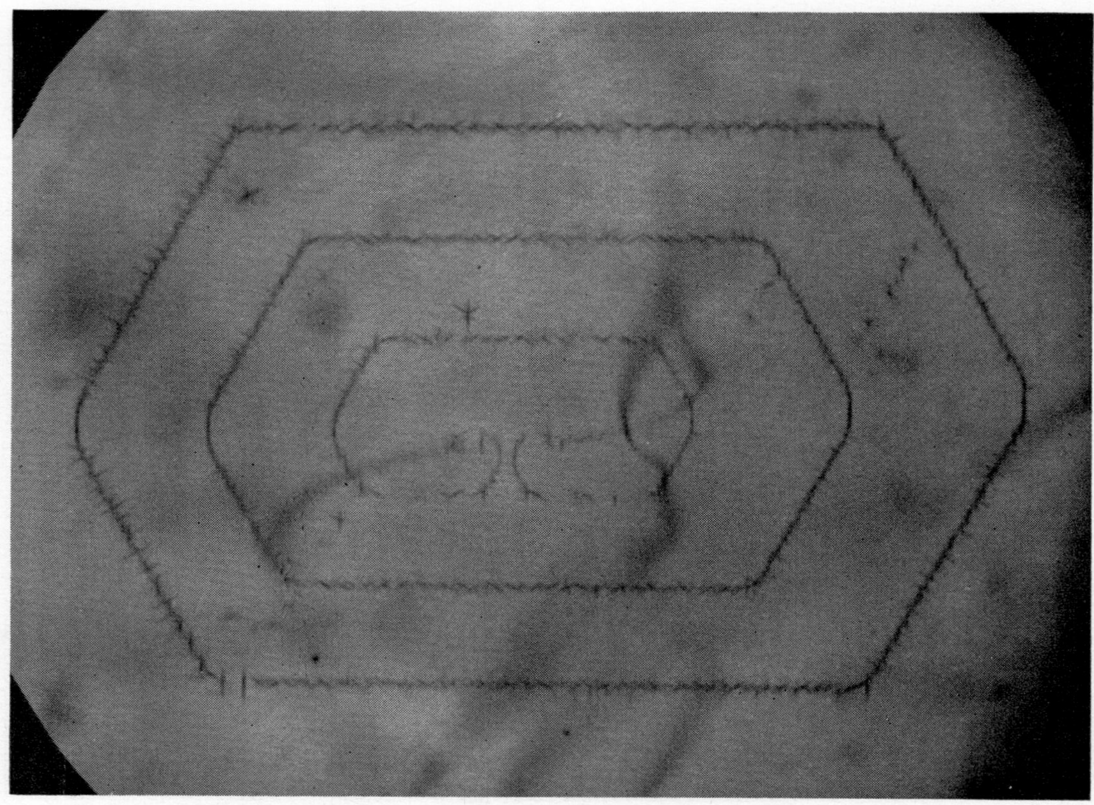

Fig. 5. Loop multiplication by a symmetrical Frank-Read source in the interior of a specimen twisted about the [111] viewing direction. The source is the central part of the s-shaped dislocation which goes out of focus below the glide plane on either side of the center.

in the lower picture locate a smaller loop which was completely etched away.

As in the case of the array in Fig. 3, there seems to be no grown-in dislocation which could serve as a source for the two sequences. Observations of this type are quite frequent in samples with low grown-in dislocation content. In some cases this may be because the etching has removed material which contained the source from which the slip started. In other cases the experiment has been done without etching the specimens, and still no source is visible at the center of the loops that have started at the surface. It seems unlikely that the sources of these arrays are grown-in dislocations.

Interior sources are seldom found in crystals with few grown-in dislocations, but many have been found upon deforming less perfect crystals. Figure 5 illustrates loop multiplication in the interior, confirming one mechanism proposed by Frank and Read.[3] The source is the central part of the s-shaped dislocation which goes out of focus below the glide plane on either side of center. The portions not in the glide plane, being immobile, anchor the ends of the mobile section. The central loop has expanded almost to the point of closing. Two completely closed hexagons have moved away from the source. From the shapes of the hexagons, a topic discussed further below, it is concluded that the source is a screw. The other grown-in dislocation to the right of center apparently does not enter the plane of the source.

Dislocation multiplication by a spiral mechanism, also proposed by Frank and Read, can be seen in Fig. 6. The source in this case is anchored by a fourfold node at one end. The other end intersects the surface, terminating nine full turns of the spiral. Figure 7 shows a combination spiral and symmetrical source which ultimately forms closed rings. Spiral sources have been found much more frequently than symmetrical sources.

For the entire temperature range in these experiments, 900°C to 1100°C, the dislocation loops have crystallographically oriented segments if the specimen is deformed as rapidly as possible consistent with avoidance of fracture. At the lower end of this range of temperatures a similar result is obtained with as little as 1% of this rate of deformation. At temperatures in the upper end of this range the configurations obtained at small rates of deformation have an entirely different appearance, as illustrated in Fig. 8. The dislocations are curvilinear and wander about the crystal unconfined to a single glide plane. Concentric rings are not found. It is possible that under the conditions of deformation the Frank-Read mechanism does not operate

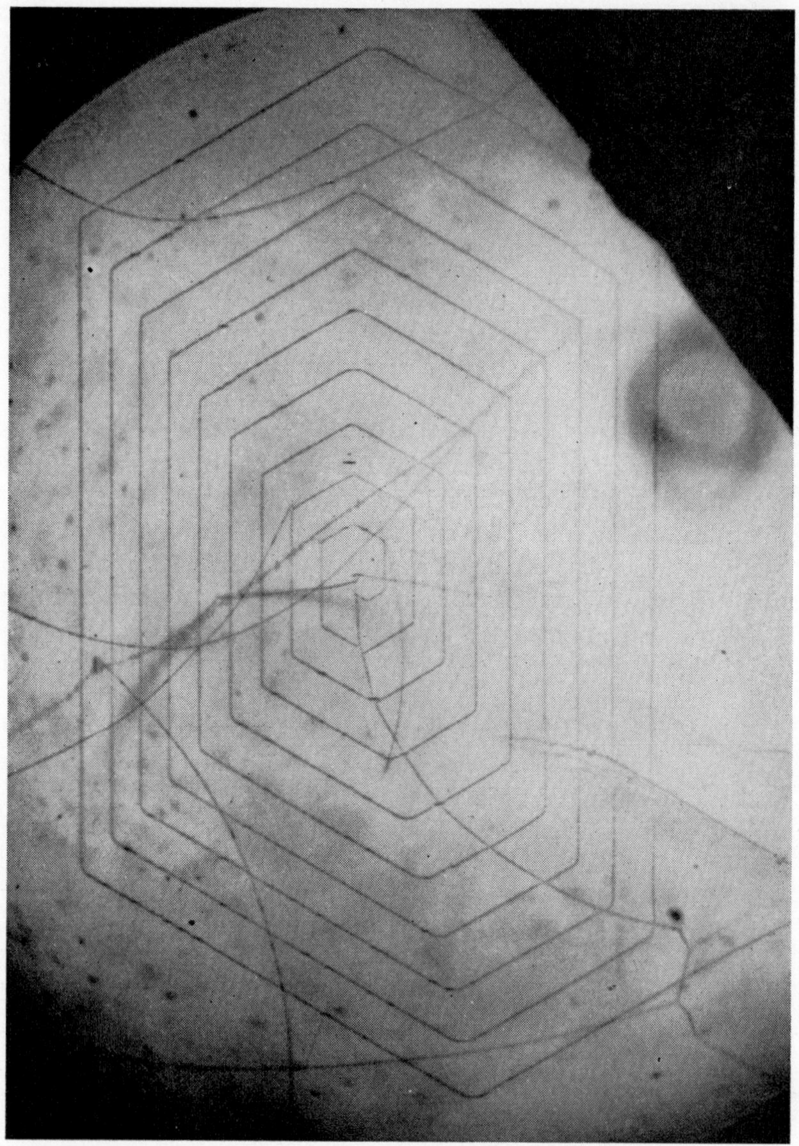

Fig. 6. Loop multiplication by the spiral Frank-Read mechanism in the interior of a specimen twisted about the [111] viewing direction.

because all segments of the dislocations can move sufficiently to eliminate the anchoring essential to this mechanism.

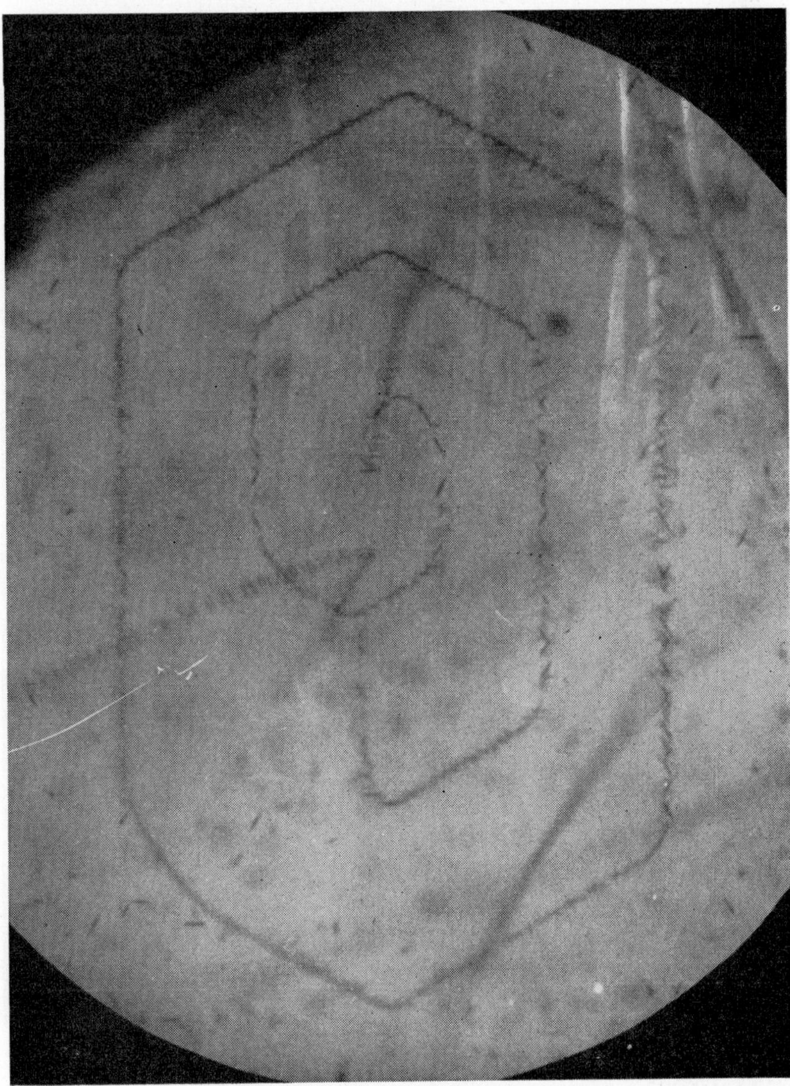

Fig. 7. Combined spiral and symmetrical source.

In Figs. 5 through 7 an elongation of the hexagons in the direction of the screw axes can be seen. It can be concluded from this that the screws move more slowly than composites. This characteristic is frequently useful for identification purposes.

A wide variation is found from sample to sample in the form of the precipitate particles and the relative amounts of decoration on the

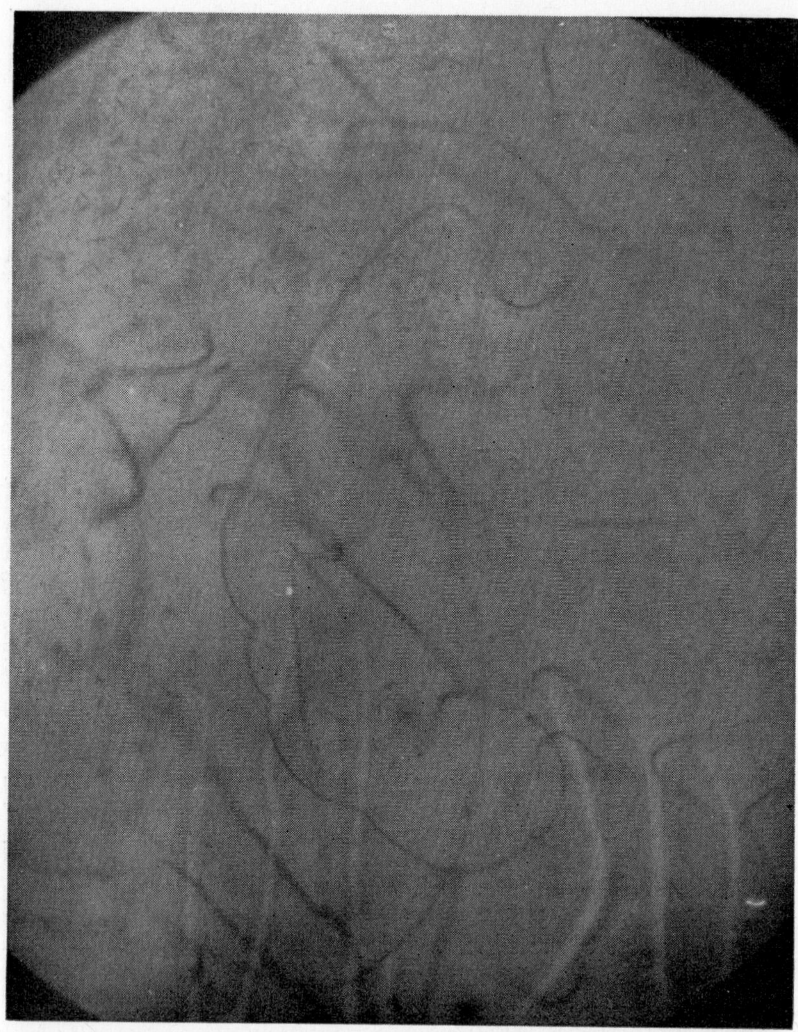

Fig. 8. Curvilinear dislocations found in specimen deformed at a slow rate at about 1100°C.

screws and composites. In Fig. 9, for example, the screws are not decorated at all. In many cases where all sections are decorated, the particles are elongated in a direction perpendicular to the Burgers vector. It has been found that the form of the precipitates can be predetermined to some degree by varying the initial copper concentration on the surface and the cooling rate. Rapid cooling of a sample saturated with copper results in uniform decoration; slow cooling of a sample with 10^{-6} to 10^{-7} atom fraction of copper results in preferential precipitation on the composites. Although this general behavior is usually observed, some specimens have been seen with screws decorated in one region and undecorated in another region a few millimeters away.

Fig. 9. Series of loops from an internal source. The screw portions are undecorated.

REFERENCES

1. W. C. Dash, *Phys. Rev.,* **98,** 1536 (1955).
2. W. C. Dash, *J. Appl. Phys.,* **27,** 1153 (1956).
3. F. C. Frank and W. T. Read, *Phys. Rev.,* **79,** 722 (1950).

ACKNOWLEDGMENT

The author wishes to express his appreciation to Professor F. C. Frank who presented this paper at the Conference.

DISCUSSION

In answer to a question of how common interior sources were, FRANK said that they are fairly common in specimens that contained a lot of grown-in dislocations and that over 100 such sources have been seen.

MITCHELL suggested that the reason why most of the sources appear to be screw dislocations is that the screw dislocations are not as strongly locked by impurities as are the edge dislocations. This is evident from the decoration with copper, where it is seen that the precipitate is heavy on the edge dislocations, and the screws are not decorated. FRANK said that Dash is doing experiments to test this idea, but that there was as yet no definite explanation as to why the sources are screw dislocations.

LOMER felt that it might not be necessary to invoke precipitation on edges to explain why it is that the screws become the sources. He suggested that whereas, in general, the grown-in dislocations run randomly through the crystal in noncrystallographic planes, the portions that are almost parallel to the Burgers vector can gain energy by moving onto the slip plane and dissociating. Therefore, one would expect the parts of the grown-in dislocation that are near screw orientation to lie on a slip plane, and these can readily act as sources. FRANK objected to this because he thought that the screw dislocations in a diamond structure should be left undissociated, so that there are no free bonds. The edge dislocation has broken bonds but the undissociated screw dislocation has none in the diamond structure.

READ pointed out that one reason why a screw would move easier is that a screw dislocation in silicon lies on two (111) planes, and it can move on whichever plane there is the higher stress.

SEEGER inquired whether there are any quantitative data on the spacing of the dislocation loops that are formed by an interior source, and on the stresses at which the sources operate. This would be of interest in view of the possible connection of the hexagons found by Dash with the dislocation arrangement in deformed f.c.c. crystals as discussed in § 6 of Seeger's paper (pages 293–294 of this volume). FRANK replied that there are no quantitative data yet.

Dislocations in Crystals of Silver Halides

J. W. MITCHELL
H. H. Wills Physical Laboratory
University of Bristol
Bristol, England

1. INTRODUCTION

In 1905, Siedentopf published a series of drawings, based upon ultramicroscopic observations, which showed the distribution of particles of colloidal sodium in additively colored and in naturally occurring blue rock salt. The boundaries between the elements of a substructure were made visible by the colloidal sodium and he recorded for the first time the presence of linear imperfections within a transparent inorganic crystal. During the next 20 years, the subject received little attention from experimental workers even though Darwin (1914, 1922) had interpreted the observed intensities of X-ray diffraction maxima on the assumption that inorganic crystals possessed a mosaic substructure.

Smekal (1929) then emphasized the role of imperfections in determining structure sensitive physical and chemical properties of crystals and sought methods whereby they might be made visible. Many papers on this subject were published by Smekal (1933) and other workers in his Institute at Halle. Among these, those of Rexer (1931, 1932a, b) who studied the diffusion of sodium into crystals of rock salt at high temperatures are of particular interest. Rexer found that linear imperfections and subboundaries within polygonized crystals were made visible at the boundary of the diffusion zone by the separation of particles of colloidal sodium. Rexer was probably the first person to observe the decoration of dislocations within an intentionally deformed and annealed transparent crystal but his work preceded the theoretical papers of Taylor and of Burgers and the concepts which were needed for its interpretation were not then available. Line imperfections in crystals of sodium chloride containing barium chloride were also observed at Halle at this time by Edner (1932).

The first observations of linear imperfections in transparent crystals after the intensive postwar development of the theory of dislocations (see Cottrell, 1953; Read, 1953) were made at Bristol by Hedges and Mitchell (1953a). Early in November 1952, during the course of their investigation of the nature and distribution of the internal photographic latent image, they found that the substructure of strained crystals of silver bromide which had been lightly annealed could be made visible by exposing them at room temperature to light with a wavelength close to the absorption edge. Hedges and Mitchell were immediately able to recognize tilt subboundaries formed by arrays of parallel edge dislocations which had previously been the subject of theoretical discussion (Burgers, 1939; Read and Shockley, 1950) and twist boundaries formed by crossed grids of screw dislocations which were to form the subject of future theoretical papers (Frank, 1955a). Their observations provided the first clear experimental demonstration of the essential validity of many of the theoretical developments (see Frank, 1955b). They also made the first observations of the behavior of dislocations within a transparent crystal during plastic deformation and it has since become evident that silver bromide is paticularly suited for work of this type. In this substance, alone among the inorganic crystals which have so far been investigated, the dislocations actually involved in plastic deformation at room temperature or at higher temperatures may be rendered immobile and made visible by exposing the crystals to light while the stress is still applied to them. The crystals do not have to be annealed at a higher temperature before the dislocations may be decorated, and as the most satisfactory results are obtained with the purest materials the segregation of a foreign impurity is unlikely to be involved in the decoration process. The deformation structures which are thus observed are modified by annealing. Many observations have been made of the probable behavior of dislocations in crystals of silver bromide during low temperature annealing (200–350°C) leading to polygonization and during high temperature annealing (350–410°C). Several hundred photomicrographs are available of particular features of the distributions of dislocations in plastically deformed and in annealed specimens.

Annealing structures in crystals of sodium chloride, probably containing traces of silver chloride (Boesman, Remaut, and Dekeyser, 1956), in which the dislocations have been rendered visible by the method developed by Rexer (1931, 1932a, b) have been studied in recent years by Amelinckx, Van der Vorst, Gevers, and Dekeyser (1955) and Amelinckx (1956) of the University of Ghent. They have published many beautiful photographs of these structures. This method cannot, however, be employed for the study of the internal behavior of dislocations during the plastic deformation of sodium chloride. For the decoration of the dislocations, the crystals have to be heated to temperatures at which rapid polygonization occurs before colloidal silver or sodium can separate along the dislocation lines.

The silver halides are thus the only ionic solids in which it has so far proved possible to observe both the probable behavior of dislocations on incipient slip bands at a definite stage during plastic deformation and the configurations of dislocations in the polygonized crystals which result from the annealing of strained specimens.

2. EXPERIMENTAL METHODS

A. Preparation of Pure Silver Halides

The preparation of pure fused silver halides for experimental work on dislocations has been described in detail in a recent paper (Clark and Mitchell, 1956). Cationic impurities are removed from the silver nitrate by suitable special methods and careful recrystallization. Anionic impurities are removed from the constant boiling point mixtures of the hydrogen halides by chemical methods and by fractional distillation. Fine particles of silica are removed from the molten silver halide by repeated filtration through fine glass capillaries after the passage through the melt for approximately 1 hr of a stream of the dry hydrogen halide in nitrogen as a carrier gas. When present, the silica particles give rise to randomly distributed etch pits (§ 3.A), and fog specks (§ 3.B, 3.C, 3.D, and 3.E), which are not related to the dislocation lines revealed by the separation of photolytic silver (§ 3.F). Further purification of silver chloride and silver bromide may then be effected by fractional distillation in high vacuum which breaks down Ag_2O and Ag_2S and removes a number of more volatile impurities such as cuprous and mercury halides and a number of less volatile and troublesome polyvalent cationic impurities. The silver halide is then heated in vacuum at 10^{-6} mm Hg for at least 8 hr and finally treated with the halogen all at a temperature about 50°C above the melting point before final crystallization. Crystals made from material prepared in this way are not spontaneously reduced to silver even when immersed for one minute in vigorous photographic developers and this, in our experience, provides a most sensitive test of purity.

B. Preparation of Large Single Crystals

Large single crystals are grown by lowering carefully evacuated and sealed-off, thin-walled, cylindrical tubes of borosilicate glass with conical ends containing the fused silver halide through a Bridgman-Stockbarger type of crystallizing furnace with the upper section at a temperature 50° above the melting point and the lower section formed by a double-walled copper jacket cooled to room temperature with a fast stream of water. Experience has shown that crystallization in a good vacuum under these conditions is necessary for the production of crystals with satisfactory properties.

The crystals are cut with a rotating thin Aloxite disk lubricated with water and then polished on soft Selvyt cloths soaked in a 1% potassium cyanide solution. A smooth polished surface can be readily produced provided that the cloths are frequently washed in the cyanide solution during polishing. It is usually necessary to polish away ½ mm from each side of the crystal to remove the deformation produced by cutting.

Sodium thiosulphate should not be used for polishing or etching because it leaves an adsorbed layer of silver thiosulphate on the surface of the crystal which may break down to silver sulphide. This sensitizes the surface of the crystal and may lead to a general surface separation of silver during exposure. It may also fog the surface so that the methods for rendering dislocations visible which depend on development cannot be employed.

C. Preparation of Thin Single Crystals

The methods used for preparing large thin single crystals of silver chloride and silver bromide with (100), (110), and (111) surfaces have been fully described (Hedges and Mitchell, 1953b; Clark and Mitchell, 1956) and such crystals have been used for the bulk of the experimental work on dislocations at Bristol.

D. Cleavage of Crystals

The thin single crystals of silver chloride and silver bromide with (001) surfaces cleave along (100) planes normal to their surfaces when they are nicked at the edge with a razor blade while resting on a glass plate after having been cooled to the temperature of liquid air. This is a valuable method for establishing the orientation of the crystals. Stars defined by cracks along [100] directions are also produced by pressing a fine needle into the surface of a cooled specimen.

We have never succeeded in cleaving large single crystals of silver chloride and silver bromide in the manner of rock salt after having cooled them down to $-183°C$.

E. Annealing of Crystals

The thin single crystals are strained as a result of the differential contraction between the borosilicate glass and the silver halide which occurs while they are cooling from the temperature of the melting point to room temperature. The most useful observations on the properties of dislocations in crystals of silver halides have been made on thin crystals which have been annealed at temperatures between 200 and 400°C for periods up to 12 hr.

The crystals are annealed in an atmosphere of the halogen, which is condensed in a side arm cooled in liquid air before the crystals are finally cooled to room temperature. They may also be annealed in vacuum without thermal decomposition if they are free from silver sulphide, silver oxide, and from silver nuclei but vacuum-annealing often leads to thermal etching which is less in evidence when the crystals are annealed in an atmosphere of the halogen.

The crystals are polygonized if annealed at a temperature below 350°C in the strained state in which they are separated from the glass plates. They may be recrystallized by passing a zone at a temperature of about 300°C slowly through them after intense local deformation such as that produced by cutting an edge with a razor blade followed by treatment with a solution of potassium bromide containing bromine to remove the iron halide and the silver produced by the operation.

F. Surface Chemical Polishing and Etching

It is sometimes desirable to remove the surface which was in contact with the glass plate during crystallization by chemical methods, leaving a smooth nonfaceted crystal surface. This is best done with a 4% solution of potassium cyanide if the crystals are subsequently to be exposed to produce photolytic silver or exposed and developed. Otherwise a solution of ammonium thiocyanate provides an excellent polishing medium.

A solution of sodium thiosulphate etches (100) crystallographic facets on the surfaces of crystals of silver chloride and silver bromide. The adsorbed layer of silver thiosulphate already mentioned in § 2.B may be removed by treating the surface with a dilute solution of potassium cyanide.

G. Deformation of Crystals

The annealed crystals have been deformed by indentation with spherical, square, pyramid, and flat based cylindrical indentors, and also by elongation and bending. Indentation has a considerable advantage for qualitative work because it is possible to trace the changes which accompany increasing degrees of deformation.

3. METHODS FOR MAKING DISLOCATIONS VISIBLE

A. Etch Pits

This has so far proved to be the least satisfactory method for establishing the distribution of dislocations in crystals of silver halides. The best results have been obtained by etching with a solution containing 5 cc of ethylenediamine and 30 cc of water for 40 sec at room temperature. With this method, there is some correspondence between the distributions of dislocations revealed by etch pits and those established by subsequently printing silver out along the dislocation lines. Dilute solutions of potassium cyanide, sodium thiosulphate, and potassium bromide have given results of low reliability. The poorest correlations between etch pits and dislocations have been obtained with the purest crystals in which the displacement of the dislocations under the action of applied stresses can be observed. It appears that the dislocations which can be etched are not mobile so that it is likely that they owe their property of etching to the segregation of foreign atoms or molecules along the dislocation lines.

B. Formation of Internal Latent Image

An internal latent image is formed during the exposure of silver halide crystals by the separation of groups of silver atoms in internal imperfections (Hedges and Mitchell, 1953b; Evans, Hedges, and Mitchell, 1955). The points of emergence of dislocations through the surfaces of the crystals may be made visible as etch pits bounded by (111) planes by the following method: (1) expose to produce an internal latent image; (2) dissolve surface of crystal with a 1% solution of potassium cyanide; (3) destroy any silver adsorbed to the free surface with a chromic acid solution containing silver nitrate; (4) wash and reimmerse very briefly in the potassium cyanide solution (a few seconds); (5) develop with a glycin and sodium carbonate suface developer; (6) remove the silver produced by reduction with a solution of nitric acid (50% by volume). After (5), the points of emergence of the dislocations are visible as black specks. These specks are replaced by etch pits when the silver is dissolved away. This is one of the few methods whereby pits bounded by apparent (111) crystallographic planes can be produced on the surfaces of crystals of silver halides.

C. Silver Diffusion

Dislocations may be made visible within a few microns of the surfaces of the crystals by allowing a film of silver deposited on the surface from an atomic beam to diffuse into the crystals at a temperature between 150 and 250°C. Excess silver is destroyed by brief treatment with a solution of chromic acid containing silver nitrate before bright or dark field microscopic examination. The presence of dislocations at far greater depths below the surface may be established by following steps (2) through (5) or (6) of § 3.B after the diffusion of the silver into the crystals (Evans, Hedges, and Mitchell, 1955).

D. Exposure Under Solutions of Halogen Acceptors

The surfaces of crystals of silver halides may be exposed while covered with a thin film of a solution of a halogen acceptor. The film is usually formed between a microscopic cover glass and the crystal surface. With certain halogen acceptors, such as 1-phenyl-3-pyrazolidinone, discrete specks of silver are produced at the points of emergence of dislocations through the surfaces of the crystals. This has proved to be a useful method for studying the properties of distributions of closely spaced dislocations because good resolution is possible at high magnifications.

E. The Use of Physical Developers

A surface latent image may be produced by exposing crystals under an acid solution of a suitable halogen acceptor, such as hydroquinone, containing a slight excess of silver ions. The surface latent image which is formed principally at the points of emergence of dislocations through the surface of the crystal then provides nuclei for the deposition of visible specks of metal from physical developers containing either silver or gold ions. In some cases, exceedingly fine filaments of metal form at screw dislocations and shapeless nodular masses at edge dislocations.

F. The Separation of Internal Silver

The networks and distributions of dislocations within strained, lightly annealed, and plastically deformed thin crystals of silver chloride and silver bromide grown between Pyrex glass optical flats are made visible to a depth of at least 30 μ below the surface by exposing them to light with a wavelength in the long wave edge of the absorption band of the crystal. Silver then separates out along the dislocation lines, and it may be observed with either bright or dark field illumination.

G. General Observations

The most valuable results have so far been obtained (1) by exposing under a dilute solution of 1-phenyl-3-pyrazolidinone as in § 3.D and (2) by exposing to cause the separation of silver along the dislocation lines as in § 3.F. The points of intersection with the surface of the crystal of all the dislocations which can be made visible by (2) can usually be established by method (1). This method does, however, sometimes give considerably greater surface densities of randomly distributed silver specks than would be deduced from the observations on the internal separation of silver. The question therefore arises as to whether all the dislocations in a specimen are made visible by method (2). At present, the conclusion must be that dislocations are only made visible by this method under certain special conditions to be discussed in § 7.

4. OBSERVATIONS ON POLYGONIZATION STRUCTURES PRODUCED BY ANNEALING BETWEEN 250 AND 350°C

A. General Discussion of Polygonized Structures

The thin strained single crystals are polygonized by annealing them in an atmosphere of the halogen at temperatures between 250 and 350°C for periods up to 12 hr. After annealing, the existence of a substructure in the crystals may be demonstrated by the methods of § 3. The dislocation lines of the subboundaries do not usually follow crystallographic directions within the crystals. The structures are sometimes not uniform throughout the thickness of the crystals. Near the surfaces, a substructure may appear on annealing which has a much finer mesh than in the interior. The dislocation networks, however, appear to be continuous within the crystals and in many crystals the substructure is quite uniform throughout. The particular behavior depends on the conditions during crystallization and cooling to room temperature between the glass plates.

Similar substructures have not yet been reproducibly observed in well-annealed large single crystals of the purest silver chloride and silver bromide grown by the Bridgman-Stockbarger technique. They have, however, been observed in a number of such silver bromide crystals containing small percentages of silver iodide.

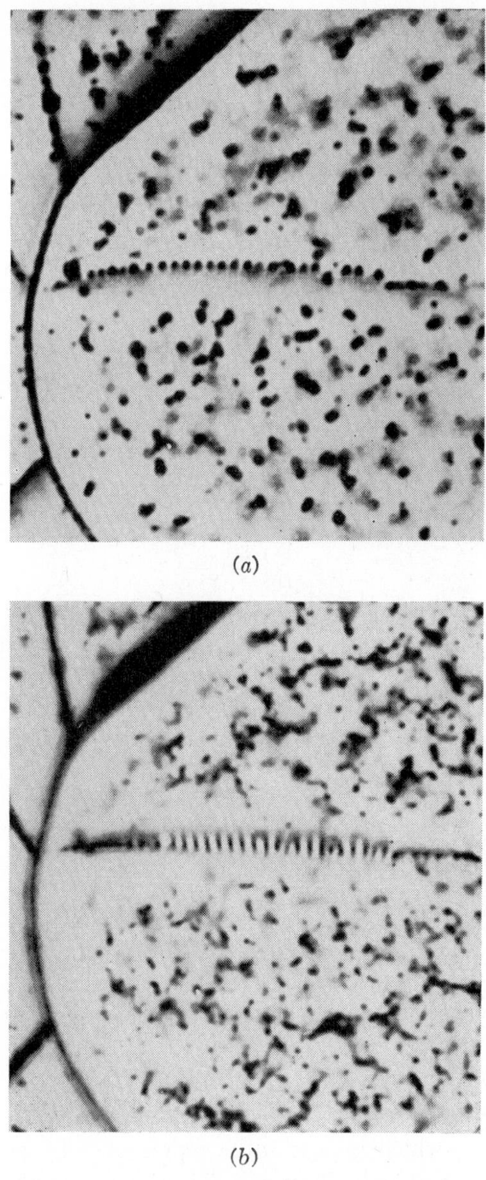

(*a*)

(*b*)

Fig. 1. (*a*) Tilt subboundary with the axis of tilt inclined at an angle to the surface of the crystal. The crystal was exposed under a dilute solution of phenyl pyrazolidinone and the points of emergence of the dislocations through the surface have been made visible by the separation of specks of silver. (*b*) Same field as (*a*), but 20 μ below the surface.

B. Tilt Subboundaries

With axis of tilt normal to the surface of the crystal. A tilt subboundary with this orientation is illustrated in Fig. 1.

With axis of tilt parallel to the surface. Polygonization leading to the appearance of a regular array of tilt subboundaries of this kind is frequently observed in the neighborhood of large angle grain boundaries. It is illustrated in the upper part of Fig. 2.

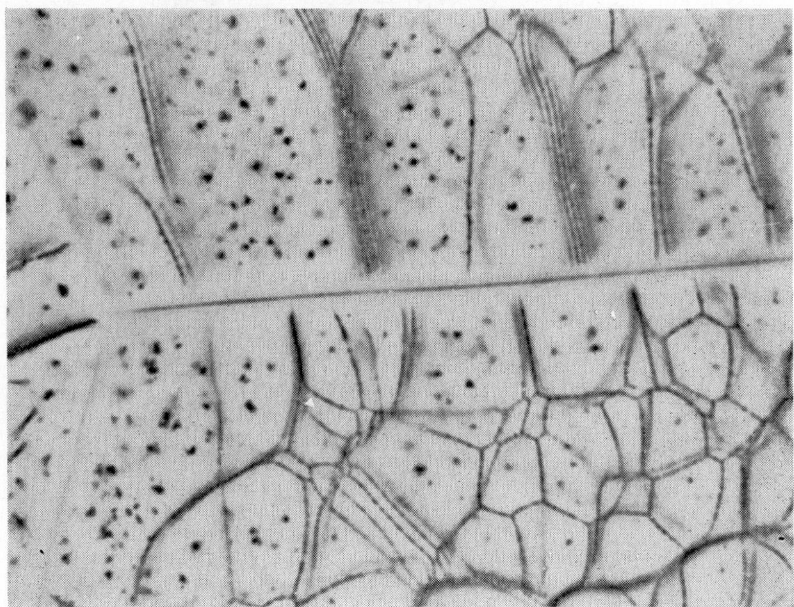

Fig. 2. Three grain boundaries intersect in the left-hand part of the field. The upper grain shows a series of tilt subboundaries with the axis of tilt nearly parallel to the surface of the specimen. The lower grain has a three-dimensional network of dislocations.

C. Twist Subboundaries

Subboundaries which appear to be represented by crossed grids of dislocations are commonly observed. They are particularly clearly defined in crystals with (111) surfaces in which they probably arise in the following way. The temperature conditions during crystallization by the method employed for producing the thin sheets are such that the leading edge of the crystal forms a tapering wedge of very small angle with its thin edge in contact with the upper plate. Disturbances accompanying the displacement of the plates during crystallization may lead to the formation of subboundaries in which the adjacent elements of the crystal are rotated on (111) planes about a [111] axis with respect to each other. Twist subboundaries are illustrated in Fig. 3.

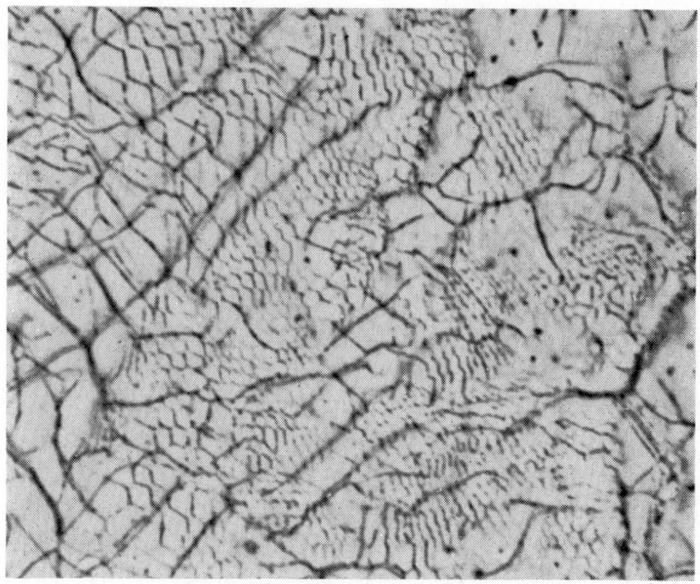

Fig. 3. Hexagonal network of dislocations.

D. General Subboundaries

Although there are usually many examples of both types of tilt subboundaries and of twist subboundaries in crystals with (001) and (111) surfaces, there are also many subboundaries in which non-coplanar arrays of interlacing dislocations of extreme complexity appear. The majority of the subboundaries are not of simple type.

E. Three-Dimensional Networks of Dislocation Lines

In most crystals many areas of several square millimeters are present in which the dislocations are arranged to form three-dimensional networks of reasonably constant mesh in which the dislocations intersect in triple nodes. The dislocations in these networks do not usually lie along definite crystallographic directions. A network of this type is shown in the lower part of Fig. 2.

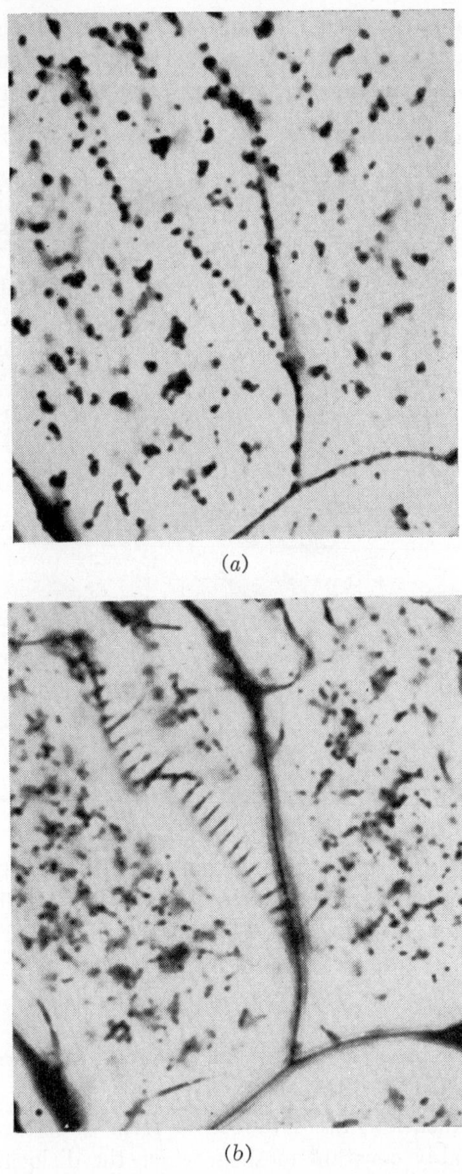

(a)

(b)

Fig. 4. (a) A fan of edge dislocations in a specimen which had been annealed at 400°C. This may represent a stage in the grouping of the dislocations into subboundaries. (b) Same field as (a), but 20 μ below the surface of the specimen.

F. Grain Boundaries

The structure of large angle boundaries has not been established either by the distribution of etch pits or by the separation of photolytic silver. Silver does not usually separate within these grain boundaries during exposure.

5. OBSERVATIONS OF STRUCTURES PRODUCED BY ANNEALING BETWEEN 350 AND 410°C

The dislocation substructures which have been described in § 4 rearrange when the crystals are annealed at temperatures above 350°C for 8 to 10 hr. The irregular subboundaries of § 4.D break up first into tangled curvilinear dislocations, leaving the tilt and twist boundaries. Regular fans of dislocations then often form at tilt subboundaries as shown in Fig. 4. Tilt boundaries with the axis of tilt normal to the surface of the crystal sometimes separate at the surface into two parallel walls composed of alternate dislocations from the original boundary.

After 8 to 10 hr at 400°C, little trace remains of the polygonized structure. The crystals are then divided into sections by relatively large angle grain boundaries along which silver does not usually separate during exposure. Within the elements thus outlined, for at least 40 μ below the surface, the dislocations which have densities between 10^5 and $10^8/\text{cm}^2$ are usually normal to the surface. Below this they form a three-dimensional network.

This material has been used for much of the experimental work on plastic deformation. Figure 5 is a photomicrograph 20 μ below the surface in the interior of a crystal element. The points are determined by the passage of dislocation lines which are normal to the surface through the focal plane of the microscope.

6. OBSERVATIONS OF DISLOCATIONS IN PLASTICALLY DEFORMED CRYSTALS

A. Large Single Crystals and Fully Annealed Recrystallized Sheets

Satisfactory observations of dislocations based upon the printing out of silver along the dislocation lines have not yet been made with sections cut from large single crystals of the purest silver chloride or silver bromide. That printing out is not fundamentally impossible has been shown by the observation of patches in some crystals where the dislocations have been made visible. This behavior, however, has never been sufficiently reliable to allow critical experiments to be carried out.

Etching procedures have also not given reliable results. Dislocations may usually be printed out and revealed by the formation of etch pits in large mixed crystals of silver bromide and silver iodide (0.01–0.1 mole %) and in a number of other mixed crystals.

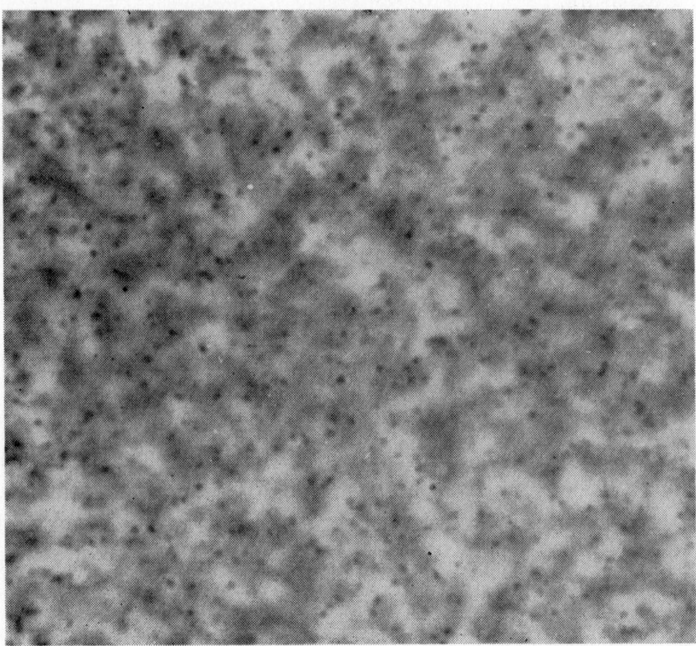

Fig. 5. Specimen annealed in bromine vapor (1 atmosphere pressure) at 400°C for 12 hr. The dislocations are normal to the surface of the specimen for 30–40 μ below the surface. The points in this photomicrograph correspond with the passage of the dislocations through the focal plane at a distance of 20 μ below the surface.

B. Thin Sheets Recrystallized at Low Temperatures After Intense Localized Deformation

These crystals form very little internal print-out silver when they are exposed without previous deformation. If they are strained at room temperature before exposure, printing out reveals the presence of groups of dislocation loops. They form smooth curves which show no tendency to develop rectilinear segments along definite crystallographic directions.

C. Thin Sheets Polygonized by Annealing at 250–350°C and then Deformed at Room Temperature

When the polygonized sheets are deformed by indentation, elongation, or bending, the regular walls and networks of dislocations which form the subboundaries break up and dislocations are then observed within all the elements of the substructure. With increasing strain a point is soon reached at which extended dislocation lines can no longer be observed. Silver then separates within the crystals to form a dense distribution of essentially random particles with, however, a greater density of particles along the positions of the subboundaries of the original structure (Hedges and Mitchell, 1953a).

D. Thin Crystals Annealed at 400°C and then Deformed and Exposed to Light at Room Temperature

The dislocations in these specimens have a density between 10^6 and $10^8/cm^2$ and they are usually normal to the surface for at least 40 μ below the surface. The specimens have been deformed with spherical or square pyramid indenters so that, by approaching the center of the indent along a radius, it is possible to pass continuously from undeformed to heavily deformed material. The observations which may thus be made allow the probable behavior of the dislocations during plastic deformation to be deduced.

The first observable deformation in crystals with (001) surfaces is mostly incipient slip on (101) and (011) planes. The density of dislocations in the space between the slip planes is reduced compared with that in the undeformed crystal whereas the density along the slip planes is considerably greater. The dislocations on a series of (011) slip planes are shown in Fig. 6. In this field, only one slip system is active. In the area illustrated in Fig. 7, two slip systems are active and slip is occurring on (110) and $(1\bar{1}0)$ planes along $[\bar{1}10]$ and [110] directions respectively. Slip involving the displacement of dislocation lines which are parallel to the surface is seldom observed because of the difficulty which attends the establishment of the corresponding stress system. In the field shown in Fig. 8, a number of slip bands terminate and are linked to adjacent slip bands by dislocation lines which are parallel to the surface of the crystal. This specimen was exposed with the load applied and the bowed character of the dislocation lines is to be noted.

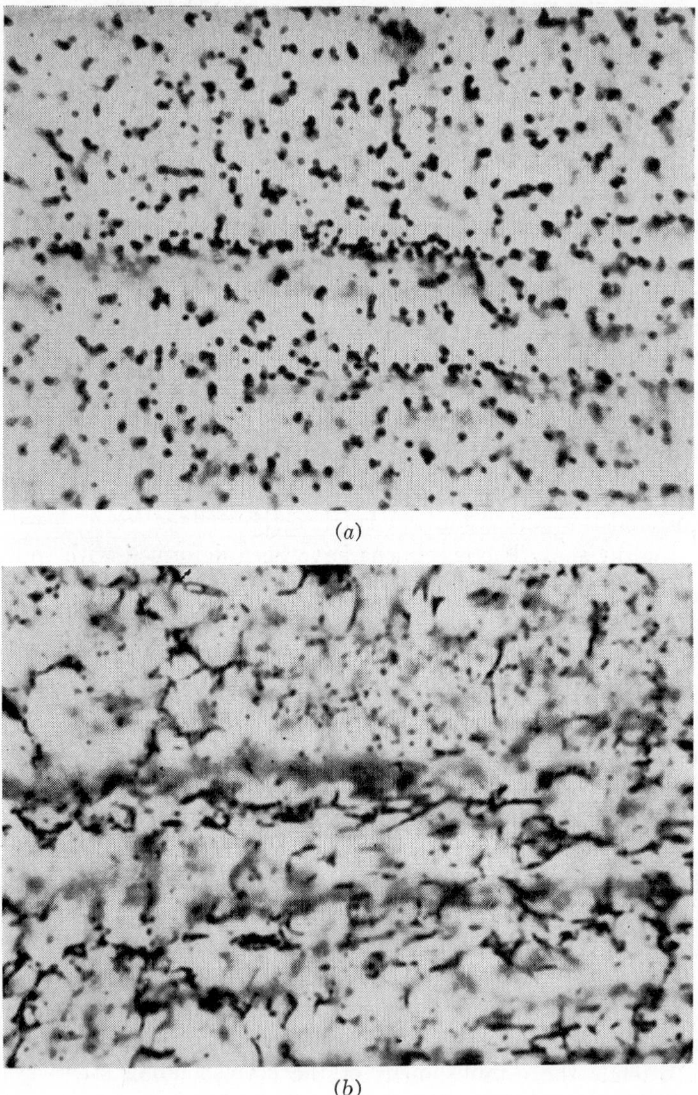

(a)

(b)

Fig. 6. (a) Photomicrograph taken at the surface of a specimen at the limit of the region of deformation produced by a hemispherical indenter. The dark bands of specks represent the intersections with the surface of two (110) slip planes inclined at an angle of 45° to the surface. Only one slip system was operative in this area. The region farthest from the indenter is at the top of the field. (b) Same field as (a) (but 20 μ below the surface) showing dislocations on inclined slip planes.

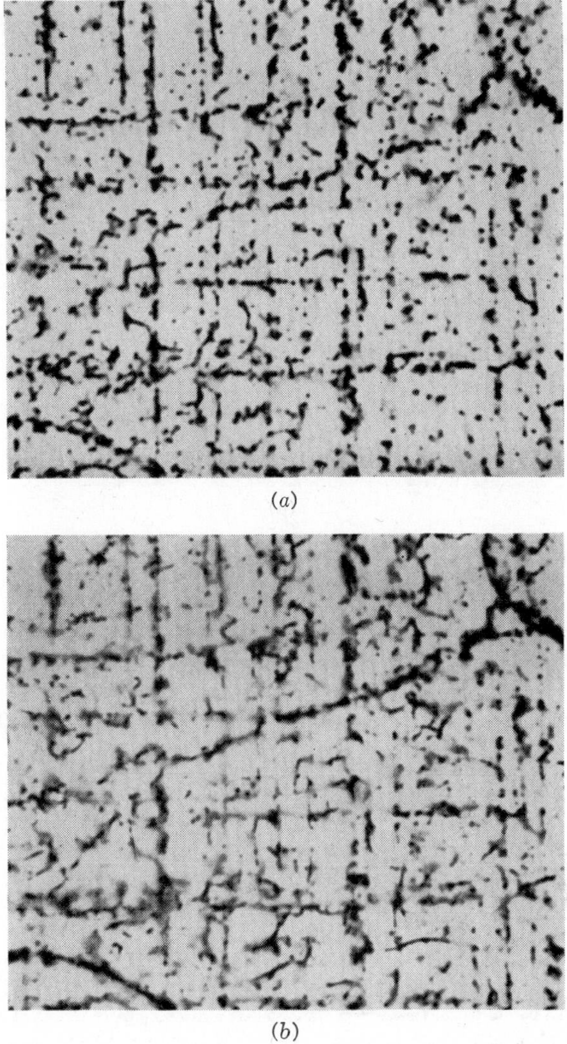

(a)

(b)

Fig. 7. (a) In this area slip has occurred principally on two sets of (110) planes which are at right angles to each other and normal to the surface. A subboundary crosses the field near the center, but there is no evidence for the piling up of dislocations. (b) Same area as (a), 20 μ below the surface.

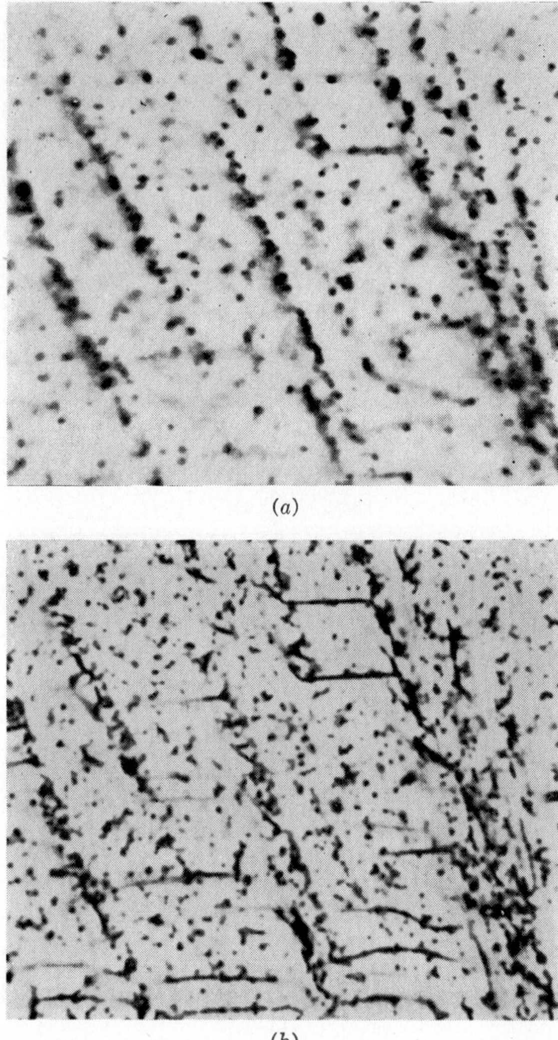

(a)

(b)

Fig. 8. (a) Near the edge of the deformed area produced by indenting a specimen, previously annealed for 12 hr at 400°C with a hemispherical indenter. The specimen was exposed with the load applied, which accounts for the curvature of the dislocation lines nearer the indent in the lower part of the field. Slip has occurred on a series of (110) planes inclined at an angle of 45° to the surface, and also on (001) planes parallel to the surface. The photomicrograph was taken at the surface of the specimen. (b) 10 μ below the surface.

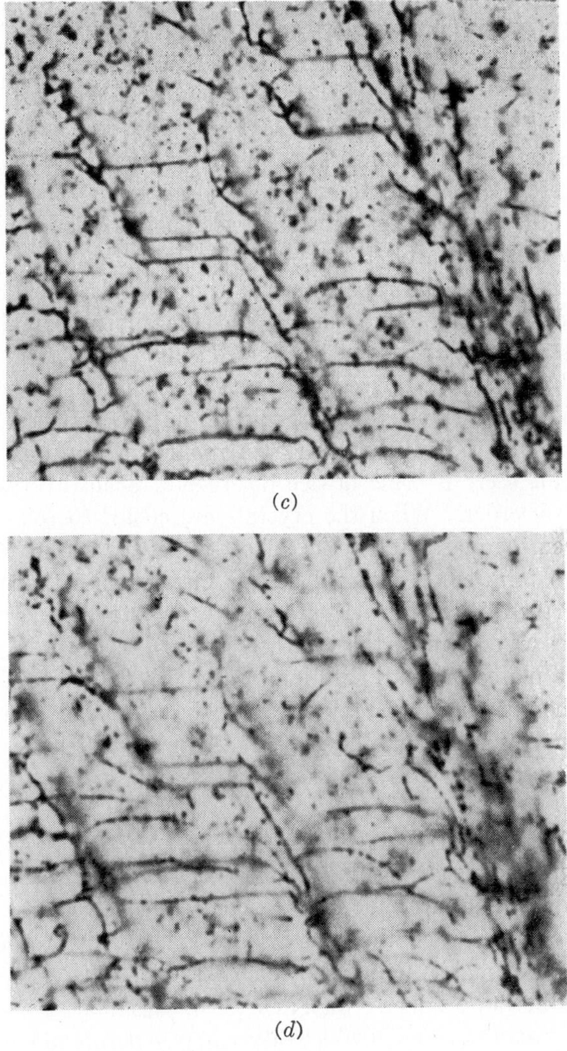

(c)

(d)

Fig. 8 (continued). (c) 20 μ below the surface. (d) 30 μ below the surface.

7. CONDITIONS UNDER WHICH DISLOCATION LINES MAY BE MADE VISIBLE IN CRYSTALS OF SILVER HALIDES

A. Conditions in Large Thin Single Crystals

The most satisfactory and reproducible observations of dislocations within crystals of silver bromide have been made with thin single crystals (150 μ in thickness) grown between plates of borosilicate glass and lightly annealed after their separation from the plates. At room temperature, before the separation of the crystals, the glass plates around the three glass rod spacers and the silver bromide crystals themselves are heavily strained. Part of this strain arises from the differential contraction between the silver halide and the glass which occurs while the system is being cooled from the temperature of the melting point of the silver bromide to room temperature. Near the melting point there is some lattice disorder of Schottky type as well as Frenkel disorder. When the crystals are cooled to room temperature between the glass plates, the Schottky defects are more likely to condense to form small internal groups of vacancies than to diffuse to the interfaces between the glass and the crystal because they will tend in this way to relax the internal strain. In crystals grown between glass plates, a small fraction of the Schottky disorder present at the higher temperature may therefore be preserved to room temperature in the form of small groups of vacancies which remain in the crystals after their separation from the glass plates.

B. Decoration of the Dislocations During Annealing

It is suggested as a working hypothesis that the small groups of vacancies dissociate into mobile pairs consisting of vacant cation and anion lattice sites when the crystals are subsequently annealed. A fraction of these mobile pairs then condenses along the edge and screw dislocation lines to produce a high density of jogs along the edge dislocations and small cavities in which silver may separate along the screw dislocations. These conditions favor the separation of silver atoms along the dislocations when the crystals are exposed to light.

C. Displacement of the Dislocations During Plastic Deformation

It must be assumed that the properties of the dislocations in annealed material which were considered in § 7.B are preserved during displacement because the dislocations may be made visible and rendered immobile by the separation of photolytic silver at any particular stage of displacement. This property is shown only by crystals of silver bromide of the highest possible purity which have been grown in an atmosphere of the hydrogen halide between plates of borosilicate glass or of silica.

D. Separation of Photolytic Silver Along Dislocation Lines

The theory of the photolysis of crystals of silver halides has been discussed in a recent paper (Mitchell, 1957). During exposure, halogen molecules are liberated and escape from the surfaces of the crystals or react with available halogen acceptors. The equivalent amount of silver is present initially in the form of conduction electrons and mobile surface or interstitial silver ions. These then combine to form groups of silver atoms along jogged edge dislocations or along screw dislocations which have previously been decorated with cavities as described in § 7.B. The interaction of electrons and silver ions with jogged edge dislocations has been discussed by Seitz (1951) (see also the detailed treatment in Mitchell, 1957). The experimental observations show that dislocations in both the edge and screw orientations in crystals of silver bromide are decorated by the separation of discrete particles of silver.

E. Dislocations in Large Single Crystals of Silver Halides

We have never been able to make the dislocations in large single crystals of the purest silver bromide visible by the separation of photolytic silver in a reliable and reproducible way. This appears to be connected with the circumstances discussed in § 7.B. If the crystals have not been plastically deformed, very little silver separates in them during exposure. Greatly prolonged exposures lead to the separation of a random distribution of particles of photolytic silver. When the crystals have been deformed so that slip lines have appeared on their surfaces with the corresponding internal slip bands, subsequent exposure causes the separation of discrete particles of silver on the slip bands as observed by Haynes and Shockley (1951) but dislocations on the slip bands outlined by linear distributions of particles of silver as described in § 6 are never observed.

As the hardness and other plastic properties of the large crystals of silver bromide are not measurably different from the corresponding properties of the thin crystals, it must be assumed that mobile dislocations are present in both types of crystals and that those in the thin crystals have modified properties which permit their decoration with particles of colloidal silver during exposure but which, in the purest crystals, do not impede their displacement during plastic deformation.

REFERENCES

Amelinckx, S. (1956), *Phil. Mag.* (8), **1**, 269.
Amelinckx, S., Van der Vorst, W., Gevers, R., and Dekeyser, W. (1955), *Phil. Mag.* (7), **46**, 450.
Boesman, E., Remaut, G., and Dekeyser, W. (1956), *J. Chem. Phys.*, **25**, 359.
Burgers, J. M. (1939), *Proc. Koninkl. Ned. Akad. Wetenschap.*, **42**, 293.
Clark, P. V. McD., and Mitchell, J. W. (1956), *J. Phot. Sci.*, **4**, 1.
Cottrell, A. H. (1953), *Dislocations and Plastic Flow in Crystals,* Oxford University Press, Oxford.
Darwin, C. G. (1914), *Phil. Mag.*, **27**, 315, 675; (1922), *ibid.*, **43**, 800.
Edner, A. (1932), *Z. Physik,* **73**, 623.
Evans, T., Hedges, J. M.. and Mitchell, J. W. (1955), *J. Phot. Sci.*, **3**, 73.
Frank, F. C. (1955a), *Report of a Conference on Defects in Crystalline Solids,* Physical Society, London, p. 159; (1955b), *Chemistry of the Solid State,* Butterworths, London, p. 1.
Haynes, J. R., and Shockley, W. (1951), *Phys. Rev.*, **82**, 935.
Hedges, J. M., and Mitchell, J. W. (1953a), *Phil. Mag.* (7), **44**, 223; (1953b), *ibid.*, 357.
Mitchell, J. W. (1957), *Die Photographische Empfindlichkeit,* Helwich, Darmstadt.
Read, W. T., Jr. (1953), *Dislocations in Crystals,* McGraw-Hill Book Co., New York.
Read, W. T., Jr., and Shockley, W. (1950), *Phys. Rev.*, **78**, 275.
Rexer, E. (1931), *Z. Physik,* **70**, 159; (1932a), *ibid.*, **75**, 777; (1932b), *ibid.*, **76**, 735.
Seitz, F. (1951), *Rev. Mod. Phys.*, **23**, 328.
Siedentopf, H. (1905), *Phys. Z.*, **6**, 855.
Smekal, A. (1929), *Z. Physik,* **55**, 289; (1933), *Handbuch der Physik,* 2nd Ed., Springer, Berlin, Vol. 24/2, p. 795.

ACKNOWLEDGMENTS

The work summarized in this paper has been carried out at intervals during the course of experimental work on the nature of photographic sensitivity by P. V. McD. Clark, T. Evans, J. M. Hedges, D. A. Jones and the author. It has been supported by a grant from Kodak, Ltd., Harrow, which is gratefully acknowledged.

DISCUSSION

SEEGER asked if all the deformation work had been done at room temperature. MITCHELL replied that one experiment had been done at high temperature and the rest at room temperature; experiments had been tried at −183°C, but the temperature was too low to allow the formation of suitable nuclei, and at $-150°C$ experiments had been unsuccessful. This appeared to be in agreement with Stasiw's work at $-150°C$, which was mentioned by SEEGER, who said that Stasiw * has obtained no formation of photolytic silver at that temperature.

JOHNSTON pointed out that the splitting of subboundaries at the surface is also found in lithium fluoride. By etching a cleaved crystal before and after annealing, it is established that a single subboundary may split into two components which move in opposite directions. Below the surface of the crystal the dislocations merge into a single boundary again.

ESHELBY described a rough analysis that he and VREELAND had discussed, and which indicated that it might be reasonable to expect the splitting of a small angle tilt boundary at the surface. In treating the elastic problem of a dislocation boundary intersecting a free plane, one can employ an image dislocation boundary. The forces between the image dislocations and the real dislocations could cause the boundary to split. The width of the splitting at the surface should be approximately equal to the depth to which the splitting extends below the surface. This prediction could be checked experimentally.

Written comment by ESHELBY:

Later calculations show that, though the elastic field of the dislocations is modified where they meet the surface, this should not give rise to splitting.

MOTT brought up the question of small dislocation loops, formed by vacancy condensation, which had been suggested during the discussion of the experiments of Gilman and Johnston described in Part I of this volume. He inquired whether such loops, of a few microns in diameter, could be detected by Mitchell's decorating technique. MITCHELL felt that if such loops existed in the silver bromide, silver would print out on them and they would be seen.

THOMSON asked if there was a difference in the precipitation of silver along screw dislocations and edge dislocations. MITCHELL said that the networks usually are uniformly decorated, but that occasionally one finds a network with lines of alternating intensity, and it may be supposed that then one set of lines has a larger screw component than the other.

* O. Stasiw, *Halbleiterprobleme,* **2,** 184 (1955) (published by Vierweg und Sohn, Braunschweig).

Direct Observations of the Arrangement and Motion of Dislocations in Aluminum

P. B. HIRSCH

R. W. HORNE

M. J. WHELAN

Crystallographic Laboratory and Electron Microscope Group
Cavendish Laboratory
Cambridge, England

1. INTRODUCTION

The nature of the dislocation structure in metals has so far only been inferred from experiments on transparent crystals, e.g., AgBr and NaCl (Hedges and Mitchell, 1953; Amelinckx, 1956), or from examination of metal surfaces, using preferential etching and precipitation techniques (Lacombe and Beaujard, 1948; Wilsdorf and Kuhlmann-Wilsdorf, 1955), or from experiments on the slip structure. Recently it has been possible to observe directly dislocations in aluminum by transmission electron microscopy using a high resolution electron microscope. Most of the specimens examined so far were prepared by beating 99.99+% Al and 99.8% Al at room temperature, followed by etching in dilute HF. The specimens were examined in a Siemens and Halske "Elmiskop" electron microscope operating at 80 kv.

2. EVIDENCE FOR THE VISIBILITY OF DISLOCATION LINES

Figures 1 through 11 show some typical micrographs obtained. The following facts leave litle doubt that individual dislocation lines are being observed:

1. Figure 1 shows that the specimens contain a substructure of subgrain diameter about 1 μ. The misorientations across the boundaries

Fig. 1. Substructure in Al annealed at 350°C after beating at room temperature. The average subgrain size is about 1 μ, the average angular misorientation about 1½°. The dislocation density is about 10^{10}/sq cm. Extinction contours are shown at *A*. (Courtesy *Philosophical Magazine*.)

have been determined by diffraction experiments and are found to be about 1° to 2°. Under higher magnification the boundaries are seen to

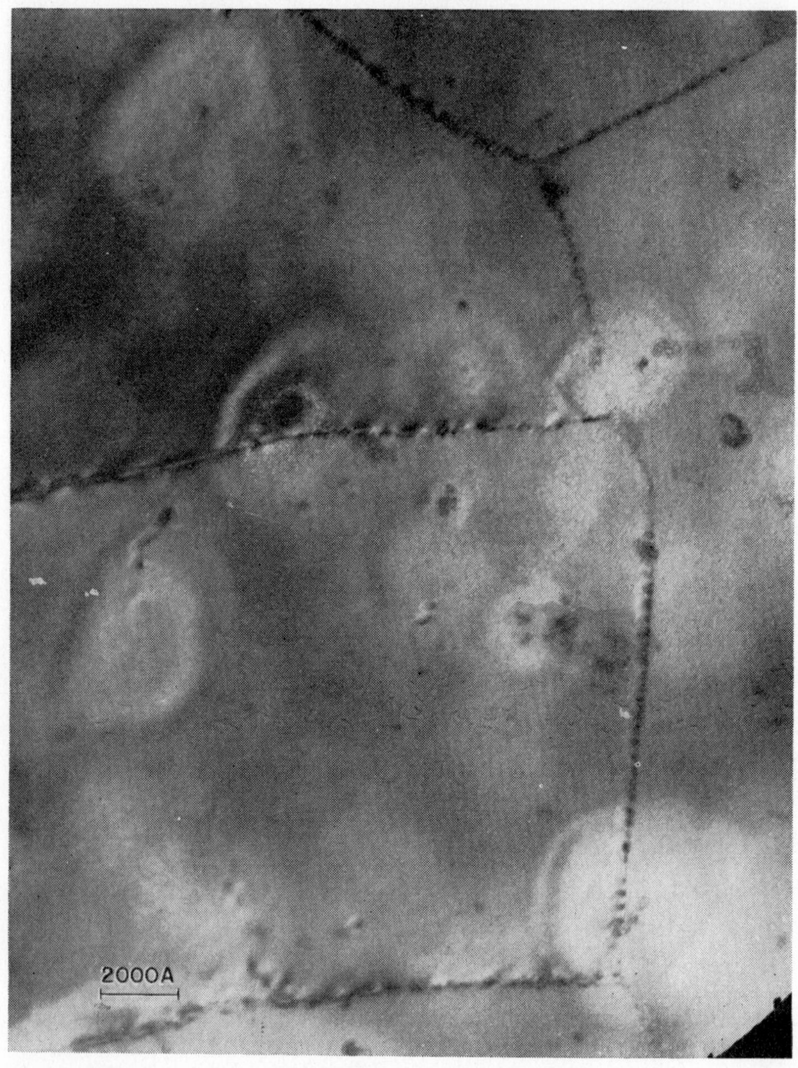

Fig. 2. A subboundary consisting of uniformly spaced dislocations. The average spacing of the dislocations is about 175 A. (Courtesy *Philosophical Magazine.*)

consist of individual lines or dots, e.g., Fig. 2. In a number of cases it has been possible to determine the angle of rotation across particular boundaries in which the individual lines could be resolved. After making reasonable assumptions about the types of dislocations present in the boundaries (based on the knowledge of the boundary planes), it is possible to compare dislocation spacings calculated from the misorientations with the observed spacings of the dislocations. Table 1 shows

TABLE 1. SUMMARY OF RESULTS OF BOUNDARY MISORIENTATION MEASUREMENTS IN THREE CASES

Plate Numbers	Normal to Foil	Type of Boundary Assumed	Rotation Axis	Component Angle of Rotation (degrees)	Calculated Dislocation Spacing (angstroms)	Observed Approximate Spacing of Dislocations (angstroms)	Resolution
94, 95	[001]	(110) Simple tilt	[$\bar{1}$12]	2.1	80	130	Poor
293, 294, 296	[001]	(211) Mixed tilt	[0$\bar{1}$1]	1.36	94	100	Good in places
299, 300, 302	[001]	Hexagonal network near (111) twist	[111]	0.35	270	300	Fair

that the agreement obtained is satisfactory, and it appears that the lines represent dislocations of unit Burgers vector.

2. On tilting the illumination or the specimen through small angles, the lines remain fixed in position, although the contrast changes. This shows that the lines are a definite property of the specimen.

3. Some of the arrangements of lines can be explained readily on dislocation theory (see below), but not on any other basis known to the authors.

4. When working with large beam currents the lines are observed to move; the movement occurs along straight lines parallel to the traces of (111) slip planes (e.g., Fig. 12). The behavior of these moving lines is identical with that expected of dislocation lines.

These observations leave little doubt that the lines represent single dislocation lines of unit Burgers vector.

3. CONTRAST MECHANISM

Dark field experiments have been carried out which show that the dislocations are rendered visible owing to the enhanced Bragg scattering near the dislocations. Most of the contrast in the electron micrographs is due to differences in diffracted intensity from different areas of specimen. The diffracted beams are prevented by a suitable aperture from reaching the image, and the electrons lost in this way give rise to the contrast. Figure 3*a* shows a bright field image of a certain region. Figure 3*b* shows the same region taken in a dark field so that the image is formed by the [200] diffracted beam. Whereas only a limited region of subgrains appears to be in a reflecting position, most of the dislocations appear to diffract strongly. Similarly, on observing

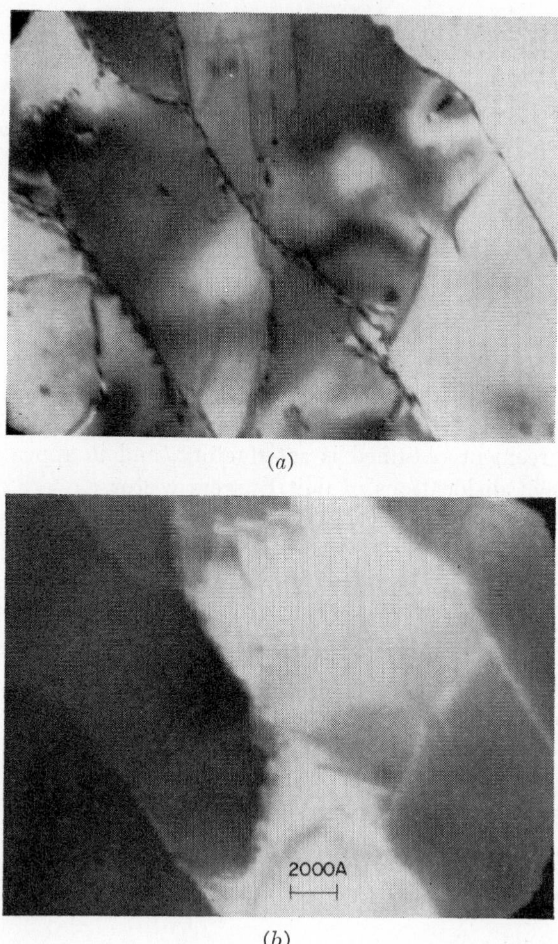

(*a*)

(*b*)

Fig. 3. (*a*) Bright field micrograph showing subboundaries and dislocations. (*b*) Dark field micrograph of same area showing reversed contrast and the preferred reflection by dislocations.

the dark field images due to other Bragg reflections, it is found that the dislocations are in a reflecting position for a number of reflections, whereas "perfect" regions give rise generally only to one or two reflections. The contrast at the dislocations is thus due to the increased probability of reflection owing to the distortion of the neighboring lattice caused by the strain field, which results in a greater loss of electrons from the direct beam.

Most of the micrographs also show "extinction contours" (Heidenreich, 1949) due to bending and buckling of the foil (e.g., Fig. 1). These represent regions where the foil is orientated so that the beam is strongly reflected from a particular set of Bragg planes.

Certain other contrast effects are also observed. Figure 4 shows a set of parallel fringes at a boundary between subgrains. Such fringes are probably due to interferences between the direct transmitted beam

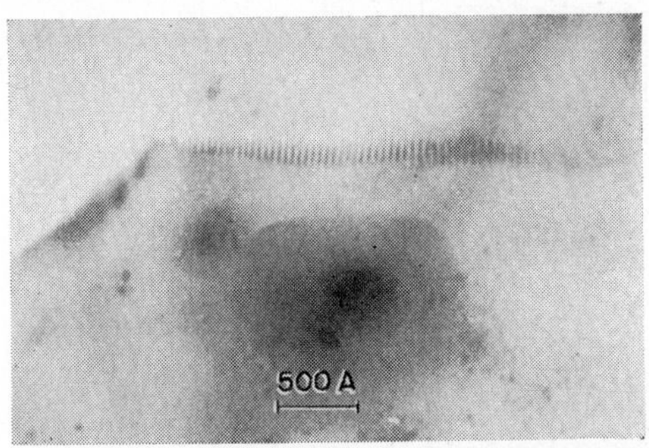

Fig. 4. Interference fringes at a subboundary.

and the beam diffracted first in one crystal and subsequently again in the second crystal so that it is nearly but not quite parallel to the direct beam. Similar interference effects could account for the "spotty" dislocation lines seen, for example, in Fig. 7. Such effects might be expected to occur for screw dislocations.

The foil is sufficiently thick for dynamical effects to become important, and these are probably responsible for the fringes sometimes observed to follow the direction of the boundary.

It is clear that the contrast effects are complicated; nevertheless it is not difficult to distinguish dislocations from interference and other effects in many cases.

4. ARRANGEMENT OF DISLOCATIONS

Figure 1 shows the substructure in Al at low magnification. The average subgrain size is about 1 μ, the average angular misorientation about $1\frac{1}{2}°$. The dislocation density measured from other photographs is of the order of 10^{10}/sq cm. All these figures are in excellent agreement with the results deduced from X-ray data (Hirsch, 1952; Gay, Hirsch and Kelly, 1953). The photographs leave no doubt at all that most of the dislocations are in the subboundaries, and relatively few within the subgrains.

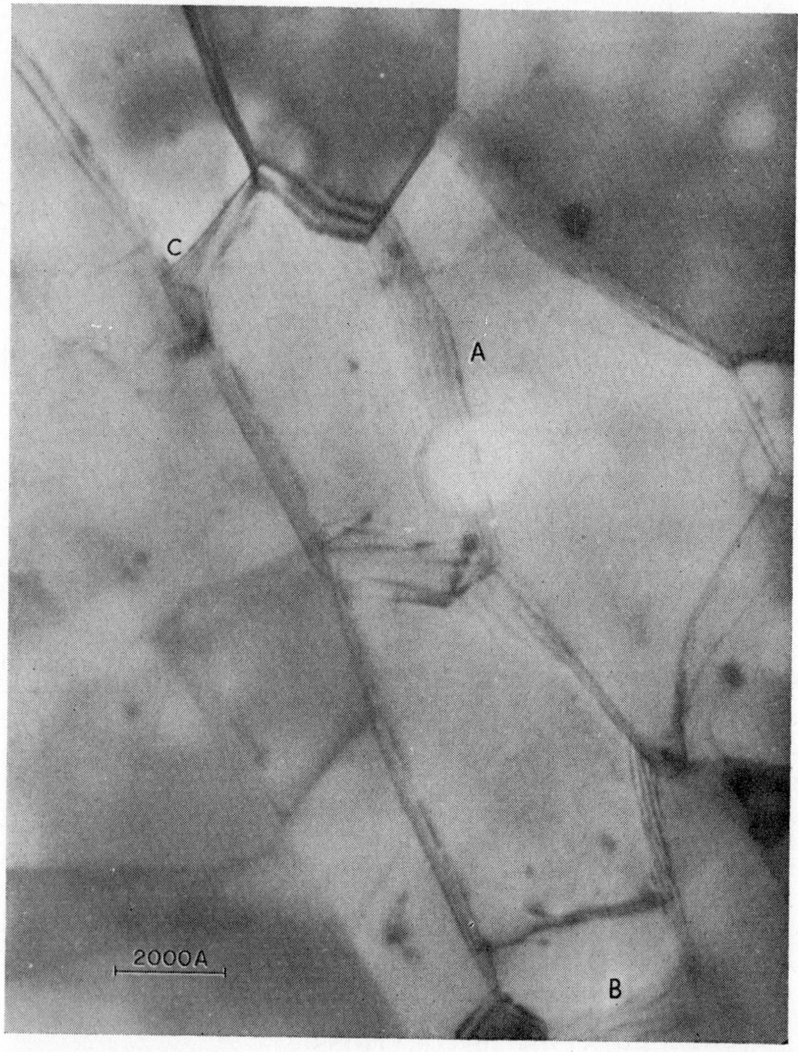

Fig. 5. Boundaries whose planes are not normal to the plane of the foil. *A:* Pure tilt boundary. *B:* Cross grid of dislocations. *C:* Dislocation nodes. (Courtesy *Philosophical Magazine.*)

Figure 2 shows dislocations spaced uniformly along a boundary. Generally the boundaries appear to be less regular. The boundary planes in this region are all nearly normal to the foil.

Figure 5 shows an area in which most of the boundaries are not normal to the plane of the foil. Some of the boundaries appear to consist of parallel dislocation lines (*A*), so that they must be pure tilt

Fig. 6. Boundaries containing dislocation networks. *A:* Square cross grid. *B:* Other networks. *C:* Dislocation nodes. *D:* Isolated dislocations. (Courtesy *Philosophical Magazine.*)

boundaries; others (*B*) appear to contain cross grids of dislocations. The micrograph shows the three-dimensional nature of the substructure; in particular, the junction of the boundaries can be observed quite clearly. In some cases nodes where three dislocation lines meet

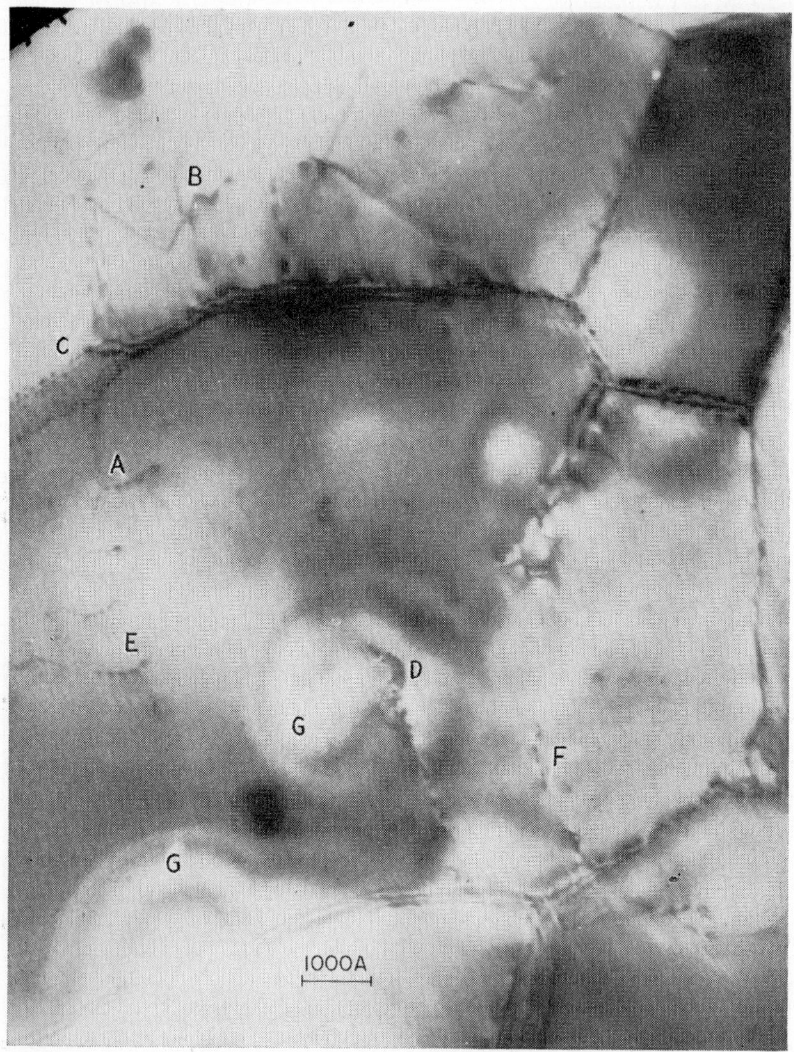

Fig. 7. *A:* Dislocation node; the "spotted" appearance of the dislocation lines is probably due to an interference effect. *B:* Crossing of two dislocations. *C:* Cross grid of dislocations. *D:* Termination of boundary. *E, F:* Single dislocations lines. *G:* Extinction contours. (Courtesy *Philosophical Magazine.*)

at a junction can be recognized, (*C*). [For a discussion of networks and boundaries in face-centered cubic crystals reference should be made to Frank (1955), Ball and Hirsch (1955), and Amelinckx (1956).]

Figure 6 shows a square cross grid of dislocations (*A*) representing probably a twist boundary on (100). Other networks can be seen at *B*; dislocation nodes can be recognized clearly in boundary junctions at *C*. A few isolated dislocations occur within the grain at *D*.

Figure 7 shows a dislocation node inside a subgrain (*A*). The dislocations appear to consist of a number of spots. This appearance may be due to an interference effect at dislocations with a screw component. At *B* two dislocations appear to cross in characteristic manner (Read, 1954). A cross grid can be seen at *C*. At *D* a boundary appears to terminate in the middle of a subgrain. The strain around this region is apparent from the curvature in the extinction contour. Single dislocation lines can be seen at *E* and *F*; at *E* the dislocations are considered to be more nearly parallel to the foil than at *F*; the spots at *E* are thought to be due to the interference effect mentioned above. At *F*, on the other hand, each pair of spots corresponds to one dislocation steeply inclined to the foil; this follows from the experiments on the motion of dislocation (see § 5). The two spots on each dislocation pair are thought to be due to the increased distortion on the top and bottom surfaces due to the oxide layer which must be present. This area shows some typical extinction contours at *G*.

Figure 8 shows hexagonal networks of dislocations (*A*, *B*). These are the only clear hexagonal networks observed so far. Many of the boundaries (e.g., *C*), however, appear to consist of more or less distorted hexagonal networks, but the clarity of the networks is spoiled by interference effects. At *D* the nodes of the dislocations at the boundary junction can again be clearly recognized.

Figure 9 shows square cross grids of dislocations of large mesh size (*A*, *B*). From a diffraction pattern taken from *B* it was shown that the dislocations in *B* are parallel to [110] directions and that the normal to the foil is almost [001]. This network therefore is likely to be a twist boundary on (001).

Figure 10 shows an irregular network, the dislocations of which are bowed out, presumably owing to some local strain.

In some areas the arrangement of the dislocations is quite complex. Figure 11 shows such a case; many complex networks can be seen (*A*). This photograph shows interesting interference effects at boundaries (*B*) and single dislocations (*C*).

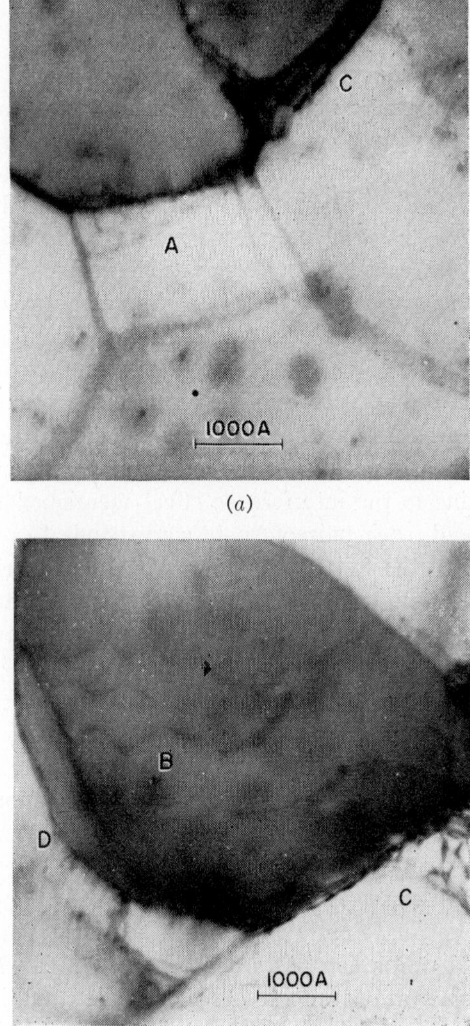

(a)

(b)

Fig. 8. *A, B:* Hexagonal networks of dislocations. *C:* Indistinct network. *D:* Dislocation nodes. (Courtesy *Philosophical Magazine.*)

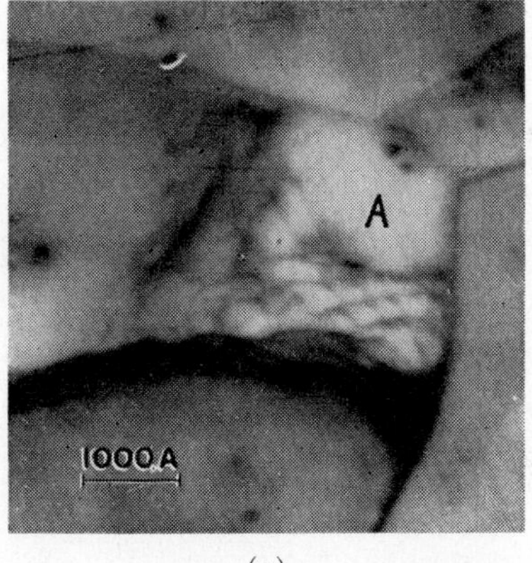

(*a*)

(*b*)

Fig. 9. *A, B:* Square cross grids of dislocations. The dislocations in *B* are approximately parallel to [110] directions. (Courtesy *Philosophical Magazine.*)

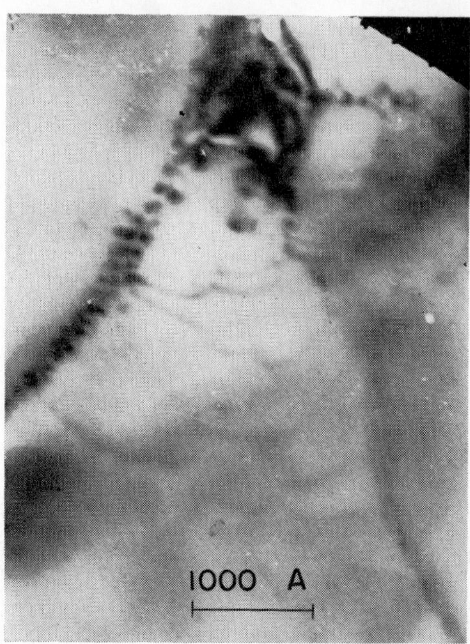

Fig. 10. Irregular network consisting of bowed-out dislocations. (Courtesy *Philosophical Magazine.*)

5. MOVEMENT OF DISLOCATIONS

When working at high beam currents and with large condenser apertures, the dislocations are observed to move. Two types of motion are observed, either rapid, or slow and jerky.

First there is a movement of the extinction contours. Subsequently the dislocation lines often bow out and in many cases move. The bowing-out effect is presumably direct confirmation of the mechanism suggested for the decrease in elastic modulus due to dislocations (Mott, 1952). The movement of the extinction contours shows that the foil buckles; the dislocations therefore move presumably under the strain; their movement may be aided by heat. The temperature rise in the specimen is not known at present.

Figure 12 is a sequence showing slip. A rapidly moving dislocation leaves behind it a broad band, the trace of which is parallel to a (111) slip plane. The edges of the band are always more intense than the middle, and after several seconds the contrast disappears. The reason for the contrast in these bands is not understood. One possibility which has been considered is that it may arise from point defects left behind after the passage of a "joggy" dislocation. The disappearance of the contrast would be due to the diffusion of the point defects away from the slip plane. Some preliminary experiments on the effect of

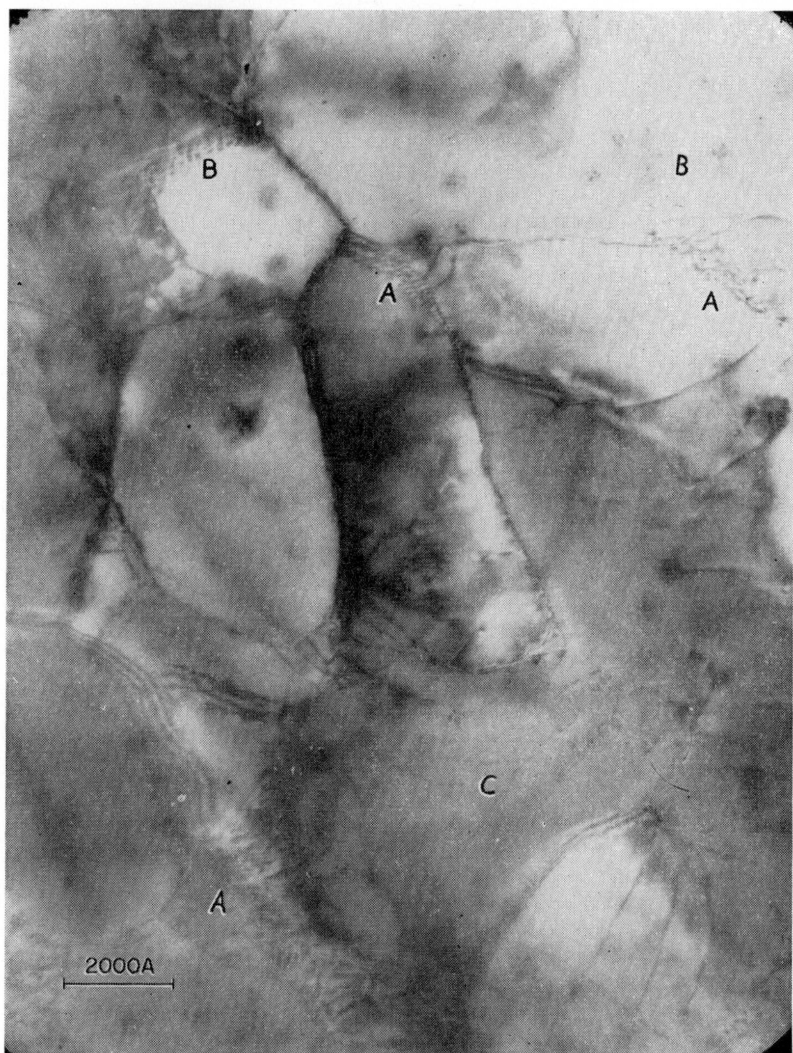

Fig. 11. Complex arrangement of dislocations. *A:* Irregular network. *B:* Interference effect at a boundary. *C:* Interference effect at single dislocations. (Courtesy *Philosophical Magazine.*)

different illumination conditions in the microscope appear to indicate, however, that the contrast disappears more rapidly with increasing temperature gradient, i.e., greater strain, than with increasing tem-

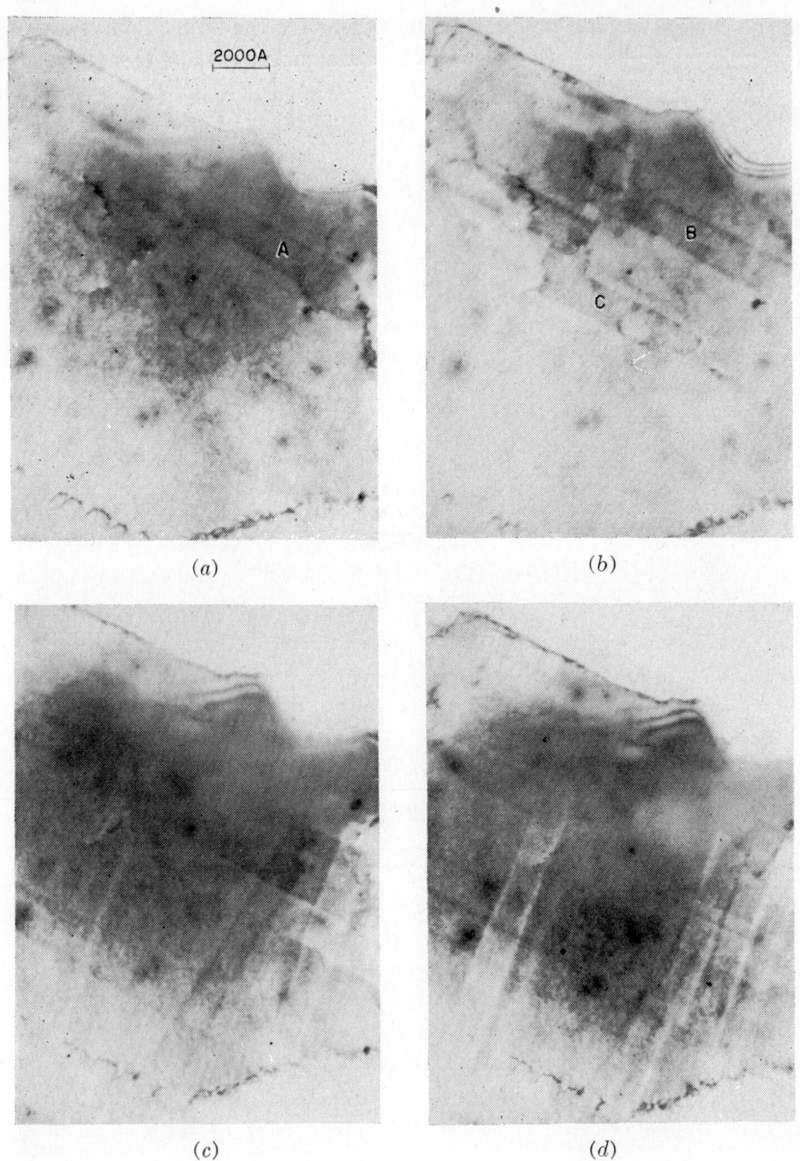

Fig. 12. Sequence showing slip. The disappearance of the contrast in the bands can be followed in the sequence. Refer to text for detailed description. (Courtesy *Philosophical Magazine*.)

perature. This suggests that the contrast may be due to the stresses set up by the interaction of the oxide film with a dislocation trying to penetrate the surface. The sequence shows clearly the disappearance of the contrast in the slip traces. For example, the slip trace *A* in Fig. 12*a* has practically disappeared in Fig. 12*b*; trace *B* is a new slip trace slightly displaced from *A*. Similarly, traces *B* and *C* in Fig. 12*b* are no longer visible in Fig. 12*c*. Complicated cross slip can also be observed, for example, on traces *A* and *C*.

The width of the slip traces can be used to determine the thickness of the foils. The thickness is found to vary from about 500 A to 1000 A.

Figure 13 shows a fine example of cross slip. It is quite clear here that a single dislocation has transferred from one slip plane to another. This represents direct proof of the Mott-Frank screw dislocation mechanism of cross slip (Mott, 1951).

Cross slip has been observed very frequently; Fig. 14 shows another example; here the dislocation started at *A* and eventually penetrated the boundary at *B*. An interesting feature about this photograph is the fact that the original line splits into two branches at *C*, *CD*, and *CE*. The precise process here is uncertain, but it may involve the splitting of a single dislocation into two. Another slip line is seen at *FG*.

Figure 15 shows a sequence in an area where the dislocations moved slowly. This type of movement may perhaps correspond to creep. In addition to subboundaries, isolated dislocations can be seen within the subgrains. The single dislocations are typically more intense at the ends. Comparing Fig. 15*a* and *b*, it is clear that a number of dislocations have moved, for example, at *A*, *B*, and *C*. The boundary at *D* has disappeared; dislocation *E* has moved to dislocation *F* which, judging from its contrast, lies in another slip plane. This suggests that *E* is held up by *F* because of the difficulty of cutting through a dislocation. However, Fig. 15*c* shows that *E* has moved on to *G* where it is again stopped. It is also clear that many other dislocations have moved; in particular, *H* has moved along the path *HIJ*. This path is quite irregular and indicates that the dislocation may move by a very intimate cross-slip mechanism, and possibly by climb. Other dislocations also appear to have moved by similar irregular paths. Motion of this type tends to be jerky when observed in the microscope.

Many observations of moving dislocations have been made in the microscope, and many complex effects have been seen. Similar observations have been made on other metals, e.g., Ag and Pd. Although the growth of dislocation loops has been observed, so far it has not been possible to locate the dislocation sources. It is clear, however, that sometimes dislocations come out of boundaries, and sometimes they originate in complex regions such as those of Fig. 11. On the whole, regions with very well formed polygons are most stable. Many of the

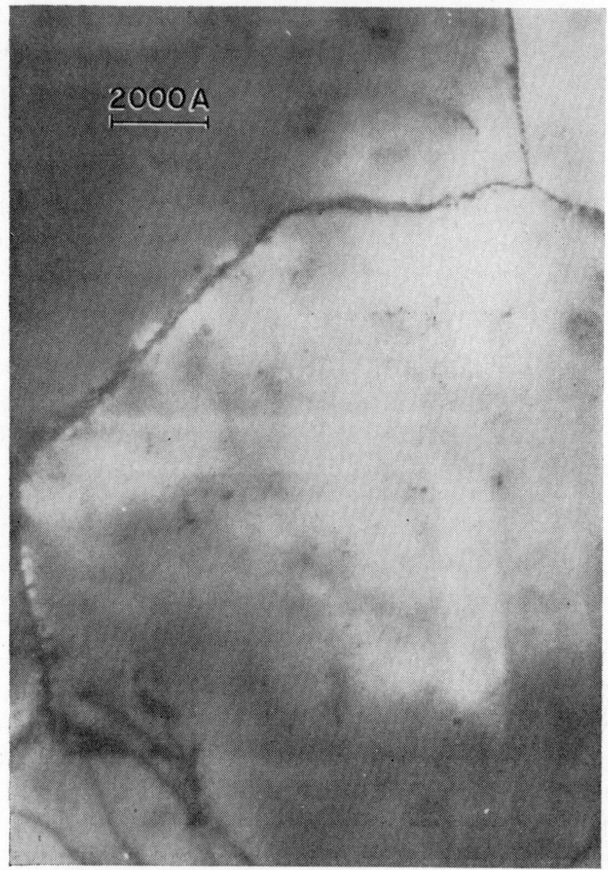

Fig. 13. Cross slip by the screw dislocation mechanism. (Courtesy *Philosophical Magazine.*)

dislocations are stopped at the boundaries; others appear to pass through them. The movement of parts of boundaries as a whole has also been observed. The detailed movement of the dislocations has been recorded on 16-mm ciné film.

Preliminary experiments have been carried out on the dislocation structure in single crystals of Al after different deformations. The results show clearly that after, for example, 5% strain the dislocations are entangled in a very complex arrangement (Fig. 16). No evidence for subboundaries has yet been found.

Experiments on heavily beaten and etched foils of Au, Ag, and Pd have revealed a very complex dislocation structure (Fig. 17). The

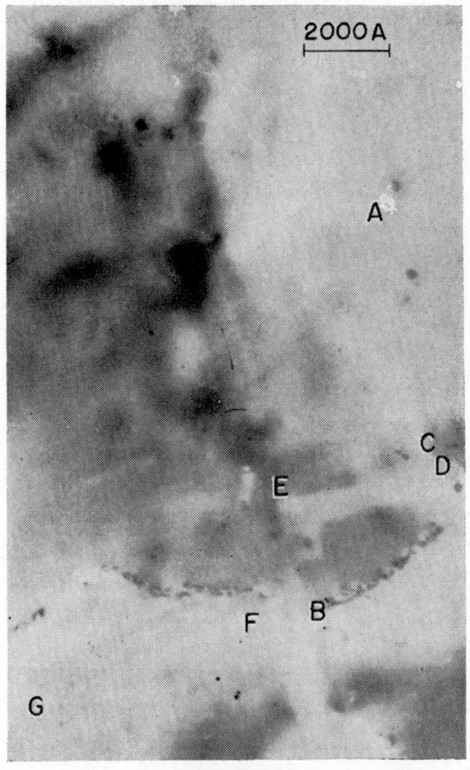

Fig. 14. Cross slip; the dislocation started at *A* and penetrated the boundary at *B*. Note that the original band splits into two branches at *C*, *CD* and *CE*. Another slip line is seen at *FG*. (Courtesy *Philosophical Magazine*.)

density of dislocations in these materials is of the order 10^{11} to 10^{12}/sq cm, and consequently the dislocations occur on a much finer scale. These specimens also contain subgrains which are smaller than in beaten Al; in Au, for example, the average subgrain size appears to be of the order of 1000 A to 2000 A in agreement with the value deduced from diffraction experiments (Hirsch, Kelly, and Menter, 1955). It is quite clear, however, that in contrast with Al many, if not most, of the dislocations occur within the subgrains. In these metals, particularly in the case of Au, there are also areas (*A*) which

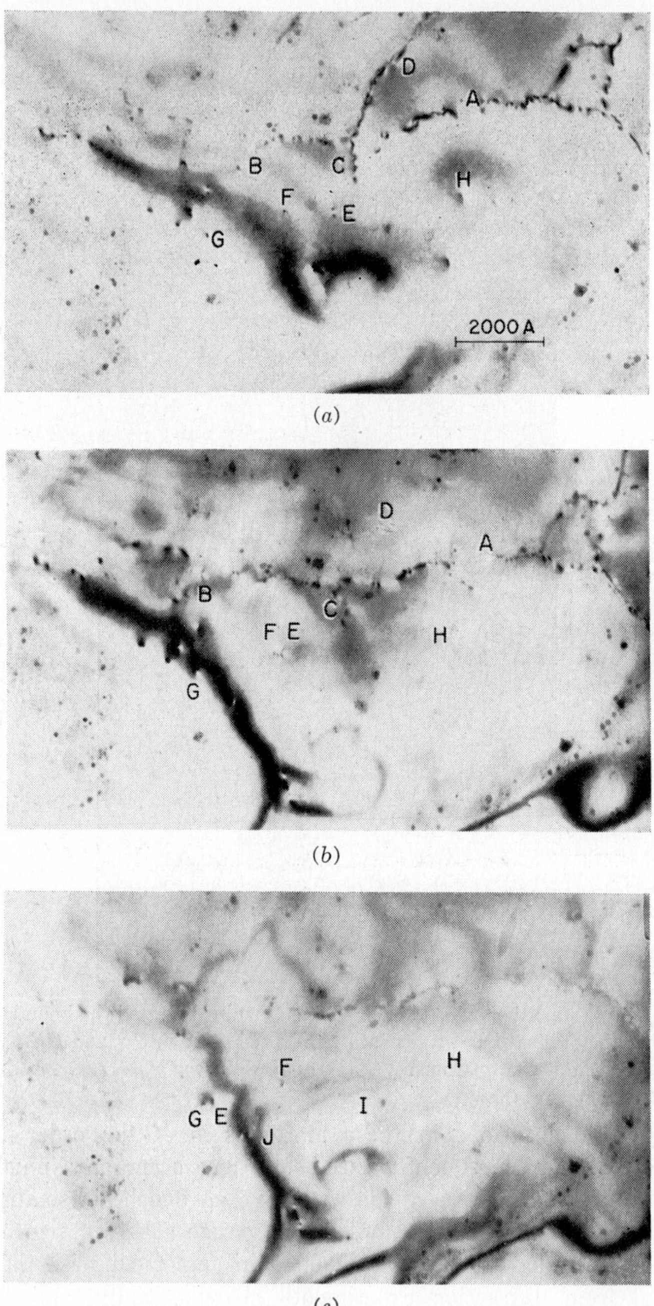

Fig. 15. Sequence showing slowly moving dislocations. Refer to text for detailed description. (Courtesy *Philosophical Magazine.*)

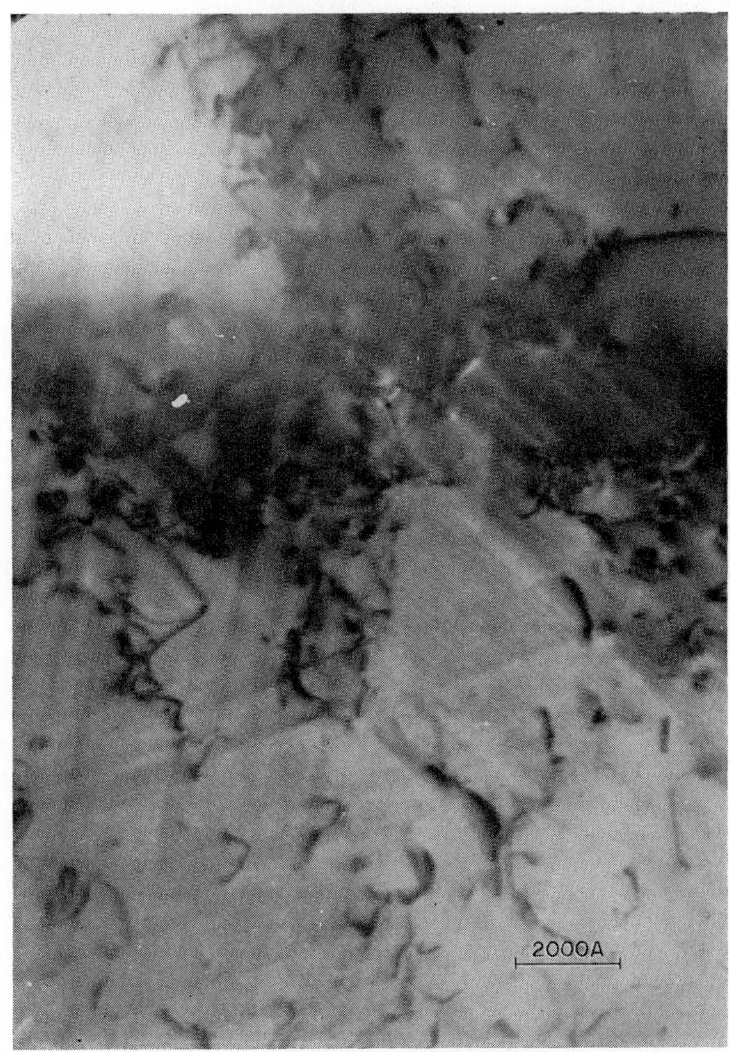

Fig. 16. Dislocations in a single crystal of Al extended 5% at room temperature.

Fig. 17. Dislocations, subgrains, and faults (A) in heavily beaten Au foils.

are heavily faulted, and there is also evidence for twins and a hexagonal phase.

REFERENCES

Amelinckx, S. (1956), *Phil. Mag.*, **1,** 269.
Ball, C. J., and Hirsch, P. B. (1955), *Phil. Mag.*, **46,** 1343.
Frank, F. C. (1955), *Report of a Conference on Defects in Crystalline Solids*, Physical Society, London, p. 159.
Gay, P., Hirsch, P. B., and Kelly, A. (1953), *Acta Met.*, **1,** 315.
Hedges, J. M., and Mitchell, J. W. (1953), *Phil. Mag.*, **44,** 223.
Heidenreich, R. D. (1949), *J. Appl. Phys.*, **20,** 993.
Hirsch, P. B. (1952), *Acta Cryst.*, **5,** 172.
Hirsch, P. B., Kelly, A., and Menter, J. W. (1955), *Proc. Phys. Soc.* (*London*), *B.*, **68,** 1132.
Lacombe, P., and Beaujard, L. (1948), *Rev. mét.*, **45,** 317.
Mott, N. F. (1951), *Proc. Phys. Soc.* (*London*), *B*, **64,** 729.
Mott, N. F. (1952), *Phil. Mag.*, **43,** 1151.
Read, W. T. (1954), *Dislocations in Crystals*, McGraw-Hill Book Co., New York.
Wilsdorf, H., and Kuhlmann-Wilsdorf, D. (1955), *Report of a Conference on Defects in Crystalline Solids*, Physical Society, London, p. 175.

EDITOR'S NOTE

P. B. Hirsch showed a motion picture film entitled "The Movements of Dislocations in Aluminum Foils," by P. B. Hirsch, R. W. Horne, and M. J. Whelan of the Cavendish Laboratory. The motion picture demonstrated quite clearly the dislocation movements that have been described in the paper.

DISCUSSION

HIRSCH explained that the foils which were photographed were not annealed prior to being placed in the electron microscope. Some experiments have been done on annealing the foils and it has been found that at 350°C the dislocations inside the subgrains are removed and the boundaries are sharpened. There was no significant increase in subgrain size. Motion of dislocations is observed in the 350°C annealed specimens as well as in the unannealed specimens.

The exact temperature at the specimen in the microscope is not known. The best estimates available indicate that under the conditions of this experiment the temperature rise should be no more than

20 or 30°C. Although the temperature rise is small, there is a high temperature gradient, since the electron beam is concentrated on a spot 5 μ in diameter. The high temperature gradient causes the specimen to be strained. This straining is observed directly because the extinction contours are seen to move. The extinction contours are regions in which the crystal is in a reflecting position, and movement of the contours implies that the foil is buckling. When a larger spot is employed, with the same current density, the specimen is heated more, but there is less movement of dislocations.

LOW observed that in the motion picture all the dislocations in a given field seemed to move in the same direction. HIRSCH said that Cottrell had suggested that this may be a stress recovery process. The small rise in temperature is putting a strain on the specimen. The dislocations are arranged in subboundaries which probably contain dislocations of only one sign, so that they may all be expected to move in the same direction under an applied stress. HIRSCH added that it is possible that in specimens of the type employed, a Frank-Read source mechanism may not be able to operate because the expanding loop will meet the surface and split up and the short segments of dislocation produced in this way may stay in that position.

SHOCKLEY raised the question of what is causing the observed relaxation in the contrast after a dislocation moves. He suggested that, instead of the dislocation staying inside the metal after slip, the situa-

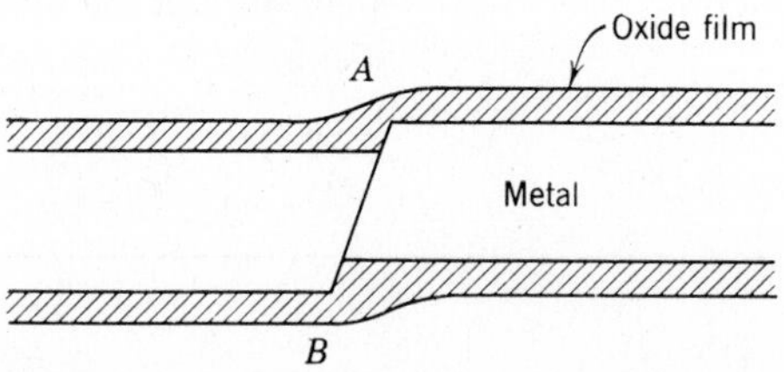

Fig. D1. Dislocation has passed through the metal film but not through the oxide film which is highly strained at A and B.

tion may be as shown in Fig. D1. The aluminum oxide film is highly strained at A and B, and the stresses can be relaxed by diffusion of the oxide film over the surface of the aluminum. This relaxation would not be observed in gold, because there is no oxide film present in that case. HIRSCH replied that some thought had been given to the role of the oxide film, but that he did not feel that the situation was understood. One does not know if the oxide film acts as an elastic skin that can be considered separately from the aluminum. The oxide film may be completely coherent with the aluminum, in which case the dislocation might be held up just below the oxide and eventually pass through. The contrast in the middle of the trace would be due to an over-all tilt of the specimen in that area. If the relaxation were merely a diffusion process, the rate of disappearance of the trace would depend strongly on temperature, whereas, preliminary observations indicate that the rate of disappearance is more sensitive to stress than to temperature. Presumably at higher stress the dislocation passes through the oxide film more rapidly.

CHALMERS recalled that Gilman and Johnston have shown * that the passage of a dislocation over a slip plane leaves dislocation loops behind, and he wondered if such loops could be responsible for the change of contrast in bands that the dislocations have passed through. HIRSCH felt that if such loops are left behind on the slip plane they should be observable, whereas they have not been observed.

* See the following paper by Gilman and Johnston.

The Origin and Growth of Glide Bands in Lithium Fluoride Crystals

JOHN J. GILMAN

WILLIAM G. JOHNSTON

General Electric Research Laboratory
Schenectady, New York

ABSTRACT

Etching techniques are described which allow direct observations of dislocation glide in LiF crystals. A chemical polishing technique is also described. A method for introducing isolated dislocation half loops into crystals is presented.

A discussion is given of the reliability of the etching techniques in revealing all the dislocations in LiF crystals. X-ray evidence of the crystal perfection is presented which confirms the etch-pit evidence of the crystal perfection.

The macroscopic plastic behavior of LiF crystals is described. Results of both compression and bend tests are presented, mostly of bend tests. The effects in bend tests of specimen shape, temperature, strain rate, and surface perfection are described.

Evidence concerning the origin of glide dislocations in LiF crystals is given. It is pointed out that dislocation loops can be nucleated at the tips of cracks in LiF crystals. Then, three sets of experiments are described which indicate that dislocation nucleation occurs at stresses as low as about 1 kg/mm^2. In these experiments dislocation loops were nucleated: (*a*) by lightly pressing balls into contact with LiF crystals; (*b*) by means of thermal stresses; (*c*) during plastic bending.

The expansion and multiplication of dislocation half loops under applied stresses is described. It is shown that a single half loop can multiply sufficiently to create a large glide band consisting of thousands of dislocations.

The multiplication process begins by the formation of new dislocation loops behind an expanding half loop. After large glide bands have been established they spawn other glide bands by new nucleation at stress concentrations and by the motion of (110) screw dislocations off (110) planes onto (100) planes.

It is demonstrated that dislocations in LiF crystals experience a large viscous lattice resistance to their motion. This lattice resistance depends strongly on temperature.

---

1. INTRODUCTION

The motion of individual, isolated dislocation lines can be observed in lithium fluoride crystals. An example of this is shown in Fig. 1. The schematic drawing (*b*) shows the position of the dislocation half loop in the crystal and how the stress was applied. In (*a*) each pair of etch pits marks the location of the two ends of the half loop; the pits with flat bottoms show the initial location of the half loop and the pits with pointed bottoms show where the half loop came to rest after an applied stress had caused it to move.

Detailed and controlled observations of dislocations such as the one above are possible because of the favorable combination of properties that lithium fluoride crystals possess. These crystals react to etching reagents in a highly sensitive way; they have a simple structure, namely the NaCl-type structure; they are unusually perfect after growth from the melt; they can be cleaved readily with negligible distortion; they are hard enough to be handled with simple precautions, and yet they are slightly plastic at room temperature. Because of this unusual combination of properties, intensive study of lithium fluoride crystals can yield answers to several important questions concerning dislocations:

1. How do dislocation loops like the one in Fig. 1 originate?
2. How do such loops multiply to form glide bands?
3. What stress is needed to move individual dislocations through a crystal of LiF?
4. How do dislocations interact with possible obstacles such as crystal boundaries and intersecting glide bands?
5. How does the velocity of a dislocation depend on the applied stress?
6. What factors determine the yield stress and critical resolved shear stress of a crystal?
7. How do dislocations behave in a creeping crystal?
8. How fast do dislocations climb at high temperatures?

An attempt will be made to answer the first three of these questions at this time. Evidence regarding the last five questions is being gathered in the course of a general study of dislocations in LiF.

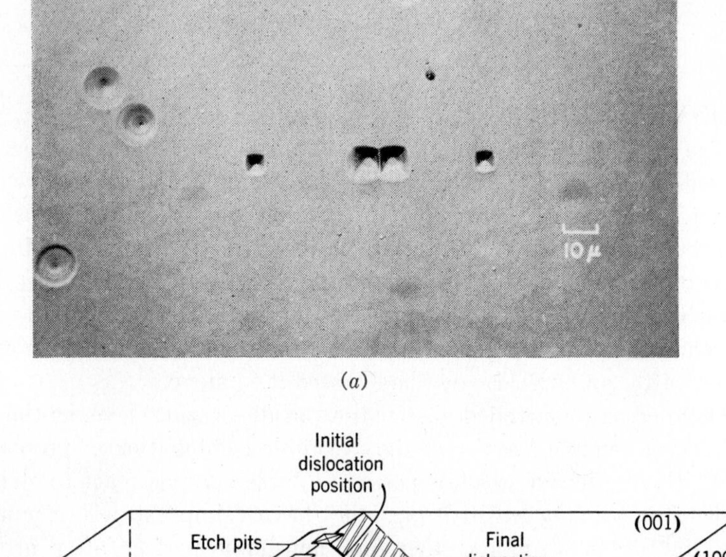

(a)

(b)

Fig. 1. Etch pits showing motion of an individual dislocation loop in a lithium fluoride crystal.

2. EXPERIMENTAL METHODS

Crystals

The crystals used in this work were purchased from the Harshaw Chemical Company, Cleveland, Ohio. The nominal composition of the crystals provided by the manufacturer was checked spectrographically. In agreement with the manufacturer's analysis, the only detectable impurity is a few parts in 10^5 of Mg. Gravimetric chemical analysis shows that the stoichiometry of the crystals is within 0.2% of ideal.

Etching reveals that the as-received crystals contain subgrains 0.8 mm average diameter and approximately 5×10^4 dislocations/cm^2 within the subgrains. The subgrain misorientations average about 5 min of arc.

Specimens were made by cleavage along (100) planes of the crystals. Good cleavages were obtained with a high-speed steel chisel tapped sharply but lightly with a ball-peen hammer. The chisel had an angle of about 30° and it was hardened to about 62 Rockwell C.

Etches

Two etches were used to reveal dislocations on (100) faces of LiF. Etch "A" attacks all dislocations equally well, whereas "W" distinguishes between annealed dislocations and fresh dislocations introduced by plastic deformation below about 300°C.

Etch "A," described earlier,[1] consists of equal parts of conc. HF and glacial acetic acid plus 1-vol. % of conc. HF saturated with FeF_3. After a 30 to 60-sec etch, a crystal is rinsed in absolute alcohol and then in anhydrous ether. The shape of the etch pits and the etching rate depend on the ferric ion concentration. This etch seems to produce a square-based pyramidal pit at each dislocation that cuts the (100) cleavage face of LiF. The base edges of the pits lie parallel to [110] directions. Dislocations that make angles as low as 10° with the (100) face are etched and they may be of either edge or screw type.

Etch "W" is a dilute aqueous solution of FeF_3 or $FeCl_3$ (1.5×10^{-4} molar). If the ferric ion concentration is low, a 2-min etch in this reagent produces large, shallow, and somewhat indistinct pits. At the proper ferric ion concentration, a 2-min etch produces sharply defined square pyramidal pits about 10 μ in size with the base edges of the pits parallel to [100] directions. Excess ferric ions reduce the size of the pits, and make them rounded. Etch "W" is followed by a rinse in alcohol, then in ether.

The two horizontal rows of dislocations in Fig. 2*a* were introduced by plastic deformation whereas the subboundaries and random dislocations were present in the crystal as grown. Notice how clearly etch "W" distinguishes between the two types of dislocation. The crystal was chemically polished to remove the pits made by etch "W," and then it was dipped in etch "A" for 1 min. In Fig. 2*b* it may be seen that etch "A" attacks all dislocations equally. Notice also the difference in orientation of the pits in the two photographs.

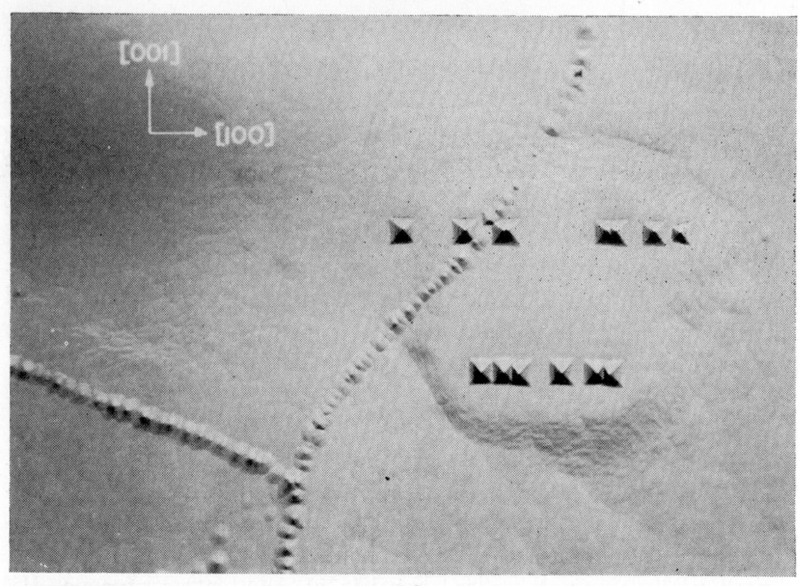

(*a*)

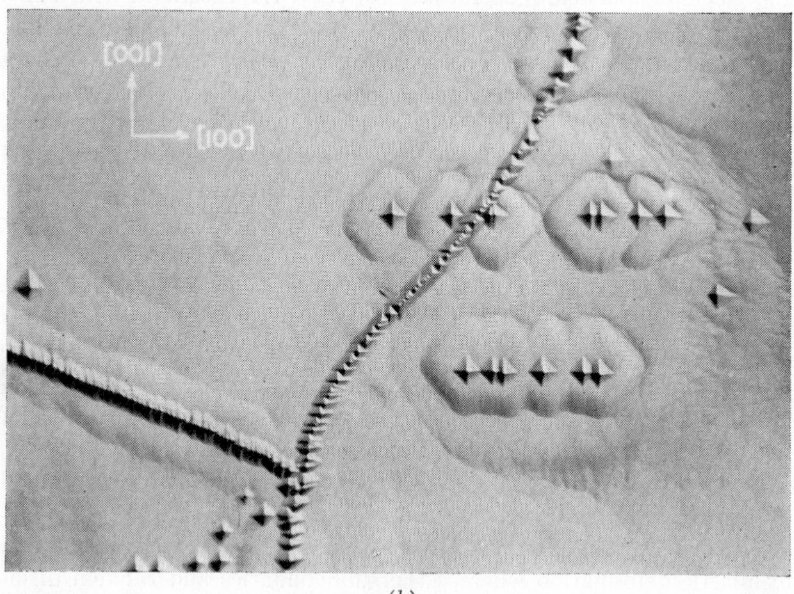

(*b*)

Fig. 2. Comparison of action of etches "A" and "W" on same field. Crystal polished between etchings. Two horizontal rows due to plastic deformation. Note difference in orientation of pits produced by the two reagents. 432×. (*a*) Etch "W" attacks fresh dislocations more rapidly than annealed dislocations. (*b*) Etch "A" attacks all dislocations equally.

The selective action of etch "W" is valuable because it enables one to readily locate a few fresh dislocations in a field containing thousands of annealed dislocations. The etch forms an indistinct pit at each annealed dislocation so their positions are also known. A possible reason for the slow attack of etch "W" on annealed dislocations is that impurities may segregate at the dislocations during annealing, thereby reducing their chemical potential.

Chemical Polishing

A technique has been developed for polishing LiF by chemical means. This technique enables one to remove a deeply etched surface which is confused by extremely large pits. For example, in Fig. 2 the pits left by etch "W" were "erased" in order to show the effect of etch "A" on the same dislocations. The chemical polish can be used to study dislocation distributions in three dimensions by polishing between successive etchings. The technique has been used to follow dislocations as far as 600 μ into crystals.

The crystal is dipped for 1 min in conc. HF, rinsed in alcohol and in ether, and then polished in a 2-vol. % solution of NH_4OH in distilled water. Vigorous agitation is necessary. At 26°C a fresh solution will remove 1.3 μ/min from the surface of a crystal. The polishing treatment is followed by an alcohol rinse, and then an ether rinse. The appearance of a polished surface can be seen between the pits of Fig. 2. The depth of polish can be accurately measured by measuring the distance between glide bands that lie on nonparallel (110) planes.

Mechanical Tests

Several shapes and sizes of rectangular specimens were cleaved from LiF crystals. The various methods that were used to apply known stresses to these specimens are illustrated in Fig. 3. The names given in the figure legend will be used in the remainder of the paper to refer to the different stressing methods.

Stress-strain curves were obtained with an Instron testing machine which is a very "hard" machine. Dead loads and impulse loads were also applied to the crystals. The impulses were obtained by bouncing balls off the bending fixtures (*d*) and (*e*) of Fig. 3.

3. CORRESPONDENCE BETWEEN DISLOCATIONS AND ETCH PITS

All of the arguments presented in this paper depend on the reliability of the etching technique to reveal dislocations, so it is desirable, before proceeding, to assess the action of the present etchants on LiF crystals.

There seems to be little doubt that the pits produced by etches "A" and "W" are located at dislocations [1] but the question as to whether all the dislocations in the crystals are being etched is not so easily answered. Only direct observations of the atoms in a crystal could give positive evidence on this question. However, a large array of circumstantial evidence can be mustered in support of the hypothesis that, indeed, all dislocations are revealed by the etchant.

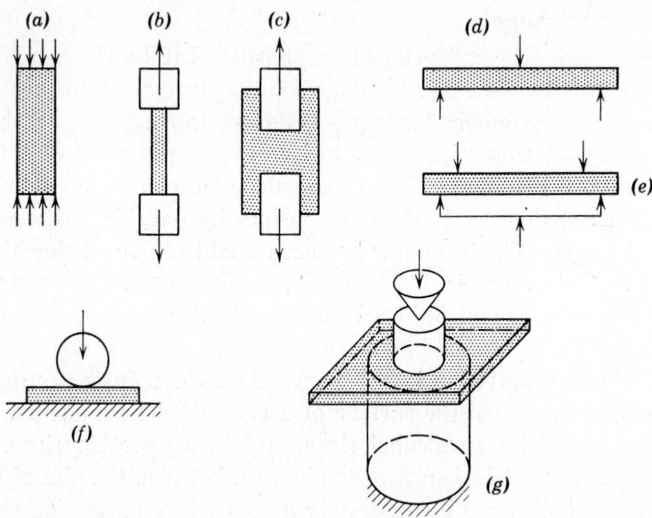

Fig. 3. Various methods used to apply stresses to lithium fluoride crystals. (*a*) Simple compression. (*b*) Simple tension. (*c*) Tension with unstressed edges. (*d*) Simple bending. (*e*) Pure bending. (*f*) Ball contact. (*g*) Concentric circular loading of plate.

The following evidence suggests strongly that all dislocations are revealed by the present etching techniques:

1. Almost identical patterns of pits appear on matched cleavage faces. This is shown in Fig. 4.

2. The etches are sensitive to defects in the crystals other than dislocations. Some of these are cleavage steps, inclusions, and evaporation pits. At these defects, the etches produce flat-bottomed pits which can be easily distinguished from the pointed pits that appear at dislocations. The fact that several kinds of defects are revealed by the etches suggests that the etches would be sensitive to more than one kind of dislocation, and hence to all dislocations.

3. The dislocations that are attacked by the etchants are attacked uniformly. In spite of the fact that the dislocations in as-grown

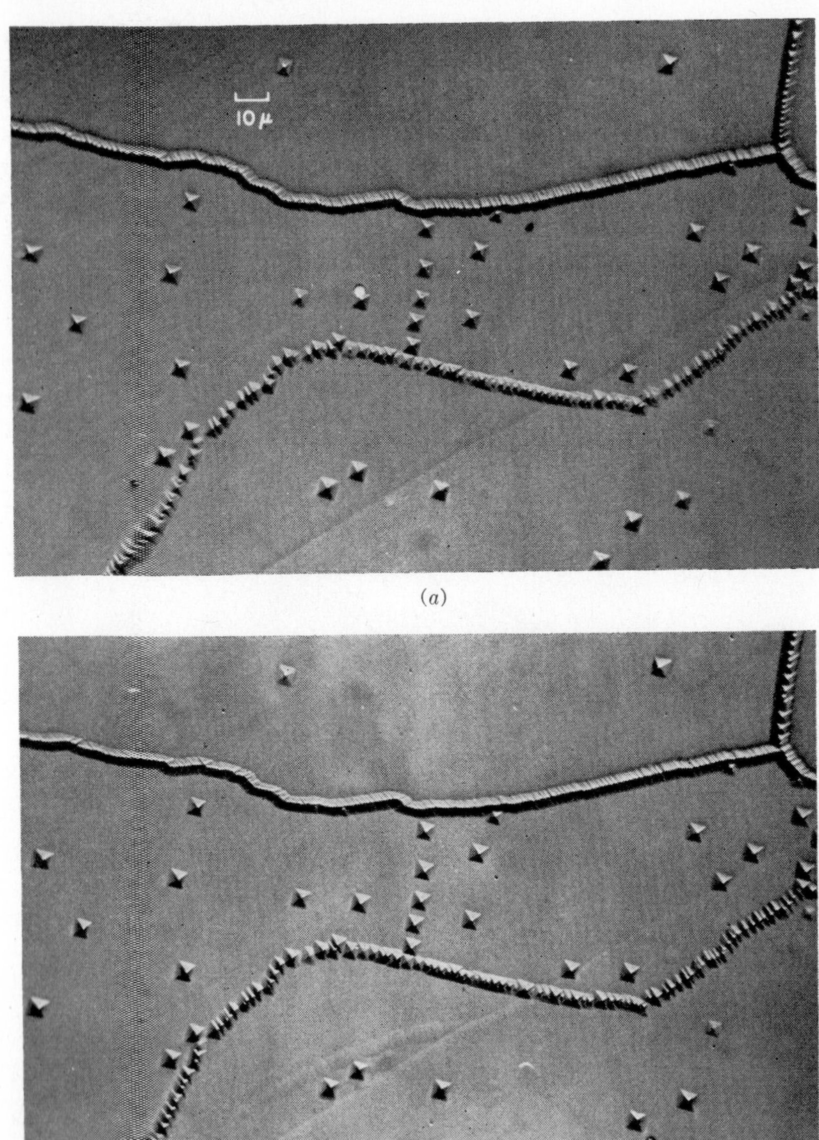

(a)

(b)

Fig. 4. Etch pits on matched opposite sides of cleavage crack in an "as-grown" crystal. Etch "A." (a) Normal printing. (b) Printing reversed to simplify comparison.

crystals probably have various Burgers vectors and certainly lie on various planes, they are all etched at very nearly the same rate.

4. Both the edge and screw orientations of (110) $[1\bar{1}0]$ dislocations are etched. They are etched at nearly the same rate, but can be distinguished because edge dislocations produce symmetric pits whereas screw dislocations produce asymmetric pits. (Fig. 5.)

5. The angle that a dislocation line makes with the (100) surface of a crystal can be estimated from the asymmetry of its etch pits. Dis-

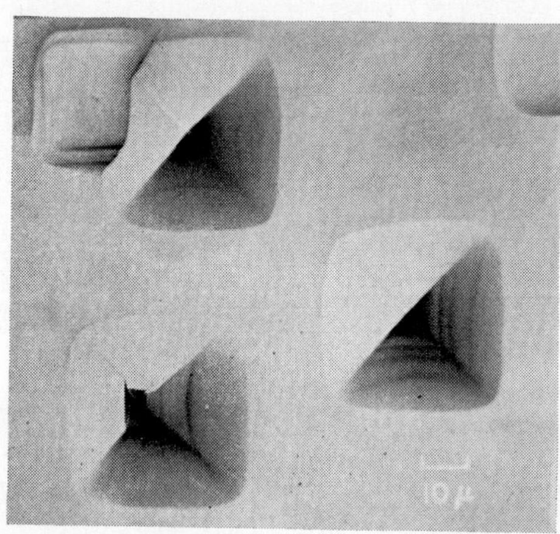

Fig. 5. Comparison of etch pits produced at edge and screw dislocations by etch "A." Lower left pit is at screw dislocation, others at edge dislocations.

locations that make angles ranging from as low as 10° up to 90° are revealed by the etchants.

6. When a dislocation moves away from the position of a pit, during subsequent etching the pit ceases to have a pyramidal shape; it becomes flat-bottomed. Thus a dislocation not only originates a pit, but its presence is necessary to maintain the pyramidal shape of a growing pit. (Fig. 6.)

7. Crystals with low etch-pit densities diffract X rays in the manner that is expected for nearly perfect crystals, whereas crystals with high etch-pit densities diffract X rays in the manner expected for imperfect crystals. Since this fact is independent of the etching behavior, perhaps it is the strongest evidence that the etch-pit technique reveals a true picture of the state of perfection of the crystals.

Striking X-ray evidence can be obtained simply by making Laue photographs of LiF crystals. If the Laue photograph of a "good" as-grown LiF crystal (disl. density $\simeq 10^5/\text{cm}^2$) is compared with the

Laue photograph of a "bad" crystal that has been quenched from 600°C (disl. density $\simeq 6 \times 10^7/\text{cm}^2$), the large X-ray extinction that occurs in the "good" crystal may be seen at a glance. For constant exposure and development, diffracted intensities of the good crystal are a factor of ten or more lower than those of the bad crystal.

Quantitative X-ray evidence was obtained using a GE XRD-3 spectrometer with MoKα radiation filtered with Zr. The diffracted intensities were detected with an argon proportional counter, recorded, and integrated with a planimeter. The results are presented in Table 1 and Fig. 7. It may be seen that the intensity of the (002) reflection from the "bad" crystal was more than 13 times greater than from the "good" crystal. Also, the measured intensity from the "good" crystal was proportional to TF while the intensity from the "bad" crystal was proportional to $(TF)^2$, where T is a factor which corrects for thermal vibrations and F is the atomic structure factor. This is in accord with the theory of X-ray diffraction in perfect and imperfect crystals.[2]

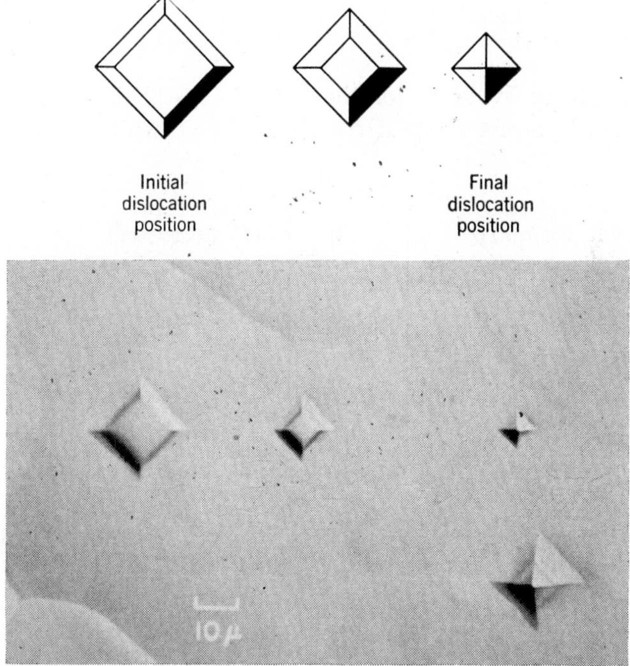

Fig. 6. Effect of dislocation motion on etch-pit shapes. Etch "A."

TABLE 1. COMPARISON OF THEORETICAL AND MEASURED X-RAY DIFFRACTION INTENSITIES FROM "GOOD" AND "BAD" LiF CRYSTALS. CORRECTION FACTORS FROM REFERENCE 2

Reflection	Angle θ (Deg)	Atomic Scattering Factors (Li^+)	(F^-)	Structure Factor $F(\theta)$	Temperature Factor $T(\theta)$, $\theta = 650°K$	Polarization Factor $P(\theta)$	Theor. Intensities TFP	$(TF)^2P$	Meas. Intensities "Good" Crystal	"Bad" Crystal
002	10.2	1.63	5.7	7.33	0.985	5.51	39.8	288	17.05	226.7
004	20.8	1.00	2.8	3.80	0.915	2.40	8.35	29	3.53	27.7
006	32.2	0.56	1.7	2.26	0.830	1.30	2.43	4.5	0.33	4.8
008	45.2	0.34	1.5	1.84	0.720	1.00	1.32	1.7	.....	0.88
010	62.5	0.30	1.35	1.65	0.570	1.62	1.51	1.4	.....	0.44

Thus the X-ray evidence for the "good" crystal demonstrates that such crystals possess the perfection that the etch-pit density implies.

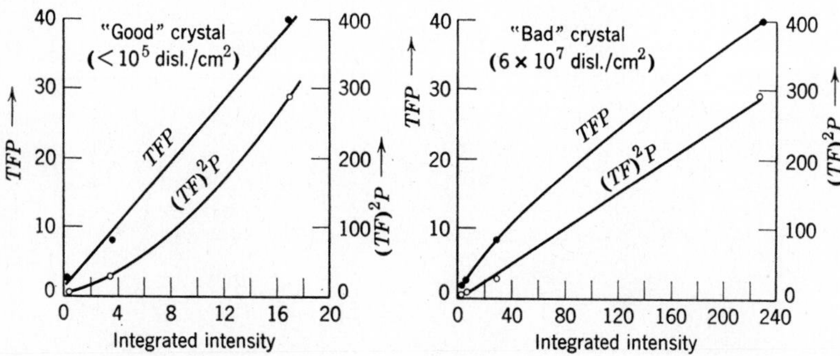

Fig. 7. Comparison of theoretical intensity factors with measured diffracted intensities for lithium fluoride crystals. (See Table 1.)

4. MACROSCOPIC PLASTIC BEHAVIOR OF LiF CRYSTALS

The authors are unaware of a description in the literature of the plastic behavior of LiF crystals. Therefore, the plastic behavior will be described here in order to orient the reader, and to provide information for subsequent discussion.

Compression Tests

Figure 8 shows the compression stress-strain curve of a typical "as-received" LiF crystal. The specimen was prepared by cleavage, and the ends were lubricated to minimize friction at the loading plattens.

The compression stress-strain curve can be divided into four parts: A, the elastic region; B, the initial yield region; C, the easy flow region; and D, the region of strain hardening. Two stresses are pertinent to the discussions of this paper: τ_y, the yield stress; and τ^*, the critical resolved shear stress. These stresses have distinct physical meanings: at the yield stress dislocation motion begins; at the critical resolved shear stress large-scale catastrophic glide occurs. The meanings of these stresses in terms of dislocations will be discussed later.

Typical values of τ_y and τ^* in compression tests are 400 and 500 g/mm^2 respectively. These values depend, of course, on the temperature, strain rate, and thermal history of a particular crystal. Because

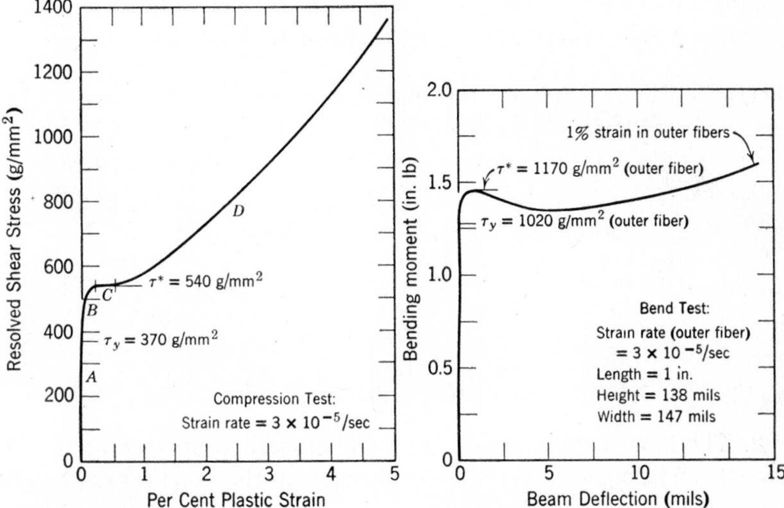

Fig. 8. Comparison of compression and bend test results on specimens from the same crystal.

of end effects it was difficult to produce uniform strains in the compression tests; and bend tests were used for a major portion of the investigation.

The brittleness of the crystals made it difficult to perform tensile tests, but the few that were performed gave results in qualitative agreement with the compression tests.

Bend Tests

A bending-moment-versus-deflection curve is compared with the compression curve in Fig. 8. Both specimens came from the same crystal. Note that the yield stress and critical resolved shear stress are higher in a bend test than in a compression test. Possible reasons for this will be discussed later.

Two factors made it necessary to compare bend tests only for specimens from the same crystal and approximately of the same shape:

1. The shape of bending-moment-versus-deflection curves depended on the specimen thickness. This was not unexpected because the maximum strain in a bent beam is given by

$$\epsilon_{\max} = \frac{t}{\Delta + c^2/4\Delta}$$

where t is the beam depth, c is the beam length, and Δ is the deflection. Thus the strain at constant deflection is proportional to the beam depth. In order to correct for this flow, stress should be compared at constant strain instead of constant deflection; Table 2.

TABLE 2. COMPARISON OF YIELD STRESSES AT CONSTANT DEFLECTION AND CONSTANT MAXIMUM STRAIN FOR LITHIUM FLUORIDE CRYSTALS

(Three mm. wide with various beam depths [beam length = 25.4 mm])

Beam Depth (mm)	Maximum Shear Stress at Yield (g/mm²)	
	Δ = const.	$\epsilon_{\max} = 10^{-4}$
1.2	930	1110
2.2	1040	1110
4.4	1080	1110
10.0	1210	1180

2. The flow stresses varied from one crystal to another in the as-grown condition, so that only specimens from the same crystal can be compared in any series of tests.

The temperature dependence of the yield stress for specimens cut from the same crystal is shown in Fig. 9. The data cannot be fitted by functions which some authors have used of the form

$$\tau_y = \tau_0 \pm KT^n \quad \text{or} \quad \tau_y = \tau_0 e^{K/T}$$

where T is the absolute temperature; however, a good fit is obtained using the function $\tau_y = \tau_0 e^{-KT}$. This function is plotted in the figure.

Changing the strain rate has little effect on the macroscopic behavior of LiF crystals; Table 3. The yield stress is proportional to

TABLE 3. EFFECT OF STRAIN RATE ON THE YIELD STRESS OF LIF CRYSTALS AT ROOM TEMPERATURE; BEND TESTS ON CRYSTAL OF FIG. 9

Beam Deflection Rate (in./min)	Strain Rate in Outer Fiber (sec^{-1})	Yield Shear Stress (g/mm²)
0.002	2×10^{-5}	1120
0.02	2×10^{-4}	1200
0.2	2×10^{-3}	1490

the ninth or tenth root of the strain rate and hence quite insensitive to it.

An important clue to an understanding of the macroscopic behavior of LiF crystals is that the stress-strain curves are very sensitive to the state of the surface. Some of these effects are shown in Fig. 10:

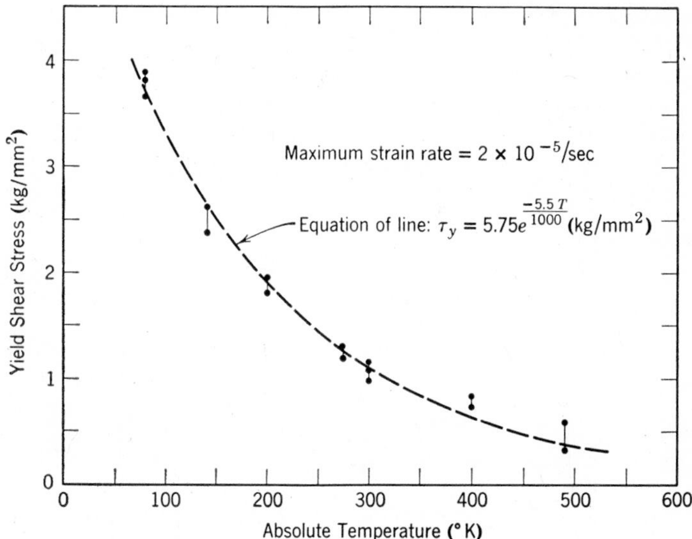

Fig. 9. Temperature dependence of the yield stress of a lithium fluoride crystal.

(*a*) An as-cleaved crystal, compared with a chemically polished crystal, and a polished crystal whose surface was sprinkled with 100 mesh carborundum particles.

(*b*) The effect of temperature on (*a*).

(*c*) Cleaved and annealed crystal; unpolished after annealing versus polished.

(*d*) An as-cleaved crystal versus deeply etched crystals.

The curves of Fig. 10 show that crystals with surface defects bend more easily and uniformly than crystals in which surface defects are removed by chemical etching or polishing. The defects on cleaved crystals are cleavage steps and dislocations introduced by cleavage; on annealed crystals they are evaporation pits (more intense at 600°C than at 400°C), and perhaps dislocations produced during cooling slowly from the annealing temperature; on polished crystals sprinkled with carborundum, they are dislocations produced at the points of contact of the carborundum and the crystal.

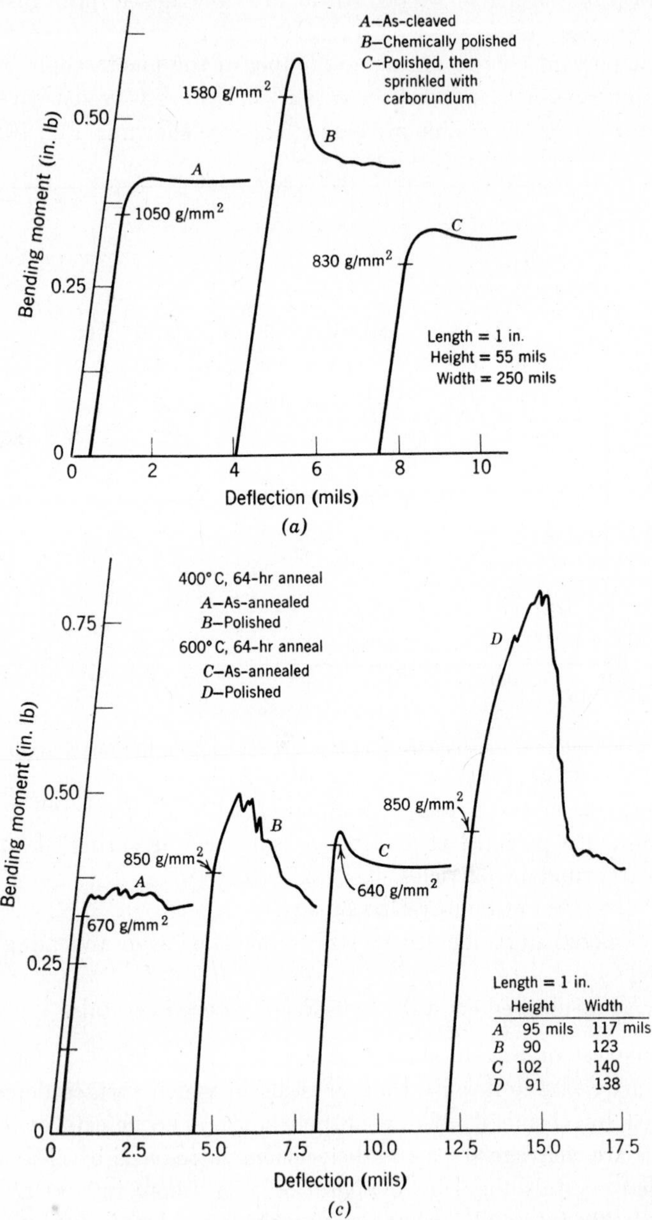

Fig. 10. Stress-strain curves showing surface effects in LiF crystals.

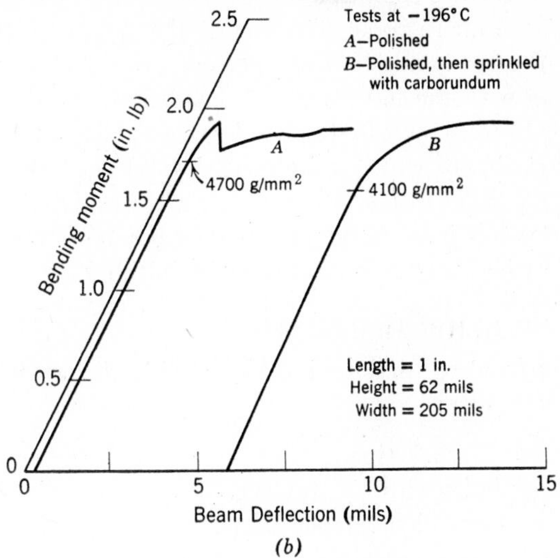

(b)

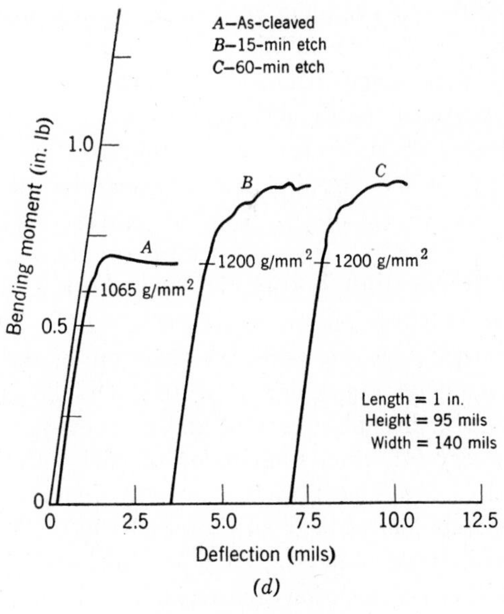

(d)

Fig. 10 (continued).

The effect of surface condition on the stress-strain curves is reflected in changes of the microscopic structure of the crystals. In particular, the number of glide bands that are present after a certain amount of strain changes with the initial surface condition. For example, after the same total strain, the first crystal (as-cleaved) of Fig. 10*d* contained 334 glide bands whereas the third crystal (heavily etched) contained only 109 glide bands. In general, after a given strain, etched or polished crystals have fewer glide bands but more strain per band than crystals whose surfaces are defective initially.

5. ORIGIN OF GLIDE DISLOCATIONS

Four methods were used to introduce glide dislocations into LiF crystals. There were:

1. Nucleation at crack tips.
2. Contacting balls with the surface.
3. Quenching from high temperatures.
4. Plastic bending of crystals.

Before these methods of originating glide dislocations are discussed, it should be pointed out that the dislocations already present in as-grown LiF crystals seem to have very little to do with initiating glide in the crystals. The "grown-in" dislocations apparently have impurities associated with them which immobilize them. Although the authors have examined many deformed crystals, they have seen no clear-cut examples of stress-induced motion of "grown-in" dislocations. Therefore, it is believed that the "grown-in" dislocations play only a passive role in the plastic behavior of the crystals.

Nucleation of Dislocation Loops at Crack Tips

If a cleavage crack is passed rapidly through a LiF crystal, the passage of the crack does not affect the structure of the crystal. This is one of the facts that Fig. 4 demonstrates. On the other hand, if a crack passes slowly through a crystal and especially if it stops somewhere inside a crystal, then multitudes of dislocations are created at the crack tip. See Fig. 11. It has been demonstrated that the dislocations form as loops ahead of the crack tip.[3] The loops do not come from Frank-Read sources. They are nucleated by the stresses at the crack tip from dislocation-free regions of the crystal.

Dislocation creation at crack tips shows conclusively that dislocations can be nucleated in LiF crystals in the absence of prior dislocations. However, this phenomenon does not define the stress at which the nucleation occurs. The nucleation stress may be extremely high

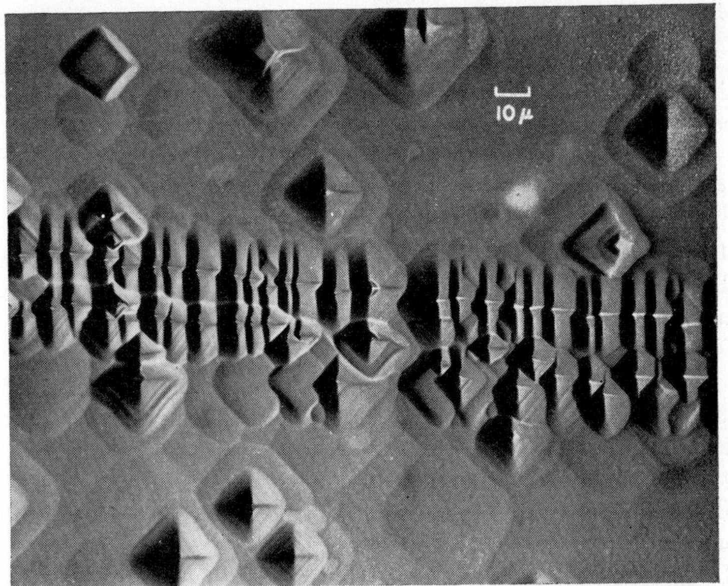

(*a*)

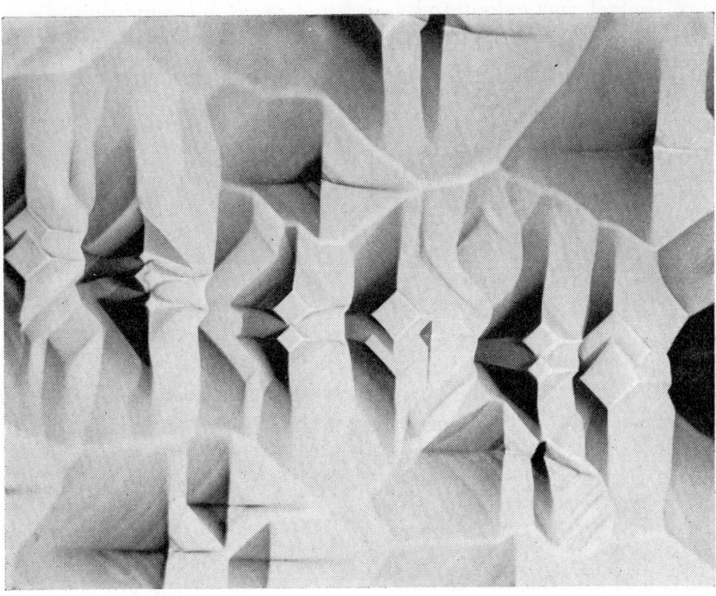

(*b*)

Fig. 11. Etch pits at dislocations that were created at region where a crack stopped temporarily in a LiF crystal. Plane of photograph is plane of crack. Etch "A." (*a*) 5-min etch. (*b*) 40-min etch; some of the dislocations have disappeared, showing that the pairs of pits represent dislocation half loops.

as it is at the very tip of the crack or it may be any lower value. Other experiments were performed to try to determine the minimum stress needed for dislocation nucleation.

Dislocation Nucleation by Balls in Contact with the Surface of LiF Crystals

If a small ball is pressed lightly into contact with the surface of a LiF crystal, it is found that dislocations are nucleated at the area of contact.

Two methods have been used to control the force of contact. One was to suspend the ball as a pendulum from the end of a long string; then, with a crystal at the zero deflection point, the pendulum was deflected and released, allowing the ball to strike and rebound from the crystal surface. From the velocity of the ball and its mass, diameter, and elastic constants, the stresses in the crystal can be calculated from the Hertz impact theory.[4] In order to simplify the calculation, a LiF single-crystal ball was used. The polished ball, ½ in. in diameter, was suspended from a 6-ft nylon thread. The velocity at the time of impact was calculated as a function of the pendulum displacement, taking air-damping into account.

For a ball that strikes a flat surface, the maximum pressure, p_0, under the area of contact is given by the Hertz theory as:

$$p_0 = \frac{1}{2}(5\rho)^{1/5}\left[\frac{2E}{\pi(1-\nu^2)}\right]^{4/5} v^{2/5}$$

where ρ = density = 2.6 g/cm^3
v = ball velocity at time of contact
$E = 1/s_{11}$ = Young's modulus = 9.45×10^{11} dynes/cm^2
$\nu = -s_{12}/s_{11}$ = Poisson's ratio = 0.27

This results in a maximum shear stress in the flat body of $\sim 0.31 p_0$ at a depth of $\sim r/2$ along the center line of the ball, where r is the radius of the area of contact and is given by:

$$r = \frac{(1-\nu^2)}{E}\pi p_0 R$$

where R is the radius of the ball. The duration of the impact is:

$$t = 2.94\left[\frac{5\pi}{2}(1-\nu^2)\frac{\rho}{E}\right]^{2/5}\frac{R}{v^{1/5}}$$

Figure 12 shows what happens at the area of contact of a ball and a LiF crystal. Figure 12a and b shows areas of crystals that were free

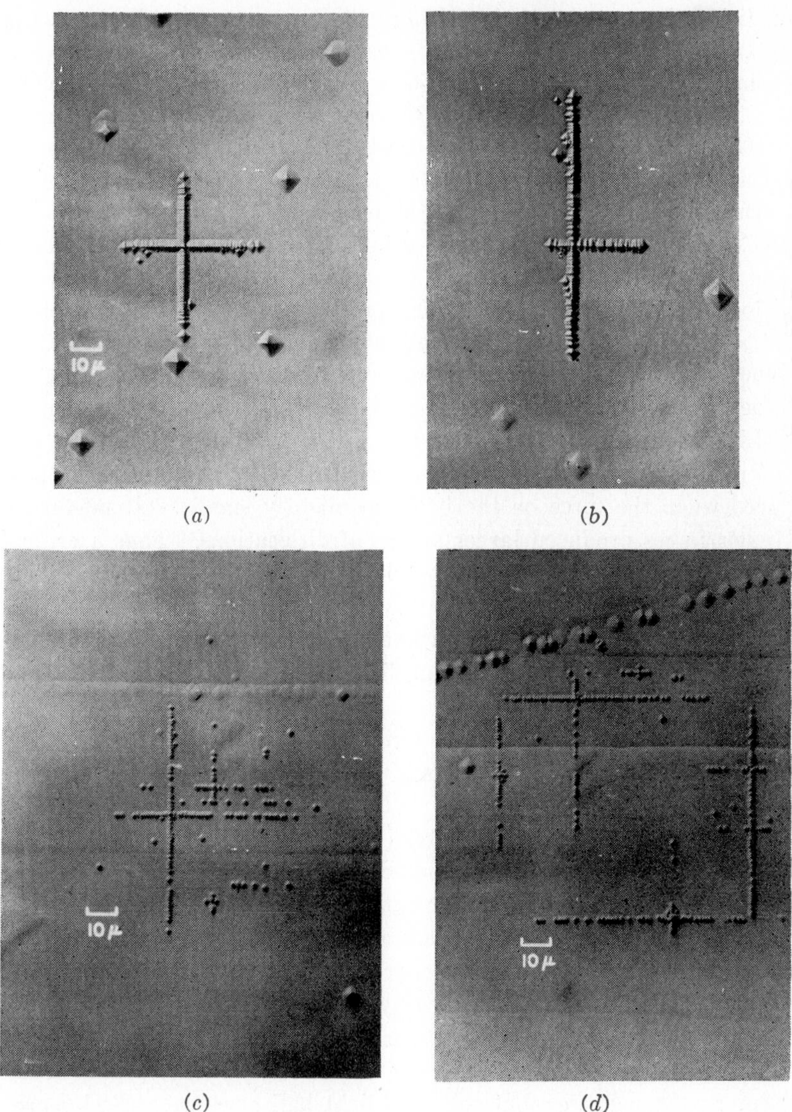

Fig. 12. Areas of contact of balls and LiF crystals—etched in etch "A." (*a* and *b*) LiF ball at −196°C. (*c* and *d*) Lucite ball at 25°C. (*a*) Cleaved, etched deeply, contacted ($v = 2.9$ cm/sec), etched lightly. (*b*) Polished, etched deeply, contacted ($v = 2.9$ cm/sec), etched lightly. (*c*) Cleaved, etched, contacted, etched ($v = 40$ cm/sec) $\tau_{max.} \simeq 4 \times 10^8$ dynes/cm^2. (*d*) Cleaved, etched, contacted, etched ($v = 40$ cm/sec) $\tau_{max.} \simeq 4 \times 10^8$ dynes/cm^2.

of dislocations at the surface before they were contacted with a LiF ball. One of the crystal surfaces was as-cleaved, and the other was chemically polished. In both cases a polished LiF ball with a velocity of 2.9 cm/sec was bounced off the crystal while the crystal was at $-196°C$. The ball was aligned with its crystal axes parallel to the crystal axes of the crystal plates. According to the Hertz impact theory, the time duration of the impact should have been about 160 μsec. The radius of the area of contact of the ball and the flat surface was about 140 μ, and therefore large compared with the size of the dislocation crosses. The maximum pressure under the ball was about 3.6×10^9 dynes/cm^2 so the maximum shear stress was about 10^9 dynes/cm^2 (and the highest shear stress at the surface was 5.5×10^8 dynes/cm^2). This may be compared with the yield stress in bending of LiF which is about 5×10^8 dynes/cm^2.

Dislocation configurations like those of Fig. 12*a* and *b* were not produced when the force on the ball was slightly smaller (about 30%). Higher forces produced larger arrays of dislocations. Thus a critical stress exists and it is approximately equal to the macroscopic yield stress.

Figure 12*c* and *d* shows somewhat larger arrays of dislocations that were produced by dropping ⅛-in. diameter polished Lucite balls onto a LiF crystal.

Similar results were produced with statically loaded balls supported on the ends of long pivoted arms. The results were essentially the same.

A complication sometimes arises if a speck of a hard substance lies within the area of contact of a ball and the crystal surface. The hard particle acts as a stress concentrator and produces a characteristic array of dislocations which we call a "rosette." Some typical rosettes and a schematic drawing of their structure are shown in Fig. 13. The rosettes of Fig. 13*b* were produced by dropping 100-mesh carborundum particles onto the surface of a crystal from a height of about 1 in. When 240-mesh particles were used, no rosettes were produced by dropping the particles, but rolling a light ball over the particles produced profuse rosettes along the path of the ball. The rosette pattern can be readily distinguished from the more open lattice patterns that are produced by balls which make contact over relatively large areas.

There is some question as to whether it is the general Hertz stresses that produce the dislocations at the contact area of a ball or more localized concentrated stresses. These more concentrated stresses might be caused by irregularities on the surface of the ball or the flat crystal or they might arise from friction combined with torques on the ball.[5] The latter is ruled out because the loading was performed so as to

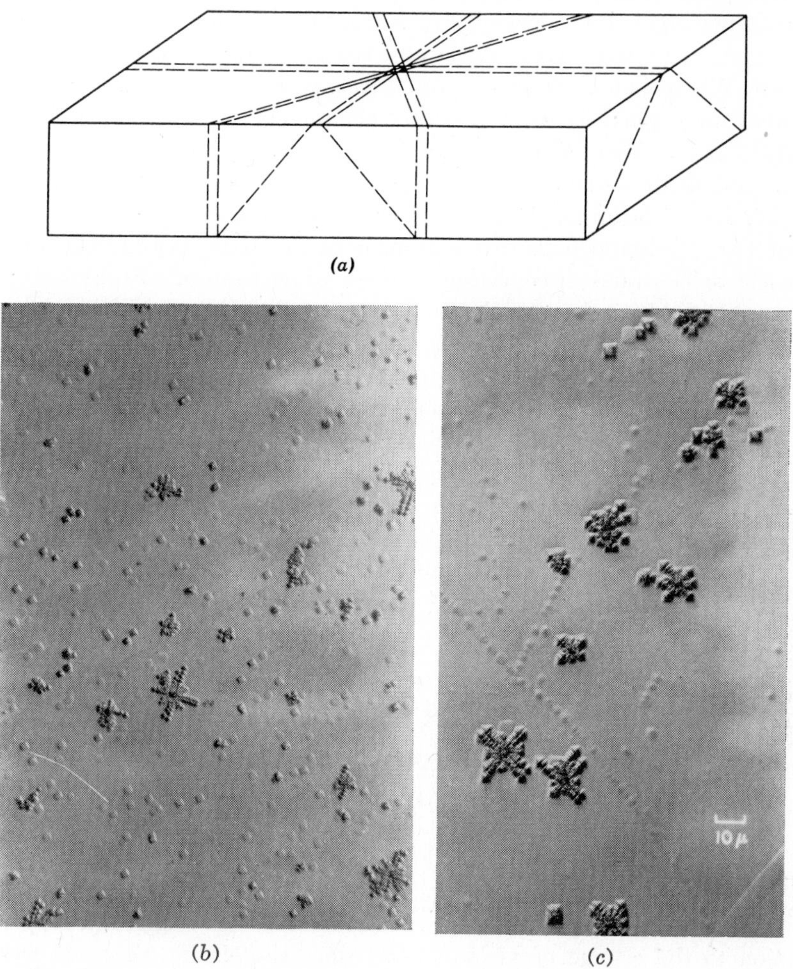

Fig. 13. "Rosettes" produced by small hard particles in contact with the surface of LiF crystals. (*a*) Drawing showing six glide planes of rosettes. (*b*) Rosettes due to 100-mesh carborundum dropped 1 in. (*c*) Rosettes due to rolling ¼-in. steel ball across surface.

make any torques negligible. The evidence regarding stress concentrations is as follows:

1. The results were not sensitive to the crystal surface preparation (cleaved versus polished—see Fig. 12) and irregularities on a chemi-

cally polished surface are expected to be little more than monatomic in height.

2. Where known surface irregularities were present in the form of cleavage steps, there was no correlation between the dislocations and the cleavage steps except for large steps pressed severely.

3. Where known surface irregularities were present in the form of small hard particles, they produced characteristic rosette patterns of dislocations easily distinguished from the dislocation patterns due to the Hertz stresses.

4. It is difficult to see how a highly co-ordinated pattern like that of Fig. 12*d* could have arisen from a single stress concentrator or a more or less random collection of stress concentrators. Note also the many "dendritic branches" and isolated individual dislocation loops in Fig. 12*d* which would have required stress concentrators to produce them unless they arose simply from the Hertz stresses.

5. Since cleavage steps do not seem to lead to dislocation production, it is not reasonable to expect that scratches on the ball would. Also, the area of contact of the ball was quite large so that scratches on the ball, if effective, should have produced a complex, irregular pattern of dislocations.

6. Balls with various elastic moduli were used:

Teflon: $\sim 5 \times 10^9$ dynes/cm^2
Lucite: 3.4×10^{10} dynes/cm^2
LiF: 9.5×10^{11} dynes/cm^2
Steel: 2.1×10^{12} dynes/cm^2

These would have various compliances with respect to surface irregularities and therefore should produce various stress concentration factors. Yet it was found that approximately the same value of the Hertz stress was needed to produce dislocations for all the balls.

7. When the hardnesses of the crystals were changed by irradiation or a change of temperature, the critical Hertz stress changed in proportion to the change of yield stress. Since the elastic constants were not appreciably changed, the stress concentration factors could not have changed; hence concentrated stresses did not seem to be responsible for the dislocations.

8. The stress concentration would have to be extremely high (a factor of 1000) and would have to extend over a volume at least 10^{-4} cm in diameter in order to satisfy the conventional theory of dislocation nucleation.

9. The critical Hertz stress needed for dislocation nucleation is remarkably close to the yield stress in bending of LiF crystals.

Dislocation Nucleation by Thermal Stresses

By cleaving a crystal into two parts and then annealing one part, it can readily be shown that LiF crystals can be annealed without changing their dislocation density. Very slow heating and cooling are essential. If, instead of being slowly cooled, a crystal is quenched from 600°C, as many as 6×10^7 disl./cm^2 will be introduced into a crystal that had only 10^5 disl./cm^2 before the quench. Intermediate rates of cooling produce intermediate numbers of new dislocations.

If a crystal is heated and cooled inside a $\frac{3}{8}$-in. diameter quartz tube with one open end, an intermediate number of new dislocations appear in the crystal after it has been cooled in air from 600°C. A large fraction of these new dislocations consists of tiny closed loops. A few of these dislocation loops can even be found in crystals cooled inside quartz tubes from 400°C.

Some of the loops in crystals cooled moderately rapidly from 400°C can be shown to be completely isolated from other dislocations in the crystals. A good example is shown in Fig. 14. Figure 14*a* shows a rather deeply etched region of the crystal (the pits are about 10 μ deep). In the center it can be seen that two small etch pits suddenly appeared. Since no large pits appear near the two new pits it is clear that there were no dislocations in a region at least 3 μ thick above the new dislocations. Upon further etching the two pits disappeared, showing that a closed dislocation loop was being etched. Still more etching revealed nothing for a depth of at least 10 μ below the closed loop. Other closed loops appeared and disappeared at other locations as the etching proceeded.

Small dislocation loops might be produced in two ways during cooling from elevated temperatures. They might form by the collapse of a plate of vacancies or they might form because of stresses.

The diameters of the dislocation loops formed on cooling from 400°C are about 3×10^{-4} cm. This would require the collapse of a plate of about 2×10^8 vacancies. From the data of Haven[6] the mobility and concentration of vacancies in LiF at 400°C can be estimated. The mobility is about 4×10^{-9} cm^2/volt-sec, corresponding to a diffusion coefficient of about 2.4×10^{-10} cm^2/sec. The concentration of vacancies is about 1.7×10^{15}/cm^3. The distance vacancies could diffuse in time t is about $x = (Dt)^{1/2}$. The maximum time t would be 30 sec. Therefore, the maximum volume which might contribute vacancies to a condensation platelet would be about $\frac{4}{3}\pi x^3 = 5.3 \times 10^{-12}$ cm^3, and the maximum number of vacancies available for plate formation would be about 9×10^3, which is 2×10^4 too low. It is concluded that the loops are not created by vacancy condensation.

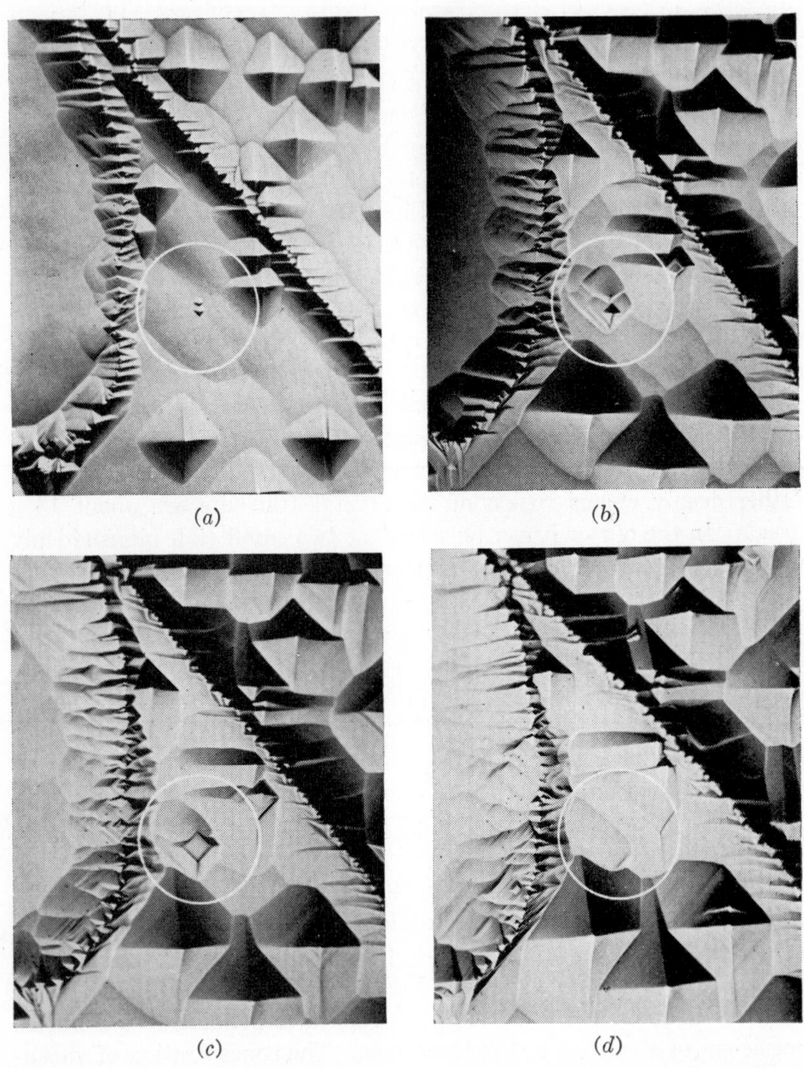

(a) (b) (c) (d)

Fig. 14. Series of photographs of same field showing existence of isolated dislocation loops in crystal cooled moderately fast from 400°C. 335×. (a) 3-min etch. (b) 6-min. etch. (c) 7½-min etch. (d) 10½-min etch (note two new loops).

The maximum stresses present during cooling of LiF crystals can be estimated in two ways. First, an upper limit can be placed because the shear stress during cooling cannot exceed the plastic yield stresses at the various temperatures that the crystal passes through. The room temperature plastic yield stress is the highest of these and hence the upper limit. Second, if the maximum temperature difference between the inside and outside of a bar is known the thermal stresses can be calculated.

In order to determine the temperature difference in a LiF crystal when it is cooled, a thermocouple was placed inside a hole in a LiF crystal and a second thermocouple was wired in contact with the outer surface. The thermocouples were connected differentially and the crystal was placed inside a quartz tube. The maximum temperature difference during cooling from 400°C averaged 19°C and it occurred about 50 sec after the crystal was removed from the furnace. The crystal was ¼ in. square and 13⁄16 in. long.

Assuming that the temperature distribution inside a cooling crystal is parabolic, the maximum thermal stress can be calculated.[4] If α is the thermal expansion coefficient and the block of LiF is approximated by a cylinder or radius b, then in cylindrical co-ordinates the radial and tangential stresses are:

$$\sigma_r = \frac{\alpha E}{(1-\nu)}\left(\frac{1}{b^2}\int_0^b Tr\,dr - \frac{1}{r^2}\int_0^r Tr\,dr\right)$$

$$\sigma_\theta = \frac{\alpha E}{(1-\nu)}\left(-T + \frac{1}{b^2}\int_0^b Tr\,dr + \frac{1}{r^2}\int_0^r Tr\,dr\right)$$

The axial stress $\sigma_z = 0$ except near the ends and the maximum shear stress is:

$$\tau_{\max} = \frac{\sigma_\theta - \sigma_r}{2}$$

Then with the parabolic temperature distribution

$$T = T_0(1 - r^2/b^2)$$

where T_0 is the temperature difference between inside and outside, and if $\alpha = 34 \times 10^{-6}$, we have:

$$\tau_{\max} = \frac{\alpha E T_0}{4(1-\nu)} = 2.1 \times 10^8 \text{ dynes/cm}^2$$

This stress is of the order of the yield stress and therefore confirms the idea that sufficient thermal stresses were present to cause yielding, and that these stresses did not exceed the ordinary yield stress by a large factor.

Dislocation Nucleation During Bending

Several crystals were chemically polished all over to remove surface dislocations and defects. At least 50 μ were removed on all sides. Then the crystals were carefully placed in bending jigs to avoid touching the crystal surfaces. The specimens were slowly cooled to $-196°C$ and plastically bent at a maximum strain rate of about 2×10^{-5}/sec until the maximum fiber strain was about 5×10^{-4} and the maximum fiber stress was about 5.5 kg/mm^2. The specimens were slowly warmed to room temperature, etched with etch "W," and examined. A control specimen was cooled and warmed without bending, to be sure that thermal stresses did not produce dislocations.

Numerous glide bands were present on the bent crystals. In addition, occasional small groups of two, four, six, etc., etch pits could be found. About four to six pairs of pits were normal. Sometimes pairs of pits were near grown-in dislocations but other times they were completely isolated. Examples are shown in Fig. 15. The pairs of pits were shown to be associated with dislocation half loops in two ways: (1) by applying a reversed bending moment they could be "popped-out" of the surface, (2) by etching them out.

No pre-existing dislocations were associated with the isolated half loops and no defects were found inside them. Therefore, it would seem that the dislocations had formed out of dislocation-free regions of the crystals at stresses small compared with the shear modulus of the crystals.

6. EXPANSION AND MULTIPLICATION OF DISLOCATION HALF LOOPS

Production of Isolated Dislocation Half Loops

In order to study the properties of individual dislocations and how they multiply, it is desirable to produce single dislocations and simple arrays of dislocations in a controllable manner. This has been done by the following two-step operation. First, a steel ball of ¼-in. diameter is rolled across the surface of a crystal. When the crystal is etched with etch "W," the trail of rosettes left by the ball is readily visible; Fig. 13. Each rosette consists of dislocations on six (110) planes, extending no deeper than about 20 μ.

The second step is to polish the crystal until only the deepest lying dislocations in the rosettes remain. Figure 16*a* shows a crystal at this stage, containing seven half loops. The nature of the half loops is shown schematically in Fig. 1*b*. The deeper lying half loops always lie on the (110) planes that make an angle of 45° with the surface.

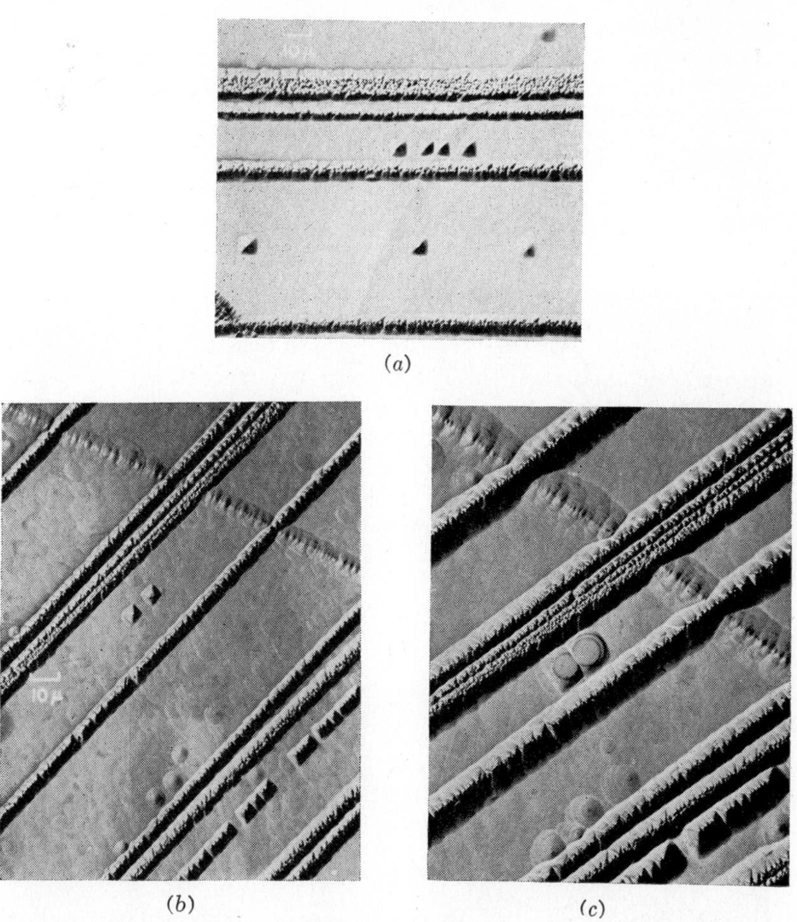

Fig. 15. Pairs of etch pits on surface of LiF crystal after plastic bending at −196°C. Etch "W." (*a*) Pairs near boundary. (*b*) Isolated pair, 1-min etch. (*c*) Same field as (*b*), 4-min etch.

Since dislocation half loops are formed by compression normal to the surface, a tensile stress applied parallel to the surface produces the proper shear stress to expand them, and compressive stress parallel to the surface contracts them.

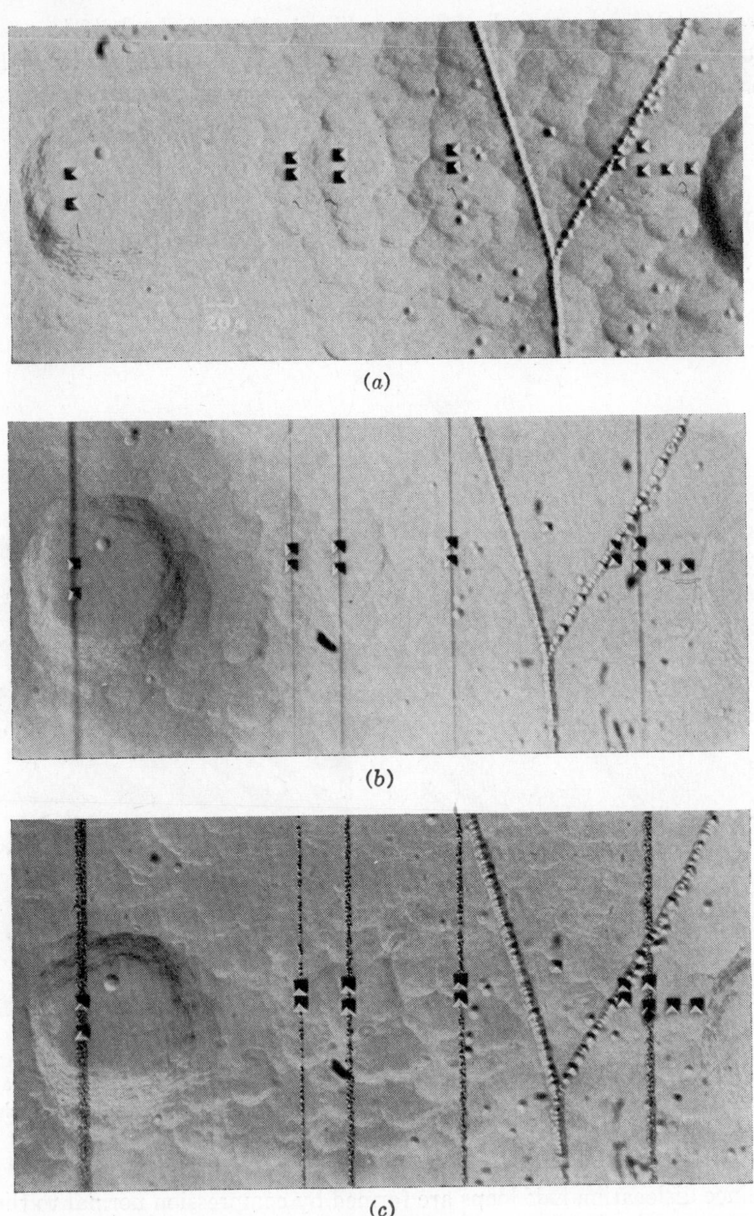

Fig. 16. Growth of glide bands from dislocation half loops. Strain rate 2×10^{-5}/sec. Etch "W." (*a*) Single dislocation half loops at the surface of a LiF single crystal. (*b*) Same crystal after bending shows glide bands passing through five of the half loops. (*c*) A light etch reveals many dislocations in each glide band.

Growth of Large Glide Bands from Single Dislocation Half Loops

When a crystal containing dislocation half loops is bent, large glide bands, consisting of tens of thousands of dislocations, grow out from the original half loops. This is illustrated in Fig. 16*b* and *c*. Figure 16*b* shows unetched glide bands under oblique illumination. Bands are distinctly visible passing through the five or six suitably oriented half loops. The seventh half loop, at the right, is oriented so that the

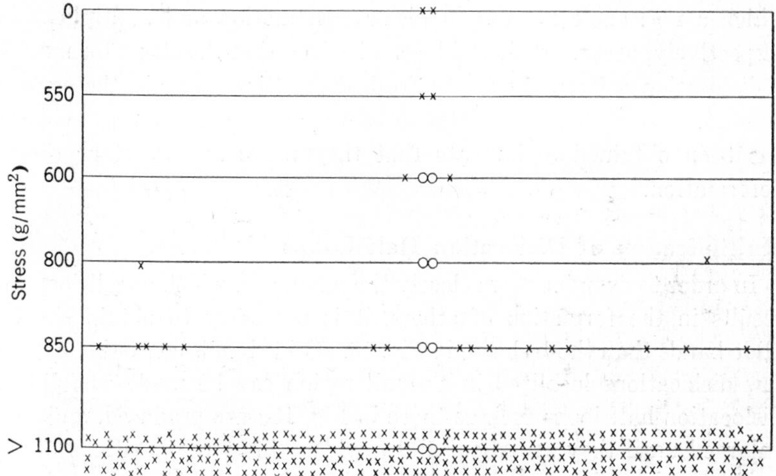

Fig. 17. Schematic drawing of the growth of a glide band from a dislocation half loop. Open circles signify the vacated positions of the original half loop. The approximate resolved shear stress at the surface is shown at each stage of the glide-band formation. Strain rate 2×10^{-5}/sec.

shear stress on it is small. Figure 16*c* shows, by means of etching, that the glide bands contain large numbers of dislocations.

The correlation between large glide bands and single dislocation half loops is good. In a crystal which contained 102 such half loops, bending produced glide bands at 87 of the half loops. In addition, there were 22 glide bands on the same glide systems but not associated with the original half loops.

The sequence of events in the growth of a glide band from a dislocation half loop can be depicted as in Fig. 17. As the stress is raised from zero to about 550 g/mm² nothing happens. Then, as the stress is increased to about 600 g/mm² the half loops begin to enlarge. At about 800 g/mm² some of the loops are as wide as 2 mm and they extend in depth about 400 (over halfway to the neutral axis). As the stress exceeds 800 g/mm² new dislocations appear within some of the enlarged loops and very lightly populated glide bands form, much lighter even than the second band from the left in Fig. 16*c*. As the stress increases further the original loop expands beyond the edges of the crystal and the glide band becomes more populated. At somewhat greater stress than 1100 g/mm^2, for a crystal with few half loops, the stress-strain curve levels off as the critical resolved shear stress of the material is reached. The glide bands then appear as in Fig. 16*c*.

The values of 600 g/mm^2 and 800 g/mm^2 $\pm$ 10% are the stresses at which a noticeable amount of dislocation motion and multiplication, respectively, occur. It should be emphasized that the stress for moving a dislocation refers only to the fresh dislocation loops in the crystal. The annealed dislocations seem to be well anchored, and no evidence has been obtained to indicate that they move at any stage of the deformation.

Multiplication of Dislocation Half Loops

In order to examine more closely the manner in which one dislocation results in the formation of others, it is necessary to obtain simpler glide bands than those shown in Fig. 16. Glide bands consisting of very few dislocations localized in a small region can be made as follows: dislocation half loops such as those in Fig. 16*a* are produced, and then enlarged until they are about 100 μ wide. After the positions of the half loops have been revealed by etching, the crystal is mounted in a bending jig (Fig. 3*c*) and given an impulse of stress by bouncing a steel ball on the jig. If the stress impulse is short, the original half loop does not expand much, but new dislocations appear within the original half loop. This is shown in Fig. 18. The flat-bottomed pits show the positions of the half loops before the stress impulse.

The structures of the glide bands shown in Fig. 18 were investigated by alternately polishing and etching the crystal. More than 60 observations were made at a spacing of 7 μ to a depth of 400 μ in the crystal, or 560 μ along the (101) glide planes. Photographs were made at intervals and the spacings of dislocations were measured with a micrometer eyepiece. From these data, maps of the glide bands were constructed, as shown in Fig. 19.

These are some of the conclusions that may be made about the maps of Fig. 19:

1. In some cases new dislocations have arisen far behind the original half loop, in a region through which the original dislocation passed, but not adjacent to it.

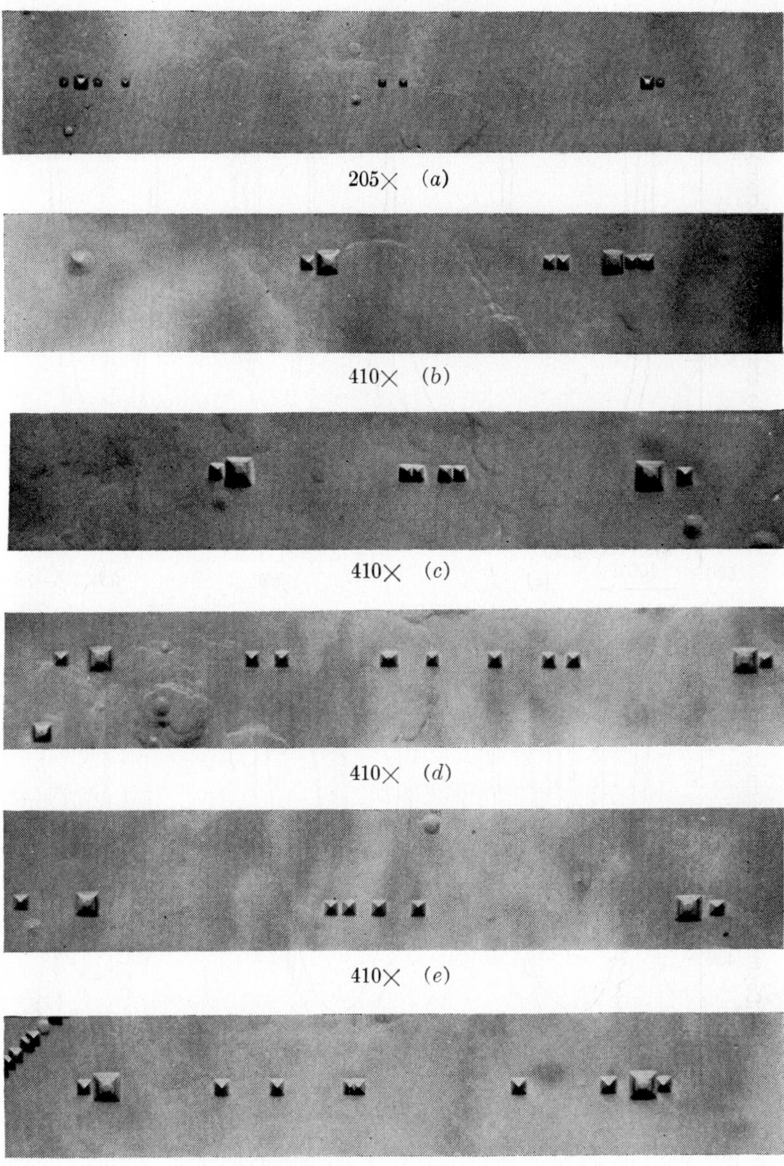

205× (a)

410× (b)

410× (c)

410× (d)

410× (e)

410× (f)

Fig. 18. Small glide bands that formed at dislocation half loops. Flat-bottomed pits show the positions of initial half loops. Letters correspond to letters of maps in Fig. 19. Etch "W."

2. The new dislocations do not all come from a single source, and they need not be coplanar; Fig. 19*b*.

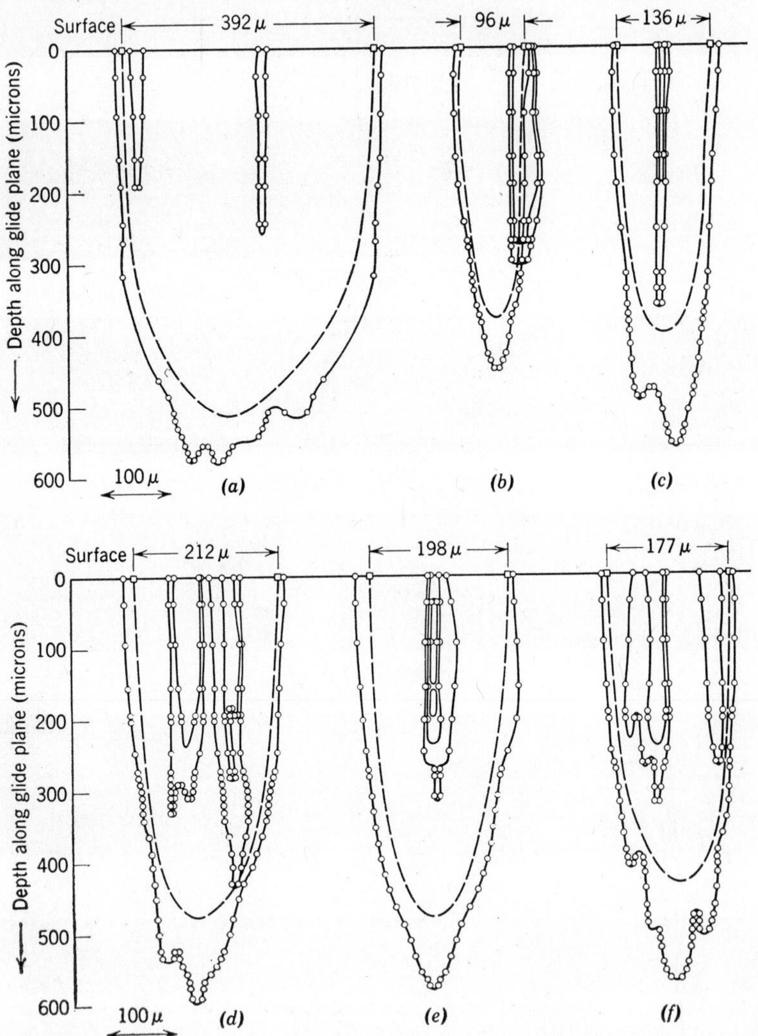

Fig. 19. Maps of six small glide bands. Solid lines show final positions of dislocations. Dashed lines indicate initial positions as deduced from measurements on other crystals.

3. The number of loops formed within an original half loop is small; sometimes none form; and there is a tendency to form multiple new loops.

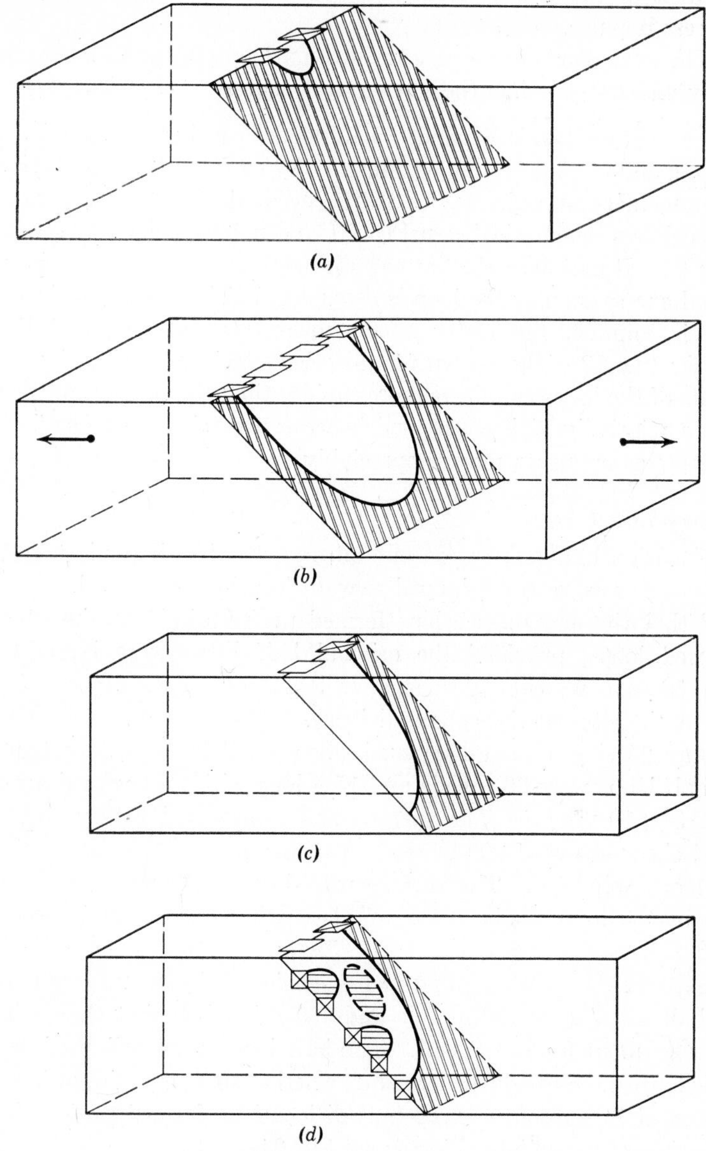

Fig. 20. Dislocations inside expanded half loops. (*a*) Original half loop. (*b*) Expanded half loop as seen from top surface. (*c*) Crystal cleaved through loop. (*d*) Crystal etched after cleavage showing loops not seen on top surface.

4. Most of the new dislocation loops extend to the surface, after the stress impulse.

5. The edge components of a dislocation loop appear to move more rapidly under stress than the screw components.

The structure inside expanded half loops was investigated by the polishing and etching technique, and also by cleaving through the loops to expose faces at right angles to the original plane of observation. This is shown schematically in Fig. 20, and photographs are presented in Fig. 21. It may be seen that new dislocation loops appear inside the original one as soon as the loop is expanded.* Then, when an impulse stress is applied, the loops extend toward the surface and break through; Fig. 22. The reason for this seems to be that the edge components of the loops can move more rapidly than the screw components under a relatively high stress, and hence can reach the surface before the screw components move appreciably.

Memory Effect

Dislocation half loops were put into a crystal, collapsed, and then the crystal was restressed until new dislocations appeared. It was found that the new dislocations formed preferentially at the sites of collapsed loops, provided the original half loops were larger than about 50 μ in width. With smaller loops new dislocations did not form at the sites of the collapsed loops.

Figure 23 shows what happened when small loops were collapsed. The half loops were 20 μ wide and 15 μ long with an enclosed area of about 3×10^{-6} cm^2. The surface was compressed lightly to a resolved shear stress of 200 g/mm^2. Etching showed that some of the half loops collapsed. The surface was then slowly put into tension. Glide bands formed only at the half loops that had not collapsed; see Fig. 23.

Figure 24 shows what happened when larger loops were collapsed. The half loops were 100 μ wide and 400 μ long, so that the enclosed area was about 3×10^{-4} cm^2. The half loops were collapsed by an applied stress. Subsequent stressing, whether slow or rapid, or in compression or in tension, showed that dislocations formed preferentially at the sites of the collapsed loops; see Fig. 24.

The structure of crystals in which large dislocation half loops had

* The act of cleavage does not create these loops. This was checked by placing a half loop near the edge of a crystal, and expanding it so that one end moved around the corner. Although no new loops appeared on the original top surface, they did appear on the side surface behind the original dislocation.

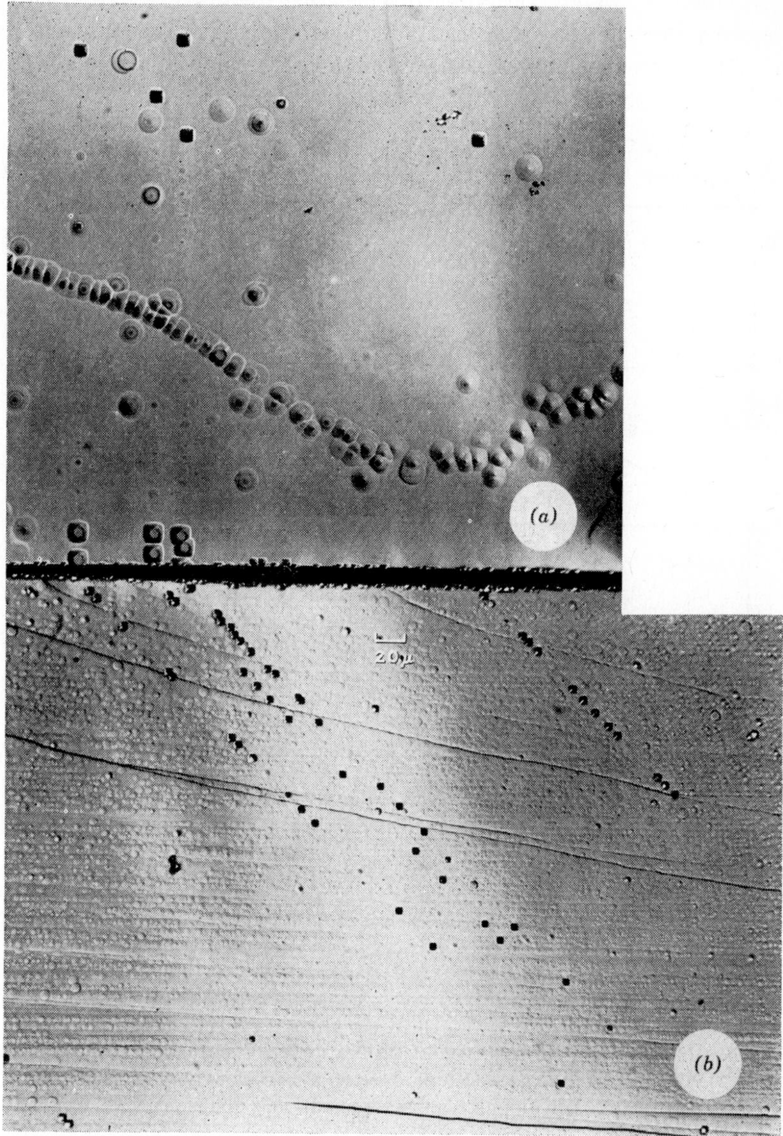

Fig. 21. Photographs corresponding to Fig. 20*c* and *d*. Etch "W." (*a*) Five half loops corresponding to top surface of Fig. 20*c*. Bottom edge of photograph at one side of cleavage crack. (*b*) Five short bands corresponding to front face of Fig. 20*d*.

been collapsed were investigated by cleaving the crystals through the regions where the loops had been. Although no glide dislocations were in evidence on the external surfaces of such crystals, dislocations were

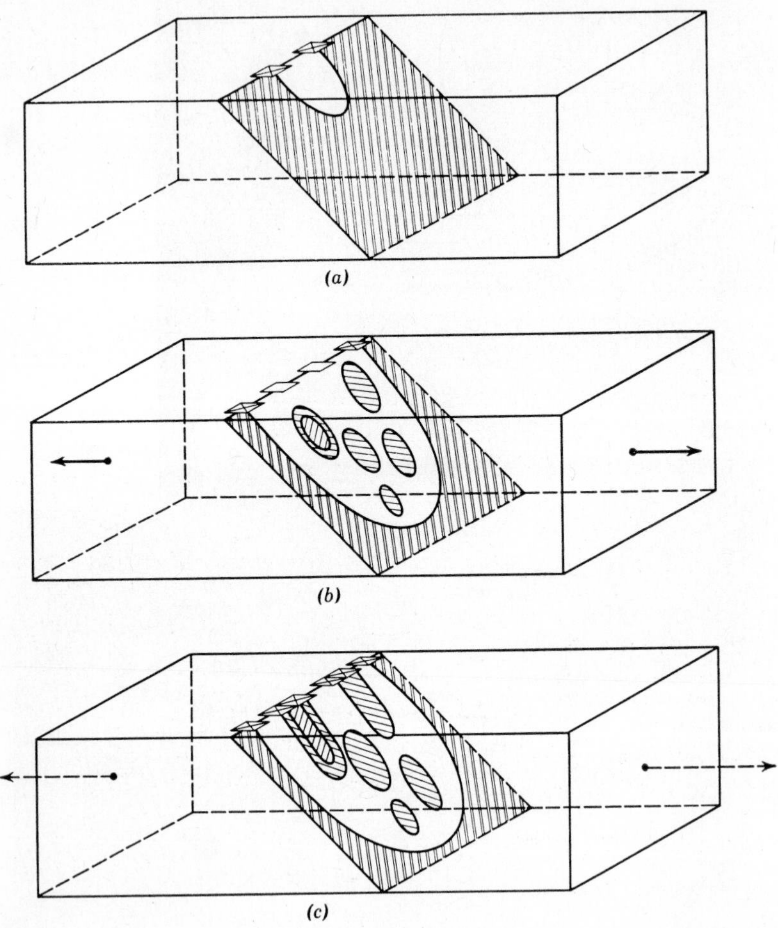

Fig. 22. Deduced growth sequence of dislocation half loops. (*a*) Original half loop. (*b*) Half loop expanded under slow stress—new loops appear inside original half loop. (*c*) Impulse stress applied—new loops expand, especially toward the surface.

found on the internal cleavage surfaces. These were parts of closed loops contained within the crystal, like those of Fig. 22*b*.

It is clear that the "memory effect" is simply a result of dislocation loops that are left inside of a crystal by a half loop that has been expanded to some critical size and then collapsed.

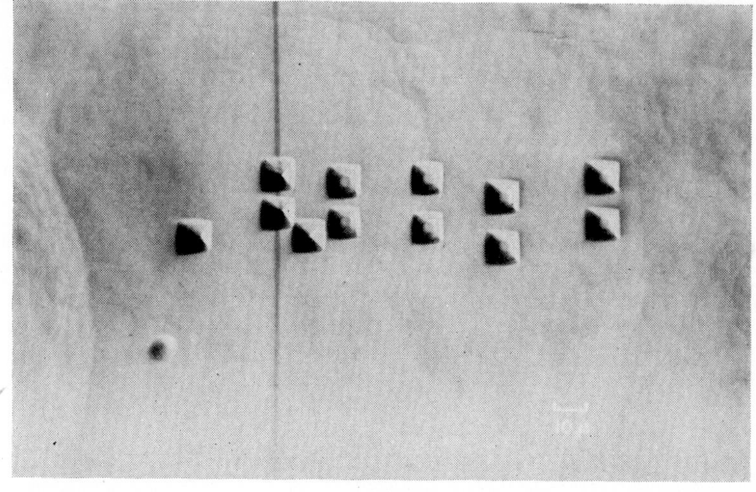

(*a*)

(*b*)

Fig. 23. Crystal with four collapsed small half loops after it was restressed. A glide band formed only at the vertical half loop that had not collapsed. Oblique illumination. (*a*) No etch. (*b*) After a light etch in "W."

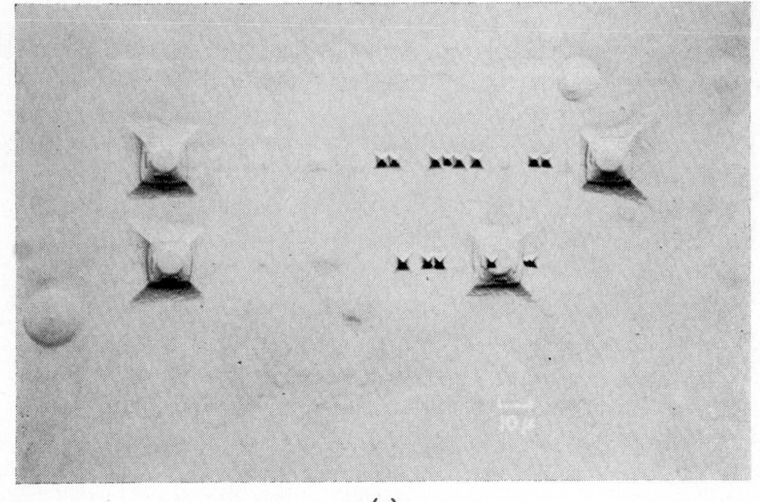

(*a*)

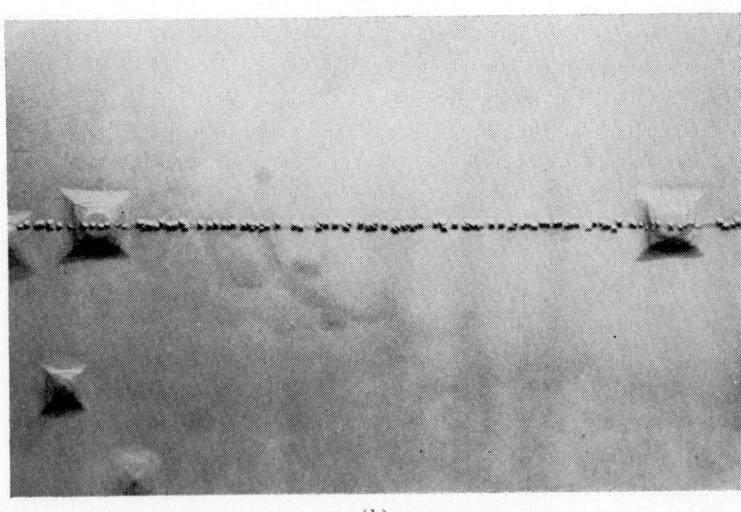

(*b*)

Fig. 24. Crystals stressed after large half loops in them had been collapsed. The new dislocations arose within the region encompassed by the original half loops. The large flat-bottomed pits mark the original sites of the half loops. Etch "W." (*a*) Rapidly applied stress. (*b*) Slowly applied stress.

"Dendritic Growth"

As deformation proceeds, the existing glide bands seem to spawn new branching glide bands. This occurs in at least two ways:

1. At glide-band intersections, places where one glide band blocks another, and at other stress concentrations, new glide bands are started through the nucleation of dislocation loops on the glide planes where the shear stress has been concentrated. Examples are shown in Fig. 25.
2. Screw dislocations lying on (110) planes move onto (100) planes under certain conditions. This is observed as a dispersion of dislocations along one side of a glide band. The dispersion is always on the side which makes an acute angle with the (100) surface. Examples are shown in Fig. 26, together with a schematic drawing of the process.

7. DISCUSSION

At the time when glide dislocations were conceived by Taylor, Orowan, and Polyanyi (1934), it was believed that plastic deformation proceeded by the gliding of the dislocations that are present in as-grown crystals. When these dislocations were exhausted from the crystal by strain, it was supposed that new pairs of dislocations were nucleated in the crystal so as to allow more and more strain. Later, calculations were made by Seitz and Read [7] which indicated that the critical energy needed for dislocation nucleation should be so high that nucleation could not occur except at very high stress levels. Since it was well known that crystals could be sheared by amounts much larger than could be accounted for by the grown-in dislocations, a search was made for mechanisms by which dislocations could reproduce themselves as they glided. Some ingenious mechanisms were proposed; the most successful of these has been the Frank-Read multiplication mechanism.[8]

The present experiments support the older view of plastic deformation in which dislocations are nucleated in dislocation-free regions of crystals as they are needed to maintain the strain rate. The experiments indicate that the stress needed to nucleate a dislocation loop in LiF is approximately 1 kg/mm^2 at room temperature and normal rates of stressing. Stresses applied in three distinctly different ways have led to the same conclusion. This interpretation is consistent with all of the plastic phenomena observed in LiF and many other crystals. However, it is in sharp disagreement with calculations of the nucleation energy. The stress at which nucleation occurs in these crystals is at least 1000 times smaller than the calculated stress.

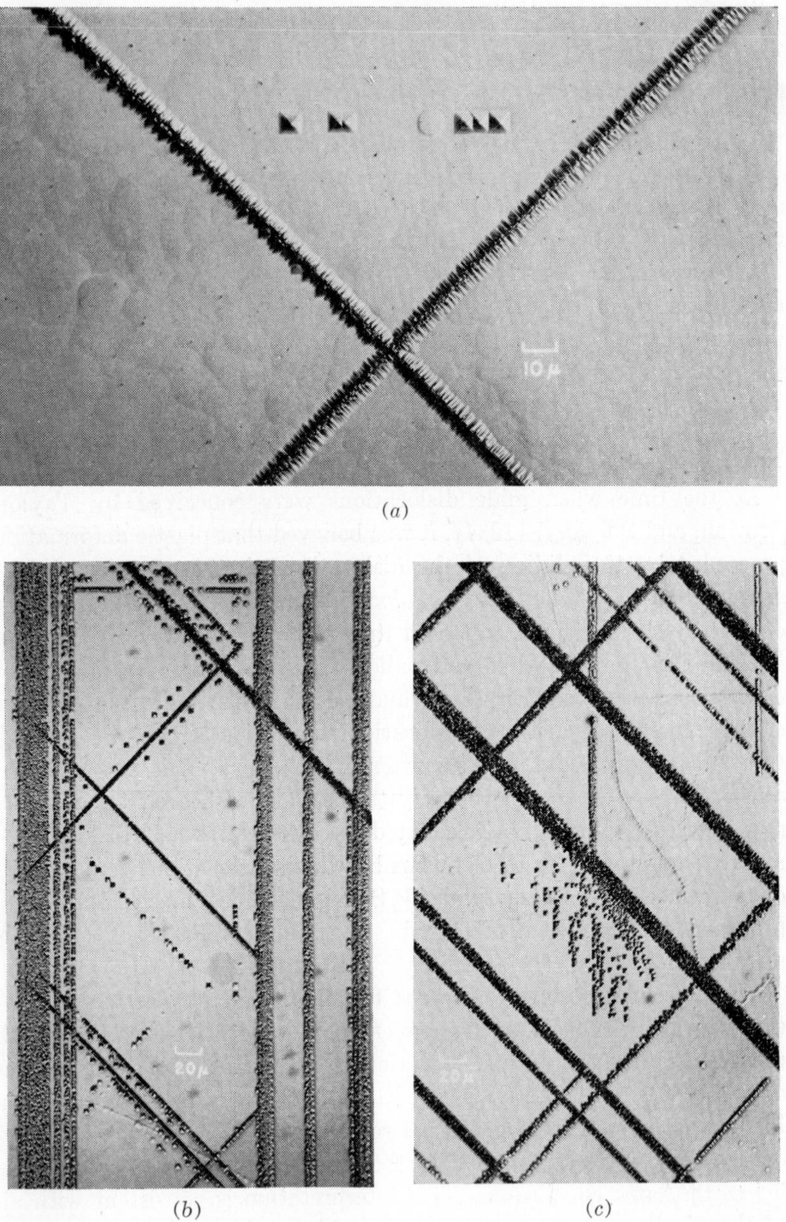

(a)

(b) (c)

Fig. 25. Examples of new glide bands starting at places where the existing bands have produced concentrated stresses.

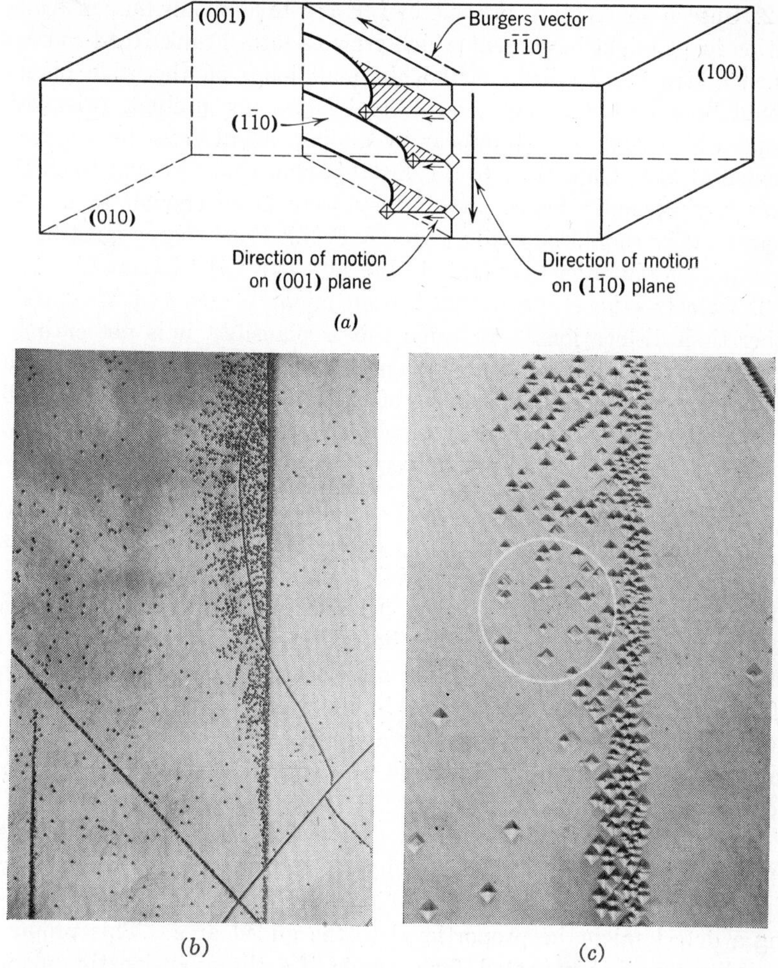

Fig. 26. Change of glide plane of screw dislocations. (*a*) Drawing showing (110) screw dislocations changing planes. (*b*) Glide band "dispersed" by process of (*a*). 75×. (*c*) Same as (*b*) at 375× showing motion of dislocations perpendicular to glide band.

Some of the possible reasons why the stress observed for dislocation nucleation is small compared to the theoretical stress are:

1. Some assumption of the theory is wrong—since the nucleation energy is predominantly elastic strain energy calculated for a continuum, it is difficult to see how this part of the nucleation theory could be in error. However, the theory might not be applicable to the behavior of real crystals.

2. Unseen sources are present in LiF crystals—small unseen dislocation loops might be present which grow to form Frank-Read sources when a stress is applied. Although small loops on the glide planes would be expected to be unstable and hence not present, prismatic loops, which could not disappear by gliding, might form by vacancy condensation.[9] Objections to this are that slow cooling ought to eliminate the prismatic loops, and if they were large enough to act as sources, they should be easily seen. A Frank-Read source must be at least 3 μ long in order to operate in LiF at a stress of 1 kg/mm^2.

3. Defects—the stress for nucleation might be reduced by defects other than dislocations. Although this is plausible, it is not entirely satisfactory. At an applied stress of 1 kg/mm^2 the critical size of a dislocation-loop nucleus would be of the order of 1 μ. Defects small compared with 1 μ such as vacancy clusters, invisible precipitates, surface steps, etc., should not be very effective in reducing the energy of the nucleus.

The heterogeneous character of plastic deformation in LiF suggests that one or more kinds of defects initiate the nucleation process. Assuming this to be true, the observed multiplication phenomena are readily understood. Apparently, the multiplication process for dislocations occurs in two steps. First, a dislocation passes over a portion of a glide plane, leaving defects in its wake. Second, the defects initiate new dislocations that move and repeat the cycle of multiplication. When a dislocation glides out of a crystal, it may leave defects behind.

If a dislocation glides over an area $\simeq 3 \times 10^{-6}$ cm^2, no defects appear to be formed. If the area is $\simeq 3 \times 10^{-4}$ cm^2, the probability that one or two defects have formed is $\sim \frac{1}{2}$. The probability for forming a defect might be proportional to the glided area. This proportionality would be expected, for example, if a gliding dislocation made defects by interacting with other dislocations that passed through its glide plane.

There are approximately 5×10^4 disl./cm^2 in annealed LiF crystals. The average number that would pass through a small half loop (3×10^{-6} cm^2 area) would be 0.15, and through a large half loop (3×10^{-4} cm^2 area) would be 15. Thus, dislocation interactions are not unreasonable as sources of defects which aid dislocation nucleation.

This investigation has demonstrated that dislocation motion is resisted by a finite force in LiF. This resistance has the nature of a viscous drag rather than the static type of force predicted by the simple Peierls-Nabarro model. A viscous lattice resistance was proposed previously in order to explain the behavior of prismatic glide in zinc,[10] but its existence is demonstrated much more clearly in the present experiments. Quantitative measurements of the lattice resistance are planned for the future, but some of its qualitative features can be pointed out now. The resistance is much smaller than the simple Peierls-Nabarro model predicts (3.5×10^{10} dynes/cm^2), but this is not surprising because the Peierls-Nabarro model would predict the (100) plane as the glide plane instead of the observed (110) glide plane. Nevertheless, the resistance is strong enough to be measured.

Three results indicate the lattice resistance most clearly:

1. The stability of small dislocation half loops.
2. The finite stresses needed to expand and contract isolated dislocation half loops.
3. The temperature dependence of glide in crystals with and without "fresh" dislocations.

It is observed that small dislocation half loops are stable in crystals until their diameter is decreased to about 4 μ. The stress that is needed to balance the line tension of a half loop with this size is about 5×10^7 dynes/cm^2.

The stress needed to expand a dislocation loop at normal rates of strain is about 6×10^7 dynes/cm^2. The stress needed to contract a loop of the same size is about 2×10^7 dynes/cm^2. Any factors tending to inhibit expansion should change sign when the stress is reversed and hence aid contraction. Therefore, the lattice resistance is about 4×10^7 dynes/cm^2.

The lattice resistance is strongly temperature-dependent. This is shown by the curves of Fig. 10*b*. Fresh dislocations were put into crystal *A* of Fig. 10*b* at room temperature. Crystal *B* of the same figure was polished so that it contained only annealed dislocations. The crystals were immediately cooled to $-196°$C and tested. They both showed about the same increase in yield stress at the low temperature, so that the factor changed by lowering the temperature must have been the lattice resistance to dislocation motion.

It appears that the stress needed to move a dislocation at a certain velocity is quite small for small velocities, but it increases rapidly as the velocity increases. At low velocities, the lattice viscosity may be Newtonian, but it probably is not for high velocities. Certainly as the dislocation velocity approaches the velocity of sound it is expected that the stress rises indefinitely. The lattice resistance is temperature-dependent and is expected to be changed by impurities, irradiation, etc.

It was shown earlier that the macroscopic behavior of LiF depends strongly on the surface condition of a crystal. The two limiting cases are: (1) the surface of a crystal contains large numbers of defects and dislocations; (2) the surface is polished and contains no fresh dislocations, only annealed dislocations. Consider what seems to happen when crystals of these two types are tested at constant strain rate in a hard machine.

Case (1), crystal with fresh surface dislocations or defects. When the applied stress reaches τ_y (yield stress), the surface dislocations begin to move at a velocity v characteristic of the stress. If there are n_0 surface dislocations per cm^2, this gives a strain rate of $\dot{\gamma} = n_0bv$ if b = Burgers vector. Initially $\dot{\gamma}$ is less than the strain rate imposed by the machine $\dot{\gamma}_M$; therefore, the stress continues to rise until it reaches a stress τ^* where the moving dislocations begin to multiply rapidly and the number of moving dislocations becomes $n = n_0 + \Delta n = \dot{\gamma}_M/bv$. The situation is complicated, of course, because v is a function of the stress and n depends not only on the rate of multiplication of dislocations but also on a recombination rate.

Case (2), crystal with polished surface. The applied stress rises until it reaches τ_0, the stress at which dislocations form in the absence of any moving dislocations (τ_0 is higher than τ^*). When the first loop begins to move, it multiplies profusely until the stress drops to τ^*, where it remains constant. The behavior results in a sharp drop in load after some strain (dislocation motion) has produced enough dislocations to allow a strain rate higher than the applied strain rate, for stresses greater than τ^*.

A distinct elastic limit, or yield stress, can be defined for LiF, namely, the stress at which dislocations begin to move at some definite velocity. The critical resolved shear stress is determined by dynamic and geometric conditions. It represents the stress at which the rate of multiplication of dislocations minus the recombination rate is sufficient to maintain enough dislocations (moving at a velocity characteristic of the stress) to keep the strain rate equal to the applied strain rate. It is not surprising that this stress is not a characteristic of a crystal, but depends on the type of test, shape of crystal, etc. The yield stress is probably a more characteristic stress.

The failure of the macroscopic mechanical equation of state can also be understood in terms of this behavior. The number of dislocations present after a given strain depends on the temperature at which the straining was carried out, on the strain rate, on the stress distribution, etc. On the other hand, an equation of state based on the microscopic parameters of a crystal might be obeyed.

A final result of interest is some insight into the reason why crystals are insensitive to strain rate. If the present interpretation is correct, this is not because dislocations move at arbitrary velocities. Rather, it results because dislocations multiply at an almost arbitrary rate (above the yield stress) so that a high macroscopic strain rate can be maintained with relatively slowly moving dislocations.

REFERENCES

1. J. J. Gilman and W. G. Johnston, "Observations of Dislocation Glide and Climb in Lithium Fluoride Crystals," *J. Appl. Phys.*, **27** (Sept. 1956).
2. *International Tables for Determination of Crystal Structures,* Vol. 2, Gebruder Borntraeger, Berlin, p. 556 (1935).
3. J. J. Gilman, "Nucleation of Dislocation Loops by Cracks in Crystals," *Trans. AIME,* **209,** 449 (1957).
4. S. Timoshenko, *Theory of Elasticity,* McGraw-Hill Book Co., New York (1934).
5. R. Mindlin, "Compliance of Elastic Bodies in Contact," *J. Appl. Mech.,* **16,** 259 (1949).
6. Y. Haven, "The Ionic Conductivity of Li-Halide Crystals," *Rec. trav. chim.,* **69,** 1471 (1950).
7. F. Seitz and T. A. Read, "Theory of the Plastic Properties of Solids," *J. Appl. Phys.,* **12,** 100 (1941).
8. F. C. Frank and W. T. Read, "Multiplication Processes for Slow-Moving Dislocation," *Pittsburgh Symp. ONR,* p. 44 (1950).
9. J. C. Fisher and F. C. Frank, private communication.
10. J. J. Gilman, "Plastic Anisotropy of Zinc Monocrystals," *Trans. AIME,* **206,** 1326 (1956).

ACKNOWLEDGMENTS

Mr. V. J. DeCarlo and Mr. D. J. Myers gave their skillful assistance to the authors during the investigation. Helpful discussions and criticisms were provided by Dr. J. C. Fisher of the General Electric Research Laboratory and Dr. F. C. Frank of Bristol University.

DISCUSSION

SEEGER inquired whether the dislocation density in the interior of the lithium fluoride is indeed as low as the 5×10^4 cm^{-2} that one sees after etching. This would imply that the critical shear stress of LiF and its temperature dependence are determined in a different way from that of f.c.c. and h.c.p. metals, which are discussed in § 4 of Seeger's paper (pages 271–277 of this volume). GILMAN pointed out that if a crystal is etched continuously the low dislocation density remains constant to whatever depth the etching is carried out; and if a crystal is cleaved into a series of thin plates, the dislocation density as revealed by etching is the same for all of the plates. Further, if there were many more dislocations below the surface than the etching indicates, then the X-ray extinction would not be as high as is observed.

In reply to THOMSON's question about how much evidence there is for the spontaneous production of dislocations in the interior of the crystals, GILMAN said that it was only with thermal stresses that one could produce the interior dislocations. With other methods of applying a stress, the maximum stress was at or near the surface.

SEEGER expressed consternation at the manner in which dislocation loops were arising at low stresses, with no obvious sources; and LEIBFRIED felt that this was impossible, and that sources must be present, perhaps in the form of small loops, which were not detected. FISHER supported the idea that small loops are already present in the crystal; these could be prismatic loops formed by the collapse of vacancy platelets. Although such loops may not be able to collapse or expand on the plane in which they lie, they may act as sources when a stress is applied.*

In response to questions by MOTT and LOMER, GILMAN said that the minimum dislocation loop size that one finds in lithium fluoride is about 3 μ. The lattice resistance needed to resist the line tension tending to collapse such loops is calculated to be about 500 g/mm^2. The loops that are formed by thermal quenching also have a minimum size of about 3 μ. When these loops are etched more than halfway through, they pop out of the surface.

SEITZ told of the experience of Professor R. L. Sproull and his group at Cornell University in cleaving additively colored NaCl. The crystals had been colored and heat-treated so as to allow the colloids to form. The work of Amelinckx shows that the colloids were formed on dislocations. The crystals were cleaved, and afterwards etching counts were made of the number of colloids at the surface. The density was 100 times larger than the statistical average, and seemed to indicate that the cleavage surface moved in such a way that it passed close to the dislocations. This would suggest that the surface of a cleaved crystal has many sources close to it.

*See the paper by J. C. Fisher in Part VI of this volume for an elaboration of this argument.

GILMAN pointed out that when rock salt is cleaved and etched, one finds that many dislocations have been introduced by the cleavage. Also, the undulations of cleavage surfaces are very small compared with the average dislocation spacing. Thus, it is not a question of the cleavage surface passing near the dislocations, but of dislocations being formed by the cleavage crack. The creation of dislocations by a crack has been demonstrated in LiF.* Such cleavage damage can be avoided in LiF by passing the crack rapidly through the crystal, but in pure rock salt even high velocity cracks cause cleavage damage.

HIRSCH and SHOCKLEY raised the question of whether obstacles to dislocations could lead to the formation of loops that could then be left behind by the dislocation. It was agreed that such loops would be of the wrong sign; i.e., the loop would tend to collapse around the obstacle. FRANK explained that in order to get overlapping of a dislocation as it wraps around an obstacle, it is necessary to have the dislocation line cross at least 100 screw dislocations of the same sign before it strikes the obstacle. If the two overlapping parts of the dislocation are on planes separated by 100 atom distances, they can be driven by each other at low stresses.

READ said that a similar problem arose in silicon. The silicon has a low etch-pit density, yet, if one etches a small specimen out of a large crystal, it is found that the strength of the small specimen is the same as that of the bulk material, despite the fact that one expects few or no long dislocations in the small specimen. READ indicated that the possibility of the existence of small loops had been considered, and annealing experiments were tried, under the assumption that the small loops would collapse at high temperatures. Annealing did not change the behavior.

Referring to the study of formation of small glide bands, SHOCKLEY inquired to what precision it could be determined whether the new dislocations were coplanar with the original one. GILMAN said that the precision was poor, certainly not closer than a micron or so. Although the first few new dislocations appear to be coplanar with the original one to within the accuracy of the observation, the subsequent dislocations are clearly not coplanar, because the glide band thickens.

* See reference 3 above.

Thermal Etching of Dislocations in Silver

E. S. MACHLIN
School of Mines
Columbia University
New York, New York

Dislocations in silver may be revealed by a thermal etch technique. It is believed pits are formed at the points of emergence of dislocations as a result of the equilibration of the dislocation line tension and the surface tension. In this technique, electropolished silver is immersed in a dynamic flow of argon containing 10 mole % of oxygen at 600°C for 5 to 10 min and then cooled to room temperature in purified argon.

Pits are formed at stationary dislocations; grooves are formed by dislocations which move slowly during the etching treatment. Screw-oriented dislocations can be distinguished from those of edge orientation in that pits at the former are several times smaller and shallower than at the edge dislocations. Pits which are formed and then vacated by the dislocation during the etching treatment are distinguished by a flat bottom. Dislocations that move rapidly during the thermal etch are not revealed by the treatment.

Inasmuch as the etching treatment needs to be carried out at elevated temperatures, this technique is most suited to a study of creep at these temperatures. Some results of this investigation will now be reported.

In crystals oriented for ideal simple glide, the density of edge dislocations often exceeds that for screw-oriented dislocations but never vice versa. There is much evidence of cross slip between slip bands and within slip bands. It appears therefore that at about 600°C in silver, screw dislocations move more easily than edge dislocations. Upon etching while the specimen is under stress, dislocation pile-ups are revealed in slip bands. If the time the specimen has been stressed at temperature prior to the etching treatment is long, then many dislocations are in the slip band. Figure 1 reveals such a slip band that

Fig. 1. Slip band produced during creep of silver single crystals. Ideal single glide orientation. At 600°C, 200 psi resolved shear stress for 7 hr. Etched during creep. Slip direction out of paper. Oblique illumination. 650×.

appears to be composed of pairs of pits, one pit lying above the other relative to the slip band. The crystal was oriented for simple glide and the surface from which the screw dislocations emerge is being observed. Under the test conditions, 600°C and a resolved shear stress of about 0.14 kg/mm^2 (200 psi), the spacing between the pits normal to the slip plane is about 0.5 μ. This is just the range at which Taylor hardening of opposite sign dislocations would be expected to operate ($d = Gb/2\pi\tau = 0.75\ \mu$). No slip bands have been found in which the spacing of the pits normal to the band exceeds 1 μ. Consequently, it is believed that Fig. 1 illustrates the operation of Taylor hardening during creep of silver. This phenomenon is also revealed in Fig. 2.

If the etching treatment is applied shortly after the stress is applied, it is possible to reveal partial dislocation pile-ups; see Figs. 3, 4, and 5.

In these instances, there is no evidence of Taylor hardening. The hardening may, however, be due to a Cottrell-Lomer reaction.

No evidence of polygonization has ever been found in specimens that are etched or annealed and etched subsequent to room temperature plastic deformation. In all such cases, the dislocations are found to be randomly distributed as shown, for example, in Fig. 6. On the other

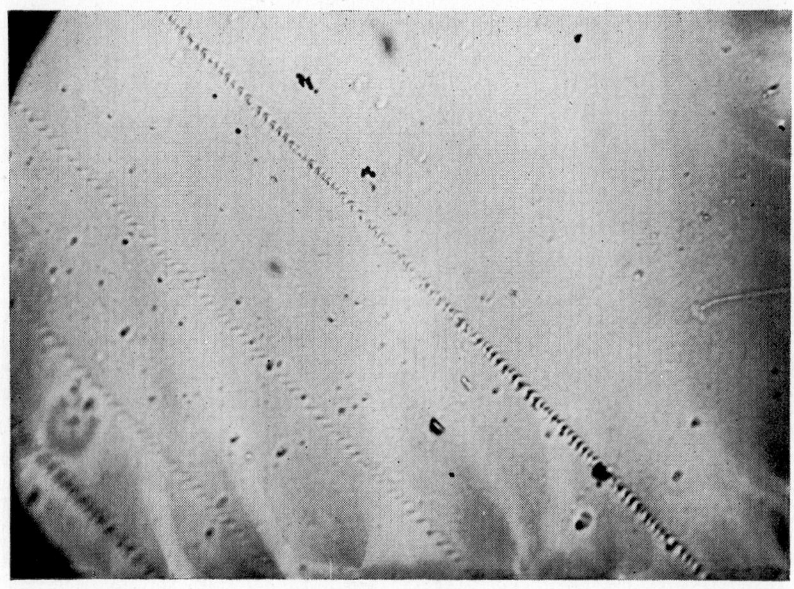

Fig. 2. Same crystal as Fig. 1, after removing stress, reducing temperature to room temperature, and then thermal-etching without an intermediate electropolish. Slip direction parallel to paper. Slightly oblique illumination. 980×.

hand, if the specimens had a creep history prior to thermal etching (in all such cases, the specimens were cooled to room temperature, polished, and thermally etched in the absence of stress), then evidence of polygonization was found. See, for example, Figs. 7 and 8. Dislocation climb during etching under stress has also been found and is revealed in Figs. 9 and 10. The grooves in these figures lie about 90° to the slip plane. Grooving has seldom been found on etching in the absence of stress. It is believed that this evidence supports Seeger's contention that climb of dislocations should be difficult in silver.[1] The mechanism of the randomization of dislocations upon annealing in the absence of stress but subsequent to plastic deformation is unknown. From the above cited evidence it does not seem likely that climb is responsible for the motion of the dislocations out of the slip bands.

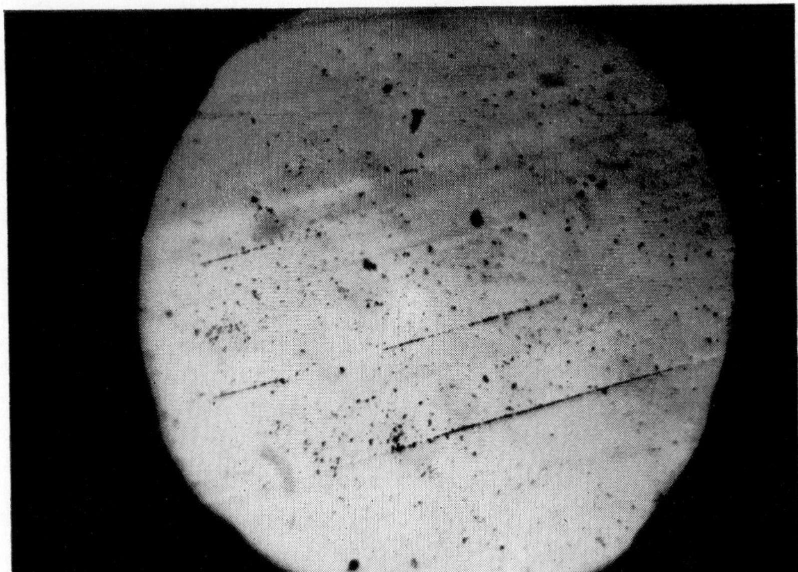

Fig. 3. Same crystal as Fig. 1, after sequence as in Fig. 2, repeated with an electropolishing step prior to the thermal-etching step, then electropolished, held at 600°C, 200 psi for 2 min, then thermal-etched while specimen is stressed. Slip direction parallel to paper. 650×.

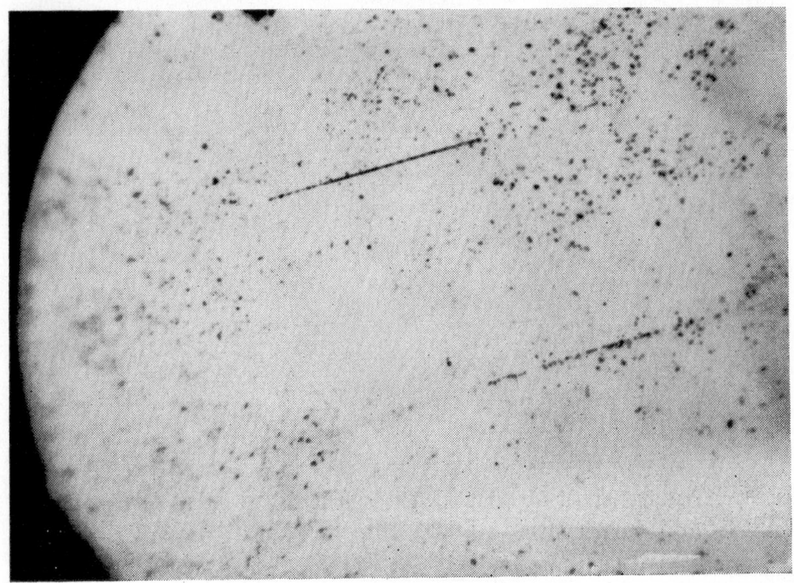

Fig. 4. As for Fig. 2. 980×.

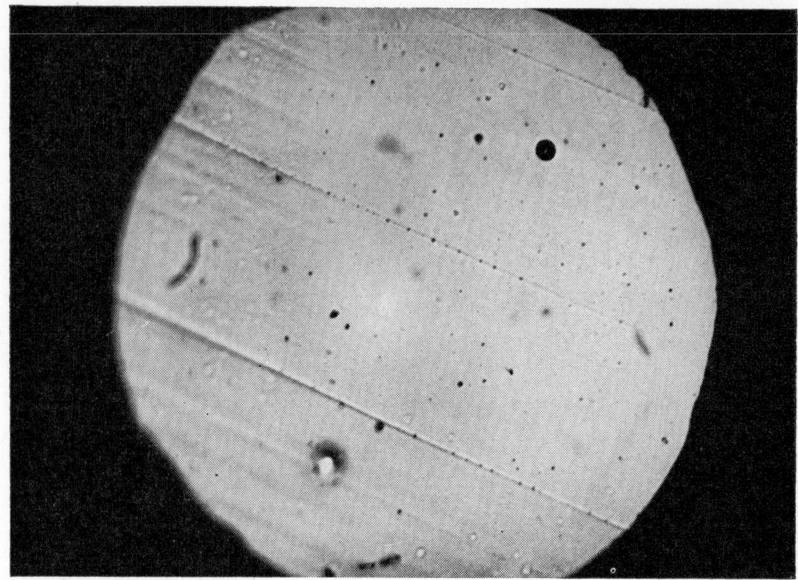

Fig. 5. As for Fig. 3 except slip direction is partially out of paper and view is of side 180° to that for Figs. 3 and 4. 650×.

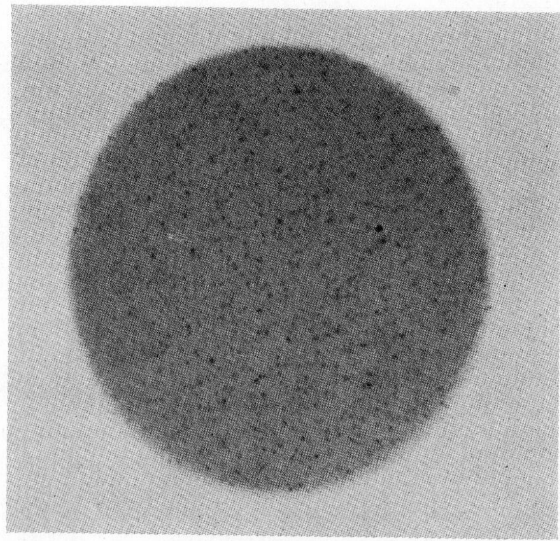

Fig. 6. Crystal oriented for simple glide, extended 33% at room temperature, polished, and thermally etched. 1000×.

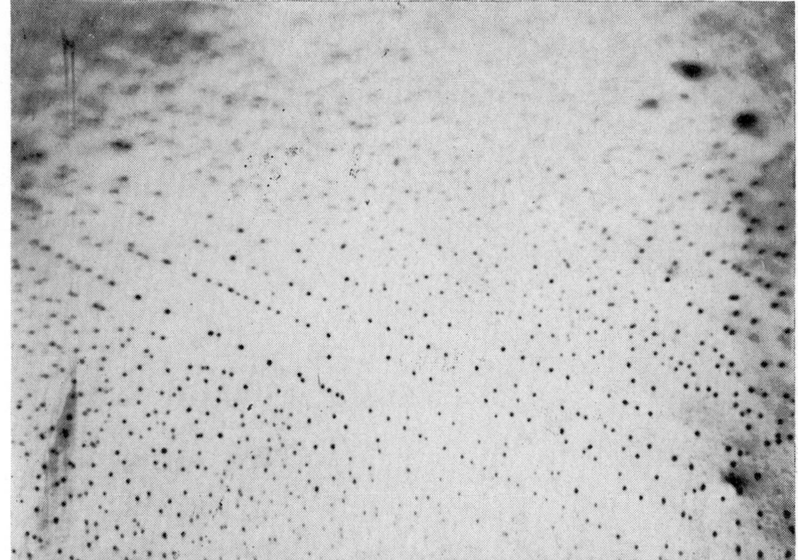

Fig. 7. Polygonization revealed by thermal etching of silver single crystal which had been subjected to 3.4% strain at 500°C and about 200 psi. Ideal simple glide orientation. Rows of pits are normal to active slip planes. Slip direction parallel to paper, normal to rows of pits. 650×.

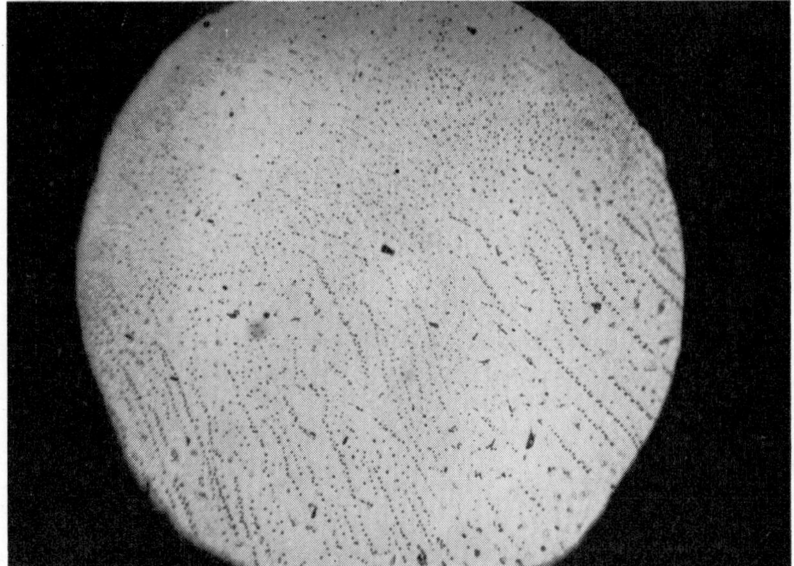

Fig. 8. Same crystal as Fig. 1, near area shown in Fig. 3, polished, then thermally etched. Slip direction parallel to paper but normal to the rows of pits. 650×.

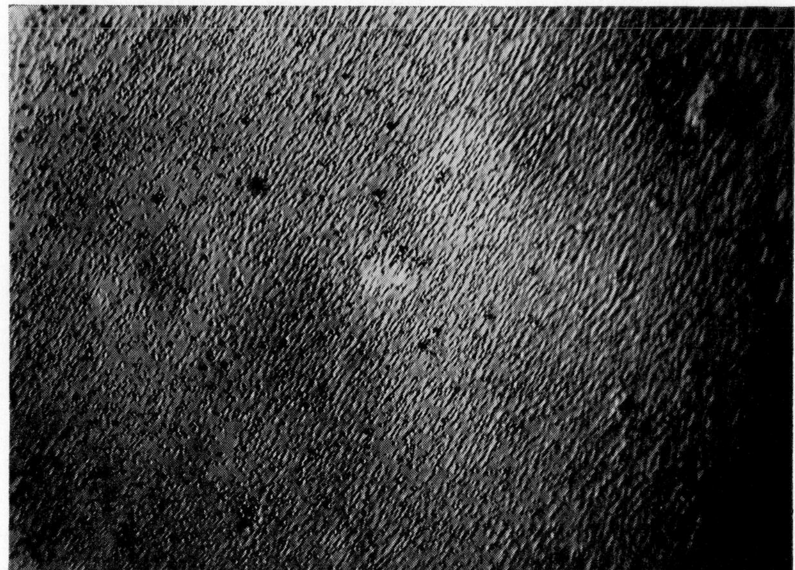

Fig. 9. Same crystal as Fig. 1, near area shown in Fig. 5. Thermally etched while specimen is stressed. Grooves appear normal to the slip planes. Oblique illumination. 650×.

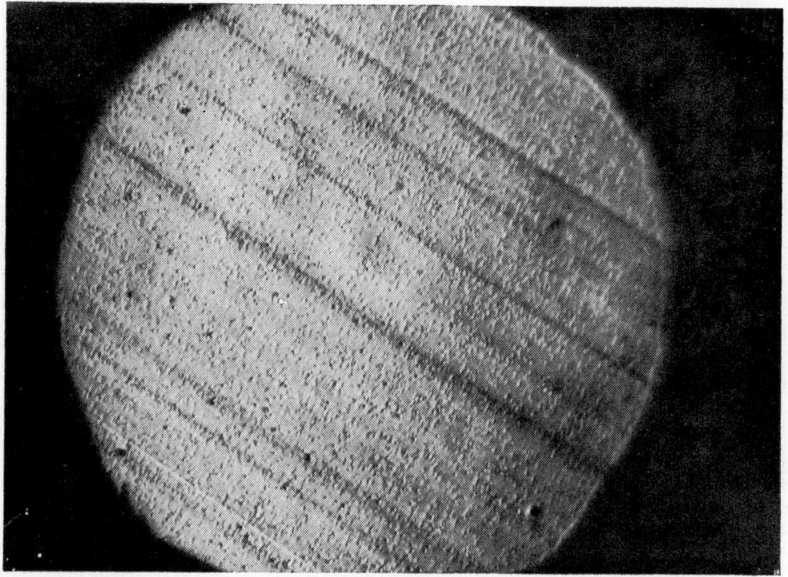

Fig. 10. As for Fig. 9, except that slip bands are visible. 650×.

REFERENCE

1. A. Seeger, *Report of a Conference on Defects in Crystalline Solids,* Physical Society, London, p. 391 (1955).

ACKNOWLEDGMENT

M. Abrahams performed the experiments and obtained the photomicrographs. His contribution is gratefully acknowledged.

DISCUSSION

MITCHELL inquired whether control experiments had been performed in which one specimen was etched without an applied stress and another etched with an applied stress. MACHLIN said that this had been done. When a crystal is thermally etched with no applied stress, circular pits are formed, and if a crystal is etched while under stress, many of the pits are in the form of grooves.

In reply to LÜCKE's question as to the direction of the grooves, MACHLIN said that they are in the direction normal to the slip, adding that dislocation etch pits do not appear along some of the slip planes that are developed during the thermal etching under stress.

JOHNSTON suggested that the etch tracks of a moving dislocation should be tapered, being smaller in the direction towards which the dislocation was moving. MACHLIN said that such a tapering of the tracks had not been observed.

The Thermal Etching of Dislocations

HIDEJI SUZUKI

Research Institute for Iron, Steel, and Other Metals
Tohoku University
Sendai, Japan

Thermal-etching techniques, such as the one reported by Hendrickson and Machlin [1] for silver, can be employed to reveal dislocations in many metals and alloys. At elevated temperatures atom movements take place to establish a mechanical balance between the surface tension and the line tension of a dislocation, so that a slight depression occurs at the dislocation. Frank [2] has discussed this subject; and according to his results, if one uses the surface tension in vacuum, the depression of the surface at a dislocation is very small in most metals and alloys. For example, in copper the depth of the depression is less than 10 A, while the diameter is about 1 μ.

If there is an oxygen atmosphere present during the thermal etching, the surface tension of the metal is decreased considerably, so that a deeper depression results. Under suitable conditions an oxide particle will form in the bottom of each depression so that the position of the dislocation is clearly marked. The thermal-etching technique can be applied to most metals and alloys, except for some metals having high vapor pressure at high temperature, such as zinc, cadmium, magnesium, and their alloys.

Some examples of Fe-Ni alloys which were oxidized at 1100°C for 30 min are shown in Figs. 1 through 4. The oxygen pressure was about 10^{-2} mm Hg. Figure 1 shows a crystal that had an uneven

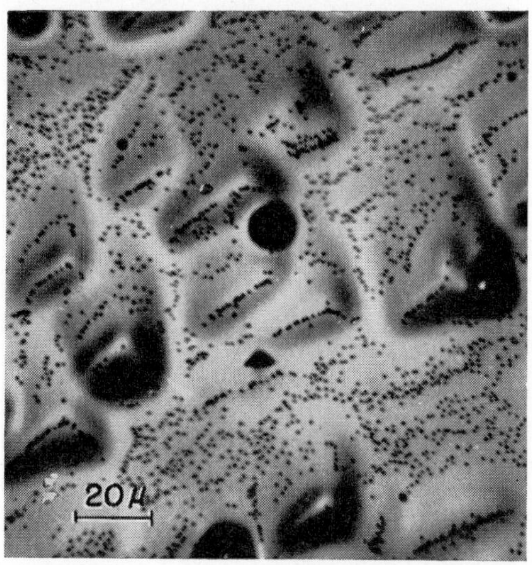

Fig. 1. Fe-Ni alloy etched at 1100°C for 30 min in an oxidizing atmosphere.

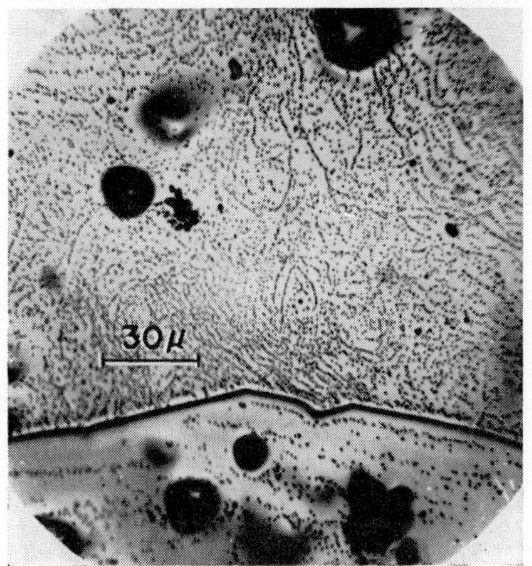

Fig. 2. Fe-Ni alloy etched thermally after mechanical polishing. The lower portion has recrystallized.

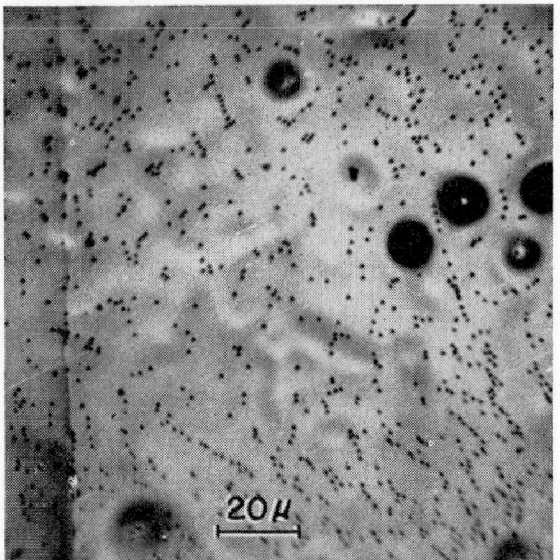

Fig. 3. Recrystallized Fe-Ni alloy, thermally etched.

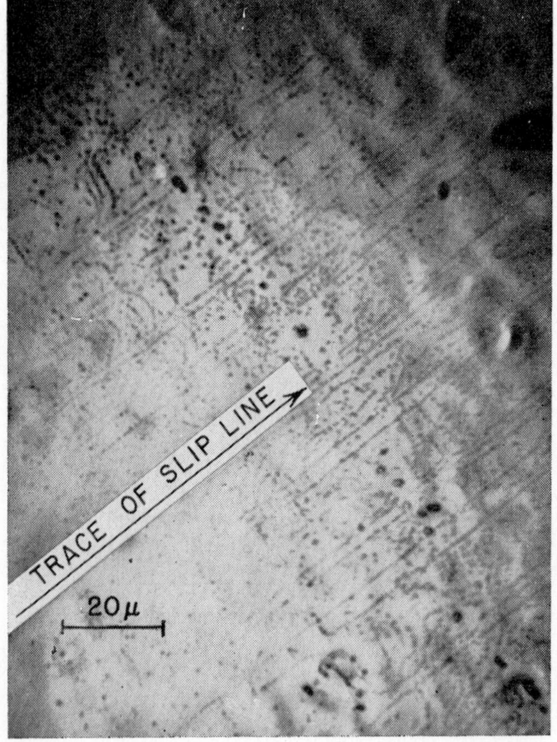

Fig. 4. Side surface of a bent Fe-Ni crystal, etched thermally.

surface, and the dislocations tend to go into the hollows in the surface in order to shorten their length.

Figure 2 shows a crystal that had been polished mechanically prior to the thermal-etching treatment. Some recrystallization has occurred, and it is seen that the dislocation density is much lower in the small recrystallized portion than in the rest of the crystal. The completely recrystallized grain shown in Fig. 3 has a low density of dislocations that are distributed rather homogeneously.

Figure 4 shows the side surface of a bent crystal, and nearly all of the dislocations are still in the slip planes. It appears, therefore, that the climb motion in Fe-Ni alloys is far slower than in the body-centered cubic Fe-Si alloys.[3]

The mechanism proposed for thermal etching suggests that, even in chemical etching, the decrease in surface energy of the crystal on dipping into the reagent is most important in order to obtain good etch pits.

REFERENCES

1. A. A. Hendrickson and E. S. Machlin, *Acta Met.*, **3**, 64 (1955).
2. F. C. Frank, *Acta Cryst.*, **4**, 497 (1951).
3. W. R. Hibbard, Jr., and C. G. Dunn, *Acta Met.*, **4**, 306 (1956).

II DEFORMATION OF PURE SINGLE CRYSTALS

Low-Temperature Deformation of Copper Single Crystals

T. H. BLEWITT

R. R. COLTMAN

J. K. REDMAN

Solid State Division
Oak Ridge National Laboratory
Oak Ridge, Tennessee

ABSTRACT

Single crystals of copper were deformed at 4.2°K and 77.3°K. At 4.2°K, after a large strain produced by normal slip, jerky flow, called discontinuous slip, occurs. From the study of reactor-irradiated crystals, it was deduced that a packet of 30 slip lines, each containing 10^4 dislocations, was released to form each jerk of the discontinuous flow. For samples of certain orientation the region of discontinuous flow was followed by a region of deformation twinning. The fact that deformation twinning was taking place was verified by X-ray methods. The twinning elements were determined to be the (111) plane and the [112] direction. At 77.3°K, discontinuous slip is not observed. In a limited range of orientations, twinning has been observed at 77.3°K. The effects of reactor irradiations on discontinuous slip and on twinning were also studied, and it was determined that the occurrence of twinning was unaffected by the irradiations.

1. INTRODUCTION

Recently the deformation characteristics of copper single crystals have been studied at temperatures ranging down to 4.2°K.[1] The initial results of this research were reported at the Conference on Defects in Crystalline Solids held at the University of Bristol, July 1954,

Bristol, England, and at the Conference on Work Hardening in Metals held at the University of Birmingham, July 1954, Birmingham, England. Included in these reports was a description of the onset of a change in the mode of deformation after large strains at liquid-helium temperature. At this time it was considered that there were reasonable grounds for suspecting that this anomalous behavior was the result of the deformation changing from a slip process to that of a twinning process. At the Birmingham Conference the suggestion that deformation by twinning was occurring in a face-centered cubic metal was not received enthusiastically. In fact, it was clear that incontestable evidence would have to be presented before such a suggestion would be accepted, though the process occurred in a temperature region and at a stress which had not been previously investigated. The unpopularity of this suggestion apparently arose as a result of numerous instances in the past where strain markings in face-centered cubic metals were incorrectly labeled as twins and as a result of Cottrell and Bilby's proposed mechanism of twinning,[2] which precluded twinning in face-centered cubic metals.

Consequently, it was the purpose of the work described in this paper to investigate more fully the deformation of copper at 4.2°K, with particular regard to the new modes of deformation which occur after large strains.

2. EXPERIMENTAL PROCEDURE

The copper single crystals were grown from 99.999% pure copper prepared by the American Smelting & Refining Co. They were grown in the shape of tensile bars with round cross sections or with square cross sections and were either ⅛ in. or ¼ in. on an edge. The exact method of growth has been described previously.[3]

The deformation was carried out in an Instron tensile machine. A simple cryostat, which is illustrated in Fig. 1, was adapted to this machine. When utilized for liquid-helium temperatures, the Dewar flask is filled with helium directly from a Collins liquefier and carried to the machine. The consumption of liquid helium including cool down is about 1 liter per 2-hr run.

After a high-temperature anneal, the crystals were loaded in the cryostat and were deformed at 4.2 or 77.3°K, the load being measured by the load cell of the Instron machine and the elongation measured by the crosshead motion. In order to test the accuracy of the crosshead motion the elongation was measured by simultaneously utilizing a traveling microscope and fiducial marks. The results showed that the elongation, as determined by these two methods, differed by less than 0.01 in. for a 1-in. gauge length.

The X-ray verification of twinning was performed by a new technique developed at ORNL.[4]

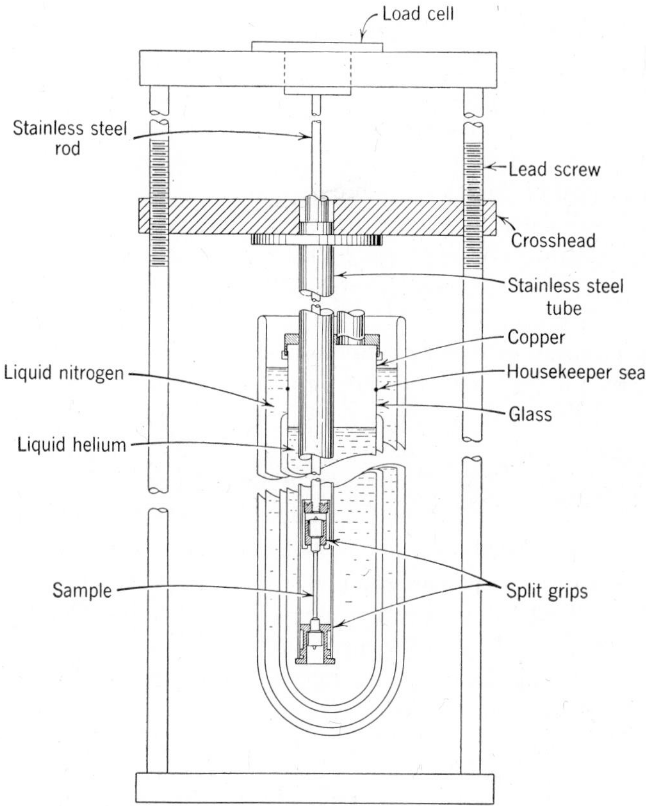

Fig. 1. Schematic diagram of cryostat mounted in Instron tensile machine.

3. RESULTS

General Considerations

The results presented here will show that mechanical twinning occurs in copper single crystals when they are deformed under certain conditions. It will be shown that temperature, orientation, and extent of deformation are important variables in determining whether mechanical twinning occurs. In order to discuss the data concisely, the general features of the process will be considered first, and the particular idiosyncrasies of various samples will be subsequently discussed. In this section, then, the over-all features of the process will be presented with the understanding that, although the samples discussed fall into the general category of typical samples, there are details of the process which differ from sample to sample.

The Load-Elongation Curves at 4.2°K

It has been previously noted that at 4.2°K the normal slip process results in a linear stress-strain curve.[1] In passing, it should be pointed out that the load-elongation curves show a similar behavior in the region where normal slip occurs. In this discussion, however, attention will be confined to the region where normal slip no longer occurs. Two types of load-elongation curves have been observed when the sample is deformed at low temperatures. These types, which will be denoted as category *A* and category *B* respectively, are illustrated in Figs. 2 and 3.

The orientation of the crystal determines whether the sample has a load-elongation curve of type *A* or type *B*. The initial tensile axes of the specimens are represented in the sterographic net of Fig. 4. Those samples whose load-elongation curves fall in category *A* are designated by an open circle, those in category *B* by a filled circle. It is well known that the tensile axis of the sample will rotate during deformation. Since a deformation of about 50% will take place by normal slip, the resulting rotation of the tensile axis must be taken into consideration in discussing the orientation effect. The crosshatched region in the spherical triangle denotes those samples whose orientation after 50% elongation will have rotated into a position on the dodecahedral plane [that plane represented in the stereographic net of Fig. 4 by the line connecting the pole of the (100) plane with the pole of the (111) plane] between the (311) plane and the (111) plane. [This demarkation zone was determined by rotating the specimen axis along the great circle connecting the initial tensile axis and the slip direction until it reached the dodecahedral plane, in accordance with the laws of single slip, after which it was rotated along the line representing the dodecahedral plane towards the pole of the (112) plane, in accordance with the laws of duplex slip.] It can be seen from Fig. 4 that only those samples with orientations in the crosshatched region had a load-elongation curve of category *B*; those with tensile axes in the open region had a load-elongation curve of category *A*.

Consider now the details of the load-elongation curve typical of category *A*, shown in Fig. 2. Beyond the region of normal slip, it is apparent from the discontinuities in the load-elongation curve that a

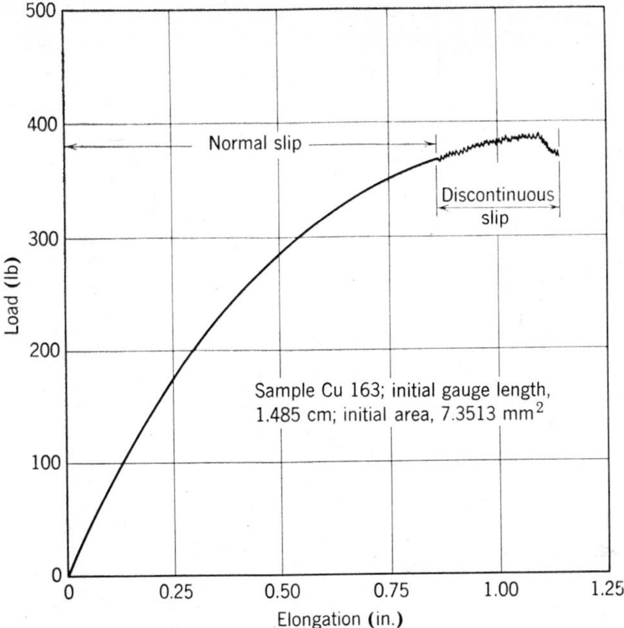

Fig. 2. Typical load-elongation curve of a copper crystal (sample **163**) deformed at 4.2°K which falls in category *A* (no twin).

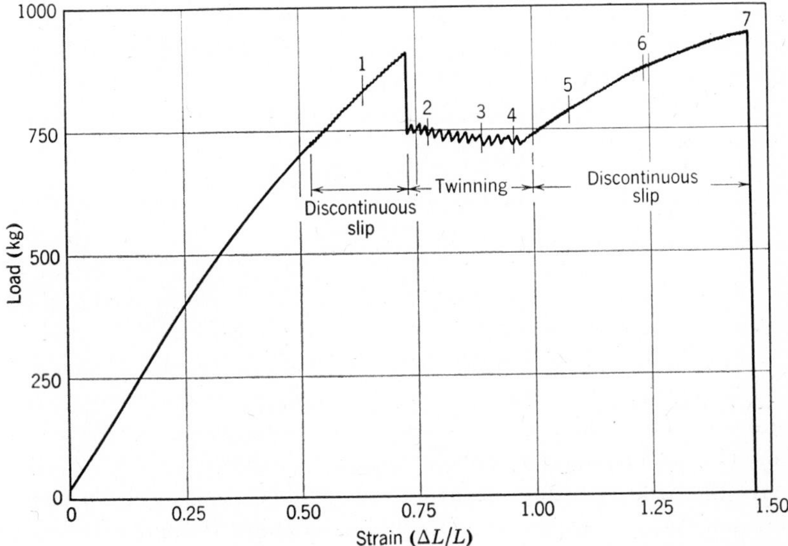

Fig. 3. Typical load-elongation curve of a copper crystal (sample 399A) deformed at 4.2°K which falls in category *B*.

high velocity localized extension occurs. This region has been designated as the discontinuous slip region. It should be noted that the sample apparently continues to work-harden with increasing deformation. A clicking noise was heard, which coincided with each discon-

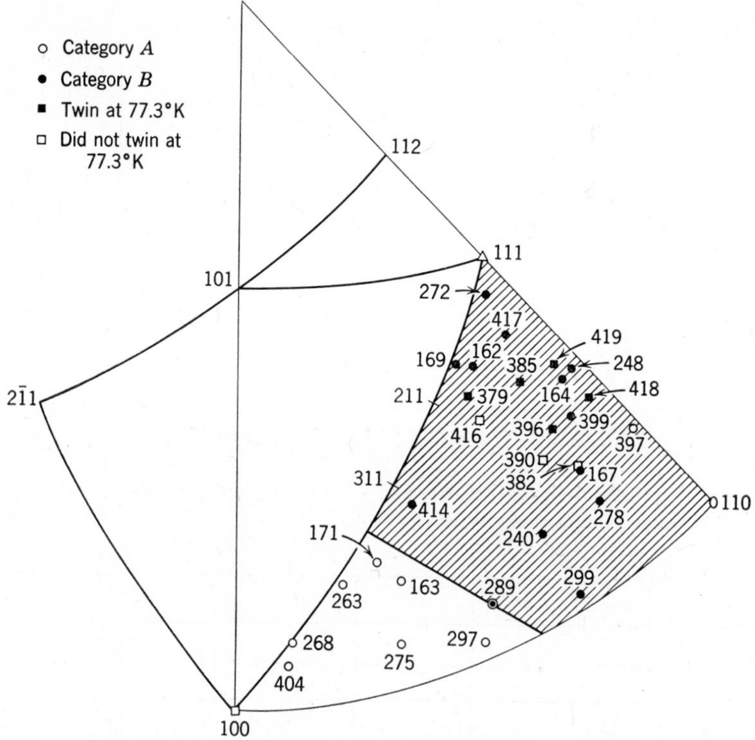

Fig. 4. Standard stereographic projection showing the tensile directions of the various samples.

tinuity in the load-elongation curve. The way in which these discontinuities appear on the strip chart is shown in Fig. 5.

After the sample was in the discontinuous slip region, it was electrolytically polished, and all strain markings were removed; the samples were then slightly extended, and the strain markings examined. The results are shown in Fig. 6.

All the strain markings in this region could be electrolytically etched off, and X-ray measurements with the spinning technique failed to show evidence for the formation of twins. After considerable deformation, the sample broke in an abrupt manner, as indicated in the load-

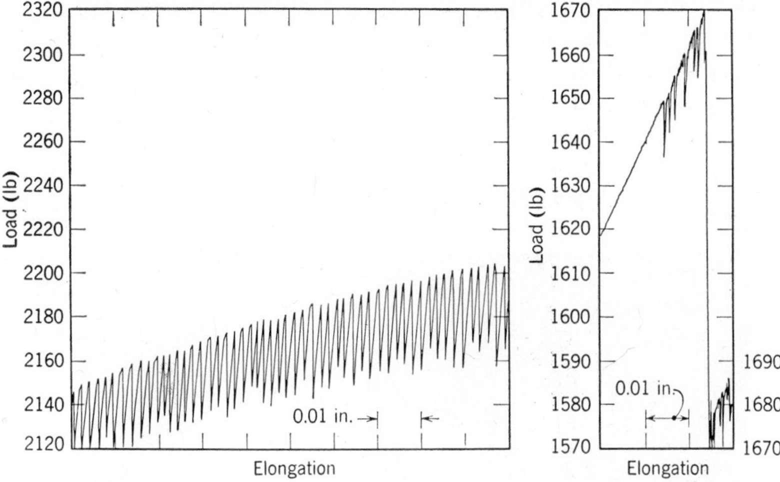

Fig. 5. Discontinuous slip region of a typical crystal (sample 404) deformed at 4.2°K.

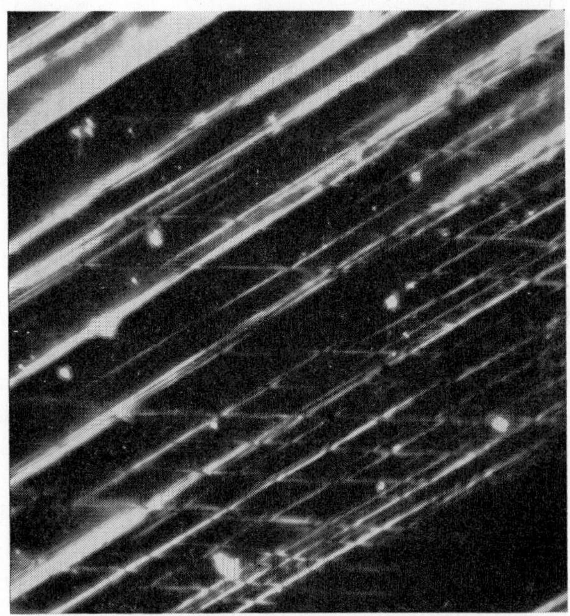

Fig. 6. The strain markings associated with discontinuous slip of a copper crystal with a load elongation of category *A* (sample 404). These markings may be removed by etching. Temperature of deformation, 4.2°K. 285×.

elongation curve of Fig. 2. The appearance of the fractured region, which is characteristic of category *A*, is shown in Fig. 7.

Consider now the load-elongation curve of category *B*. The load-elongation curve of sample 399A, which is representative of this category, is shown in Fig. 3. There is the usual region of slip in which the stress-strain curve is linear; this is followed by a region of discontinuous slip similar to that found in category *A*. The beginning of a new region, that of twinning, originates with a sharp release of load. In sample 397A, the tensile test was stopped when this occurred. The sample was mounted, polished, and etched. The resulting photomicrograph of the initial strain marking, which is believed to be the initial twin, is shown in Fig. 8. A loud report was heard when this twin formed. After the initial twin formation, the load-elongation curve shows no evidence of work hardening, since the load oscillates slightly with elongation. Periodically the sample was removed from the tensile machine and etched so that progress of the twin growth could be followed. Macroscopic pictures of the sample showing this growth are given in Fig. 9. The numbers in the illustration correspond to the numbers in the load-elongation curve. It can be seen from Fig. 9 that when the sample has completely twinned, work hardening once

Fig. 7. Appearance of typical fractures of copper single crystals with load-elongation curves of category *A* (samples 171 and 404). Temperature of deformation, 4.2°K. 2×.

more occurs. Finally, as in the case of samples in category *A*, the category *B* sample fractures abruptly; the fracture is, however, different from that of specimens of category *A* in that the fractured surface seems to be along a plane. Figure 10 shows a typical fracture for samples which have load-elongation curves that fall into category *B*. It is believed that fracture for both categories *A* and *B* occurs as a result of stress exceeding the theoretical strength. Mackenzie [5] has

Fig. 8. Initial twin nuclei of copper crystal sample 397A. Deformation temperature, 4.2°K. 57×.

estimated the theoretical strength as one-thirtieth of the shear modulus. For the case of copper this amounts to about 100 kg/mm^2. In the case of sample 399A the stress was determined from the load and the measured area of the fracture surface and found to be about 120 kg/mm^2.

The Load-Elongation Curve at 77.3°K

Twinning has been observed at 77.3°K in a limited number of specimens. As in the case of deformation at 4.2°K, the orientation seems to determine whether or not twinning occurs. Only a limited number of crystallographic orientations result in the appearance of deformation twins. Those orientations in which twinning has been observed are represented in the stereographic projection of Fig. 4. The load-elongation curves of samples showing twinning (corresponding to category B at 4.2°K) are shown in Fig. 11. Figure 12 shows the load-elongation curve for a sample which did not show twinning. It should be noted from the load-elongation curve, apart from the twinning

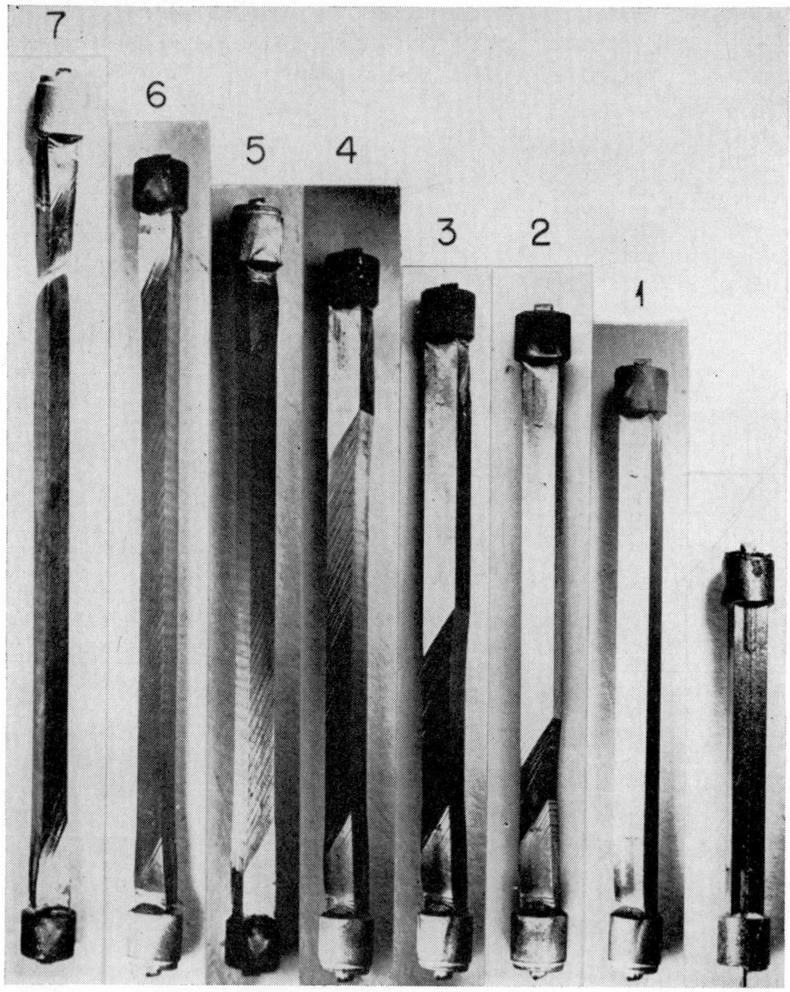

Fig. 9. Twin growth of sample 399A. The numbers correspond to the numbers on the load-elongation curve (Fig. 3).

phenomenon, that the plastic flow occurs by a normal slip process in both cases A and B, without the presence of a discontinuous slip region. Moreover, it is interesting to note that there is a slight necking down immediately prior to the twinning; then there is an abrupt decrease

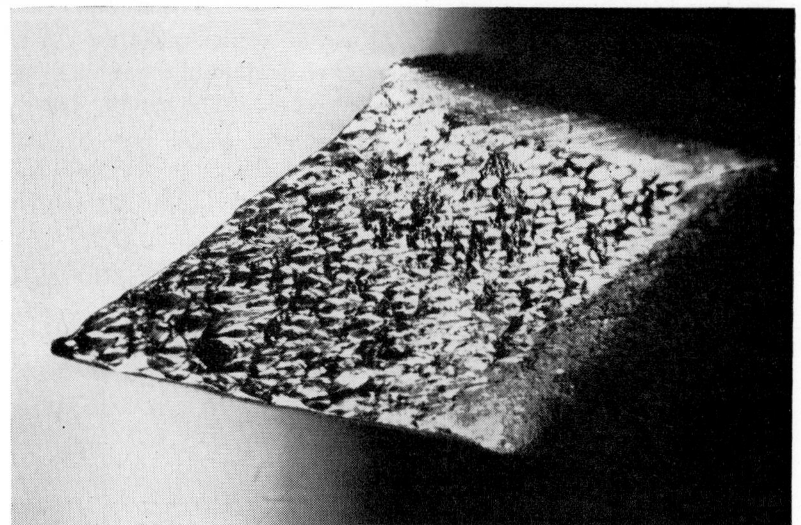

Fig. 10. Fractured surface of sample 399A. 9×.

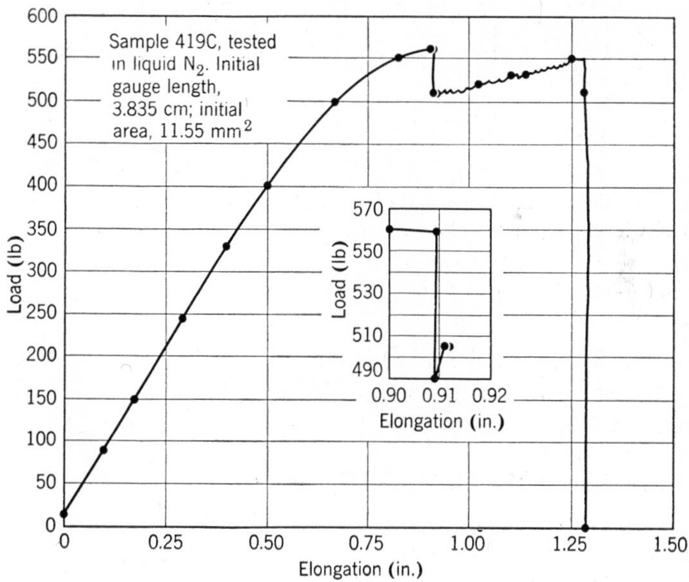

Fig. 11. Load-elongation curve for sample 419, which is typical for samples which show twinning at 77.3°K.

in load, and the twinning phenomenon occurs. It has been found that the twinning nucleates in the original necked region. The growth of the twin has been studied as a function of elongation in the same manner as was done for samples deformed at 4.2°K. The results showed a high degree of similarity in the two processes. It can be seen from Fig. 11 that, after the twinning material filled the gauge length of the sample, deformation again proceeded by a normal slip process. Some

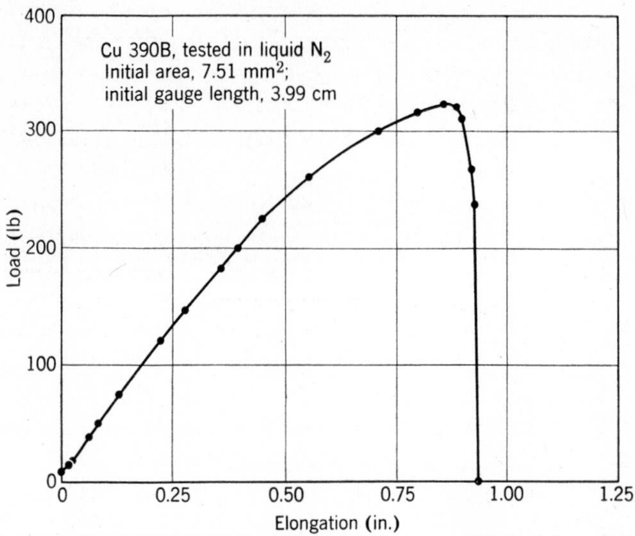

Fig. 12. Typical load-elongation curve for sample 390 which was deformed at 77.3°K without any anomalous effects.

degree of necking occurred, and the sample then fractured in an abrupt fashion. The fractured surface appeared similar to that of samples deformed at 4.2°K. On the other hand, those samples which deformed without twinning fractured with a chisel edge in the normal shear-type manner.

Determination of the Twinning Elements

Cahn [6] gives the following definition of twinning: "Two crystals present together in a single coherent piece of solid are said to be in the twin relation to each other if their lattices are related by symmetry about some crystallographically important axis or plane." Twinning will thus be proved if the symmetry criterion indicated by Cahn can be shown to exist. This was done by utilizing a special

X-ray technique developed at ORNL, and described elsewhere.[4] The usual X-ray techniques could not be used because of the extreme amount of distortion present in the crystal when the twinning phenomenon occurred. This special technique was utilized in the study of many samples deformed at both liquid-nitrogen and liquid-helium temperatures. The results, which are described below, were obtained from one of these samples and are quite typical of the others studied.

Sample 164 was deformed at liquid-helium temperatures until a large twin formed. Figure 13 is a photograph of this sample after deformation. A section about ½ in. long, containing approximately equal areas of twinned and parent material, was removed from this sample; and the orientation of each was determined by the special spinning technique. Alternate portions of the sample were covered with lead foil, and, as a consequence, it was possible to deduce that the untwinned parent area was a single crystal, whereas the twinned region consisted of two crystals. The orientation of each of these crystals was studied by this technique, and it was determined that one of the crystals in the twinned region had an identical orientation with the parent crystal, whereas the second crystal had an orientation which bore a symmetry relationship to the parent crystal about the (111) plane. The results are shown in Fig. 14 and in Table 1. It should be remembered that, since the (112) plane makes an angle of 90° with the (111) plane, the

TABLE 1. THE ORIENTATION OF CRYSTAL *A* (MATRIX MATERIAL) AND CRYSTAL *B* (TWIN MATERIAL) IN SAMPLE 164

	Crystal *B*		Crystal *A*			
	Measured		Measured		Required for *A* to Be Twin of *B*	
Plane	α	ω	α	ω	α	ω
			Side I			
400	32	0	31	100	33	100
220	16	130	18	340	17	335
222	26	235	27	235	28	228
420	10	50	10	50	10	47
331	14	185	14	290	14	278
			Side II			
400	34½	0	14½	145	14½	142
220	10½	227	28½	328	29	330
222	42½	268	42½	268	42½	266
222	28	116				

symmetry could also be referred to the (112) plane. It is significant, however, that the X-ray results can only be interpreted if one of the (111) planes is common to both crystals, thereby establishing that the (111) plane is the twinning plane. It can further be noted from Fig. 14 that, in this particular case, the (111) plane utilized in the primary slip system is in actuality the twinning plane.

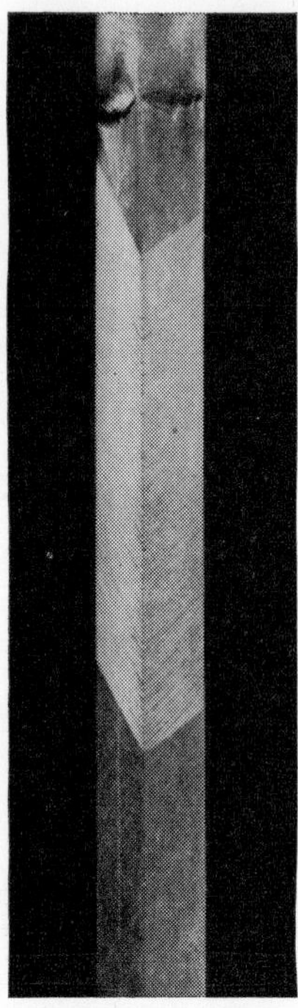

Fig. 13. Twin formation in sample 164 following deformation at 4.2°K. A section from this sample containing both twinned and parent regions was utilized for an X-ray analysis. 3×.

Consider now the atomic motions on the (111) plane which will result in twin formation. It is commonly accepted that slip proceeds on the (111) plane in the [110] direction. It is furthermore accepted that the atomic motions are in the [112] and [211] directions, with a resultant net motion in the [110] direction, as is illustrated in the vector diagram of Fig. 15. It can also be seen from Fig. 15 that a net atomic motion in the [112] direction (i.e., if only half of the slip occurs) will change the stacking, since it will move an atom from a B site to a C site. The stacking will thus change from $A\ B\ C\ A\ B\ C\ A\ B\ C$ to $A\ B\ C\ A\ C\ A\ B\ C\ A$. This is called a stacking fault. If, however, a number of adjacent planes glide over each other in this fashion, the stacking becomes $A\ B\ C\ A\ C\ B\ A\ C\ B\ C\ A\ B\ C$, the region between the vertical lines being a twin. The amount of shear, S, associated with this twinning is constant, with a value of 0.707. The amount of elongation associated with this shear will, of course, depend upon the orientation of the crystal relative to the tensile direction. It is given by the following equation:

$$\frac{l}{l_0} = \sqrt{1 + 2S \sin \chi \cos \lambda + S^2 \sin^2 \chi}$$

where l_0 is the initial length, l is the final length, λ is the angle between the twin plane and the tensile axis, and χ is the angle between the twin directions and the tensile axis.

On utilizing the orientation of sample 164, it was found that $l/l_0 =$ 1.27. For this particular sample, the areas of both the twinned and parent samples were measured. The strain determined from this measurement was 1.29. Thus, there is some indirect evidence that the twinning direction is the [112] direction, although it would be most difficult to expect any other direction after it had been deduced that twinning occurs on the [111] plane.

At the time that twinning was first suspected, an effort was made to determine the orientation of the twin lamellae by measurement of the

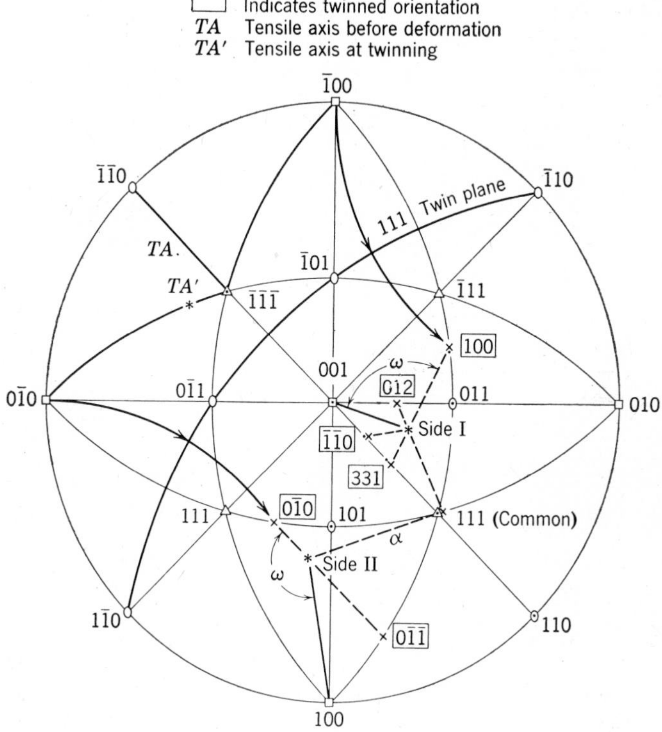

Fig. 14. Standard projection of a face-centered cubic crystal showing the rotations of the principal planes for a twin relationship. The experimental determination of the twinned principal planes is indicated by a segment of a circle. The initial tensile axis is denoted by *TA* and the axis at the onset of twinning by *TA′*.

macroscopic angles that the lamellae made on the crystal surface, together with the angles between the surfaces. Invariably, these results showed that the twin lamellae were some 3 to 5° from the (111) plane; since the accuracy of this method is not high, this departure was attributed to experimental error. It is apparent from Fig. 8 that this discrepancy arose from the fact that the macroscopic boundary of the twin is composed of a series of twin lamellae which fail to run through the sample and which make an angle of about 5° with the boundary.

In some cases twinning occurred on two conjugate (111) planes. The twin formation in sample 167 is an example of this phenomenon. Figure 16 shows the macroscopic appearance of these twins, and Fig. 17 shows a photomicrograph of the interaction of the conjugate twins. Although several interpretations are possible, in the region shown in the photomicrograph it would appear that the two twins formed simul-

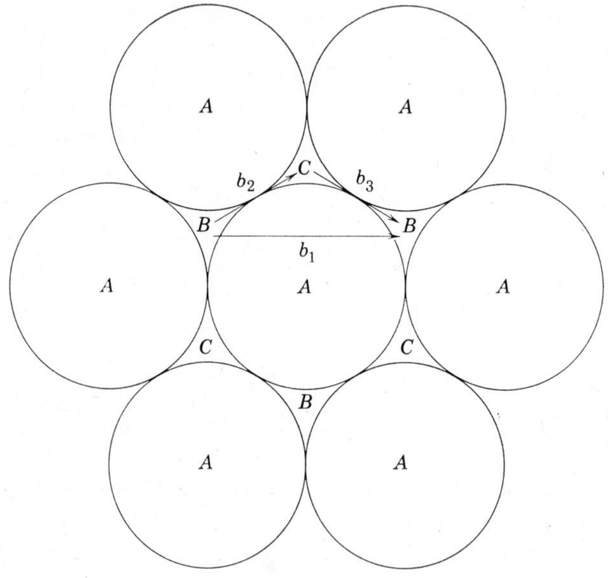

Fig. 15. Vector diagram indicating the atomic motions resulting in slip. The voids between the spheres will be the sites for atoms in the plane below and the plane above. These positions are denoted by C and A respectively. (From Cottrell, *Dislocations and Plastic Flow in Crystals,* Clarendon Press, Oxford, 1953.)

taneously and then interacted with each other. Apparently, one twin lamella finds it difficult to penetrate the other. Twinning on conjugate planes was observed generally in those samples in which this initial orientation was close to the dodecahedral plane. In an earlier paper,[4] considerable attention was devoted to the X-ray determination of the orientation of the conjugate twins of sample 167.

In certain instances strain markings have been observed which have not been identified. A photomicrograph of such markings is shown in Fig. 18. An additional group of short secondary markings is also apparent at high magnification. The fact that secondary markings change direction when they pass through the unidentified markings would suggest that this region has a different orientation from that of the matrix. It may be that these markings are the result of twinning of unidentified elements.

To obtain the photograph of Fig. 18 the sample was mounted in bakelite for metallographic polishing; thus the temperature reached 150°C for a few minutes. This was sufficient to result in recrystallization, as is evident in Fig. 18. It can thus be deduced that the region is in a high state of strain relative to the matrix. This preferential recrystallization of the twinned crystal on heat treatment appears to be the general rule. An additional photomicrograph showing the twin boundary of sample 164 following a 25-min heat treatment at 150°C is presented in Fig. 19. It will be noted here that in only one case did a recrystallized grain penetrate through the twin boundary. Sample 399, which had completely twinned, was observed to be recrystallized after it was stored for about 1 year at room temperature. The heaviest density of recrystallized grains was visible near the fractured end. The fractured end itself was a fine-grained surface.

Fracture

In the case of the samples which have twinned, it is believed that fracture occurs as a result of literally pulling the atomic planes apart; i.e., the theoretical strength has been reached. Consider sample 399A. The cross-sectional area of fracture was measured and was utilized to compute, in conjunction with the load, the fracture stress on the fracture plane. The stress on this plane was found to exceed 100 kg/mm^2. The theoretical strength has been estimated to be one-thirtieth of the shear modulus, which is in accord with the measured value.

Attempts have been made to determine the crystallographic orientation of the fracture, but the results have been inconclusive. However, it can be said that the orientation is within 10° of the (111) twin plane, which is common to both orientations.

The exact details of the fracture vary somewhat from sample to sample, in that the degree of necking varies. Sample 399A shows less necking than is usually encountered.

Fracture of untwinned samples varies in certain details. Particularly, it is not planar. Flow has been so drastic in the case of these samples that the two halves of the sample cannot be arranged so that the fractured surfaces fit together. Apparently the untwinned lamellae exert an influence and make an apparent planar surface when fracture occurs in the twinned region. The two types of fracture probably result from exceeding the theoretical strength.

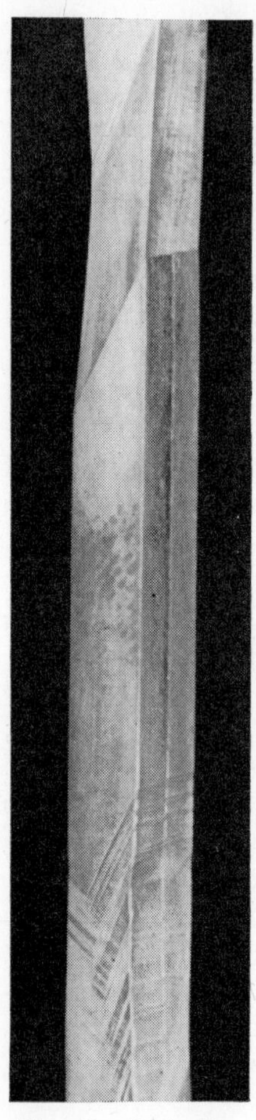

Fig. 16. Twin formation at 4.2°K in a sample (no. 169) whose initial orientation was near the dodecahedral plane. A twin has formed at one end of the crystal. At the other end, two twins, each with its twinning plane on one of the conjugate slip systems, can be seen. 2½×.

The Effect of Neutron Irradiation on Discontinuous Slip and Twinning

It is well known that reactor bombardment substantially alters the deformation properties of copper single crystals. The investigations of the effects of nuclear bombardments on the mechanical properties, however, have been largely concerned with the study of the normal slip process. The effect of nuclear bombardment on the anomalous deformation processes in copper, i.e., on discontinuous slip and twinning, has been studied as part of the present investigation.

The study was made on samples which were bombarded at 30°C in a natural uranium cylinder in the center of the ORNL Graphite Reactor to an integrated flux of 1×10^{18} nvt and on samples bombarded at 80°C in a fuel element in the ORNL low intensity test reactor to an integrated flux of 1.5×10^{20} nvt.

Two sets of samples, 419 and 396, were bombarded for 1×10^{18} nvt. The orientations of these samples, which are given in Fig. 4, were such that twinning would occur at 77°K. The results of the deformation of 419C (nonirradiated) and 419B at 77°K are shown in Fig. 20. Similar results were found for the 396 series.

On deformation at liquid nitrogen it can be seen that irradiated samples differed from unirradiated samples only in that the strain at which twinning occurred was somewhat less in the irradiated samples. This may be a consequence of the irradiation reducing the ductility, which results in necking at the lower strains. In the previous section, it was noted that necking occurs before the onset of twinning at 77°K, and this is not altered by irradiation.

The irradiations of samples 416 in the Low Intensity Test Reactor were carried out for the purpose of establishing whether irradiation could induce twinning in a sample whose orientation was unfavorable to this process and, in addition,

Fig. 17. Twins formed on conjugate slip planes in sample 169 deformed at 4.2°K. 150×.

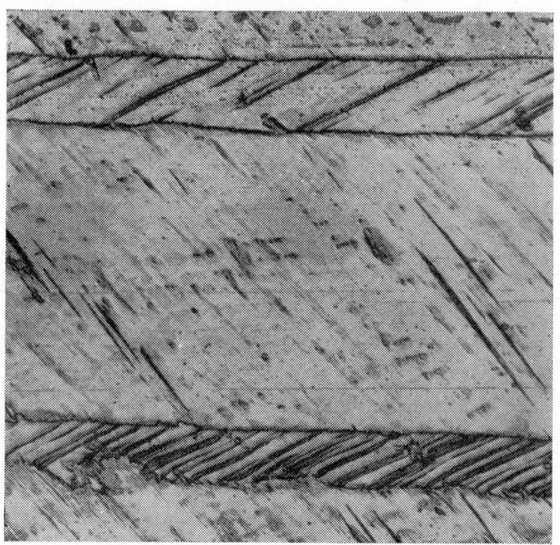

Fig. 18. Photomicrograph of an unidentified strain marking. 90×.

Fig. 19. Recrystallization in the twinned region following an anneal at 150°C for 25 min. 50×.

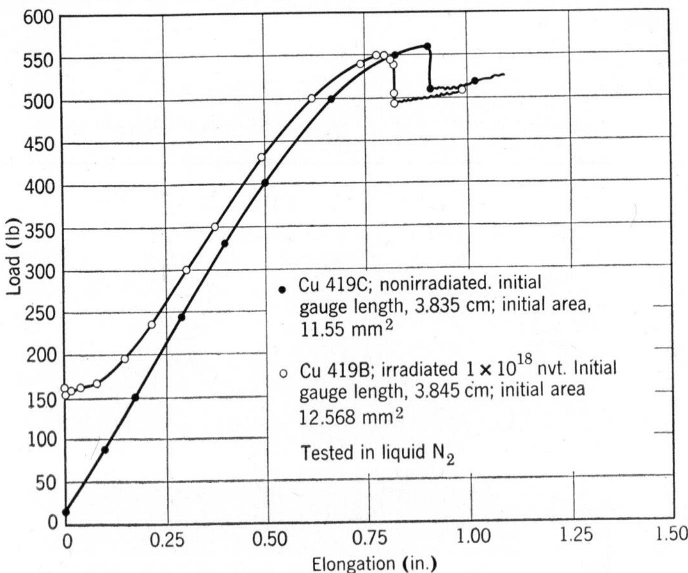

Fig. 20. The load elongation of samples 419B and 419C. Both samples are of the same orientation with sample 419B being reactor-irradiated. The temperature of deformation was 77.3°K. The drop in the load after strains of the order of 0.80 is the result of twinning. Both samples necked down slightly before twinning occurred.

to secure an irradiation which would raise the initial shear stress above the level where twinning was previously observed. Consequently, a sample whose orientation was such that it would not twin at 77°K but would twin at 4.20°K was desired. It will be noted in Fig. 4 that the orientation of the 416 series fits these requirements and, in point of fact, is very near that orientation which twins at 77°K. Experimentally, it was found that the irradiation of 1.5×10^{20} nvt did not induce

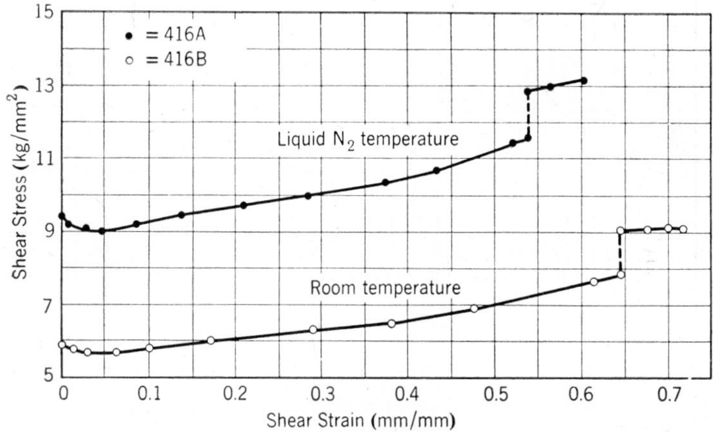

Fig. 21. The stress-strain curves for samples 416A and 416B. Both samples are of the same orientation and they were both irradiated simultaneously to an integrated flux of 1.5×10^{20} nvt at about 340°K. Sample 416A was deformed at 77.3°K and sample 416B at 300°K. The rise in the flow stress at large strains is the result of the slip system changing from the primary system to the conjugate one. The last point on each curve is the point at which necking occurred. Both samples fractured from this point without evidence of twinning.

the sample 416A to twin at 77°K, indicating that neutron irradiation will not induce twinning in a sample unfavorably oriented for twinning. The stress-strain curves of sample 416A deformed at 77.3°K and of sample 416B deformed at 300°K are shown in Fig. 21.

The load-elongation curve of sample 416E deformed in tension at 4.2°K is shown in Fig. 22. It is apparent that this sample whose critical shear stress has been raised to 13.5 kg/mm at 4.2°K by the irradiation has a typical load-elongation curve of category *B* in that discontinuous slip and twinning are observed. It is also apparent, however, that the irradiation results in some modification of the load-elongation curve. First, it is observed that the irradiation completely suppresses normal slip, i.e., the discontinuous slip starts immediately; second, it is seen that there is no apparent work hardening in the region of discontinuous slip indicating Lüders band formation; and third, the amount of elongation prior to fracture (ductility) is considerably reduced. These factors make the irradiated sample ideal for studying discontinuous slip and twinning as the effects of normal slip are not present to obscure these phenomena.

In order to study the nature of discontinuous flow sample 416 was

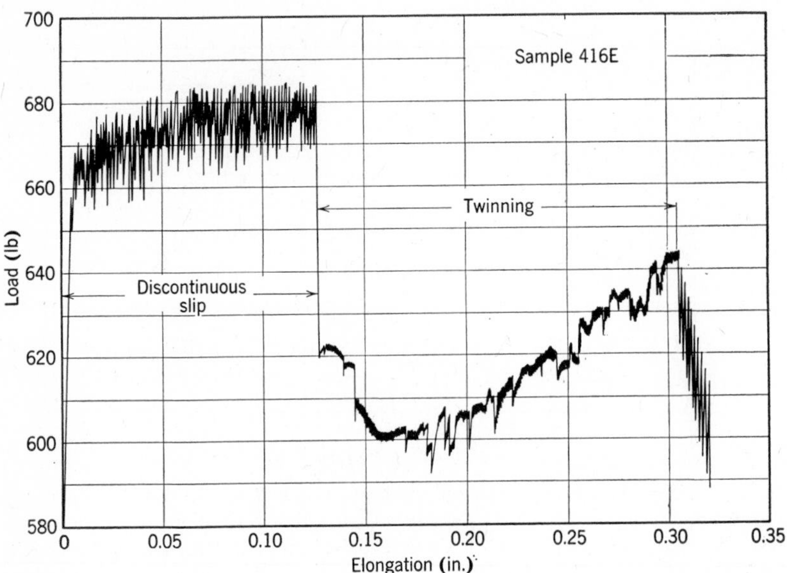

Fig. 22. The load-elongation curve of sample 416E. The sample was bombarded for 1.5×10^{20} nvt at 340°K and deformed at 4.2°K. Periodically, the sample was examined for slip lines and twinning. The load-elongation curve shows that discontinuous slip starts without the preliminary normal glide. The large drop in load is the result of twinning.

elongated a small amount (0.005 in.) and the strain markings were studied; see Fig. 23. It was found that these appeared in a cluster, confirming the indication of deformation by Lüders bands. Altogether, about 150 slip lines were observed after the deformation. With the exception of lines at one end of the band, each of the slip lines at low magnification appeared to make a trace that went completely around the sample. It was obvious that the step heights were quite high. Upon examination of the bands at higher magnification, there was some indication that there were some jogs in the lines due to cross slip. This is illustrated in Fig. 3. An estimate of the step height can be made if it is assumed that no fine slip occurs. In view of the jerky nature of discontinuous slip, it would seem reasonable to assume that the majority of the slip is associated with the strain marking. Taking then the measured elongation, one finds that approximately 10^4 dislocations are associated with each line. It was also deduced from the fact that five discontinuities (or jerks) in the load-elongation curve produced 150 slip lines that 30 slip lines or 3×10^5 dislocations were associated with each discontinuity.

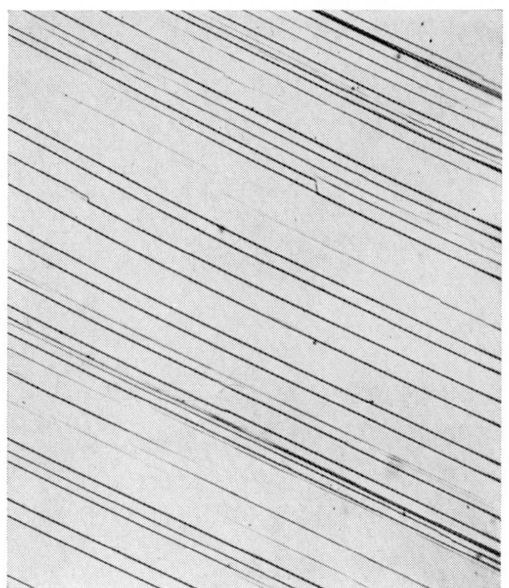

Fig. 23. Discontinuous slip lines after an elongation of 0.005 in sample 416E. This photomicrograph was taken in the center of the Lüders band. 250×.

The twinning was studied by periodically examining the progress of the twin formation. It was particularly desired to observe whether twinning could occur in an undeformed sample. Since the discontinuous slip proceeded by a Lüders band formation, there would be a deformed and undeformed portion of the crystal if the twin formed before the Lüders band swept through the crystal. This was observed on crystal 416E. The sample was extended, after preliminary study of discontinuous slip, until the load fell abruptly, indicating the formation of the twin lamellae, at which point the test was immediately stopped and the sample examined without prior etch. Figure 24 shows the appearance of the initial twin nuclei with slip lines formed by discontinuous slip prior to the twinning passing through the sample. It was observed that the Lüder's band had swept through about one-half of the length of the sample. Light scratches were inscribed on the sample to indicate the extent of the Lüders band and the sample was then deformed to fracture. It was observed that the twinned region did not extend into the undeformed region of the crystal; instead, after the twinned region had filled the region of the Lüders band, the sample commenced to deform by discontinuous slip in the twinned region, and after a small amount of necking an abrupt fracture occurred.

It is not clear just why the twin does not extend into the unde-

Fig. 24. The twin nucleus in sample 416E. This photomicrograph was taken after the sample had been deformed to the point where the large decrease in load occurred (see Fig. 22). The slip lines are horizontal in the untwinned region and are deflected in the twin band due to the shear strain of the twin. The sample was unpolished after the photomicrograph of Fig. 23 was obtained. 250×.

formed portion of the crystal. It may simply be a geometrical factor as the area of the deformed region is reduced by 18%, raising the flow stress by that factor in the deformed region. On the other hand, it is observed in Fig. 25 that twinning does occur near the end of the Lüders band where the density of the discontinuous slip lines is slight and the geometrical consideration would be small. It was observed that these twin bands did not pass completely through the sample, however, possibly indicating the necessity of previous deformation to the formation of twinning.

It is interesting to note that the twinning plane in the case of the irradiated sample is not the active slip plane, but rather is the conjugate slip plane. It was previously pointed out that in the case of the unirradiated copper the twinning plane seemed to coincide with that of the slip plane having the largest amount of slip. In the case of the irradiated sample, however, the situation is somewhat different as the amount of deformation is relatively small and the rotation of the tensile axis is correspondingly small. The tensile axis of sample 416E has not, for example, rotated sufficiently to allow it to fall on the dodecahedral plane. Under these conditions, there is a greater resolved shear stress for twinning on the (111) plane associated with the conjugate slip system than in the case of the (111) plane associ-

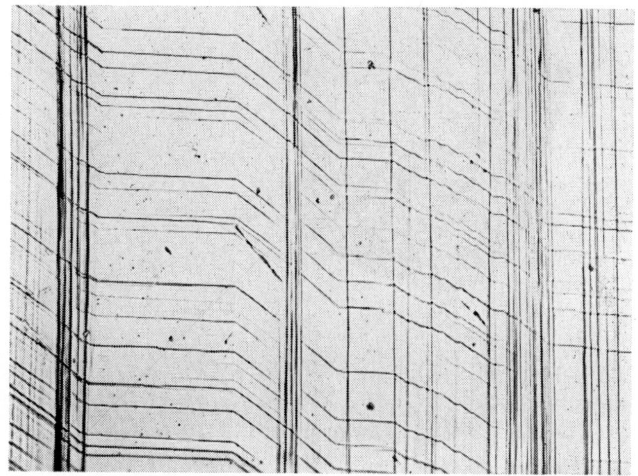

Fig. 25. Twin lamellae and slip lines near the boundary of the Lüders band in sample 416. This photomicrograph was taken after fracture. The sample was unpolished following the photomicrograph of Fig. 23. The slip lines are horizontal in the untwinned portion of the crystal and the boundaries of the twin are vertical. 250×.

ated with the primary slip system. This geometrical effect is apparently sufficient to account for the difference in behavior of irradiated and unirradiated samples.

The raising of the critical stress by irradiation reduced the strain required to produce twinning to such a degree that it was possible to obtain Laue back-reflection photograms of sufficient resolution to determine the orientation of both the twinned and untwinned portions of the crystal. It was possible by this technique to verify that the twinned region had the required orientation relative to the matrix material. In addition, it was possible as a result of the small strain and high step height of the slip lines to clearly view the change in direction of slip lines due to the twinning shear. This made it possible to determine the twinning shear by the measurement of the deflection of the slip lines induced by the twinning shear. Sample 416 was particularly suited for such a measurement, as the [112] twinning direction lay near to one of the crystal faces, making the deflection angle, observed in Fig. 4, a good approximation to a shear strain. The tangent of this angle measured 0.70 compared to the 0.707 which is required for twinning on the (111) plane in the [112] direction. It is

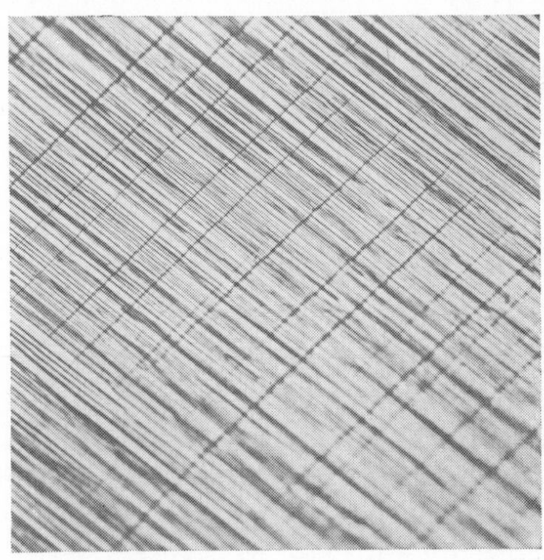

Fig. 26. Unidentified strain markings and slip lines in sample 416E. The unidentified markings are parallel to the twin boundaries. This photomicrograph was taken at the same point in the deformation process as Fig. 24, i.e., at the formation of the original nucleus. 250×.

also interesting to note that slip lines in the twin are straight, indicating a homogeneous shear strain.

It is of further interest that the initial twin lamellae formed in a region of the Lüders band which was undistinguishable from any other portion. Why the twin formed where it did rather than in some other location is not clear. The fact that this seems to be somewhat accidental is verified by the fact that in the four samples of the 416 series bombarded for 1.5×10^{20} nvt and deformed at 4.2°K, all of them twinned at a different strain and, in the case of one of them, the sample was completely filled with slip lines before the twin nuclei formed. In this latter case, the sample completely twinned prior to fracture.

In addition to the twin lamellae described, strain markings parallel to the lamellae were also observed after the initial twin lamellae formed in the Lüders band region. The markings are shown in Fig. 26. From their appearance, it does not seem that they are strain markings from discontinuous slip. It may be that they are very small twin lamellae, and these serve as nuclei during the subsequent twin growth.

4. CONCLUSIONS

1. The deformation of copper single crystals at 4.2°K proceeds by three different mechanisms. At low flow stresses, ordinary glide occurs; at intermediate flow stresses, a process called discontinuous slip occurs; and finally, at high flow stresses for certain sample orientations, twinning occurs.

2. The discontinuous slip process occurs as the result of an avalanche of slip lines. There are approximately 30 slip lines released for each discontinuity in the flow curve with each line producing a displacement of 2×10^4 A.

3. The discontinuous slip process has not been observed at 77.3°K or at higher temperatures. At 4.2°K it has been observed in samples of all crystal orientations.

4. It has been experimentally established that mechanical twinning occurs at 4.2°K at high flow stress when the tensile axis lies between the [111] and [113] direction on the dodecahedral plane. It is believed that significance is to be drawn from the fact that the [311] direction is the symmetry point between the [112] and [$2\bar{1}1$] directions. Twinning occurs only when the resolved stress in the [112] direction is greater than in the [$2\bar{1}1$]. (A twin forms by glide in the [112] direction.)

5. Twinning can occur at 77.3°K when the tensile orientation is near the [111] direction.

6. The twinning occurs by the formation of a twin nucleus which results in a decrease in the flow stress. This twin nucleus grows and completely fills the crystal. There is no evidence that slip is occurring in the twinned region until after the sample has been filled with twin at which point discontinous flow occurs.

7. The twinning plane is the (111) plane and the twinning direction is the [112] direction in copper.

8. There is no evidence that there is an initial shear stress for twinning. There is considerable variation in the twinning stress—in the (111) plane and [112] direction—for samples of different orientations.

9. Reactor irradiation will not affect the orientation dependence of twinning; it will, however, completely suppress the normal glide process at 4.2°K if the dose is heavy enough. In this case, deformation proceeds directly by discontinuous slip with the deformation occurring by a Lüders band process. In samples of the correct orientation, twin-

ning will occur in the Lüders band. After this band has been filled with twin, the sample fractures.

10. Fracture occurs because the flow stress exceeds the theoretical strength in some cases. In all cases, however, the fracture is abrupt at 4.2°K. At 77.3°K, normal shear fracture occurs unless a twin is formed in which case an abrupt fracture is observed.

11. The fact that twinning occurs in copper does not affect the validity of the dislocation process of twinning suggested by Cottrell and Bilby. The stress fields set up at these low temperatures greatly exceed those considered by this theoretical treatment.

REFERENCES

1. T. H. Blewitt, R. R. Coltman, and J. K. Redman, *Report of a Conference on Defects in Crystalline Solids,* Physical Society, London, p. 369 (1955).
2. A. H. Cottrell and B. A. Bilby, *Phil. Mag.,* **42,** 573 (1951).
3. T. H. Blewitt, *Phys. Rev.,* **91,** 1115 (1953).
4. F. Sherrill, M. Wittles, and T. Blewitt, *J. Appl. Phys.,* **28,** 526 (1957).
5. J. R. Mackenzie, Thesis, University of Bristol, Bristol (1949).
6. R. W. Cahn, *Nuovo Cimento, Suppl.,* **N.4** (1953).

ACKNOWLEDGMENTS

The authors are indebted to D. S. Billington for the encouragement and cooperation which he offered throughout the period of research. We are also appreciative to D. K. Holmes, T. S. Noggle, and C. E. Klabunde for the helpful suggestions made during frequent discussions, to F. A. Sherrill who grew the crystals, and to L. D. Roberts and J. B. Capehart who kindly supplied the liquid helium.

DISCUSSION

SEEGER gave his interpretation of the occurrence of discontinuous glide and its temperature dependence. He referred to evidence to be given in his presentation (pages 301–302) that in copper, at low temperature, there are pile-ups of 20 to 25 dislocations. This gives a stress at the head of the pile-up of the order of one-tenth or one-twentieth of the shear modulus, which is of the order of the theoretical shear strength. A spontaneous generation of dislocations may set in, giving rise to discontinuous glide. Discontinuous glide is not observed well above liquid-nitrogen temperature because the extended dislocations are squeezed together and glide by cross slip before these high stresses are reached. COTTRELL asked if these ideas raised difficulties for the theory of fracture from pile-ups which is used to explain fracture in higher as well as low temperature ranges. SEEGER did not think the pile-up theory of fracture could be used for higher temperature ranges in copper, unless the edge dislocations in polycrystalline material (which would be responsible for the fracture) are arranged very differently from the screw dislocations to which the cross slip argument refers.

Observations on Slip in Aluminum*

†T. S. NOGGLE
JAMES S. KOEHLER
University of Illinois
Urbana, Illinois

Some experiments done at the University of Illinois are described in this paper (see also ref. 1). The experiments were on 99.99% pure aluminum single crystals. The deformation was performed at helium temperature, at liquid-nitrogen temperature, and at room temperature. Figure 1 shows a plot of the resolved shear strain versus shear stress for the three different samples. One sees that at helium temperature the curve above 0.1 shear strain is approximately straight; at nitrogen temperature the curve begins to show stage III; and at room temperature the entire region seems to be in stage III of work hardening.

Figure 2 shows an electron micrograph of a slip band in aluminum at room temperature. The strain at this point is 10%. The large wedge in the figure is an etch pit, and the electron microscope picture was taken by the oxide replica method. At room temperature, 85% of the deformation occurs by means of slip bands. About 15% occurs in fine slip, but the fine slip is not observable on this figure. Figure 3 shows a sample at the same temperature with about 17.5% deformation. One sees that the slip band is wider in this case.

Figure 4 shows aluminum at liquid-nitrogen temperature. The shear

* Research partially supported by the Office of Naval Research.

† Now in Solid State Physics Division, Oak Ridge National Laboratory, Oak Ridge, Tenn.

strain is about 40%, and in this case nearly all of the slip is by means of fine slip. One sees here what might be termed a kind of fluctuation in the density of the fine slip. Slip lamellae were detected in which the total amount of slip was about 15 A.

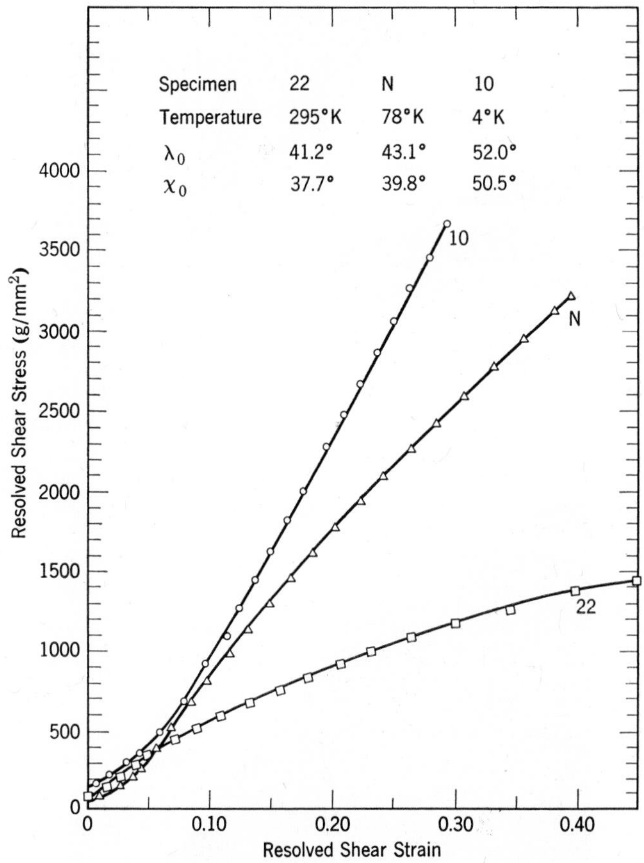

Fig. 1. Comparison of stress-strain behavior at various temperatures.

Figures 5, 6, and 7 show the structure of the surface at liquid-helium temperature. We note that all of the deformation is by means of fine slip.

In Fig. 8, we see a picture of an etch pit on a crystal which had been deformed at liquid-nitrogen temperature to a strain of 90%. One does not see any cross slip evidence here. This replica was unshadowed. The other replicas were shadowed with gold chromium. On the basis of these experiments, one would be tempted to say there was no cross

Fig. 2. Slip-band structure of specimen S deformed at room temperature to a shear strain of 10.3%. 20,000×.

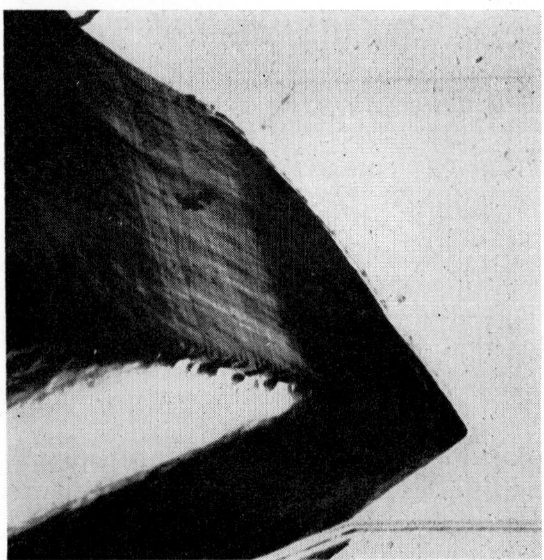

Fig. 3. Slip-band structure of specimen M deformed at room temperature to a shear strain of 17.5%. 20,000×.

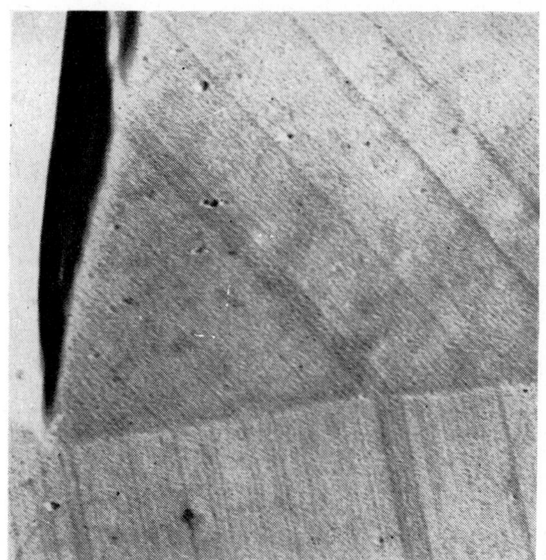

Fig. 4. Thin sheet specimen 3 ST, deformed at 78°K, $\gamma = 0.138$ (γ is the resolved shearing strain). 50,000×.

Fig. 5. Specimen PCI, deformed at 4°K, $\gamma = 0.191$. 20,000×.

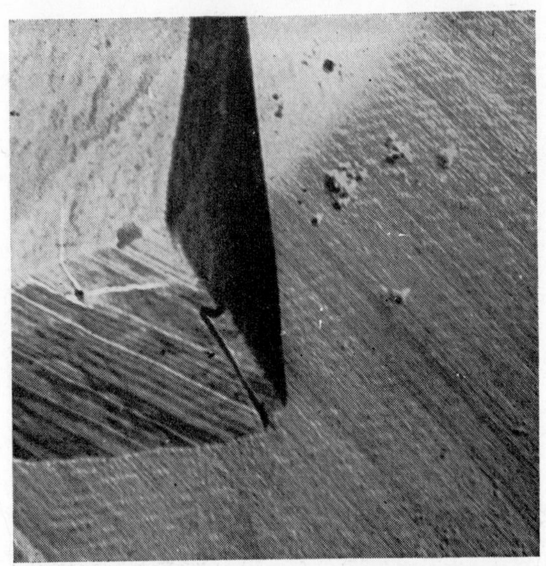

Fig. 6. Specimen EE, deformed at 4°K, $\gamma = 0.522$. 20,000×.

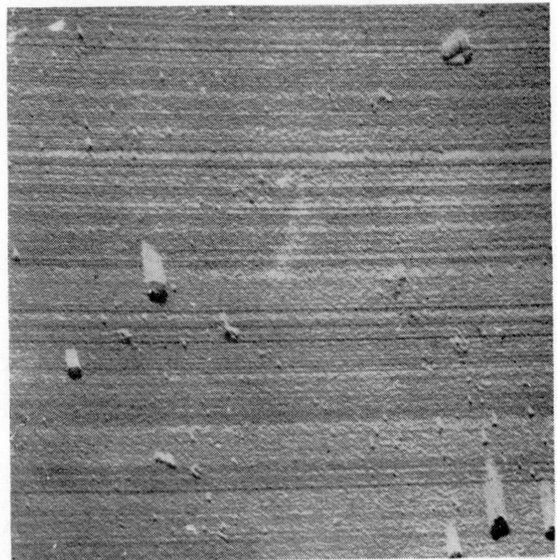

Fig. 7. Specimen EE, deformed at 4°K, $\gamma = 0.522$. 20,000×.

slip evident at liquid-nitrogen temperature even for extremely large amounts of shear.

Fig. 8. Specimen DD, deformed at 78°K, $\gamma = 0.878$, unshadowed. 20,000×.

REFERENCE

1. T. S. Noggle and J. S. Koehler, *J. Appl. Phys.*, **28**, 53 (1957).

DISCUSSION

MOTT asked if the fine slip, its spacing, step height, etc., depended on the initial conditions of the specimen. For example, do these things depend on the microstructure in the metal? Would they be the same for a mildly polygonized specimen, or are they inherent properties of the material? KOEHLER answered that he did not know in detail how the slip spacing and step height depended upon the initial conditions of the experiment, but that some of the details of the stress-strain curve and slip bands did seem to depend upon the thickness of the material. For instance, some of the specimens were only 20 mils thick and showed a somewhat different structure from specimens ⅜ in. in cross section.

BLEWITT said that superficially there seemed to be a difference between Noggle's results and those reported by Seeger and co-workers.* He asked if impurities in the material had anything to do with the presence of cross slip because Seeger's sample differed from Koehler's in the amount of impurity present. Seeger's experiments were done on copper, but BLEWITT said that there should be a greater tendency to cross-slip in aluminum than in copper. KOEHLER answered that no experiments had been done on impure specimens, so that he was unable to answer the question.

SEEGER remarked that the experimental results reported by Koehler appeared to be in good agreement with both the theory and the experiments presented in Seeger's paper (pages 243–328 of this volume). In the latter work, in order to see the cross slip in stage III, the specimens had to be polished to erase all of the slip markings of stage II. SEEGER said that the experiment at liquid-helium temperature was in good accord with the theory: at the stresses used by Noggle one would not expect to obtain stage III at helium temperature and would thus not obtain slip bands. As shown by the theory, in particular by eqs. 36 and 36(b) of Seeger's paper (page 302), the difference between a low stacking fault energy metal like copper and a high stacking fault energy metal like aluminum becomes rather small at very low temperatures, contrary to the situation at room temperature.

HONEYCOMBE remarked that there seemed to be several variables being juggled at once. For instance, one would not really compare copper with aluminum at room temperature. The temperature comparison is not fair, and the purity may be different. He pointed out that the purity of a metal could have considerable effect on its slip structure. HONEYCOMBE remarked that one should see little difference between slip in metal specimens of the same purity but with different substructures and suggested that the sensitivity of the method was insufficient to show up any differences due to substructure. MOTT said that the number of slip lines and hence the step height of a slip band for a given strain ought to depend on the number of sources, and that the number of sources should be dependent on the state of the material with which one begins. HONEYCOMBE said that there was a great deal of fine slip at the start of the deformation so that the subsequent evidence was obscured. He suggested that the only way one could find evidence of this sort would be to do an experiment in which the original fine slip was etched off. Both KOEHLER and MOTT suggested that even the fine slip should be a function of the source density.

* J. Diehl, S. Mader, and A. Seeger, *Z. Metallkunde,* **46,** 650 (1955).

Surface Sources and Plastic Flow in KCl Crystals*

† TAIRA SUZUKI

Physics Department
University of Illinois
Urbana, Illinois

1. INTRODUCTION

During the study of plastic deformation in alkali-halide crystals, the author has met with many facts which suggest the great importance of surface sources to the onset of plastic flow in the crystals. In this paper, experimental work specially performed to test this hypothesis will be described.

Many experiments concerning the influence of surface effects on plastic flow of crystals are related to thin films of other substances, e.g., oxide or hydroxide, formed on the surfaces of the crystals surrounded by various inorganic solutions. These effects might be called the Rhebinder effects after the name of the first investigator.[1] Such films are surely important practically, since any metal crystal will be covered by some such a film. There also exists another remarkable effect concerning the important role of the surface in plastic flow of crystals. This was found originally in ionic crystals like rock salt by Joffé.[2] The Joffé effects have been understood as the effects due to the dissolution of surface layers of crystals by the surrounding sol-

* This work was partially supported by the Office of Naval Research.

† On leave from the Research Institute for Iron, Steel, and Other Metals, Tohoku University, Sendai, Japan.

vents, resulting in an improvement of plasticity. Although no satisfactory explanation has been given as yet, the effects are not explicable only in terms of surface films formed or removed by inorganic reagents as in the former case. It was first theoretically suggested by Hollomon [3] and Fisher [4] that surface sources for slip should be very important during the initiation of plastic flow. The stress necessary for the operation of a surface source is about one-half of the stress required to operate an inner source of the same length. This conclusion can be drawn simply from the Frank-Read mechanism for slip.[5]

The present work aims first to check the above point, and then to show that the Joffé effects will relate to the operation of surface sources through certain fundamental processes associated with plastic flow of crystals. The specimen crystals to be used have two advantages: first, we can provide the crystals after anneal with surfaces practically free from films of other substances, and second, we can observe directly stress patterns inside the crystals corresponding with the formation of slip bands. These conditions cannot be found in metal crystals.

2. EXPERIMENTAL PROCEDURE

Specimen

Crystals of KCl were obtained from the Harshaw Chemical Co. From these original blocks of the crystal, specimen crystals of cubic form (about $0.6 \times 0.6 \times 1.5$ cm^3) were cleaved and then annealed at 600°C for 10 hr in air except for special cases described later. They were slowly cooled to room temperature to avoid a plastic deformation by thermal stress and also to avoid retaining an excess amount of point defects.

Polishing

Even cleavage surfaces carefully obtained are not usually flat enough for the compression tests used here. Hence, the surfaces were polished carefully before anneal with a wet silk cloth on a flat plate of Lucite.

Apparatus

The specimen crystals were compressed at room temperature between two quartz plates mounted on steel compression stages, which are guided by two parallel columns of steel. The external stress to be applied was measured by reading the amount of contraction of a steel spring with known constant by use of a dial gauge. The compression stresses are 264 gr for one spring and 48.1 gr for the other per unit scale of the dial gauge (1×10^{-3} in.). These are 7.34 and 1.34 g/mm^2, respectively, for a specimen of the size mentioned. The stress was applied stepwise by hand by advancing a screw of very small pitch. A unit step of loading normally corresponds with the above values. The strain was determined by use of a dial gauge measuring to 10^{-5} in. To eliminate the strain in the quartz plates and the upper, steel stage, which is rigidly fixed, we used another dial gauge of the same accuracy to measure compression in these parts. Final reading will thus give a strain equal to 0.0017% for the specimen mentioned above.

The birefringence of deformed crystals was observed using a Cooke polarizing microscope. Birefringence bands could be observed only by use of polarized light parallel to the glide planes concerned.

3. RESULTS

Microscopic Observations

The microscopic observations concerning the initiation of slip in the crystals will be described here. When the crystals are compressed in the direction parallel to a cubic axis, the four glide systems, $\{[\bar{1}01]/(101)\}$, are equally oriented to the applied stress. Therefore, geometrically considered, we cannot expect single glide to occur. In the initial stage of deformation up to 1 to 2% strain, however, the crystals occasionally deform, apparently by the action of a single glide system. The general form of stress-strain curves is quite similar to that of face-centered cubic metal crystals as already pointed out by Pratt.[6] The crystals deformed within this initial stage were carefully polished so as to allow examination through the parallel specimen surfaces normal to the glide direction (Fig. 1). The birefringence bands were then observed by using polarized light normal to the above surfaces, i.e., the $(\bar{1}01)$ faces. As shown in Fig. 2, these bands are seen only in the regions near the free surfaces (cube faces), and very few, weak bands exist below the surface regions. The strain in this case was 0.28%. At this stage, the number of bands increases with applied stress, as well as the depth of the regions. At a strain of 0.3 to 0.4%,

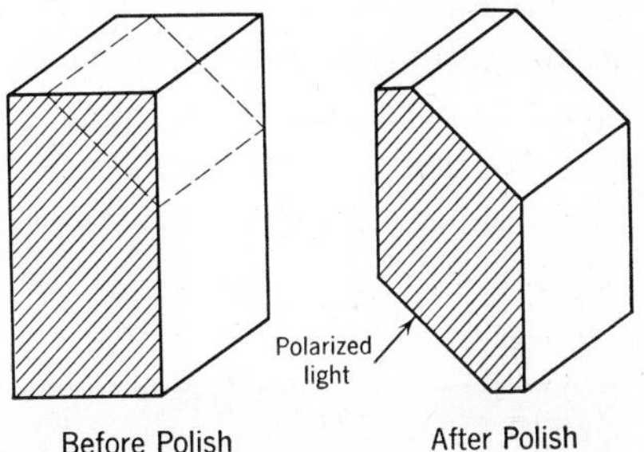

Fig. 1. The way of polishing crystal surfaces to observe birefringences by use of polarized light parallel to the slip direction concerned.

new bands begin to appear in the central regions of the crystals. This is illustrated in Fig. 3. Thereafter, they will cover all the regions throughout the crystal. On the other hand, when crystals are deformed to the end of the initial stage, strong birefringence bands due to the second slip begin to be observed. In almost all cases, the latter system

Fig. 2. Birefringence bands observed by use of polarized light parallel to the slip direction. The bands are concentrated in surface layers. The strain of the crystal was 0.28%. The arrows indicate the free surfaces. 13×.

is perpendicular to the first one, i.e., their Burgers vectors are normal to each other.

It is quite reasonable to suppose that dislocations moving on the second slip system encounter barriers opposing the propagation in the direction normal to its Burgers vector, since it must cut through the first slip bands. One has therefore a great opportunity to investigate the onset of plastic flow by careful observations of the second bands.

Fig. 3. Birefringence bands in the central parts of a crystal which begin to be observed at a strain of about 0.4%. 14×.

Figure 4 shows good examples of this. Figure 4*a* was observed by focusing just on a free surface, and Fig. 4*b* by focusing at about 250 μ below the same position on that surface. We can see the second bands only in the regions just below the surface. This will be shown more clearly by an observation similar to that of Fig. 2. In this case, however, the crystal was polished to reveal the surfaces parallel to the glide plane of the first slip. Hence, the birefringence bands thus shown in Fig. 4*c* correspond with the second bands, which are concentrated below the surface. The observations lead us to conclude that slip initiates from a free surface. When a deformation goes into the second stage, these bands also go through the crystal.

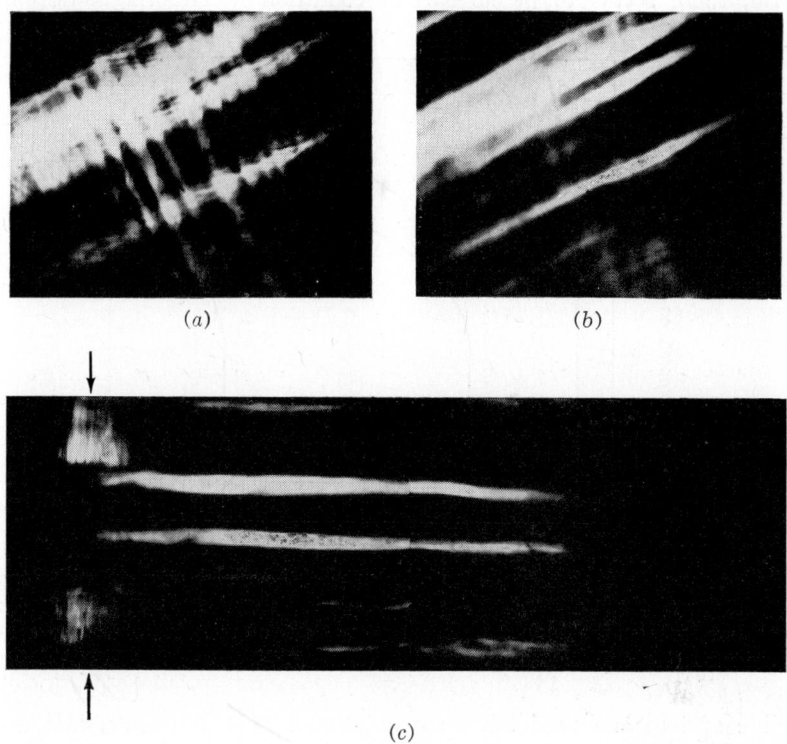

Fig. 4. Birefringence bands corresponding to double slip: focused just on the surface, (*a*); 250 μ below the same position on the surface, (*b*); the birefringence due to the minor slip in (*a*) observed by use of polarized light parallel to the corresponding slip direction and normal to the slip plane of the major one, (*c*). The strain was 0.68% in (*a*) and (*b*), and 0.78% in (*c*) on the same crystal. 53×.

The birefringence bands due to the second slip are normally so weak and so restricted in narrow surface layers at the beginning of deformation that they are hardly observed. The asymmetry in the pattern of the main bands in Fig. 2, however, is actually found to be caused by a small amount of the second slip just mentioned, which is observed only in the cube face on the corresponding side of the photograph.

It is important in connection with the above conclusion concerning the onset of plastic flow to note the following facts: (1) It is sometimes observed in the early stages of deformation that the birefringence bands appearing on opposite faces of a crystal are due to glide on two different slip systems. Double slip occurs in the above cases from the beginning of deformation. This fact may suggest that, in general, there seems to be no special condition determining how one

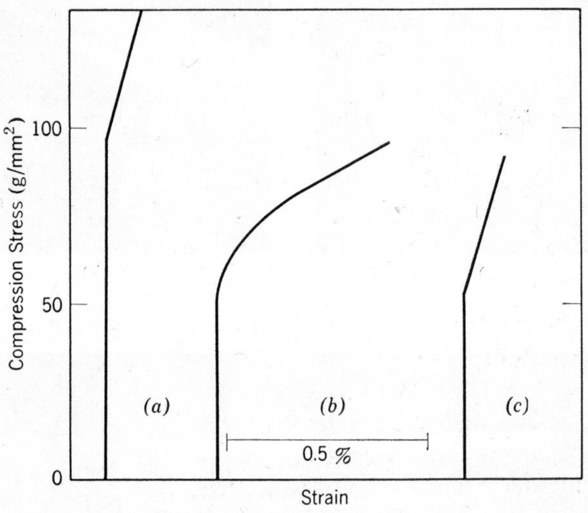

Fig. 5. Stress-strain curves of crystals annealed in a high vacuum without a special precaution to avoid the excess vaporization of one constituent (*a*); polished through the surface layers of a few tens of microns, which are contaminated (*b*); only one surface polished (*c*).

glide system can predominate over others. (2) When crystals are annealed in a high vacuum at 600°C for several hours and then cooled slowly, the surface of the crystals becomes a little opaque, which may be due to the excess vaporization of metallic ions. Such crystals show a critical shear stress twice as large as the normal value, as illustrated in Fig. 5*a*. These surface layers are normally very thin, of a few tens of microns, and easily polished away by the method mentioned earlier. The stress-strain curve after polishing the surface layers is shown in Fig. 5*b*, which is quite normal. If we polish only one surface, however, the critical shear stress is normal, although the hardening rate is still high, as seen in Fig. 5*c*. It is noticeable that birefringence bands in this case can be seen only in the narrow regions below the polished surface, not below the unpolished surfaces. From the present results, the effective sources for the onset of plastic flow can be supposed to be not only surface sources but in particular only those whose Burgers vectors lie in that cube face. The dislocation loops must elongate along their slip directions parallel to the surface.

Work Hardening and Internal Stress of Crystals

Based upon the above results we will study the nature of work hardening in the crystals. After the deformation of crystals,* when the yield stress increased from σ_0 to σ_1, the surfaces were polished, and birefringence bands were observed as illustrated in Fig. 6. Let us take the depth of the second polish as Δd, and the yield stress for the following compression in the same direction as the first one as σ_2. $(\sigma_2 - \sigma_0)/(\sigma_1 - \sigma_0)$ is plotted against Δd in Fig. 7. It drops very rapidly to a constant value of about 0.46 at $\Delta d \approx 50\ \mu$. It should be emphasized that this value of Δd is independent of strain as seen in Fig. 7. Since the internal stress at active slip sources will be written as $\sigma_i = \sigma_2 - \sigma_0$, σ_i is thus found to be only one-half of $(\sigma_1 - \sigma_0)$, hardening stress, from Fig. 7, in the regions below the surface layers of about 50 μ in thickness; an important hardening occurs in these surface layers. It will not be unreasonable to suppose that polishing the surfaces of deformed crystals can reveal the new sources, becoming surface sources, with a yield stress equal to $\sigma_0 + \sigma_i$. This is because the dislocations pinned at both ends of various lengths are supposed to be distributed statistically at random throughout the crystal. This will be checked by removing the surface layers after the second deformation to see if $(\sigma_2 - \sigma_0)$ again falls down.

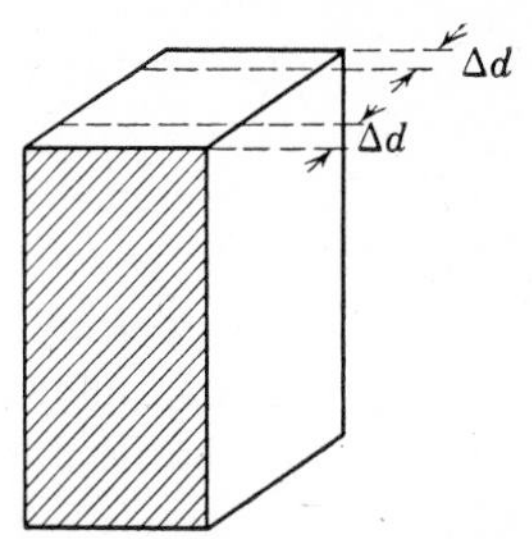

Fig. 6. Polishing the surface layers of Δd in thickness, where birefringence bands are observed. The following compression is made in the same direction as before.

For such successive deformations, which were interrupted by the surface polish before each deformation, the initial yield stress, the final stress, the strain, and the amount of removal of the surface layers in thickness before the corresponding deformation are shown in Table 1. We should consider here the difference in each mechanical state attained. For instance, the final stress in the second deformation in Table 1 is 126.5 g/mm^2, which is smaller than the one for the first

* The surfaces of crystals were polished before the deformation for comparison with the following tests.

TABLE 1

	Initial Stress (g/mm^2)	Final Stress (g/mm^2)	Strain (%)	Δd (in.)
1	67	127.9	0.361	
2	108	126.5	0.028	0.0058
3	116	147.2	0.046	0.010
4	128	...	...	0.017

deformation, but the crystal deformed plastically during this second loading through a strain of 0.028%. To get a relation corresponding to the one shown in Fig. 7, therefore, it may be reasonable to take σ_0' in place of σ_0 in the expression $(\sigma_2 - \sigma_0)/(\sigma_1 - \sigma_0)$, where σ_0' is the initial yield stress for the deformation just before the removal of the surface layers concerned. Thus we will put $\sigma_0' = 108$ for $\Delta d = 0.010$, and $\sigma_0' = 116$ for $\Delta d = 0.017$. This gives 0.43 and 0.46, respectively, for the corresponding ratio. These values almost coincide with the value previously mentioned. Therefore, we are able to conclude that an important hardening in the surface layers of about 50 μ in thickness, which is independent of strain, occurs in each case. Taking into account the conclusion obtained by the microscopic observations, this supports the above-mentioned idea that polishing the surfaces of deformed crystals can reveal new surface sources in place of the sources already operated and hardened. The thickness of the above layers will be shown later to be of the order of the effective length of surface sources.

Effects of Surface Polish on Critical Shear Stress

In general, the dislocations ending at a free surface would be expected to be longer after anneal than those forming the double-ended Frank-Read sources inside a crystal. This is because other dislocations near the surface are supposed to escape from the crystal with the aid of the image force [7] and the interaction between them. Hence, surface-polishing before deformation will reveal the surface sources to be of shorter length than those in unpolished crystals. The following experiments were performed to check this. Each point in Fig. 8 is the mean taken from 20 to 30 crystals, which were cleaved from a single block of KCl crystal. In other words, Fig. 8 shows the results obtained from ten different blocks of the crystal. One point is obtained from the specimen crystals sealed in vacuum (2×10^{-6} mm Hg) with a certain amount of powdered crystals to avoid a deficiency of one constituent by vaporization during anneal, which happened in the case shown in Fig. 5. No special behavior of such crystals could be found

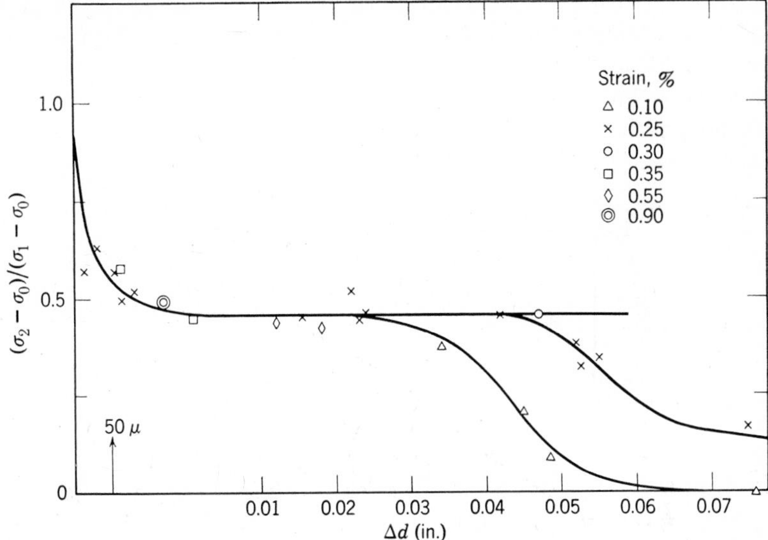

Fig. 7. $(\sigma_2 - \sigma_0)/(\sigma_1 - \sigma_0)$ plotted against Δd. σ_1 is the maximum stress for the initial deformation, and σ_2 the yield stress for the following deformation after polishing off surface layers of Δd in thickness. The strains listed on the figure correspond to σ_1 for the initial deformation.

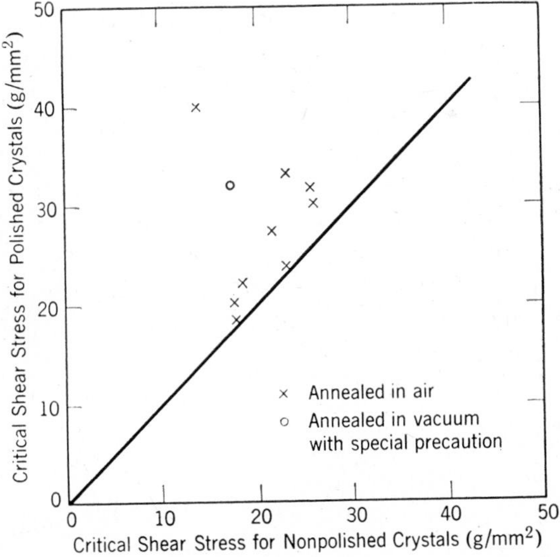

Fig. 8. Effects of surface polish on the critical shear stress of crystals. Each point corresponds to the mean of the results on 20 to 30 crystals obtained from a single block of the crystal.

as compared with the crystals annealed in air. The atmosphere during anneal, accordingly, does not seem to give an important effect on the onset of plastic flow. As illustrated in this figure, polished crystals always show higher critical shear stresses and smaller hardening rates than nonpolished crystals. Figure 9 gives some examples of stress-strain curves.

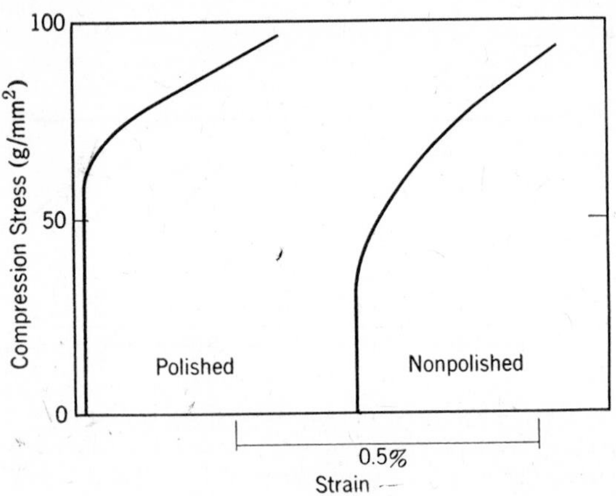

Fig. 9. Stress-strain curves of polished and nonpolished crystals after the same heat treatment.

We may have to consider the mechanical effects of polishing, although we could not find any trace of deformation under the polarizing microscope. This will be described later.

When the critical shear stress of polished crystals is below about 30 g/mm^2, the discrepancy between the critical shear stress of polished crystals and that of nonpolished crystals becomes small. There is another point to be noticed, which is the diversity of the points in Fig. 8 in spite of the same heat treatment. These two facts will be of interest from the point of the influence of annealing on the distribution of dislocations. Since the critical shear stress is inversely proportional to the effective length of the slip source,[5] the length of the source increases as the critical shear stress of a crystal decreases. Accordingly, we may be able to take the separation distance between dislocations corresponding to $\sigma_0 = 30$ g/mm^2 as somewhat critical for the dislocations near the surface to escape from the crystals within practical annealing periods such as are used here. The second fact suggests that the dislocation networks once built in crystals grown from the melt are fairly stable.[8]

Writing the effective length of surface sources as $2l_0$, the critical shear stress σ_0 will be equal to $Gb/2l_0$. Taking the values as $\sigma_0 = 30$ g/mm^2 $= 2.9 \times 10^6$ dynes/cm^2, and $G = 4 \times 10^{11}$ dynes/cm^2, we will get $2l_0/b = 1.38 \times 10^5$, where b is the Burgers vector. Thus, it follows that $2l_0 \approx 50\ \mu$, which is roughly the depth of the surface effects previously described.

4. DISCUSSION

General

Although polishing the surfaces of virgin crystals increases the critical shear stress, the surface polish of deformed crystals has been found to release a part, at least one-half, of the work hardening and to increase the plasticity of the crystals. This is an explanation of the Joffé effects. In other words, the above polishing gives an effect similar to the dissolution by solvents of the hardened surface layers of crystals.

The hardening of surface layers will be caused by the same mechanism which makes possible the observations of the birefringence concentrated just below the free surface. The birefringence near the surface only shows that many dislocations get stuck near the surface. Some dislocations must traverse the center to give rise to plastic strain there. It can be mentioned in the ranges of small deformation, however, that many dislocations initialed from surface sources would be stopped after traveling for a rather short distance, depending upon the applied stress and the density of dislocations of different glide systems to be crossed through. The latter are supposed to be mostly the dislocations produced at other surface sources. This will cause a source hardening. This is particularly apt to happen in the case of ionic crystals of NaCl type, since there are always at least two equivalent glide systems for an external stress in any direction. With regard to this, it may be concluded that metal crystals would show generally little Joffé effects as compared with the above crystals. The importance of surface sources to the onset of plastic flow may be the same, however.

Birefringence Bands

It is important to note that birefringence bands could be observed by the polarized light parallel to a glide direction. This fact cannot be explained by a uniform distribution of edge dislocations of one sign such as Nye [9] studied in AgCl crystals. It will be necessary to assume in the present case the presence of screw dislocations as well as edge dislocations lying in a glide plane to give the birefringence. In connection with this fact, it should be remarked that, in general, the bands have tapered ends, resulting in a shape of an oblate spheroid. Such an intensity distribution of the birefringence may be given by the group of the dislocations of concentric ellipses.

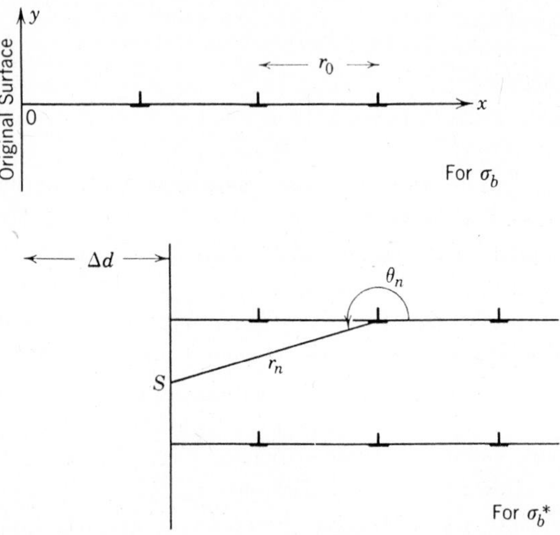

Fig. 10. A model of the hardening of surface layers. The dislocations produced at surface sources are arranged parallel to the z-axis along the (x, z) planes. Δd is an amount of removal of surface layers.

Hardening of Surface Layers and Internal Stress in Deformed Crystals

In the following, we will discuss approximately how the relation, $(\sigma_2 - \sigma_0)/(\sigma_1 - \sigma_0) \simeq 0.5$, will be explained on the basis of an idea already mentioned of a sort of exhaustion of surface sources and of the operation of new surface sources after the removal of the surface layers. Suppose there is a simple arrangement of dislocations produced at the surface sources. For the sake of simplicity, we assume the dislocations to be of pure edge type, of which axes are parallel to the z-axis, and arranged with a spacing equal to r_0 in the parallel glide planes, (x, z), where $r_0 \gg b$. Take the origin of the co-ordinates on the surface as illustrated in Fig. 10. The hardening stress, σ_b, for a surface source already operated will be given in taking account of only the influence due to the single row of n dislocations produced at the source concerned as

$$\sigma_b = -\frac{2Ab}{r_0} \sum_{n=1}^{n} \frac{1}{n} \tag{1}$$

where
$$A = \frac{G}{2\pi(1 - \nu)}$$

G is the shear modulus, and ν Poisson's ratio. The numerical factor 2 in eq. 1 is due to the images of the above dislocations. By use of polar co-ordinates, the vector $\mathbf{r}_n$ from the nth dislocation to a point on the surface will be designated as (r_n, θ_n), where θ_n is the angle between $\mathbf{r}_n$ and the positive direction of the x-axis. Then, the stress at this point on the surface will be given by

$$\sigma_b = \sum_{n=1}^{n} \frac{2Ab}{nr_0} \cos \theta_n \cos 2\theta_n \cos (\theta_n - \pi) \tag{2}$$

The stress necessary for the operation of new surface sources, which appear after the removal of the surface layers of Δd in thickness, where $\Delta d \ll nr_0$, is supposed to be given by $\sigma = \sigma_0 + \sigma_b{}^*$. $\sigma_b{}^*$ will be given, using eq. 2, as follows:

$$\sigma_b{}^* = -4\frac{Ab}{r_0} \sum_{n=1}^{n} \frac{\cos^2 \theta_n \cos 2\theta_n}{n} \tag{3}$$

taking account of the nearest neighboring rows of the dislocations. If we take the average of eq. 3 with respect to the angle θ, it follows that

$$\begin{aligned} \langle \sigma_b{}^* \rangle &= -4\frac{Ab}{r_0} \sum_{n=1}^{n} \frac{\langle \cos^2 \theta_n \cos 2\theta_n \rangle}{n} \\ &\simeq -\frac{Ab}{r_0} \sum_{n=1}^{n} \frac{1}{n} \end{aligned} \tag{4}$$

From eqs. 1 and 4, it follows that

$$\begin{aligned} \sigma &= \sigma_0 + \sigma_b{}^* \\ &\cong \sigma_0 + \tfrac{1}{2}\sigma_b \end{aligned}$$

Since σ_b is taken as $(\sigma_1 - \sigma_0)$ and σ as σ_2 by use of the preceding notations,

$$\sigma_2 - \sigma_0 = \tfrac{1}{2}(\sigma_1 - \sigma_0) \tag{5}$$

Plastic Behaviors of Polished and Nonpolished Crystals

The fact that polished crystals show smaller hardening rate than nonpolished crystals (Fig. 9) may be interpreted as follows. As stated before, two kinds of possible sources of different glide systems will play an important role on the onset of plastic flow in a pair of parallel free surfaces. The rearrangements of dislocations resulting in a stable network inside a crystal will occur during anneal much more quickly than will the increase of the length of dislocations near the surface. The reason is that the latter process should depend on the geometry of the dislocation arrangements inside the crystal. As a result, any fluctuation in the above arrangements near the surface will appear as a stronger one in the length of surface sources. We can thus expect that the fluctuation of the length of surface sources in nonpolished crystals will be greater than that in polished crystals. As a matter of fact, we observe that multiple slip occurs from the very beginning of deformation on nonpolished crystals much more frequently than on polished crystals.

Finally, we should note one important thing. It is about the mechanical effects of the polishing, if any. Although we believe no serious effect on the results to be obtained is produced by the present procedure of polishing, it is well to compare the present results with others. Dommerich [10] and Sperling [11] studied the effects of water on the critical shear stress of rock-salt crystals. Dommerich removed the crystals from the water just before deformation. Sperling, however, kept the crystals immersed continuously in water during tests. In both cases, no mechanical effects were associated with the removal of surface layers. They concluded that the critical shear stress was the same within experimental error in a wet condition as in a dry condition. On careful examination of their data, however, it seems to be certain that wet crystals have higher critical shear stress than dry crystals; e.g., see Tables 5 and 10 of Sperling, and also Table 2 of Dommerich. As a result, any removal of fresh surface layers after anneal, irrespective of the procedure, will cause a certain increase in critical shear stress of crystals insofar as a clean surface is obtained.

REFERENCES

1. A. H. Cottrell, *Dislocations and Plastic Flow in Crystals,* Oxford University Press, Oxford, p. 55 (1953).
2. E. Schmid and W. Boas, *Kristallplastizität,* Julius Springer, Berlin, p. 271 (1935).
3. J. H. Hollomon, *Report of 9th Solvay Conference,* Stoops, Brussels, p. 576 (1952).
4. J. C. Fisher, see A. H. Cottrell, *op. cit.,* p. 55.
5. F. C. Frank and W. T. Read, *Phys. Rev.,* **72,** 722 (1950).
6. P. L. Pratt, *Acta Met.,* **1,** 103 (1953).
7. J. S. Koehler, *Phys. Rev.,* **60,** 397 (1941).
8. T. Suzuki and T. Imura, *Report of a Conference on Defects in Crystalline Solids,* Physical Society, London, p. 347 (1955).

9. J. F. Nye, *Proc. Roy. Soc.* (*London*), *A,* **198,** 190 (1949); **200,** 47 (1949).
10. K. H. Dommerich, *Z. Physik,* **80,** 242 (1933).
11. G. F. Sperling, *Z. Physik,* **76,** 476 (1932). See also Schmid and Boas, *op. cit.,* p. 271.

ACKNOWLEDGMENTS

This work has been supervised by Professors F. Seitz and J. S. Koehler of the Department of Physics, University of Illinois. It is a great pleasure to thank them for their continued interest and discussions. The author is also indebted to M. Doyama for his kind help.

DISCUSSION

COTTRELL reported that some work done by Adams and Cottrell in Birmingham seemed to lead to the same conclusion, i.e., that surface sources are important in the onset of plastic flow. An experiment was done on copper single crystals which were known from previous work not to show yield points or strain aging of the impurity type. A very small amount of zinc was diffused into some samples. The diffusion penetrated the surface to a depth of the order of 50 μ, and the concentration at the surface was about 1% zinc. The crystals then showed a weak yield point and strain aging which were assumed to be due to the operation of surface sources which were weakly locked by the zinc atoms. When the zincified surface was polished off, the metal became softer and the yield point and strain-aging behavior were no longer to be seen. Alternatively, when the zinc content in the surface was raised to 8%, then the observed behavior was that the crystal became harder (about a factor of two), but it no longer showed a yield point or strain aging after light deformation. The interpretation was that the surface sources became very strongly locked and slip thus preferred to begin on the interior sources at approximately double the critical stress of the untreated copper crystals.

COTTRELL commented on Suzuki's observation of two sets of glide bands which penetrated from the surface. COTTRELL suggested that this experiment was an ideal example of the type of situation he had discussed (in Part VI of this volume), where two sets of screw dislocations approaching each other try to intersect. The intersection is of the type that would produce interstitial jogs. One would expect that the dislocations would provide very severe obstacles to one another and that one set of dislocations might push the other back out of the crystal. COTTRELL asked if Suzuki had ever observed one set of dislocation lines eliminating the other in this way. SUZUKI replied that he had seen some cases where the birefringence occurred on both sides of the crystal, and where, after continued deformation, one of the birefringence patterns disappeared.

LEIBFRIED said that Cottrell had done an experiment in which only the surface sources were locked. He asked if one could get any idea about the contribution of the surface to the interior by also doing the reverse experiment and locking the interior sources. COTTRELL replied that such an experiment had been done—a preliminary experiment in which zinc had been homogeneously diffused throughout the material. The critical yield stress of this sample turned out to be 20% to 30% greater than that of the natural copper.

LÜCKE asked if Cottrell had any idea why the sources of the deformation should work more easily when the sources were near the surface. He asked if it is only due to the Fisher effect. COTTRELL replied that the network was a bit more free at the surface; that annealing produces larger sized networks there. He suggested that not only was there an apparent lengthening due to the Fisher effect but also there was a real physical lengthening because the network size became coarser near the surface. LÜCKE asked if there was any difference of opinion about the cause of the yield point. Did people agree that it was due to the production of loops from a Frank-Read source, or was the yield point due to the cutting of dislocations through a forest, as suggested by Seeger? SEEGER replied that either point of view would lead to the same result in this case. One could interpret Cottrell's suggestion to be that the dislocation density is lower at the surface, hence τ_g is less there. SEEGER indicated that if it is true that dislocation densities are lower at the surface, then it might account for a discrepancy which he felt exists between the observations of dislocations by the etch-pit technique and calculations of the dislocation density from the flow stress data.

KOEHLER commented that the strains which were obtained were such that the interior of the crystal must have suffered considerable plastic deformation, and yet no birefringence was ever observed there. He suggested that it probably meant that dislocations traversed the center of the crystal but were never trapped there. LOMER said that the birefringence technique did not necessarily show everything that went on in the crystal. He pointed out that the only stress component which produces birefringence and which can change discontinuously at the slip band is that due to the compressive stresses parallel to the slip planes. All one can see is the excess number of edge dislocations of a particular sign; and the fact that the birefringence is high at the surfaces of the crystal and zero in the middle may not actually yield any indication of the distribution of slip. It may be that there is an unbalance between the two different types of edge dislocation only at the surfaces. Hence, it would be rather risky to draw conclusions from the intensity of birefringence about the over-all distribution of dislocations within the crystal. In addition, there was the point that perhaps the dislocations were present on close planes but could not be resolved by the method used. SUZUKI replied that he had performed his observations on the surface normal to the Burgers vector. Suppose edge dislocations of one sign were in excess and uniformly distributed and gave rise to a uniform lattice bending in fairly large volume. Then it would be very hard to observe discrete birefringence bands parallel to the glide plane. On the other hand, the experiments showed that such bands were very clearly observed.

EGLI inquired about what solvents were used in the final stage of the polishing. He suggested that if films were left behind, the solvent could make a considerable difference in the energy of the surface. SUZUKI replied that he had only used water, but that he had also looked at this problem. There was evidence that surface films, if present, did not seriously affect the properties which were studied. SUZUKI said that he would like to take issue with some old experiments done on the Joffé effect. In the text by Schmid and Boas,* it is stated that there is no increase of critical shear stress when a dry crystal has been wet. SUZUKI has found upon careful examination that in the wet condition the critical shear stress is always higher than for completely dry crystals. He thinks, however, that this is not caused by surface films, but by the existence of longer surface sources in crystals as annealed than those in wet or polished crystals.

* E. Schmid and W. Boas, *Plasticity of Crystals,* F. A. Hughes & Co., London, p. 258 (1950).

Experimental Indications of Surface Sources

B. CHALMERS

R. S. DAVIS

Harvard University
Cambridge, Massachusetts

We wish to describe two recent experiments. In the first, aluminum crystals of rectangular cross section are so oriented that one slip system is favored. The experiment is to stretch such a crystal to a point within the easy glide range, about 0.5%, anneal it, and then examine it by the Schultz technique. After stretching, the Schultz picture, which is essentially a high-resolution Laue spot, is rectangular. After annealing, it is still rectangular, but is broken up into parallel bands which are separated from each other. This is interpreted as evidence of the formation of arrays of edge dislocations, all of the same sign in the region of the specimen from which the Schultz picture is derived. The sign of the dislocations is such that their motion is away from the surface during the plastic deformation in tension. This observation supports the proposal that the dislocations that move during the early stages of plastic deformation of single crystals originate at Frank-Read sources of which one end is free to move on the surface of the crystal.

The second experiment [1] relates to the corresponding behavior in the vicinity of a crystal boundary. The experimental sample is a bicrystal of rectangular section with a large-angle boundary in the center. If the sample is deformed in tension, each crystal deforms on its primary slip system. These slip systems do not coincide for the orientation relationships that we have used. In order that the two crystals may deform equally at the boundary, it is necessary for each crystal to deform on at least one additional system. The second system is not necessarily the system with the second highest externally applied shear stress on it; it is the system that has the greatest component of the shear stress that is developed at the boundary by the "pile-up" of dislocations at the boundary from the primary system in the other crystal. Microscopic examination shows that the second slip system is observable close to the boundary, but frequently not elsewhere. It is, therefore, concluded that the second system originates in the region very close indeed to the boundary, where the transmitted shear stress due to the piling up of dislocations is very large.

It follows that surface sources of a different kind may be important in bicrystal, and therefore, in polycrystalline specimens in which most of the crystals do not have any free surface.

REFERENCE

1. J. D. Livingston and B. Chalmers, *Acta Met.*, **5**, 322 (1957).

DISCUSSION

SHOCKLEY referred to some experiments which were done by Heidenreich and which were discussed at the 1947 Bristol Conference. Heidenreich observed that sudden loading on aluminum single crystals produced something rather different than nice slip bands. It was proposed that this was a surface effect due to the starting of a lot of slip systems at once by a very high load which was not kept on very long. SHOCKLEY suggested that actual measurement of the velocity of motion of a dislocation may clarify this point.

READ called attention to one clear-cut experiment in which the sources were definitely not all at the surface, namely Vogel's experiments * on bending germanium and counting the etch pits. The number of etch pits after deformation was considerably in excess of the number one would calculate from bending, which means that both signs of dislocations were generated, those that produced the

* F. L. Vogel, Jr., *Trans. AIME,* **8,** 946 (1956).

bending and those that would tend to produce bending in the other way. The unwanted dislocations could only have come from an internal source. If all the dislocations had been formed at the surface, the unwanted ones would have tended to go out and not in.

GILMAN pointed out that in all experiments of this sort one has to be very careful about how the surface is prepared. One would expect a relatively large dislocation density near the surface when the surface is prepared by cleavage of a relatively soft crystal or by solidification in a hard mold, or even in so-called soft molds. One would expect to have to polish down at least 50 μ or perhaps as much as several hundred microns in order to get rid of this excess dislocation density. CHALMERS replied that they electropolished by at least that much before doing the experiments described above.

HONEYCOMBE pointed out that when the critical strain method of preparing crystals is employed this problem does not arise. Very good crystals can be obtained without surface defects. Aluminum crystals are best prepared by this method, but one must be careful in subsequent handling of the crystals if accidental defects are to be avoided. GILMAN added that nothing should be allowed to touch such crystals. Very gentle contact with other solids can introduce surface dislocations.

Deformation of NaCl Crystals

F. R. N. NABARRO

University of the Witwatersrand
Johannesburg, South Africa

This is a preliminary report of some work done by E. C. H. Silk at Johannesburg, which is related to the work of T. Suzuki (pages 215–229). Sodium chloride crystals were made from the melt, perhaps of considerably lower quality than the crystals Suzuki was using, and with the same sort of angular deviations that P. L. Pratt [1] had in his crystals.

The crystals were strained by two different methods, but chose to deform by four mechanisms. The two methods were compression and the Bausch-type apparatus. The Bausch apparatus is shown schematically in Fig. 1. The grips are translated as shown and in this way one gets a very nonuniform shear stress but enforces, one hopes, a homogeneous shear strain. The intention of this work was to see whether by enforcing slip on a single system one would cut down the rate of shear hardening. The resolved shear stress was plotted against the sum of the glides on all operating systems and the rate of shear hardening compared for the two methods.

Considerably less shear hardening was observed in simple shear in the Bausch apparatus than in compression, except in the case of deformation by kinking in compression. One could tell rather well whether one was seeing slip lines or kinking, and those crystals which kinked hardened at about the same rate as those which were forced into pure shear by the Bausch apparatus. In order of increasing rate of shear hardening, the deformation mechanisms were (1) Bausch deformation and kinking, (2) single slip, (3) double slip, and (4) quadruple slip.

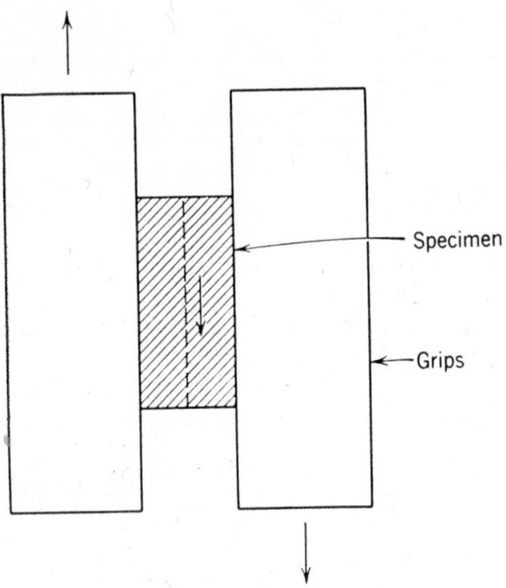

Fig. 1. Schematic of the Bausch apparatus showing a trace of the slip plane and the slip direction of the crystal.

It was found that in the Bausch apparatus the initial critical stress was higher than in any of the other tests. This may be due to the fact that in the Bausch apparatus the shear stress is zero on those surfaces in which edge dislocations would be nucleated. However, the possibility of stress concentrations at cleavage steps in the compression tests is not excluded. We thought that if the reason that crystals deformed in the Bausch apparatus are initially stronger was that the surfaces were free from stress, then the crystals should soften if they were wetted. We wetted the surface, but the crystals did not soften.

REFERENCE

1. P. L. Pratt, *Acta Met.,* **1,** 103 (1953).

DISCUSSION

LOMER asked if slip lines and kink bands were actually seen. NABARRO replied that faint slip lines and much coarser lines almost, but not quite, at right angles to them were seen between crossed polaroids. Silk decided that the specimen deformed by kinking if the illumination in polarized light showed markings which were not quite at right angles to the slip direction. LOMER mentioned that Pratt observed much the same in his tests, and asked if there was no observable difference between kinking and single slip work hardening. In reply, NABARRO said that the difference observed was thought to be because the so-called "single slip" had a good deal of slip on the conjugate system while the kinking was really simple slip.

The Effect of Pressure on the Plastic Deformation of Ni and Al

C. S. BARRETT

Institute for the Study of Metals
University of Chicago
Chicago, Illinois

Dr. Peter Haasen of the Institute for the Study of Metals, University of Chicago, has investigated the effect of hydrostatic pressure on the plastic deformation of single crystals of Ni and Al. This is a brief report of some of his work.

The effect of hydrostatic pressure on the stress-strain curve of Al is shown in Fig. 1, with pressures up to 5200 atmospheres. The effect of increasing the pressure is to increase the flow stress. If the pressure

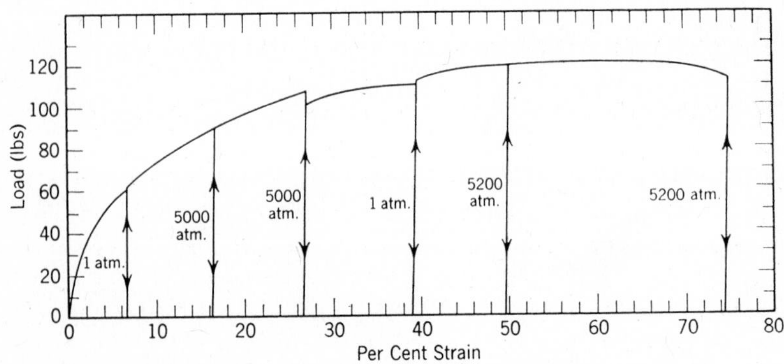

Fig. 1. The effect of hydrostatic pressure on the plastic deformation of Al single crystals.

is decreased, the flow stress decreases. There is a slight transient immediately upon reloading after the pressure is changed, but there is clearly a difference in flow stress. In all cases the crystal fractured by necking down; the type of fracture did not change under pressure.

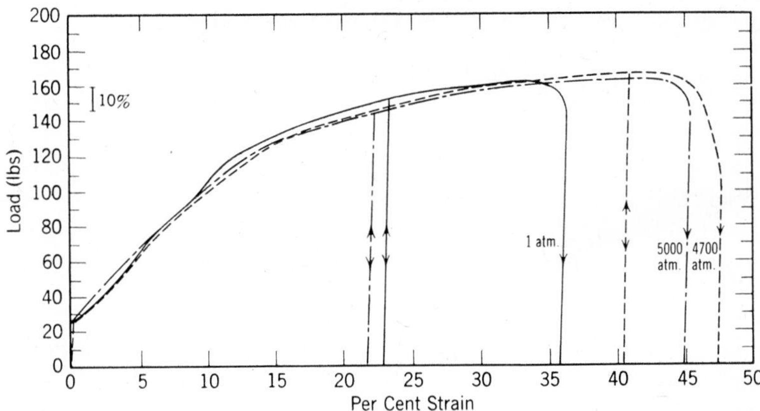

Fig. 2. The effect of hydrostatic pressure on the stress-strain curve of Ni single crystals.

Figure 2 shows that the total elongation in Ni is greater at high pressures than at 1 atmosphere, but there is *less* strain hardening at the higher pressures. This result was quite unexpected.

DISCUSSION

SEEGER said that the interpretation is straightforward in the case of aluminum, because both the dislocations and the vacancies increase the volume, whereas the interstitials leave the volume roughly unchanged (as indicated by unpublished calculations), so that high pressure would tend to inhibit plastic flow. SEEGER felt that in the case of nickel there is a magnetic effect, adding that at Stuttgart creep experiments had been done with nickel single crystals in a magnetic field; * they found that there is a rather large interaction between magnetostriction and domain walls on one hand and dislocations on the other.

* H. Blank, *Naturwissenschaften,* **43,** 494 (1956).

HONEYCOMBE described similar negative yield effects in single crystals of age-hardening alloys (Al-2%Ag) which had been quenched to a supersaturated state. When such a crystal is strained slightly, unloaded, and then reloaded, there is a negative yield effect which is a transient effect. It is presumably due to the redissolving of G-P zones which have been formed by the previous cold work.

BARRETT emphasized that although there is a slight transient in the pressure effects in Al, there is a large nontransient effect that amounts to a shifting of the entire stress-strain curve when the pressure is changed. He added that Haasen had encountered some severe troubles in the pressure tests in alpha-brass, which prevented reproducible results. The brass behaved as if there were pores closing up at high pressures.

BOAS suggested that it would be worthwhile to measure the change in electrical resistivity of specimens deformed the same amount at various pressures in order to determine if the high pressure does suppress the generation of vacancies.

III WORK HARDENING AND RECOVERY

The Mechanism of Glide and Work Hardening in Face-Centered Cubic and Hexagonal Close-Packed Metals

ALFRED SEEGER

Max Planck Institut für Metallforschung and Institut für theoretische und angewandte Physik der Technischen Hochschule Stuttgart, Germany

ABSTRACT

A theoretical picture is given for the dislocation processes governing the plastic properties of face-centered cubic metals and alloys and of hexagonal metals with basal glide. It is based on the similarities and dissimilarities of the dislocations in face-centered cubic and hexagonal close-packed structures and in metals and alloys with low and high stacking fault energies. It accounts for the critical shear stress of pure metals and dilute alloys, work hardening, recovery, surface markings (slip bands), and creep. Most of the discussion refers to single crystals, but a short account is given of the cell formation in polycrystals. The contents:

1. Introduction.
2. Dislocations in close-packed crystals.
3. Survey of the principal experimental facts.
4. The flow stress of pure metals and dilute alloys.
5. Work hardening and recovery of hexagonal close-packed metals.
6. Work hardening of face-centered cubic crystals.
   - A. Stage I.
   - B. The transition from stage I to stage II.
   - C. Stage II.
   - D. Latent hardening and Bauschinger effect.
7. Dynamical recovery and work softening of face-centered cubic metals.
8. Formation of slip bands and cell boundaries.

9. Influence of alloying elements on work hardening and work softening.
10. Creep of close-packed metals.

---

1. INTRODUCTION

This paper is a report on recent investigations of the dislocation mechanisms governing the plastic deformation of face-centered cubic and hexagonal close-packed metals. Among the hexagonal metals we focus our attention on plastic glide in Zn, Cd, Mg, and Co. In these metals at low and moderate temperatures, glide occurs mainly on the basal plane, the close-packed directions ($\langle 11\bar{2}0 \rangle$) in this plane being the possible glide directions (for other hexagonal metals see below). From the crystallographic point of view this mode of glide (basal glide) is closely related to the so-called octahedral glide which predominates in all face-centered cubic metals, the $\{111\}$ glide plane corresponding to the basal plane and the $\langle 110 \rangle$ glide direction corresponding to the $\langle 11\bar{2}0 \rangle$ glide direction in the hexagonal crystals.

A consequence of this relationship is the fact that the dislocations involved in the plastic deformation of these two structures are very similar from a geometric (or crystallographic) point of view. There are, however, distinct differences in the processes that these dislocations can undergo in the two crystal structures under consideration. They are related to the fact that a hexagonal crystal has only one set of basal planes, whereas a face-centered cubic crystal possesses four sets of octahedral planes, intersecting each other at an angle of $70°32'$. These differences in the dislocation properties will be explained in more detail in § 2; keeping them in mind will assist us in determining the dislocation processes responsible for the work-hardening characteristics, etc., of face-centered cubic and hexagonal close-packed metals.

Even if we confine ourselves to the same crystal structure, e.g., the face-centered cubic lattice, there is still room for individual features of the dislocations in various metals that can be correlated with experimental results. Such differences are to be expected since the details of the metallic binding vary from metal to metal (compare, e.g., the series Cu, Ni, and Al).* The essential point is that in the case of face-centered cubic or hexagonal close-packed metals these differences can be rationalized in terms of the magnitude of a single quantity, namely the stacking fault energy γ. As was first pointed out by Heidenreich and Shockley (1948), the dislocations with which we are

* We leave aside "trivial" features that stem from the differences in elastic constants or in lattice parameters.

concerned are "extended" ones. The degree of the extension (which is determined by a dimensionless quantity containing γ) and some dislocation properties depending on it may vary from metal to metal, thus giving rise to individual features of the plastic deformation which are detectable on a macroscopic scale (Seeger, 1954b, 1955a).

In order to supply the theoretical background for the discussions along the lines indicated above, we start in § 2 with a brief description of extended dislocations in both the face-centered cubic and the hexagonal close-packed lattice. Theoretical and experimental evidence as to the magnitude of the stacking fault energy γ and the degree of extension will also be given in § 2.

The dislocations which are most important for glide in the hexagonal metals Zr and Ti belong to the same glide directions (Burgers vectors) as those occurring in Zn, Cd, etc. Their preferred glide planes, however, are not the basal planes, but prismatic and pyramidal planes. These dislocations do not show the features in which we are most interested. We therefore exclude hexagonal metals with predominantly prismatic or pyramidal glide from our considerations. (These metals are characterized by subnormal axial ratios.) From now on *"hexagonal close-packed"* always refers to metals whose principal glide plane is the basal plane.

The major part of the experimental data on this latter group, particularly on Zn, Cd, and Mg, was accumulated in the early period of the investigation of the plasticity of crystals and is reported in Schmid and Boas' (1935) classic book. Some of the fundamental investigations on *face-centered cubic metals* were also carried out in the period around 1930. Due to the greater complexity of the empirical situation, however, it was not until recently that the experimental data were detailed enough to establish a complete picture for the face-centered cubic metals. In § 3 we shall briefly summarize the essential features of this picture and contrast it with the corresponding observations on hexagonal metals.

The main object of the present paper is to describe the *dislocation mechanisms* that govern the work-hardening characteristics of f.c.c. and h.c.p. metal crystals. Since individual crystals in the as-grown and annealed state may differ widely in their dislocation patterns and, to a lesser extent, in the way in which the dislocation arrangement changes during cold work, the purpose of a theory of cold work and work hardening cannot be to derive the stress-strain curve of a crystal from first principles. Its main task rather is to find out what are the fundamental processes hidden behind the individual behavior of the crystals.

In some instances we shall be able to supplement this descriptive approach by relating the experimental findings to quantities that can be calculated from dislocation theory, or by using dislocation theory as a link between different types of observations.

The first step in a *theory of work hardening* is to develop a *theory of flow stress,* i.e., to determine the resolved shear stress τ under which extensive plastic flow in a (unstrained or prestrained) crystal begins * (§ 4). The dislocation arrangement is assumed to be known and enters into the theoretical expression through parameters characterizing the dislocation density. The next step is to determine how the dislocation arrangement changes with strain, and, in some cases, also with time. Combining this with the theory of flow stress, we obtain the slope $\theta = d\tau/d\epsilon$ of the stress-strain curve as a function of strain ϵ and strain rate $\dot{\epsilon}$, i.e.,

$$d\tau/d\epsilon = \theta(\epsilon, \dot{\epsilon}) \tag{1}$$

Integration gives us the equation of the stress-strain curve $\tau = \tau(\epsilon)$ for a given strain rate $\dot{\epsilon}$.

As indicated before, this ambitious program of calculating the stress-strain curve from first principles cannot be carried through completely. At the present state of the theory we have to content ourselves with a semiquantitative interpretation of the experimental facts in terms of dislocation theory. This will be done for hexagonal crystals in § 5 and for face-centered cubic crystals in § 6. In § 7 we shall discuss the nature of the recovery process occurring at moderate temperatures and high stresses during the plastic deformation of face-centered cubic crystals. It is found to be closely related to characteristic changes in the dislocation pattern as revealed by X-ray techniques, e.g., the microbeam technique, and to the surface markings on deformed face-centered cubic crystals (§ 8).

Experimental data on face-centered cubic alloys are not nearly as complete as those on "pure" metals. There are, however, some observations on stress-strain curves and surface markings that lend themselves to an interpretation along the lines established for pure metals. It turns out that many features can be attributed to either the influence of the solute atoms on the stacking fault energy or their interaction with dislocation lines.

Equation 1, the fundamental relation of the theory of work hardening, is also fundamental to the study of creep. Instead of considering the strain rate as a parameter, in a creep test the flow stress τ is kept constant. The result of the test is the creep curve

* The flow stress of the unstrained crystal is the critical shear stress.

$$\epsilon = \epsilon(t, \tau) \tag{2}$$

i.e., the strain ϵ (or the strain rate $\dot{\epsilon} = d\epsilon/dt$) as a function of time t, the applied stress τ being a parameter. Equation 2 can be obtained from eq. 1 by integration. In principle, creep tests can therefore give the same information as stress-strain tests (tensile tests). At the present time creep data on single crystals in the interesting range of parameters are still rather scarce; we will therefore confine ourselves to a mainly qualitative discussion in § 10.

2. DISLOCATIONS IN CLOSE-PACKED CRYSTALS

The relationship between the hexagonal close-packed structure and the cubic close-packed structure (which is identical with the f.c.c. lattice) stems from the fact that both of them may be built up by *stacking close-packed planes of spheres* over each other; the close packing of spheres is shown in Fig. 1 with crystallographic notations corresponding to the face-centered cubic lattice.

Starting with a plane of atoms whose centers are in the positions A of Fig. 1, we put the centers of the atoms of the next layer on top of the B positions. When we come to the third layer we may either put the centers on top of the C positions or on top of the A position. In the latter case the third layer of atoms lies right above the first one. If we choose the C positions for the third layer and continue this pattern, i.e.,

$$A\ B\ C\ A\ B\ C\ A\ B\ C\ A\ B\ C$$

we arrive at the face-centered cubic structure. If we choose the A positions for the third layer and continue this pattern, i.e.,

$$A\ B\ A\ B\ A\ B\ A\ B\ A\ B\ A\ B$$

we obtain the close-packed hexagonal structure, the close-packed planes now being the basal planes (0001).

Without destroying the close packing we may have breaks in the stacking order, e.g., in the cubic case

$$\begin{array}{cccccccc} A & B & C & A & C & A & B & C & A \\ & & & \uparrow & \uparrow & & & & \end{array}$$

or in the hexagonal case

$$\begin{array}{ccccccccc} A & B & A & B & C & A & C & A & C \\ & & & & \uparrow & \uparrow & & & \end{array}$$

The arrows indicate where the breaks in the "correct" stacking order occur, each pair of breaks defining a "stacking fault." There are further possibilities for stacking faults in the f.c.c. or h.c.p. structure (see Read, 1953, Chap. 7), but those considered above are the only ones of importance in the theory of extended dislocations.

The quantity that enters the theory of extended dislocations is the *stacking fault energy* γ, defined as the surplus free energy of a stacking

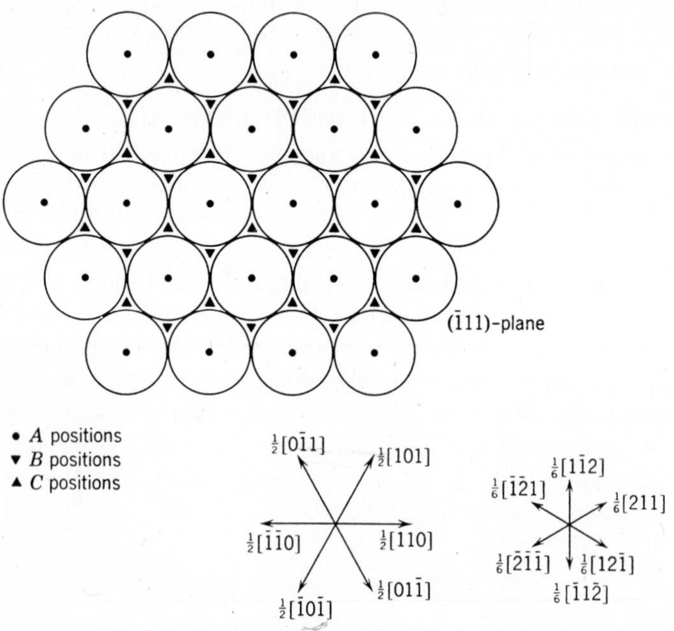

Fig. 1. A close-packed $(\bar{1}11)$-plane of a face-centered cubic lattice. The markings A, B, C indicate the projections of the positions of the centers of spheres in A, B, C layers. The pattern is the same in the basal plane of the hexagonal close-packed structure. The crystallographic notations in Fig. 1, however, refer to the face-centered cubic lattice.

fault of unit area. We shall postpone for the moment the problem of the absolute magnitude of the stacking fault energy and discuss first the question of the relative magnitude of γ in different *nontransition metals*. The answer to this question, both from theory and from experiment, is that monovalent metals (Cu, Ag, Au) have a small stacking fault energy whereas multivalent metals (Al, Pb, Mg, Zn, Cd) have a large one (Seeger, 1955a). The argument is as follows: A stacking fault leaves the number and the distance of nearest neighbor atoms unchanged. This means that in nontransition metals the contribution of the core electrons to the cohesive energy remains essentially unchanged by the introduction of a stacking fault into an otherwise perfect crystal. The same holds for the interaction between the conduction electrons and the ion core, since the volume of the atomic cell in the stacking fault is the same as in the perfect structure. The fact that in a stacking fault the number and the distance of next nearest neighbors of an atom deviate from the normal case is felt, however, by the conduction electrons, due to their wave nature. The conduction electrons feel the structure of a crystal mainly through the existence of the Brillouin zone boundaries. This means that the main change in the energy of the electron gas (Fermi energy) comes from electrons whose wave vectors are near to a zone boundary. The direction of this change must be such that the introduction of a stacking fault results in an *increase* of energy, since otherwise the crystal structure would be unstable. In *monovalent* metals, where the region of the wave-number space occupied by the conduction electrons does not overlap and is unlikely even to touch the boundaries of the first Brillouin zone, this increase in energy and therefore also the stacking fault energy is relatively small. In all *multivalent* metals, however, there is some overlap of the occupied region into the second Brillouin zone. In these cases we expect a large increase in energy of the conduction electrons and therefore a large stacking fault energy.

The available theoretical discussion of the magnitude of the stacking fault energy of *transition metals* (Seeger, 1955c, d) is much more involved and on a less well-founded basis. The main idea is that in transition metals interactions between the *d*-electrons of both nearest and next nearest neighbor atoms are very important for the cohesive energy, and that the difference in energy between the hexagonal and the cubic close-packed structures and the stacking fault energy are determined by the bonding between next nearest neighbors provided by the *d*-electrons. From discussions along these lines it is possible to predict whether the stacking fault energy of a transition metal should be small or large. Experimental evidence is available on only very few transition metals. We therefore see little point in going into more details. An interesting observation however is that Ni, Co, and Re are predicted to be low stacking fault energy metals. For Ni and Co there is experimental evidence supporting this. The outstanding high-temperature mechanical properties of Re, which are beginning to be of technological importance, may be related to the low stacking fault energy of this metal which distinguishes it (in addition to the difference in melting point) from other hexagonal metals like Zn or Cd.

An *experimental order of magnitude estimate* of the stacking fault energy of face-centered cubic metals can be obtained from measurements of the energy of coherent twin boundaries. A coherent twin boundary in a face-centered cubic lattice corresponds to one break in the correct stacking order of {111}-planes as indicated by the arrow in the sequence

$$A\ B\ C\ A\ B\ \underset{\uparrow}{C}\ B\ A\ C\ B\ A$$

In a picture based on interatomic forces between neighbor atoms and next nearest neighbor atoms, a stacking fault has twice the energy of such a coherent twin boundary. The latter is approximately known in copper and aluminum (Fullman, 1951); from these data stacking fault energies of $\gamma = 40$ ergs/cm^2 in copper and $\gamma = 200$ ergs/cm^2 in aluminum have been derived (Seeger and Schoeck, 1953). This intuitive approach based on forces between next nearest neighbors differs from the electron theory approach which we have outlined above. It is unlikely to give exactly the same results. The rather good agreement between experimental data and the theoretical deductions based on the stacking fault energies given above, however, indicates that the next nearest neighbor approach does give the right order of magnitude. It is certainly useful for establishing a qualitative correlation between stacking fault energies and the energies of coherent twin boundaries in face-centered cubic metals. We mention as an example that the well-known observation of a more frequent occurrence of annealing twins in Zn-rich alpha-brass than in copper indicates a lower twin energy and therefore also a lower stacking fault energy in alpha-brass than in copper. This is a conclusion in good agreement with independent experimental results which will be mentioned presently.

Several workers have investigated the occurrence of stacking faults in heavily cold-worked copper and alpha-brass, the most detailed investigation being that of Warren and Warekois (1955). These authors showed that the frequency of stacking faults increased with increasing zinc content of the alloy. This is most easily interpreted as being due to an increasing extension of the stacking fault ribbons of extended dislocations and therefore decreasing stacking fault energy with increasing zinc content. Since the arrangement of atoms in the stacking fault is the same as that in a thin slab of close-packed hexagonal material, the stacking fault energy is also related to the difference in free energy between the hexagonal close-packed structure and the face-centered cubic structure. It is therefore gratifying that Barrett and Massalski (1956) have observed that brass with a composition just beyond the boundary of the alpha phase transforms on cold work to a structure which is thought to be close-packed hexagonal. This is indicative of a small difference between the free energies of face-centered cubic and hexagonal close-packed Zn-rich alpha-brass, and therefore also of a small stacking fault energy. The situation is very similar to that in cobalt, where the existence of a phase transformation, h.c.p. to f.c.c., shows that the stacking fault energy of cobalt is very small. For further discussions reference may be made to Seeger (1955e, sect. 90).

After this brief survey of stacking faults and stacking fault energies we turn to a description of extended dislocations. For the sake of simplicity Fig. 2 refers to edge dislocations. Extended screw dislocations are very similar; instead of an *inserted* pair of a and b $\{110\}$-planes we have a *helix* of such a pair of planes.

Figure 2a shows an unextended edge dislocation in a face-centered cubic lattice or in a hexagonal close-packed structure. The "inserted plane" is a pair of two planes with the same pattern of atoms, the b-plane, however, being shifted with respect to the a-plane by half a lattice vector as shown in Fig. 3a (f.c.c.) and Fig. 4a (h.c.p.). The elastic strain energy of such a complete dislocation can be reduced if these two inserted planes are separated from each other as shown in Fig. 2b. The edge of each of these two planes now forms a partial dislocation.* The Burgers vector $\mathbf{b}_c$ of the complete dislocation and the Burgers vectors $\mathbf{b}_{pa}$ and $\mathbf{b}_{pb}$ of the two partial dislocations are connected by the equation

$$\mathbf{b}_c = \mathbf{b}_{pa} + \mathbf{b}_{pb} \tag{3}$$

The explicit form of this equation is for a dislocation oriented as shown in Fig. 2 in the face-centered cubic case (Heidenreich and Shockley, 1948)

$$\tfrac{1}{2}\,[110] = \tfrac{1}{6}\,[211] + \tfrac{1}{6}\,[12\bar{1}] \tag{3a}$$

and in the hexagonal close-packed case

$$\tfrac{1}{3}\,[11\bar{2}0] = \tfrac{1}{3}\,[10\bar{1}0] + \tfrac{1}{3}\,[01\bar{1}0] \tag{3b}$$

As shown in Fig. 2b, between the two partial dislocations an area of misfit is created on the glide plane of the dislocation. This can be seen from the fact that the (110)- or $(11\bar{2}0)$-planes between the two partial dislocations change over from a-character to b-character and vice versa. This is shown more clearly in Fig. 3b and Fig. 4b, where pairs of these planes have been drawn. The breaks which are evident from a comparison with Figs. 3a and 4a constitute the same types of stacking faults as discussed at the beginning of this section. This can be seen from the lettering of the $(\bar{1}11)$- or (0001)-planes by A, B, C.

* For simplicity we have neglected in Fig. 2b the fact that the partial dislocations are not of pure edge character.

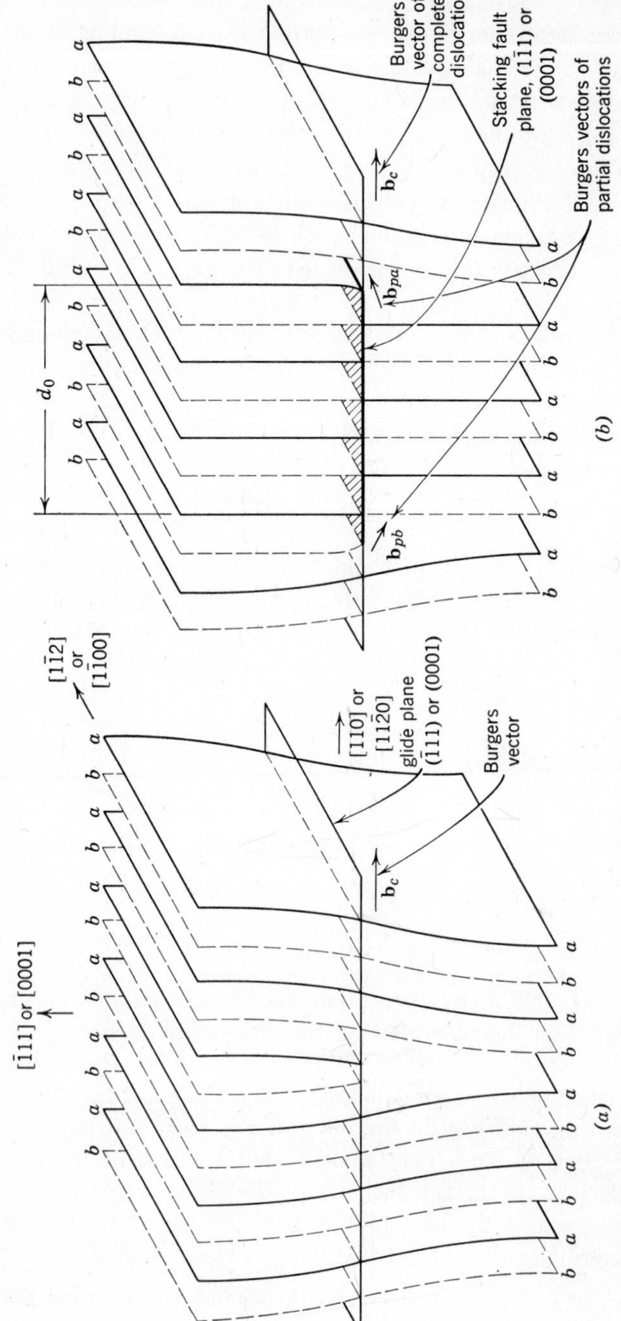

Fig. 2. Edge dislocations in the face-centered cubic lattice and the hexagonal close-packed structure. (*a*) Unextended dislocation. (*b*) Extended dislocation with $d_0 = 3b$. For the pattern of atoms in the *a*- and *b*-planes see Figs. 3 and 4.

It can further be seen that a stacking fault in a face-centered cubic lattice constitutes a thin slab of hexagonal close-packed material and

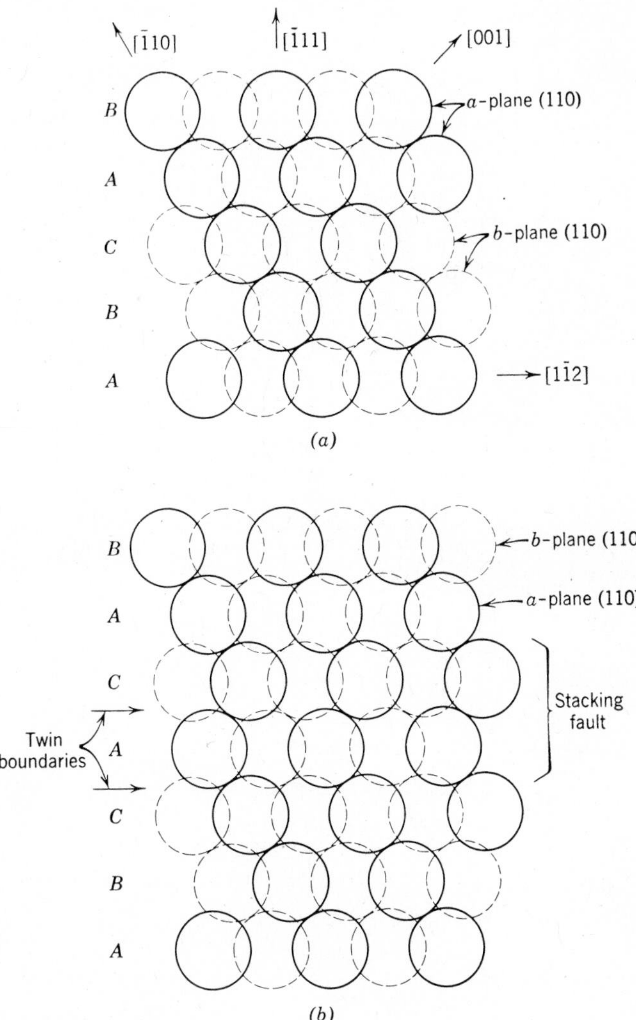

Fig. 3. (110)-planes in a face-centered cubic lattice. (*a*) Without a stacking fault. (*b*) Intersecting a stacking fault. The letters *A*, *B*, *C* refer to the stacking of ($\bar{1}$11)-planes. (Compare Fig. 1.)

vice versa, and that a stacking fault in the f.c.c. lattice can be considered as being bounded by two coherent twin boundaries separated by one (111)-plane, although the position of these twin boundaries is not

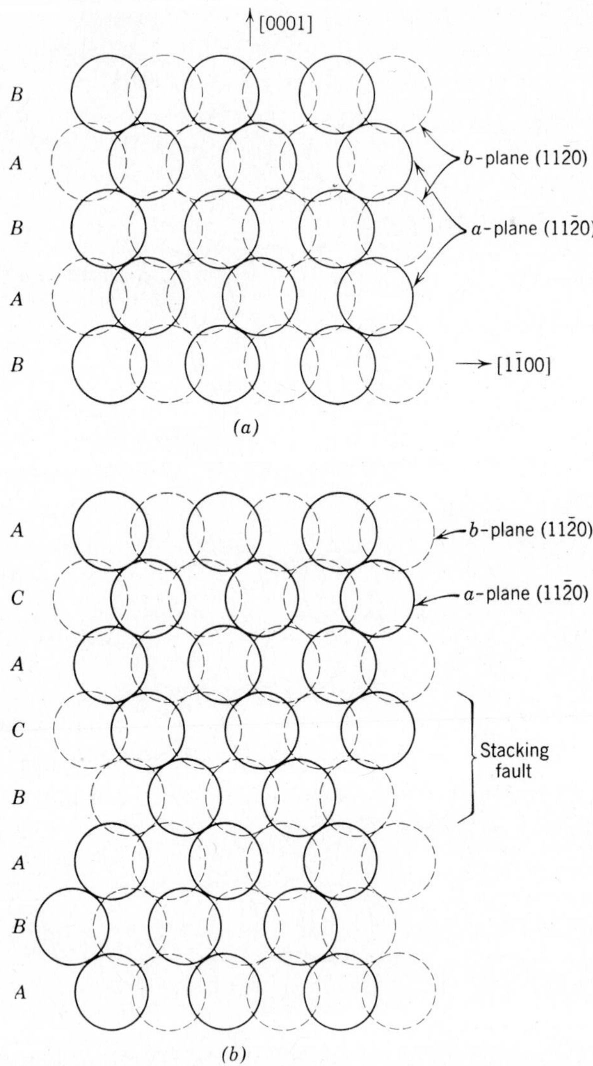

Fig. 4. (11$\bar{2}$0)-planes in a hexagonal close-packed structure. (*a*) Without a stacking fault. (*b*) Intersecting a stacking fault. The letters *A*, *B*, *C* refer to the stacking of (0001)-planes. (Compare Fig. 1.)

uniquely defined. [A similar situation does not hold for the hexagonal structure, since the (0001)-plane is a symmetry plane.]

The "surface tension" of the stacking fault energy γ opposes the elastic repulsion between the partial dislocations and binds them together at a finite equilibrium separation d_0. The theory of this separation, allowing for the anisotropy of the elastic properties of crystals and also for some of the non-Hookeian interaction between the partial dislocations by using Peierls' model as developed by Leibfried and Dietze (1951), has been given by Seeger and Schoeck (1953—for the correction of printing errors see Seeger 1955e, sect. 73). The dimensionless parameter determining the equilibrium separation (or extension) d_0 is $\gamma c/Gb^2$. Here G is the shear modulus (in the glide plane), c the separation between neighboring glide planes, and b the separation between neighboring atoms in the glide plane (or the modulus of $\mathbf{b}_c$). If this parameter is larger than 10^{-2}, the separation between the partial dislocations is of the order of b only, and rather insensitive to the exact value of γ. In this case, typified by aluminum ($\gamma c/Gb^2 = 2.3 \times 10^{-2}$), we speak of high stacking fault energies. The stacking fault energy is called low if the parameter is smaller than 10^{-2}. This is the case for copper, where $\gamma c/Gb^2 = 4 \times 10^{-3}$. Then the partial dislocations are well separated (in copper: $d_0 = 12b$ for an edge dislocation, $d_0 = 5b$ for a screw dislocation). The equilibrium separation in this case is rather sensitive to the exact value of γ and also to the character of the complete dislocation (e.g., whether edge or screw).

The partial dislocations bounding the stacking fault ribbon of an extended dislocation are also called incomplete dislocations, since their Burgers vectors (which are the vectors $\frac{1}{6}$ <121> shown in Fig. 1) are not lattice vectors. There are several processes in which the incomplete dislocations have to recombine to form an unextended (complete) dislocation over a certain length of the dislocation line. For example, for the intersection of dislocation lines it is necessary to form so-called constrictions, an example of which is shown in Fig. 5. The energy of constrictions has been calculated by Stroh (1954), Seeger (1954b), and in more detail by Schoeck and Seeger (1955). The two last-mentioned calculations show that the constriction energy in copper is considerably larger than that in aluminum. Qualitatively, the same result holds for the energies of jogs in dislocation lines. The dependence of d_0 on the dislocation character causes a corresponding variation of the jog energy, however. We will have the opportunity to return to the question of jog energies later.

Another problem which involves constrictions is the *cross slip* of extended dislocations, which was also treated by Schoeck and Seeger

(1955). The physical situation of interest is in general as follows: An extended screw dislocation—Burgers vector ½ [110], stacking fault plane $(\bar{1}11)$—has been held up by an obstacle in its glide plane. The width d of the stacking fault ribbon may either be equal to the equilibrium distance d_0, or differ from d_0 because of applied or internal stresses. If the dislocations are piled up against an obstacle as shown in Fig. 7, their width may be considerably reduced. If a shear stress τ_Q acts in the glide system [110], $(1\bar{1}1)$, which is called the cross-slip system, there is a certain tendency for the screw dislocation to leave its original plane $(\bar{1}11)$ and change over to the cross-slip plane $(1\bar{1}1)$. It is rather difficult to treat the rate of this process theoretically, since we

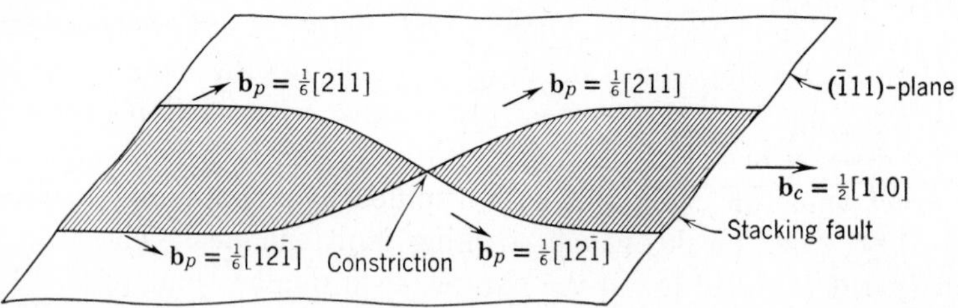

Fig. 5. Constriction in an extended dislocation. The drawing corresponds to a screw dislocation in an f.c.c. lattice.

are dealing with a many-particle problem. The application of the simple one-particle theory of reaction rates to the cross-slip process is therefore not straightforward. What seems to be a reasonable model is shown in Fig. 6. In the first stage of the cross-slip process the partial dislocations in the original glide plane have to be brought together over a certain length $2l_0$ of the dislocation line (Fig. 6*a*). Over this length the geometrical situation is symmetric with respect to the two possible glide planes $(\bar{1}11)$ and $(1\bar{1}1)$; the acting stresses will in general help the dislocation to spread in the cross-slip plane $(1\bar{1}1)$ as shown in Fig. 6*b*. The stress τ_Q will then tend to increase the area in the $(1\bar{1}1)$-plane swept out by the dislocation line (Fig. 6*c*).

The state of highest energy (which determines the activation energy) in this process is when the dislocation passes through the stage shown in Fig. 6*a*. The activation energy depends on the length $2l_0$. A good choice of this quantity seems to be such that a dislocation loop of length $2l_0$ is just able to expand in the $(1\bar{1}1)$-plane under the action of the shear stress τ_Q. The calculations of Schoeck and Seeger (1955) along these lines refer to dislocations with $d = d_0$. Their result is that for *aluminum* with $\tau_Q = 100$ g/mm^2 the activation energy lies between 1.0 ev and 1.1 ev. This implies that in aluminum cross slip should be

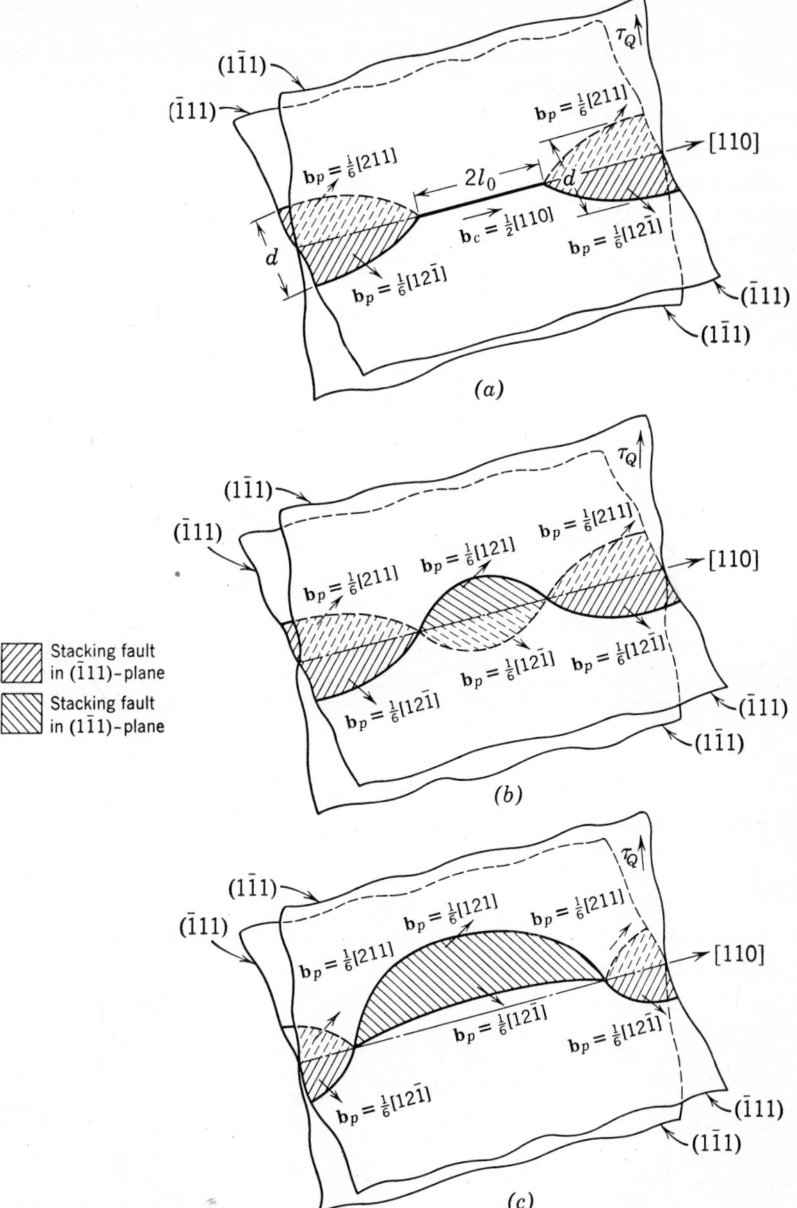

Fig. 6. Three stages of the cross slip of an extended screw dislocation from a ($\bar{1}$11)-plane to a (1$\bar{1}$1)-plane. (*a*) The partial dislocations have been brought together over a length $2l_0$ to form an unextended dislocation. (*b*) The unextended dislocation spreads into an extended dislocation in the (1$\bar{1}$1)-plane. (*c*) The portion of the dislocation line lying in the (1$\bar{1}$1)-planes spreads in this plane under the action of the resolved shear stress τ_Q in this plane.

quite frequent under rather low stresses in the temperature range just above room temperature. This prediction has been verified recently by the observations of cross slip in stress annealing of aluminum by the electron transmission technique of Hirsch, Horne, and Whelan (1956). The result for copper is that the activation energy of cross slip is so high that it can only occur if the extension d of the screw dislocations is reduced appreciably below the equilibrium separation d_0, e.g., in a pile-up.

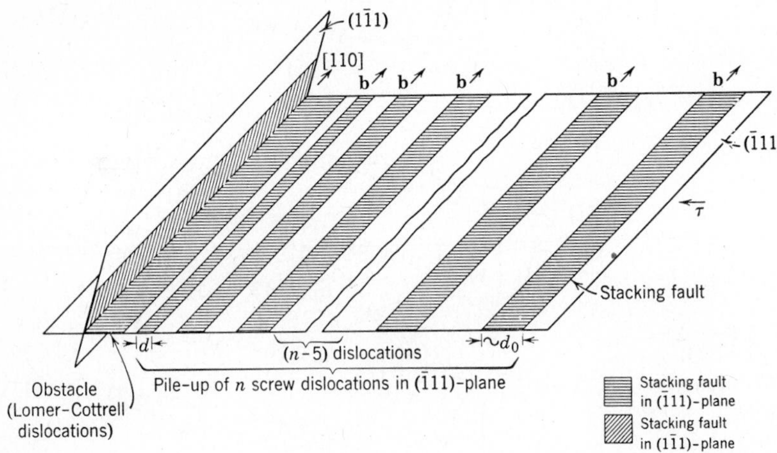

Fig. 7. n extended screw dislocations in a ($\bar{1}$11)-plane piled up against a sessile Lomer-Cottrell dislocation under the action of the applied shear stress τ. The width of the extended dislocations is smallest at the head of the pile-up.

If the number n of dislocations in a pile-up and the applied stress acting on these dislocations are large enough, it is possible to bring completely together the two partial dislocations of an extended screw dislocation at the head of the pile-up. This is an interesting situation, since the screw dislocation is now able to undergo cross slip without thermal activation. This is the situation that should prevail at very low temperatures, provided we are justified in neglecting quantum effects.

The stress acting on the leading dislocation of a pile-up of n dislocations is n times the applied stress τ acting on the group (Cottrell, 1949; Eshelby, Frank, Nabarro, 1951). The force on the leading dislocation exerted by this stress is balanced by the force exerted by the obstacle against which the piled-up dislocations are pressed. In the case of screw dislocations piled up against a Lomer-Cottrell dislocation, the reaction force is mainly due to non-Hookeian interactions.* For the following discussions we assume that this force is of such a short range that that partial dislocation of the leading dislocation which is adjacent to the Lomer-Cottrell dislocation is kept in a fixed position. The equilibrium position of the other partial dislocation is determined by the balance of the repulsion by the first dislocation (including the attracting effect of the stacking fault "surface tension") and by the force (per unit length) exerted by the applied stress and the other piled-up dislocations. If the extension of the dislocation is small, the latter quantity is $n\tau b/2$, since the other stress component in the glide plane is not to be multiplied by the factor n and can therefore be neglected. For the repulsive force per unit length we obtain in the notation of Seeger (1954b), again under the assumption of a negligible extension:

$$\left.\frac{dE(\eta)}{d(2\eta)}\right|_{\eta=0} = \frac{1}{2}f'(\eta_0) = \frac{bG\sqrt{2}}{8\pi} - \gamma \tag{4}$$

Equating this to the external force, we obtain for the shear stress necessary to bring completely together the two partial dislocations of the leading screw dislocations:

$$\tau = \frac{1}{n}\left(\frac{\sqrt{2}}{4\pi}G - \frac{2\gamma}{b}\right) = \frac{2G}{n}\left(0.056 - \frac{\gamma}{Gb}\right) \tag{5}$$

Here G is the shear modulus in the glide plane, γ the stacking fault energy, b the dislocation strength of the complete dislocations, and n the number of dislocations in the pile-up. We shall employ eq. 5 in § 7 for the discussion of experiments.

In Fig. 7 we have introduced a Lomer-Cottrell dislocation as an obstacle holding up screw dislocations in their glide planes. Lomer-Cottrell dislocations are a particular form of extended dislocations and have been discussed in the books by Cottrell (1953, sect. 14.8.) and by Read (1953, sect. 7.12.). They can be generated by a "dislocation reaction" between two suitably chosen extended dislocations on intersecting {111}-planes. The Lomer-Cottrell dislocation oriented as shown in Fig. 8 can be the result of two different types of dislocation reactions which are given in Table 1. The energy gain in such a reaction comes from the combination of one of the partial dislocations in the $(1\bar{1}1)$-plane with one in the $(\bar{1}11)$-plane to form a "stair-rod" partial dislocation with Burgers vector $\frac{1}{6}[1\bar{1}0]$ (Thompson, 1953) by the reaction

* The Lomer-Cottrell dislocations holding up screw dislocations are formed by reactions involving dislocations of other glide systems (see Table 1).

$$\tfrac{1}{6}\,[\bar{1}\bar{2}\bar{1}] + \tfrac{1}{6}\,[211] = \tfrac{1}{6}\,[1\bar{1}0]$$

or

$$\tfrac{1}{6}\,[21\bar{1}] + \tfrac{1}{6}\,[\bar{1}\bar{2}1] = \tfrac{1}{6}\,[1\bar{1}0]$$

The resulting Lomer-Cottrell dislocation can be described as a wedge-shaped stacking fault ribbon lying in the [110]-direction, bounded by two partial edge dislocations and containing in the edge of the wedge a partial edge dislocation of the stair-rod type. It is obvious that in the $(\bar{1}11)$-plane two more Lomer-Cottrell dislocations are possible, running in the $[01\bar{1}]$- and [101]-directions.

Since under ordinary conditions an extended dislocation is confined to the plane of its stacking fault, Lomer-Cottrell dislocations are confined to the line of intersection of the glide planes of the two original

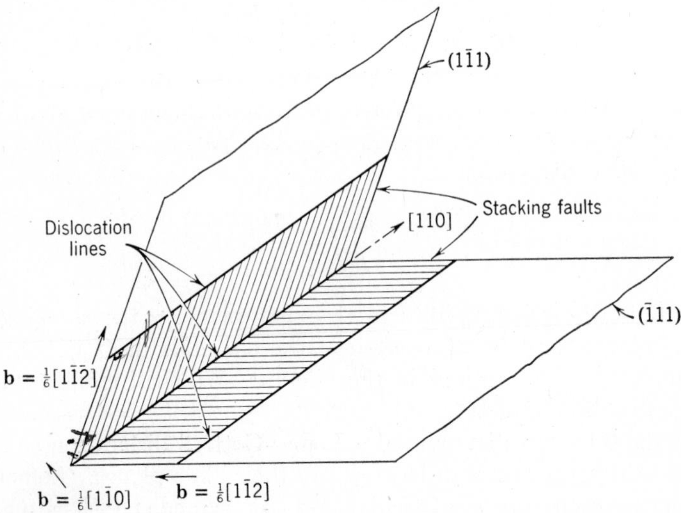

Fig. 8. Lomer-Cottrell sessile dislocations consisting of three partial edge dislocations.

TABLE 1. DISLOCATION REACTIONS LEADING TO A LOMER-COTTRELL DISLOCATION CONSISTING OF $\tfrac{1}{6}\,[1\bar{1}2]$ AND $\tfrac{1}{6}\,[1\bar{1}\bar{2}]$ "SHOCKLEY" PARTIAL DISLOCATIONS, AND A $\tfrac{1}{6}\,[1\bar{1}0]$ "STAIR-ROD" DISLOCATION

	Burgers Vectors of Complete Dislocations	Burgers Vectors of Partial Dislocations		Glide Plane
Reacting pair of dislocations	$\tfrac{1}{2}\,[0\bar{1}\bar{1}]$	$\tfrac{1}{6}\,[\bar{1}\bar{2}\bar{1}]$	$\tfrac{1}{6}\,[1\bar{1}\bar{2}]$	$(1\bar{1}1)$
	$\tfrac{1}{2}\,[101]$	$\tfrac{1}{6}\,[211]$	$\tfrac{1}{6}\,[1\bar{1}2]$	$(\bar{1}11)$
Reacting pair of dislocations	$\tfrac{1}{2}\,[10\bar{1}]$	$\tfrac{1}{6}\,[21\bar{1}]$	$\tfrac{1}{6}\,[1\bar{1}\bar{2}]$	$(1\bar{1}1)$
	$\tfrac{1}{2}\,[0\bar{1}1]$	$\tfrac{1}{6}\,[\bar{1}\bar{2}1]$	$\tfrac{1}{6}\,[1\bar{1}2]$	$(\bar{1}11)$

extended dislocations. They are "sessile" (Frank, 1949) and are therefore able to act as obstacles to the glide motion of "glissile" dislocations. If a group of such glissile dislocations is piled up against a Lomer-Cottrell dislocation, the width of the stacking fault wedge may be reduced in the manner discussed above. If this reduction is sufficiently large the Lomer-Cottrell dislocation may collapse, e.g., by becoming a glissile dislocation and gliding away. Various conceivable modes of collapse have been considered by Stroh (1956). Seeger, Diehl, Mader, and Rebstock (1957), however, have shown that in the case of screw dislocations piled up against a Lomer-Cottrell dislocation under increasing stress (the case we are most interested in), the screw dislocations will leave the pile-up by cross slip before the Lomer-Cottrell dislocation collapses.* We shall see in later sections that there is strong experimental evidence in support of this conclusion.

3. SURVEY OF THE PRINCIPAL EXPERIMENTAL FACTS

The object of this section is to give a brief account of the main experimental results on stress-strain curves of face-centered cubic metal crystals. Figure 9 shows the temperature dependence of the stress-strain curve of gold single crystals as measured by Andrade and Henderson (1951). The interpretation of these results and similar data on silver and nickel single crystals by the same authors and on copper crystals by Blewitt (1953) was complicated by the fact that crystals of different crystallographic orientations had been used. At about the same time the orientation dependence of the stress-strain curve of aluminum single crystals deformed at room temperature and liquid air temperature was studied in great detail by Masing and Raffelsieper (1950), Lücke and Lange (1952), Diehl and Kochendörfer (1952), Röhm and Diehl (1952), Lange and Lücke (1953), and Staubwasser (1954). The orientation dependence of the stress-strain curve of aluminum crystals deformed at room temperature appeared to be so marked that it was thought to overshadow the temperature dependence. By considering all the data available for face-centered cubic metals and primary alloys, however, Diehl (1954a, b, 1955) was able to show that they fit into the following schemes (see Diehl, Mader, and Seeger, 1955, and Fig. 14): The stress-strain curve of a face-centered cubic metal may or may not show an easy glide region (later on called stage I), depending on the crystal orientation and the impurities present.

* The argument is based on the fact that the forces tending to press together the extended dislocations are the same for the Lomer-Cottrell dislocation and the leading screw dislocation, but the repulsive forces are larger for the Lomer-Cottrell dislocation than for the screw dislocations.

Most characteristic for face-centered cubic crystals is the stage of rapid work hardening which follows the easy glide region (stage II). In this region the ratio of work-hardening coefficient to the shear modulus (or some other suitable elastic constant) is practically inde-

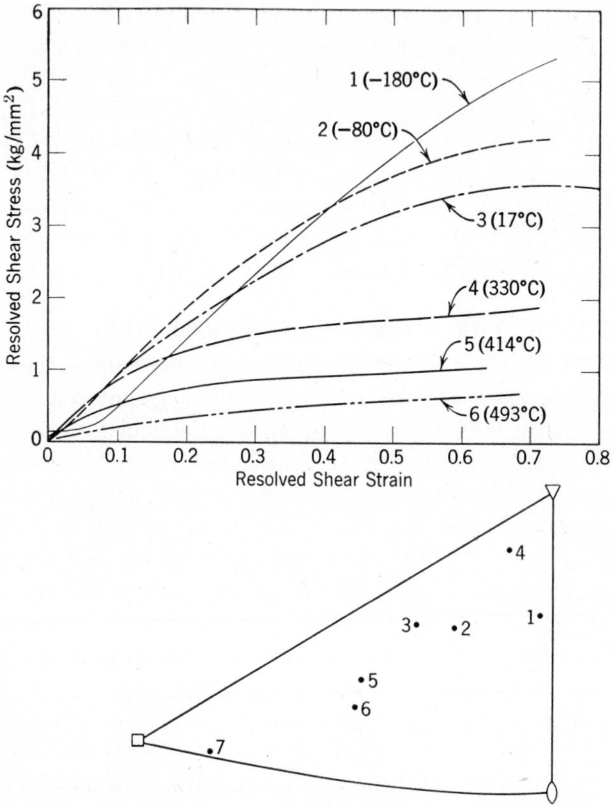

Fig. 9. Temperature dependence of the stress-strain curves of gold single crystals of varying orientation (Andrade and Henderson, 1951).

pendent of the applied stress and the temperature, not very dependent on the crystal orientation, not sensitive to the impurity content (cf. Fig. 31), and of the same order of magnitude, namely about 4×10^{-3}, for all face-centered cubic metals (see also Friedel, 1955). The understanding of the rapid work hardening in this stage seems to be basic for the understanding of the plastic deformation of face-centered metals, and we shall concentrate on this problem in § 6. At larger strains the slope of the stress-strain curve diminishes with increasing strain. The stress at which this stage, III, begins depends markedly on temperature, and Diehl proposed to ascribe this to a kind of "dynamic recovery." The term "recovery" is meant to indicate that temperature acts to reduce the work-hardening coefficient relative to that of stage II. The word "dynamic" refers to the fact that this occurs

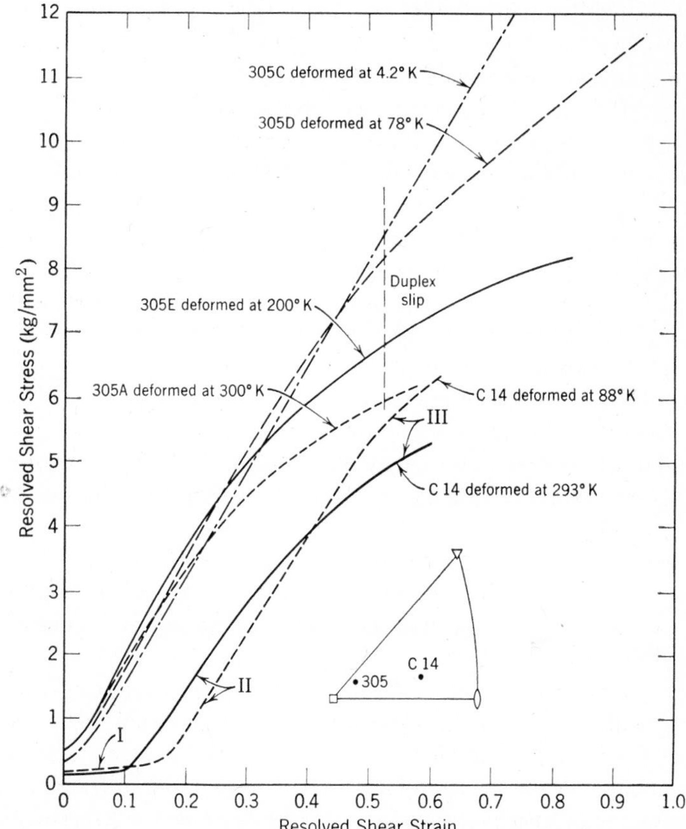

Fig. 10. Temperature dependence of copper crystals of identical orientations according to Blewitt, Coltman, and Redman (1955), and Diehl, Mader, and Seeger (1955).

during the deformation, but not necessarily in the unloaded crystal. It is well known, for example, that deformed copper crystals do not show mechanical recovery at room temperature after unloading. We shall call the "normal" recovery of crystals (either unloaded or well below the flow stress) "static" recovery as opposed to the dynamic recovery which occurs during plastic deformation. It should be pointed out that there are cases in which the situation is different from the one we have been discussing, and in which static and dynamic recovery are due to the same mechanism (see § 5).

Some points of the preceding discussion are illustrated in Fig. 10 where the orientation dependence has been removed by using crystals of the same orientation. The orientation 305 is taken from Blewitt, Coltman, and Redman (1955). It shows the constancy and temperature independence of the work-hardening coefficient of stage II and the marked temperature dependence of the beginning of stage III. It does not show stage I. This may be due partly to the orientation of the crystal, partly to a possible prestress during growth from the melt, since the critical shear stress of these crystals is considerably higher than normal. All stages of the stress-strain curve are shown by the data on the crystals of the orientation C 14, taken from Diehl, Mader, and Seeger (1955). It shows that the critical shear stress at liquid air temperature is higher than at room temperature (as is normally the case), and that the region of easy glide is longer at the lower temperature. These two features, together with the temperature dependence of stage III, lead to a characteristic twofold crossing of stress-strain curves taken at different temperatures. This is already shown clearly by the data of Andrade and Henderson (1951). In particular, some of their silver crystals exhibit very extended easy glide regions at liquid oxygen temperature.

The orientation dependence of the stress-strain curves of copper crystals at a given temperature is shown in Fig. 11, taken from Diehl (1956a). We shall give a brief description only; for more details see Diehl (1956a, b). At first sight the orientation dependence seems to be very pronounced. Closer consideration, however, shows that most of the orientation dependence comes from the extension (ϵ_2) and the slope of the easy glide region (θ_I). They vary by about a factor of ten through the whole range of orientations. All the other characteristic quantities (critical shear stress τ_0, resolved shear stresses τ_2 and τ_3 at the beginning of stages II and III, slope θ_{II} in stage II) are much less orientation-dependent and vary at best by a factor of about two. The variations of the stresses ($\tau_2 - \tau_0$) and τ_2 are the strongest ones among the "weakly orientation-dependent parameters," according to Figs. 9 and 10 in Diehl's (1956a) paper; it seems therefore to be unjustified to put particular emphasis on the "orientation independence" of these quantities, as has been done by Rosi (1954) and Garstone, Honeycombe, and Greetham (1956).

A discussion of the orientation dependence is incomplete without an investigation of the reproducibility of the individual quantities both for different crystals of the same orientation and for different parts

of the same crystal. Diehl (1956b) has shown that th
eters show considerable scattering, this being largest
orientation-dependent parameters $\theta_{\rm I}$ and ϵ_2 and smalle
However, the fluctuations are in no case so large that

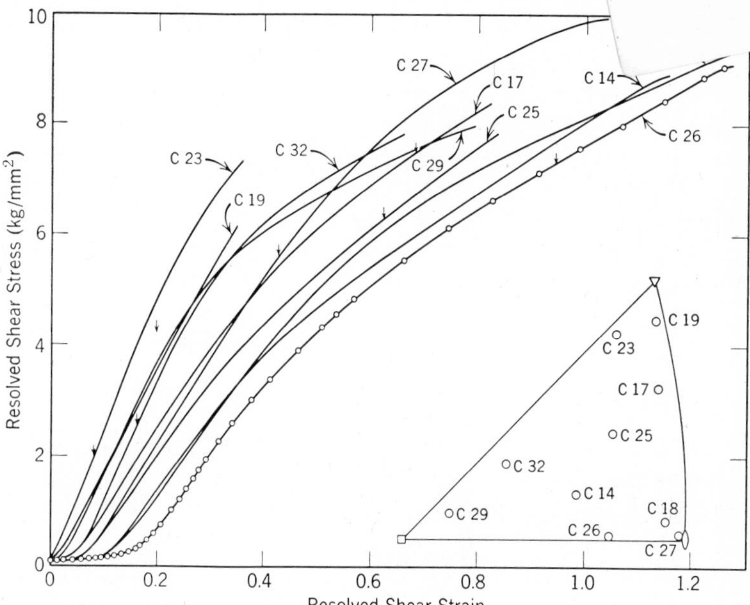

Fig. 11. Orientation dependence of the stress-strain curves of copper single crystals (purity 99.98%, diameter 4 mm) deformed at room temperature. After Diehl (1956a).

validate the above statements on the systematic orientation dependence.

It might be mentioned that the subdivision into stages I, II, and III shows up not only in the tensile stress-strain curves but also in the magnetic behavior of plastically deformed nickel crystals. Dietrich and Kneller (1956) have recently investigated the approach to magnetic saturation of nickel crystals after tensile deformation at room temperature. Representing the differential susceptibility at high magnetic fields, H, in the form

$$\chi = \chi_0 - \frac{C_2}{H^2} - \frac{C_3}{H^3} \tag{6}$$

with three field-independent parameters χ_0, C_2, and C_3, they found that C_2 as a function of prestrain ϵ and orientation of the tensile axis beves qualitatively as the flow stress $\tau(\epsilon)$, exhibiting stages I–III for orientations in the interior of the stereographic triangle and showing stages II and III only for symmetric orientations.

The reader may have noticed that so far we have been discussing data mainly on low stacking fault energy metals. In Fig. 12, data

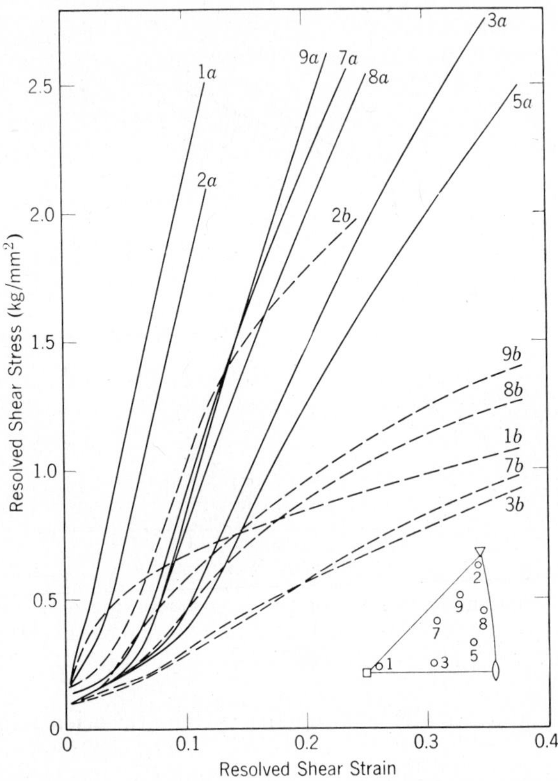

Fig. 12. The orientation dependence of the work-hardening curves of aluminum single crystals at room temperature (dashed curves) and at −195°C (solid curves) according to Staubwasser (1954).

selected from Staubwasser (1954) show the orientation dependence of the stress-strain curve of aluminum single crystals at liquid air temperature and room temperature. The situation at liquid air temperature is the same as with copper crystals at room temperature. The early stages of the stress-strain curves depend markedly on the orientation of the crystals. A straight stage II is followed by a stage III with decreasing work-hardening coefficient. Due to the apparatus limitations the stress-strain curves of some orientations, particularly the one with tensile axis near a <111>-direction, end before stage III is reached. There is, however, little doubt [particularly if the data of Sosin and Koehler (1956) are also considered] that the stress-strain curves of aluminum crystals deformed at low temperatures fit well into the scheme given above.

The situation is, however, somewhat different at room temperature. Only in some special orientations of high symmetry, in particular in the [111]-corner of the stereographic triangle, do the stress-strain curves show a fully developed stage II. Orientations in the interior of the stereographic triangle assume the steepest slope $\theta_{\max}$ of the stress-strain curve only in an inflection point; in most cases $\theta_{\max}/G$ is considerably less than the liquid air value. The interpretation of this behavior is that stage III already begins at a stress where stage II is not yet fully developed. The same situation will prevail in Cu, Ag, Au, and Ni at sufficiently high temperatures. This is indicated in the stress-strain curve of crystal 6 in Fig. 9.

It should be stressed that this quantitative difference between aluminum and, say, the noble metals is not just due to the difference in melting points and the corresponding adjustment in the scale of the absolute temperature. Aluminum at 78°K corresponds roughly to copper at room temperature, which is about four times as high a temperature. The ratio of the absolute temperatures of the melting points, however, corresponds to a factor of only about 1½. It will be shown later that this difference in the temperature scales is due to the differences in the stacking fault energies and in the width of extended dislocations (Seeger, 1955a).

The data on the other high stacking fault energy f.c.c. metal, lead, are not as extensive as that on aluminum. The results of Feltham and Meakin (1957) indicate that the situation is similar to that of aluminum.* The width of the extended dislocations in lead seems to be at least as small as that in aluminum, since at room temperature stage II appears to be even more suppressed than in aluminum.†

Turning now to hexagonal metal crystals, virtually no data are available on low stacking fault energy metals. A considerable body of evidence exists on the high stacking fault energy metals Mg, Zn, and Cd. Since the empirical situation is much simpler we shall merely mention a few experimental results. Considering as an example the case of zinc single crystals, it appears from the work of Fahrenhorst and

* This is also suggested by the surface appearance of lead crystals deformed at room temperature (Wilsdorf, 1954). Compare the discussion of slip bands in § 8.

† For quantitative considerations it must be kept in mind that both the melting point and the dislocation line energy are lower in Pb than in Al.

Schmid (1930), Lücke, Masing, and Schröder (1955), Deruyttère and Greenough (1956), and others that at low temperatures (below −30°C) and high temperatures (above 180°), the stress-strain curves can be represented very well by a straight line. In the intermediate temperature range the stress-strain curves are very nearly straight up to strains of the order one to two, and then show a bend upwards to not more than twice the original slope This same phenomenon is also observed in cadmium (Boas and Schmid, 1930) and magnesium (Schmid, 1931), and extends in these metals even to lower temperatures. The orientation dependence of the tensile stress-strain curve

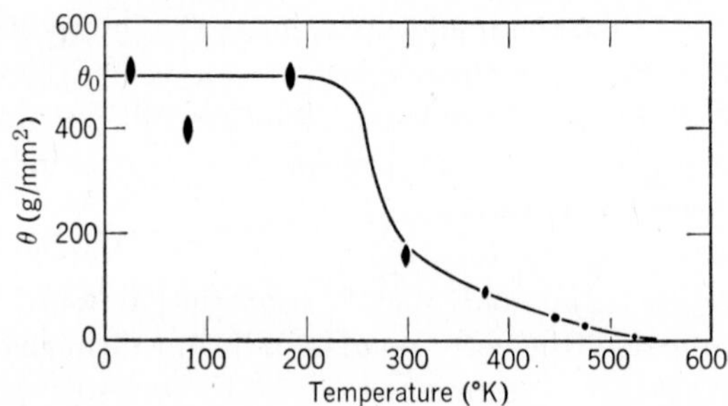

Fig. 13. The temperature dependence of the coefficient of work hardening θ of zinc single crystals according to Fahrenhorst and Schmid (1930).

which has been observed in zinc by Fahrenhorst and Schmid (1930) and in great detail at room temperature by Lücke, Masing, and Schröder (1955) is negligibly small over nearly the whole of the fundamental stereographic triangle. Only if the resolved critical shear stress is very nearly the same in two of the basal glide systems is there a systematic orientation dependence to speak of. We shall, in general, exclude these critical orientations from our considerations.

The slope θ of the stress-strain curve shows the following behavior as a function of temperature (see Fig. 13): Below the temperature interval from −30°C to −50°C the slope is very nearly temperature-independent. It will be denoted by θ_0. This behavior is predicted by the theory (Seeger, 1954c), which will be discussed in § 5. A minimum in the temperature dependence of θ which was observed in zinc crystals at liquid air temperature by Fahrenhorst and Schmid (1930), in agreement with recent measurements of Deruyttère and Greenough (1956), is not understandable on the basis of the theory (which does not allow for possible surface effects due to the temperature bath) and is at present unexplained. In the temperature region around room temperature θ decreases rapidly with increasing temperature, and is also rather sensitive to the strain rate. In this temperature range the recovery of cold-worked zinc crystals proceeds to a measurable extent during the time of typical experiments. Polanyi and Schmid (1929) therefore proposed to interpret the temperature dependence of the work-hardening coefficient as a thermal softening superimposed on an athermal hardening process. The softening process was considered to be the ordinary ("static") recovery process and possibly (at higher temperatures, and in polycrystalline material) recrystallization. The view that in the hexagonal metals Zn and Cd the mechanisms of static recovery and dynamical recovery are essentially the same will be supported in § 5. As was mentioned above, this situation differs profoundly from that in the face-centered cubic metals where dynamical recovery can occur at temperatures far below the temperatures at which an unloaded crystal recovers at a measurable rate.

Another important difference between Zn, Cd, and Mg on one hand and the face-centered cubic metals on the other hand is the stress dependence of the dynamical recovery. In the hexagonal metals the temperature at which θ begins to decrease with increasing temperature is rather well defined and therefore not markedly dependent on the applied stress (or the prestrain). From our description of the experiments it is obvious that the contrary is true for face-centered cubic metals, and that τ_3 (see Fig. 14) depends very strongly on temperature. This will be interpreted in § 7.

Conrad and Robertson (1957) find for cadmium that $\theta_0/G = 1.4 \times 10^{-4}$. Leaving aside the anomaly mentioned above, the corresponding value for zinc is about the same (Fahrenhorst and Schmid, 1930). The order of magnitude is the same as the lowest θ_I/G-values for copper crystals at room temperature, the minimum being $\theta_I/G = 1.7 \times 10^{-4}$ (crystals C 26 and C 14 of Fig. 11). This suggests strongly that the athermal work-hardening process of hexagonal crystals is essentially the same as the hardening process in the "unperturbed" easy glide which is observed in suitably oriented face-centered cubic crystals and which seems to be temperature-independent too.

Finally we turn to the questions of size and surface effects on the work-hardening curve. Paterson (1955) has investigated the stress-strain curves of copper single crystals of 1.5-mm diameter at room temperature. He obtains longer and flatter easy glide regions than Rosi (1954) does with crystals of 9.5-mm diameter, and he points out that this implies a size effect in the easy glide region. Paterson's stress-strain curves are in good agreement with Diehl's (1956a) (who used crystals of 4-mm diameter). The most detailed investigation of this size effect was published by Suzuki, Ikeda, and Takeuchi (1956) who investigated (also at room temperature) the stress-strain curves of copper crystals with diameters between 0.06 mm and 1 mm. Garstone, Honeycombe, and Greetham (1956) demonstrated the size effect with crystals grown from the same seed, and showed also that elements like silver or gold alloyed to copper in small concentrations increase the

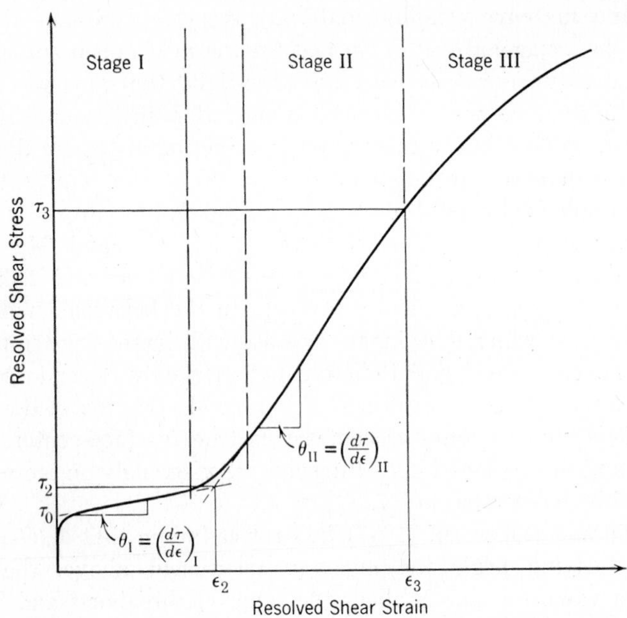

Fig. 14. Schematic representation of the typical stress-strain curve of a face-centered cubic metal crystal with its characteristic parameters.

length of the easy glide region, but do not influence its slope very much. Finally, Rebstock (1957) found the size effect, working with tubular crystals rather than with thin solid crystals.

With this impressive list of experimental investigations there can be no doubt about the existence of a strong size effect on stage I, and about the slight or negligible influence of the specimen diameter and the surface conditions on the later stages of the work-hardening curve. The size effect allows us to understand some of the results of Andrade and Henderson (1951) who worked with thin crystals and obtained extended regions of easy glide.

Although there are several reports in the literature on size and surface effect on the *critical shear stress* of hexagonal crystals (quoted, e.g., by Seeger, 1954c), published observations of such effects on the *work-hardening coefficients* of these metals do not seem to exist. Diehl (1956a) has drawn attention to the desirability of size effect experiments in hexagonal metals in view of the relationship to stage I of face-centered cubic metals. As will be shown in § 6.A, we do not expect a size effect if the majority of the dislocations slip out of the crystal. A surface coating that is able to prevent the dislocations from doing so, however, should raise the work-hardening coefficient of hexagonal metals at low temperatures.

4. THE FLOW STRESS OF PURE METALS AND DILUTE ALLOYS

It was pointed out in § 1 that a theory of flow stress is prerequisite to the development of a theory of work hardening. It was mentioned that parameters describing the dislocation density, which in general are not known a priori, enter into the theory of flow stress. The theory of the critical shear stress is included as a special case in which the dislocation density and the dislocation arrangement are that of an undeformed crystal. The theory has been developed in a series of papers (Seeger, 1954a, c, 1955d, 1956a) and will not be repeated here in detail.

The basic idea is that in a tensile test the rate of straining $\dot{\epsilon}$ is (at least in an idealized situation) prescribed by the experimental situation. What is measured is the applied stress which is required to move a sufficiently large number of dislocations per unit time over a sufficiently large area in the glide plane. If we confine ourselves to dislocations in one glide system only, the shear strain is connected with the dislocation strength b (modulus of Burgers vector), the number of dislocations per unit volume N, and the area A swept out, by the well-known formula

$$\epsilon = bAN \tag{7}$$

The dislocation movement will in general be resisted by obstacles which can be overcome with the aid of thermal energy and the applied stress. We assume that the thermal activation can be described by ordinary rate theory with an activation energy $U(\tau)$ depending on the applied shear stress τ. The strain rate is then given by

$$\dot{\epsilon} = bAN\nu_0 \exp\left[-\frac{U(\tau)}{kT}\right] \tag{8}$$

where ν_0 is a frequency factor which depends on the nature of the obstacle and the way in which it is overcome, and k is Boltzmann's constant. The equation of the flow stress as a function of the absolute temperature T and the strain rate $\dot{\epsilon}$ is obtained by solving eq. 8 for τ. For this it is necessary to know the function $U(\tau)$ explicitly. We base its calculation on the following model:

The critical shear stress or the flow stress of a crystal is reached when a sufficiently large number of dislocations in the glide plane are able to move over distances large compared with the mean separation between dislocations. The applied shear stress must be large enough to overcome the opposing action of the stress fields of the dislocations surrounding a moving dislocation. The main contribution comes from dislocations which are roughly parallel to the moving one and have the same Burgers vector. If these dislocations are distributed in a random pattern, and if the density per unit area is N', this opposing stress is given by

$$\tau_G = \alpha b G \sqrt{N'} \tag{9}$$

G denotes the shear modulus, and α is a constant of the order $1/5$ whose exact value depends on the details of the dislocation arrangement, Poisson's ratio ν, and the character of the dislocations involved. The wavelength of the fluctuating internal stresses which give rise to the opposing stress (eq. 9) is of the order of the mean distance between dislocations, i.e., 10^{-4} cm in annealed metal crystals and somewhat smaller in cold-worked ones. In all cases of practical interest it is so large that thermal fluctuations do not assist the applied stress in overcoming these opposing stresses. They give rise to a contribution to the flow stress which is temperature-independent except for a small indirect dependence due to temperature variation of the elastic constants. This has been indicated by the index G.

The other contribution to the flow stress of pure metals comes from the dislocations that penetrate the glide plane more or less perpendicularly, and which therefore have little or no elastic interaction with the dislocations moving in the glide plane. These dislocations have been called the "dislocation forest" by Cottrell who first considered them in the theory of transient creep (Cottrell, 1952). The theory of the dislocations cutting through the forest is very complicated. Depending on the dislocations involved, the number of jogs formed may be zero, one, or two. The energy of these jogs may depend strongly on the character of the dislocations, as mentioned in § 2. Some of the jogs created during cutting through the forest are able to generate vacancies and interstitials as they move along with the dislocation line.

In view of these complexities we confine ourselves to the simplest version of the theory. We assume that there is just one activation energy (U_0) that is rate-determining, and that the apparent activation energy depends linearly on the applied stress. We have

$$U = U_0 - v(\tau - \tau_G) \tag{10}$$

where v is an "activation volume." The stress effective in lowering the activation energy U_0 is the difference between the applied stress τ and the opposing internal stress τ_G, since the strain rate is determined by those parts of the forest which are situated in the adverse regions of the internal stress field.

If the dislocations of the forest are considered as being rigid (which of course is only an approximation), the activation volume is given by

$$v = bdl_0' \tag{11}$$

where b is the dislocation strength of the intersecting dislocation, d is the "diameter" of the intersected dislocation and measures the distance through which work is being done by the applied stress during the cutting process, and l_0' is the distance between the trees at which the moving dislocation line is "hung up." If we deal with unextended dislocations, d is of the order of the interatomic distance b (Cottrell, 1952); if we deal with extended dislocations, it is related to the width of the stacking fault ribbon (Seeger, 1954b).

Assuming d and l_0' to be independent of $(\tau - \tau_G)$, we obtain for the flow stress as a function of temperature T and strain rate $\dot{\epsilon}$

$$\tau(T) = \begin{cases} \tau_G + \dfrac{U_0 - kT \log (NAb\nu_0/\dot{\epsilon})}{v}, & T \leq T_0 = \dfrac{U_0}{k \log (NAb\nu_0/\dot{\epsilon})} \\ \tau_G, & T \geq T_0 \end{cases} \tag{12}$$

Friedel (1956) and Donth (1955) have refined these expressions by allowing for the stress dependence of l_0'. We shall not discuss these refinements and compare them with experiment here, since it is of equal importance to treat the dependence of the activation energy on the force acting at the point of intersection in more detail; in other words, to consider the stress dependence of d as well. Calculations on this problem have been under way for some time at Stuttgart, but are not yet completed.

The important features of eq. 12, which are unchanged by the refinements just mentioned, are the following ones (Fig. 15): the ratio τ/G of flow stress and shear modulus is independent of the temperature above the critical temperature T_0 (eq. 12). It rises almost linearly with decreasing temperature below T_0. The flow stress at absolute zero, which according to eq. 12 is equal to

$$\tau(0) = \tau_G + U_0/v \tag{13}$$

consists of about equal contributions of the forest (which will later on be referred to as τ_S) and of τ_G (Seeger, 1954c). This general behavior is in agreement with the observations on the hexagonal or trigonal metals Mg, Zn, Cd, and Bi (Seeger, 1954c), and on the face-centered cubic metal aluminum (Seeger, 1954c; Cottrell and Stokes, 1955). The

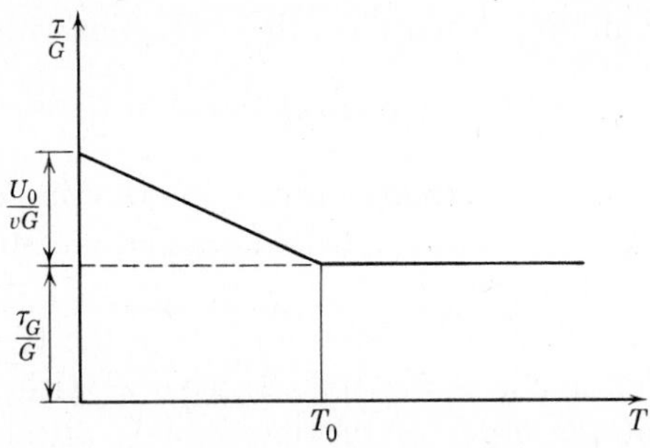

Fig. 15. Temperature dependence of the flow stress, τ, according to eq. 12.

magnitudes of the activation energies derived from experiment are as predicted by the theory (Seeger, 1955a, 1956a).

In all the metals just mentioned the extension of the dislocations is unimportant. This is essentially the reason why the theory based on a single activation energy (that for jog formation) works. In low stacking fault energy metals the temperature dependence of the flow stress is more complicated, as demonstrated by the measurements of Adams and Cottrell (1955). The theory shows (Seeger, 1955d) that we have different rate-determining processes in different temperature intervals and that one of them is the thermally activated generation of vacancies by jogs in screw dislocations. The temperature above which τ_S is unimportant is above the temperature range accessible to experiments. At room temperature we have therefore a substantial contribution of τ_S to the critical shear stress of metals like copper or nickel, whereas τ_S is virtually zero for aluminum crystals deformed at normal rates of strain at room temperature. It might be mentioned that Adams and Cottrell (1955) find very accurately a linear τ-T relationship in the temperature interval where, according to the theory, vacancy generation is rate-determining. This is exactly what we must expect on theoretical grounds, since in this case the assumptions leading to such a relationship are much better fulfilled than for the jog formation. (The role of l_0' is now played by the distance l_j between the jogs in a dislocation line.)

The concept that the critical shear stress of a pure metal is determined (according to eq. 12 or a more elaborate expression) by the temperature-independent contribution of the internal stress field (eq. 9) plus the temperature-dependent contribution from the dislocation forest (τ_S) is strictly contrary to two hypotheses which have been dominating the literature for some years, namely the "dynamical hypothesis" and the "critical length of Frank-Read sources" hypothesis. The latter hypothesis assumes that the critical shear stress is determined by the length of the longest Frank-Read sources and usually implies that the early hardening stages of a deformed metal crystal are due to the "exhaustion" of Frank-Read sources.

The arguments against the dynamical hypothesis have been given elsewhere (Leibfried and Haasen, 1954; Seeger, 1954a). Since this hypothesis, which assumed that the kinetic energy of a dislocation could easily reach the magnitude of its potential energy, seems now to be abandoned by the majority of its former supporters, we shall not repeat the arguments here. We shall also not repeat the arguments against the "length of Frank-Read sources" hypothesis (Seeger, 1954a), but mention just one point which might prove useful for future investigations. It seems to be generally accepted by now that the flow stress in strongly cold-worked metals is of the type proposed in Taylor's (1934) model of work hardening, namely that due to the elastic interaction of nearly parallel dislocations as discussed above, plus a superimposed "forest" contribution. This is the same picture as the one which we have adopted for the critical shear stress. If the critical shear stress were due to other contributions (Frank-Read mechanism, Peierls stress), there would have to exist a critical strain at which the changeover to the high strain mechanism occurs. This should manifest itself in a break in the flow stress-temperature relation as a function of prestrain. Such a break was never observed in pure metal crystals (Adams and Cottrell, 1955; Cottrell and Stokes, 1955; Seeger, Diehl, Mader, and Rebstock, 1957). On the other hand, such a break might be observable in materials like germanium, lithium fluoride, alpha-iron with carbon, and other alloys, and might help to study quantitatively the contribution to the flow stress of other mechanisms such as impurity locking, short- and long-range order, and Peierls stress.

So far we have been discussing the critical shear stress of hexagonal (or trigonal) and face-centered cubic metals without considering their purity. It is well known, however, that impure metal crystals show a higher critical shear stress than pure crystals grown in essentially the same way. In some cases, the best known being that of alpha-iron with carbon, it is generally accepted that this influence is due to the direct interaction between the impurity atoms and the dislocation lines. In the hexagonal close-packed and face-centered cubic metals this inter-

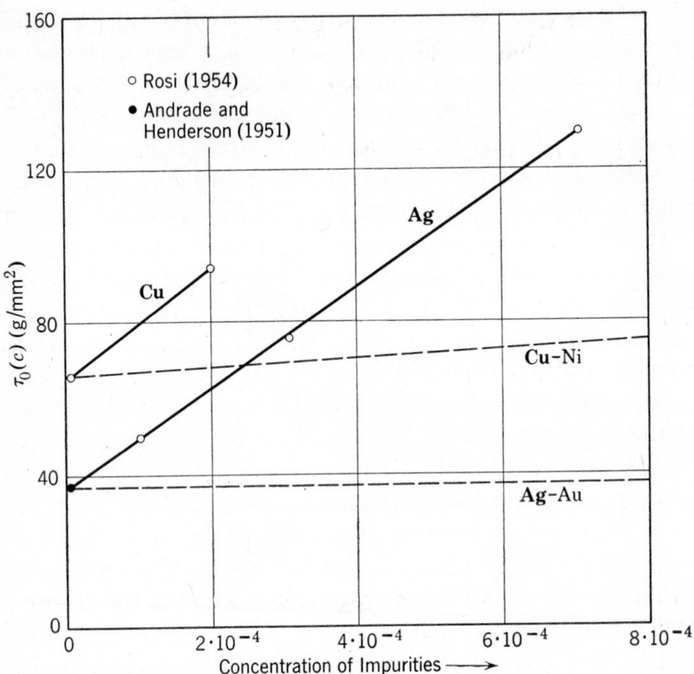

Fig. 16. The dependence of the critical shear stress of copper and silver single crystals at room temperature on the impurity content. The dashed lines are extrapolated from higher concentrations according to the measurements of Osswald (1933) (Cu-Ni) and Sachs and Weerts (1930) (Ag-Au).

action is far weaker. We believe that the main influence of the impurities on the critical shear stress of these metals comes about in an indirect way. The dislocation density which is introduced during the growth of a crystal depends on the impurity content and is higher the more impure the specimen. From the point of view of the present discussion the main effect of the impurities is to increase the quantity N' of eq. 9 and to decrease the length l_0' of eq. 11. Since these quantities are treated as parameters to be determined from experiment anyway, our theory holds for impure specimens just as well as for pure ones. This partly explains why the understanding of the plastic properties of close-packed metals has progressed so much further than that of body-centered cubic metals in which we always deal with both the "direct" and the "indirect" effects of impurities.

The experimental evidence for the proposed explanation is as follows: The temperature dependence of the critical shear stress is the same for pure and impure specimens, and, as mentioned above, the same as that for the flow stress at larger strains. Pinning effects (e.g., Cottrell locking) that would be strongly temperature-dependent can therefore be excluded. Now let us consider short-range ordering effects, in the widest sense of the word, which might give rise to a temperature-independent contribution to the flow stress. (See also Suzuki's paper in Part IV of this volume.) All these effects require a sufficiently high concentration c of impurity atoms in order to be both effective and not strongly temperature-dependent. An upper limit for their contribution $\tau(c)$ as a function of the concentration c can be obtained by assuming that this is proportional to $c(1 - c)$ and adjusting the constant of proportionality for concentrations of the order ½. This has been done in Fig. 16 (taken from Seeger, 1956b). We see from these two examples (and others) that small concentrations of impurities raise the critical shear stress much more than we would predict on the assumption of a concentration-independent dislocation density. We conclude, therefore, that the main effect comes through the increased dislocation density.

5. WORK HARDENING AND RECOVERY OF HEXAGONAL CLOSE-PACKED METALS

We have seen in § 5 that eq. 12 applies to hexagonal metals like Zn and Cd. We start with a discussion of the temperature dependence of the work-hardening coefficient θ based on that equation. Differentiating eq. 12 with respect to the strain ϵ and neglecting the small strain dependence of the logarithmic term, we obtain

$$\theta \equiv \frac{d\tau}{d\epsilon} - \begin{cases} \dfrac{d\tau_G}{d\epsilon} + \dfrac{dv}{d\epsilon}\dfrac{kT}{v^2}\log\dfrac{NAb\nu_0}{\dot{\epsilon}}, & T \leq T_0 \\[2ex] \dfrac{d\tau_G}{d\epsilon}, & T \geq T_0 \end{cases} \tag{14}$$

If we have basal glide only (as is the case in Zn and Cd to a good approximation) l_0', and therefore also v, will be strain-independent. We are left with the equation

$$\theta = d\tau_G/d\epsilon \equiv \theta_G \tag{15}$$

Equation 15 combined with eq. 9 says that the work-hardening coefficient is independent of temperature and strain rate as long as the variation of the dislocation arrangement and the dislocation density N' with strain are temperature-independent. If we work below the temperature of recovery there is no reason why the dislocated state of the material should depend on the temperature or strain rate. As can be seen from the discussion in § 3 and from Fig. 13, this conclusion is in agreement with experiment (Seeger, 1954c).

In the recovery range, which begins at about $-50°C$ for cadmium and at about $-30°C$ for zinc (Drouard, Washburn, and Parker, 1953), N' does depend on temperature, since the recovery tends to reduce the dislocation density to that of the undeformed crystals. In the temperature range at about room temperature we have therefore a competition between the recovery process on the one hand and the work-hardening process on the other hand, which tends to build up the same dislocation density and the same τ_G as deformation at low temperatures does. This competition accounts for the very pronounced dependence of the work-hardening coefficient on temperature in this interval (Boas and Schmid, 1930). At higher temperatures the recovery "wins." The coefficient of work hardening is very small and strain-rate insensitive in the usual range of strain rates. The work hardening created during the plastic deformation is almost instantaneously removed by recovery.

It has been mentioned that Polanyi and Schmid (1929) had already given this explanation in terms of softening during deformation by recovery. We believe that the process common to both static and dynamic recovery in the hexagonal metals Zn, Cd, and Mg is the climbing of edge dislocations or dislocations with a substantial edge component. To our knowledge the first to discuss recovery in terms of dislocation climb was Mott (1952, 1953). A theoretical treatment of the temperature dependence of θ based on a climb mechanism has not yet been published. It has been shown, however, that the strain-rate dependence of the work hardening of hexagonal metals at room temperature is in agreement with the rate of static recovery at that temperature (Seeger, 1956b), thus supporting the assertion of the identity of the static and the dynamic recovery mechanism.

From the preceding discussion it follows that the work-hardening process of hexagonal metals should be studied at low temperatures. Very few detailed observations in this temperature range are available. Therefore the knowledge of the work-hardening mechanism of the hexagonal metals is not nearly as advanced as that of the face-centered cubic metals. We shall not attempt a systematic treatment but content ourselves with a few remarks.

Mott (1952) has already mentioned the
distance of the dislocations in the hexagonal m
substantial proportion of them slip out of the c
no longer contribute to the flow stress. The followi
that this must indeed be the case or that the slip dis
least be comparable with the specimen diameter. Supp
are N'' sites per unit area where dislocations can be he
number n of dislocations at each site is assumed to increase w
If we eliminate n from the equations

$$\epsilon = nbN''L \tag{16}$$

and

$$\tau_G = \alpha n b G \sqrt{N''} \tag{17}$$

we obtain

$$\theta_G = \frac{\tau_G}{\epsilon} = \frac{\alpha G}{\sqrt{N''}L} \tag{18}$$

We think that N'' will hardly exceed 10^6. Putting $\theta_G = 10^{-4}$, $\alpha = 1/5$, we obtain $L = 5 \times 10^{-4} \times 10^3$ cm $= 5$ mm. Our considerations are of course too crude to tell us whether the slip distance is large, but still smaller than the diameter of the crystal (as assumed in eqs. 16, 17, and 18), or whether the majority of the dislocations slip out of the crystal as we will suppose in eqs. 19 through 23. Equation 16 gives $n = 14$ for $\epsilon = 1$. The estimate that L is of the order of magnitude of the crystal diameter is in agreement with the observation that the length of the slip lines is of the same order of magnitude. The estimated size of the pile-up is also not too unreasonable, since it is hard to see how large groups of dislocations could be held up in a hexagonal metal with one glide plane only. Possible exceptions are regions of crystal bending, where groups of edge dislocations are used to create the lattice curvature. This can be done in essentially two ways: At low temperatures all the edge dislocations of such a group will lie in the same glide plane and give rise to internal stresses which can lead to brittle failure. At higher temperatures these dislocations would be able to change into a polygonized arrangement and to avoid the building up of big stresses. This was suggested as the explanation for the coincidence of the temperature interval of beginning recovery and of the brittle-ductile transition in zinc (Seeger, 1956b).

Finally, we shall devote a few remarks to the question of latent strain hardening and the magnitude of the Bauschinger effect. Both effects were examined in shear tests on zinc crystals at $-196°$C by Edwards and Washburn (1954). They found that the latent harden-

of the slip systems whose glide directions made angles of 60° or 120° with the original glide direction was larger than that of the original system, and that it increased with increasing strain. This result cannot be understood in terms of τ_G; the authors considered the possibility of the formation of dislocation lines of low mobility by reactions between the dislocations of the original and the new glide system. We prefer an alternative explanation, however, which suggests that due to the mobility of the nodes of the dislocation network in the basal plane the Frank-Read sources of the latent systems are gradually eliminated during straining (Seeger, 1954b). It accounts also for the orientation dependence of the work hardening if two glide directions are about equally favored by the applied stress.

According to the preliminary picture which we have drawn above for the work hardening of hexagonal metals, we do not expect the cold-worked state to be very stable against deformation in the reversed direction. Some of the dislocations are presumably held up by lineage boundaries and regions of lattice curvature; the majority of the dislocations causing the work hardening are likely to be accommodated in the potential wells of the internal stress field of the dislocated structure of the undeformed crystal. This is a relatively stable situation as long as the work hardening is considerably smaller than the critical shear stress, which measures the depth of these potential wells. The instability increases with increasing strain which is what Edwards and Washburn observe.

6. WORK HARDENING OF FACE-CENTERED CUBIC CRYSTALS

The empirical results on the stress-strain curves of face-centered cubic metals were summarized in § 3. In the present section we shall discuss stages I and II. Stage III will be dealt with in § 7.

A. Stage I

In § 3 we have already mentioned the connection between the stress-strain curve of the hexagonal metals at low temperatures and stage I. This connection has been considered by several authors, in particular Mott (1952, 1953), in terms of dislocations slipping out of the crystal. The size effect discussed in § 3 indicates indeed that the slip distance of the dislocations is of the order of the specimen diameter. This is in agreement with electron microscope observation of faint slip lines on copper crystals in stage I which show that these lines extend over macroscopic distances (Mader, 1956). A common explanation of the easy glide phenomenon is that we have glide in one glide system only, thus implying that no sessile Lomer-Cottrell dislocations (see § 2) can form.

The most striking feature about stage I is the strong dependence of θ on the orientation of the tensile axis. As was particularly stressed by Diehl (1956a), this presents a difficulty for the accepted picture of glide in one system only. A part of the orientation dependence may be accounted for by the size effect, since for a given diameter the area of the slip plane depends on the crystal orientation (Garstone, Honeycombe, and Greetham, 1956). There is, however, no doubt that for normal diameter (1 mm to 1 cm) there is a genuine large effect. We think the explanation of the orientation dependence of the work-hardening rate and the extension of stage I is as follows:

The smallest slope θ_I (in Fig. 11 for crystals C 26 and C 14) corresponds indeed to unperturbed slip on one glide system (the so-called primary system) only. There may be some dislocation movement in other glide systems (so-called secondary systems), too, but this cannot cut down the slip distance effectively unless sessile Lomer-Cottrell dislocations are formed. [As can be seen from eqs. 18 and 33(*a*) and (*b*), a decrease in the slip distance means an increase in the work-hardening coefficient if the law of work hardening is linear.] For the formation of Lomer-Cottrell dislocations it is necessary that a sufficiently large number of dislocations be generated either in that secondary glide system that is able to form Lomer-Cottrell dislocations with the primary glide system, or in two secondary glide systems whose dislocations can give Lomer-Cottrell dislocations by reacting with one another. The crystallography of the dislocation reactions in the face-centered cubic lattice leading to sessile dislocations was discussed in some detail by Haasen (1953) and, with the present object in mind, by Seeger, Diehl, Mader, and Rebstock (1956). (The latter discussion is in terms of the orientation dependence of the *extension* of the easy glide region rather than of its *slope*. The orientation dependences of these two quantities are simply related to each other, since the orientation dependence of shear stress τ_2 at the end of stage I is smaller by one order of magnitude.)

The basic idea of these discussions is that the probability to produce a certain number of dislocations in a secondary glide system is greater the larger the resolved shear stress in this glide system. This argument neglects, of course, the latent hardening of the secondary systems, but it should be not too bad an approximation for small strains. The result of the discussion is shown in Figs. 17 and 18. In Fig. 17 it has been assumed that the primary slip system is [101], $(11\bar{1})$, i.e., that the tensile axis is situated in the triangle with the corners [100], [111], and

[110]. Triangles which are near to this "fundamental" triangle are hatched in such a way that the dislocations belonging to triangles containing the same kind of hatching lines are able to form Lomer-Cottrell

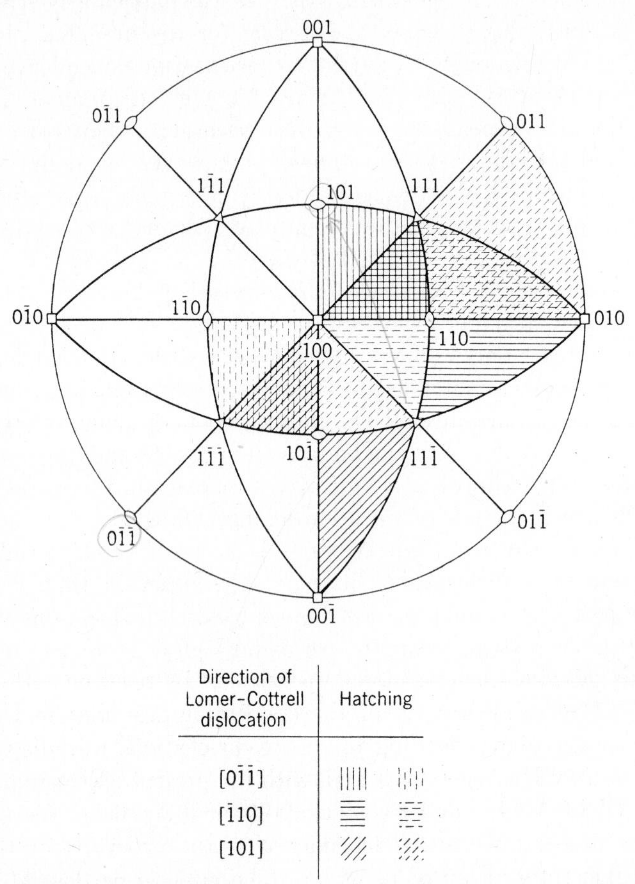

Fig. 17. Stereographic projection showing the combinations of glide systems capable of yielding Lomer-Cottrell dislocations. Dislocations whose triangle of maximum shear stress are hatched by the same pattern are capable of forming Lomer-Cottrell dislocations together. The crystallographic direction of the Lomer-Cottrell dislocations is related to the direction of the hatching lines.

dislocations with one another. (An exception is the triangle of the slip system [110], $(1\bar{1}\bar{1})$, which is represented twice among the hatched triangles of Fig. 17.) For more details see Seeger, Diehl, Mader, and Rebstock (1957).

The shaded area in Fig. 18 indicates the range of orientations where the probability of the formation of Lomer-Cottrell dislocations in the primary glide plane is smallest. The probability rises towards the [110]-corner, where sessile dislocations lying along the [$\bar{1}$10]-direction can be formed (by two different reactions) and towards the great circle (01$\bar{1}$) (connecting [100] and [111]), where sessile dislocations lying along the [0$\bar{1}\bar{1}$]-direction can be formed by the dislocations of the primary and the conjugate slip system. In the [100]- and the [111]-corners there are, of course, additional possibilities.

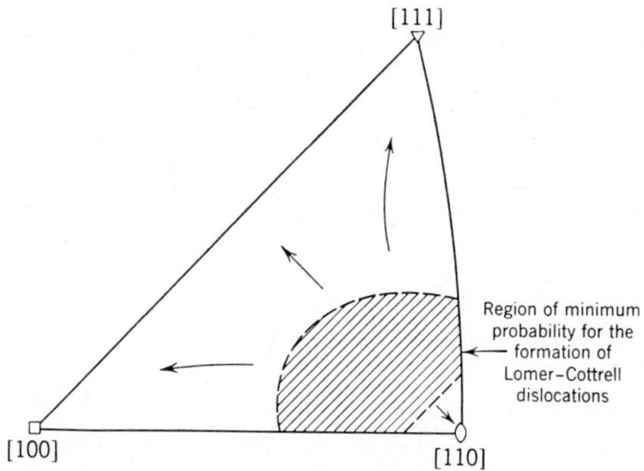

Fig. 18. The probability of formation of Lomer-Cottrell dislocations is smallest if the tensile axis lies in the shaded part of the orientation triangle. It rises in the directions of the arrows.

This orientation dependence represents strikingly well the orientation dependence of the work-hardening coefficient θ_I in stage I according to the measurements of Suzuki, Ikeda, and Takeuchi (1956), Diehl (1956a), Paterson (1955), and Rosi (1954) on copper, and of Staubwasser (1954) on aluminum.* This supports the picture that only for crystals within the shaded area do we have "unperturbed single glide" as in the hexagonal crystals, and that only in these crystals do the dislocations move all the way through the crystal. If we work with crystals of "normal" thickness, the dislocation movement in crystals oriented outside the shaded region is impeded, at least in some direction of motion, by the formation of Lomer-Cottrell dislocations. The corresponding slip distance is reduced and the coefficient of work hardening is increased, though not as much as if sessile dislocations of all three

* It would seem desirable to mention here that contrary to statements widespread in the literature, the measurements of Diehl (1956a–copper) and Staubwasser (1954–aluminum) show that the work-hardening coefficient θ_1 is not a minimum for [110]-crystals, but rises as the tensile axis moves from the shaded area of Fig. 18 towards the [110]-direction.

possible types (see § 3) were formed. The possible importance of Lomer-Cottrell dislocations in the easy glide region has already been discussed by Haasen (1953).

Strong experimental evidence for our view comes from the observations of Suzuki, Ikeda, and Takeuchi (1956) on the dependence of θ_{I} on crystal diameter for diameters smaller than 1 mm for different crystal orientations. For orientations in the shaded area of Fig. 18 they find θ_{I} to be diameter-independent, which is to be expected since the dislocations slip out of the crystal anyway. For orientations on the great circle $(01\bar{1})$, however, the slip distance is still large, but (at least in some direction) limited by sessile dislocations. Reducing the diameter therefore increases the probability of the dislocations slipping out of the crystal, thereby reducing the work-hardening rate. If the diameter is sufficiently small the holding-up of moving dislocations by sessile ones becomes unimportant. Then the work-hardening coefficient should become diameter-independent and equal to the value of the orientations of "slow hardening." This is indeed observed for a crystal diameter of about 0.2 mm.

We shall now summarize our discussion of stage I and supplement it by a few formulas. In the orientations of slow hardening (shaded area of Fig. 18) we have only "basic hardening" (Seeger, 1954a), in which most of the dislocations slip out of the crystal and only a small fraction are held up in sufficiently deep potential wells of the dislocated structure of the undeformed crystal. This is presumably the same situation as for hexagonal crystals with tensile axes in the interior of the orientation triangle. The shear strain is determined by the total number of slipping dislocations per unit area (N') and by the average diameter L_p of the slip plane in the crystal according to the equation

$$\epsilon = bN'L_p \tag{19}$$

Only those dislocations that are held up inside the crystal contribute to the work hardening. Their density $\bar{N}'$ is proportional to L_p and N'. We can therefore write

$$\bar{N}' = N'L_p/L_\infty \tag{20}$$

where L_∞ is the mean slip distance after which all dislocations were held up in an infinitely large crystal. Equation 20 holds only if L_p is smaller than L_∞.

Combining eqs. 19 and 20, we obtain the equation

$$\epsilon = b\bar{N}'L_\infty \tag{21}$$

which contains as the only variable on the right-hand side $\bar{N}'$. This is the quantity that determines the work hardening. We have therefore derived the result that the basic hardening is independent of the crystal diameter, provided this is not too large. This is in agreement with the experiments of Suzuki, Ikeda, and Takeuchi (1956). Rosi (1954) investigated copper crystals of 9.5-mm diameter and the same purity as Diehl's (1956a) thinner crystals. His minimum slopes in stage I are considerably larger than Diehl's. This might be interpreted as L_∞ being about 1.5 cm.

The preceding discussion is quite general and independent of the mechanism of basic hardening. A derivation of the numerical value of the work-hardening coefficient θ_{I} is more difficult, since we are concerned with the particularly difficult range where the work hardening $(\tau - \tau_0)$ is of the same order of magnitude as the critical shear stress τ_0. To show the orders of magnitude we use tentatively the same model as in § 5, and assume that during the plastic deformation an increasing number n of dislocations is held up by N'' fixed and randomly distributed obstacles. We then have

$$\bar{N}' = nN'' \tag{22}$$

and find, using eq. 17, that

$$\theta_{\mathrm{I}} = \frac{\alpha G}{L_\infty} \frac{1}{\sqrt{N''}} \tag{23}$$

Inserting $\alpha = 1/5$, $L_\infty = 1.5$ cm, $\theta_{\mathrm{I}}/G = 1.7 \times 10^{-4}$ (see § 3) into eq. 23 gives

$$N'' = \tfrac{1}{2} \times 10^6/\text{cm}^2 \tag{24}$$

which is a reasonable order of magnitude.

Equation 23 is formally the same as eq. 18. It appears, therefore, that it does not matter whether L_∞ is smaller or larger than L_p. This is, however, a consequence of the special assumption that the work-hardening process in stage I and in the hexagonal metals leaves the mean slip distance of the dislocations unchanged. We know that this is not so in stage II, but our present experimental knowledge is insufficient to decide this point for stage I.

Basic hardening involves the concept that no serious obstacles to glide be formed by the interaction of two glide systems. For the orientations outside the shaded area in Fig. 18 such obstacles, namely Lomer-Cottrell dislocations of a certain crystallographic direction, will be generated relatively frequently. They will cut down the average slip distance to a value smaller than L_∞ and in many cases smaller than L_p. We find then some "interaction hardening" superimposed on the basic hardening, provided the crystal diameter is not smaller than the mean slip distance as limited by the sessile dislocations. A quantitative theory for this type of hardening is not yet available and will probably have to be preceded by a theory of latent hardening.

B. The Transition from Stage I to Stage II

Our picture of stage I is that in some crystal orientations practically no Lomer-Cottrell dislocations are formed (unperturbed easy glide). In other orientations, however, the resolved shear stress in certain secondary glide systems is large enough to generate dislocations which can form Lomer-Cottrell dislocations in one of the three <110>-directions of the primary glide plane. This accounts for the larger hardening rate θ_I of such crystals through a reduction of the mean slip distance in *some* directions. With increasing plastic deformations a stress high enough for the generation of a sufficiently large number of Lomer-Cottrell dislocations along at least two of the three <110>-directions will eventually be reached. From there on the slip distance in all directions is limited by Lomer-Cottrell dislocations. We think that stage II is fully developed if Lomer-Cottrell dislocations of all three types possible in the primary glide system are formed in significant numbers.

We shall now discuss how the dependence of the transition stage I–stage II on orientation, temperature, and impurity content is accounted for by our picture. Rosi (1954) and Garstone, Honeycombe, and Greetham (1956) stated that $(\tau_2 - \tau_0)$ (see Fig. 14) is orientation-independent. As already mentioned in § 3, this is not in agreement with the results of Diehl (1956a), who covered a larger part of the orientation triangle than the other authors did. He showed that $(\tau_2 - \tau_0)$ is roughly orientation-independent in the middle of the stereographic triangle, but that it rises quite pronouncedly towards the boundaries and in particular the corners of the triangle. This is what we have to expect in our picture. In order to produce all three types of Lomer-Cottrell dislocations simultaneously, we must have a sufficiently large resolved shear stress in glide systems whose triangles of maximum resolved shear stress lie on different sides of the triangle of the primary system (Fig. 17). It is obvious that a smaller resolved shear stress in the primary system is needed to achieve this objective if the tensile axis is situated in the middle of the orientation triangle than if it lies near one of the boundary lines.

The explanation of the temperature dependence of the beginning of stage II and of the extension of stage I (for the experiments see § 3) has already been given by Seeger (1954). It was pointed out that in order to create a substantial number of dislocations in a secondary glide system the resolved shear stress in that system minus the latent hardening must at least be equal to the critical shear stress. Since the critical shear increases, in general, with decreasing temperature (as does the latent hardening *) the stress to activate the secondary system is larger the lower the temperature. Since the work-hardening coefficient in stage I is either temperature-independent (basic hardening) or (by the argument just given) decreases somewhat with decreasing temperature (if Lomer-Cottrell dislocations interfere with the dislocation movement), the extension of the easy glide region is larger the lower the temperature. This has been observed by a number of authors, most recently by Garstone, Honeycombe, and Greetham (1956), whose interpretation is essentially the same as ours. These authors also considered the effect of small impurity concentrations and were able to show that the increased length of the easy glide region can be accounted for by the increase in the critical shear stress of the alloys. The same tendency can be seen from a comparison of Paterson's (1955) and Diehl's (1956a) work. Paterson, who used purer copper, finds shorter easy glide regions than Diehl does for corresponding orientations.

C. Stage II †

After the discussions of § 6.A and B it is straightforward to base the discussion of the present section on the assumption that at the beginning of stage II the slip distance of the dislocations in the primary system is limited by Lomer-Cottrell dislocations. For the processes occurring during stage II, two different theories had been proposed. Friedel (1955) assumes that at the beginning of stage II a very large number of Lomer-Cottrell dislocations are formed by a sort of catastrophic process using up all the Frank-Read sources available in the secondary glide systems. Thus a fixed number of Lomer-Cottrell barriers is created, serving as obstacles for the pile-up of dislocations. The number of dislocations increases proportionally to the strain. The formal theory is therefore the same as used in § 5, and accounts for the linearity of the work-hardening curve.

This linearity is explained in quite a different way by Seeger (1956a). He assumes that the formation of Lomer-Cottrell barriers continues throughout stage II. This gives rise to a decrease of the slip distance with increasing strain (roughly as the first inverse power of the strain) and to small dislocation groups of essentially constant size, piled up against the barriers and distributed more or less at random. As we

* For the discussion of the temperature dependence of latent hardening see § 6.D.

† The discussion of the present section and also of §§ 7 and 8 will be rather brief. For more details and references the papers by Seeger, Diehl, Mader, and Rebstock (1957) and Mader (1957) should be consulted.

shall see later (eqs. 29 through 33), this picture also accounts for the linearity of the stress-strain curves.

Experiments to decide between the two theories were carried out (Diehl and Rebstock, 1956; Seeger, Diehl, Mader, and Rebstock, 1957; and Rebstock, 1957) and were found to be in full agreement only with the second theory.

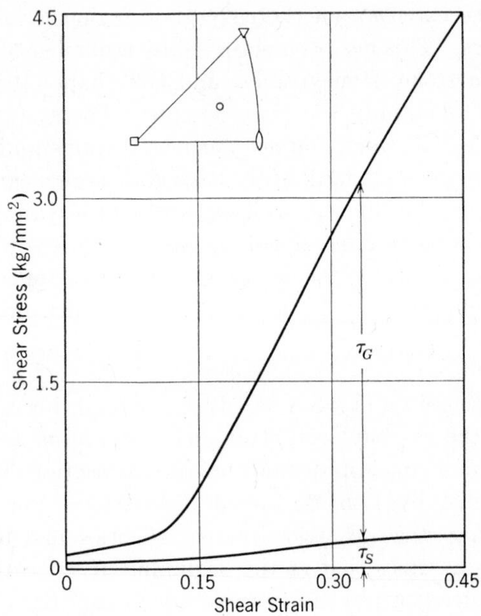

Fig. 19. The division of the stress-strain curve of a copper crystal deformed at room temperature into $\tau_S(\epsilon)$ and $\tau_G(\epsilon)$.

The first step was to decide whether the strong increase of flow stress in stage II comes from the temperature-dependent contribution τ_S of the dislocation forest or from the temperature-independent contribution of the stress fields of the dislocations lying in the primary slip plane. Figure 19 (taken from Seeger, Diehl, Mader, and Rebstock, 1957) refers to a copper crystal deformed at room temperature. It shows that τ_S and τ_G contribute to a comparable extent to the critical shear stress. The large increase of flow stress in stage II, however, is due nearly exclusively to an increase in τ_G, so that at the end of stage II τ_G is an order of magnitude larger than τ_S. The same type of change-in-temperature experiments as used for the preparation of Fig. 19 were carried out by Adams and Cottrell (1955–copper) and by Cottrell and Stokes (1955–aluminum). Their results refer mainly to stage III, however, and are therefore not directly related to the present question.

The unimportance of the change in τ_S for the work hardening in stage II had already been deduced indirectly by Diehl (1956a). It was confirmed further by tensile experiments on tubular copper crystals carried out after intermediate twists (Rebstock, 1957; Seeger, Diehl, Mader, and Rebstock, 1957). Such a confirmation was necessary in view

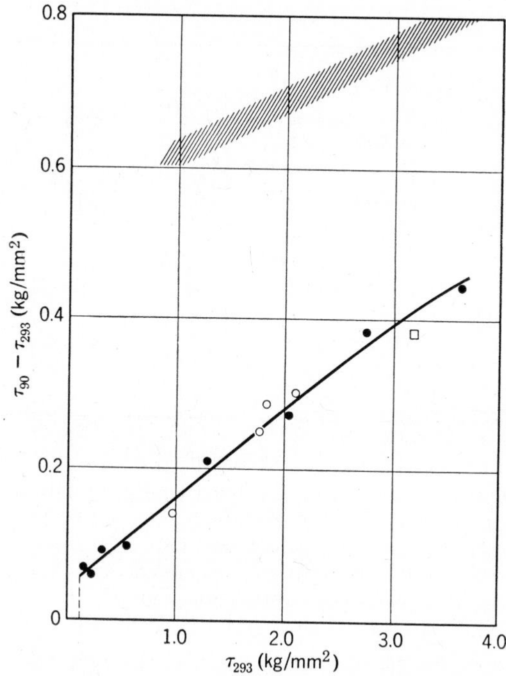

Fig. 20. Difference in flow stress at 90°K (τ_{90}) and 239°K (τ_{293}) as a function of τ_{293}. The open circles refer to crystals that have undergone twists with shears γ between 0.01 and 0.02; the open square refers to an intermediate twist with $\gamma = 0.1$. (See text.)

of the results of Paxton and Cottrell (1954) who had concluded from intermediate twisting experiments on solid aluminum crystals that the increase in flow stress is due to the increase of forest density during the twist, or, in our language, due to τ_S. Figure 20 shows that this is not so. It represents the change in flow stress accompanying a change in temperature from 90°K to 293°K as a function of the flow stress of copper crystals at 293°K. Full circles were obtained by tension alone, empty marks after one or two intermediate twists. The hatched area indicates which experimental points would have been obtained if the increase in flow stress after a twist corresponding to a surface shear $\gamma = 0.02$ had been due to an increase in τ_S only. It can be seen that within experimental accuracy the total increase in flow stress comes from τ_G. Since the only conceivable way in which dislocations on glide planes intersecting the primary slip plane can increase τ_G substantially is by forming barriers in the primary plane, these results can be taken as a confirmation of the view that slip on secondary systems

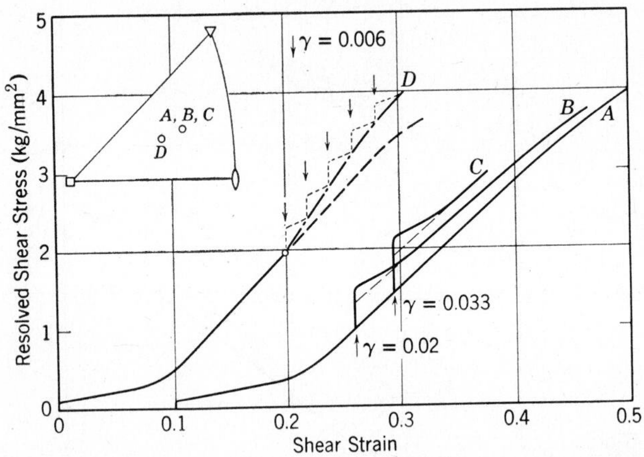

Fig. 21. Tensile stress-strain curves of tubular copper crystals at room temperature. (The origin of curves A, B, C is shifted to $\epsilon = 0.1$.) The arrows indicate intermediate twists with shears γ. The dashed branch of D is obtained by extrapolation from the tensile curve without intermediate twists and shows that repeated twists increase the average work-hardening rate.

influences the stress-strain curve mainly through the formation of barriers (sessile dislocations).

The twisting experiments on tubular crystals, which avoided possible complications due to the elastic core, disagreed in still another way with the results on the solid aluminum crystals. A single intermediate twist was found to raise the flow stress, but not the work-hardening coefficient in tension (Fig. 21), contrary to Paxton and Cottrell (1954), who observed a considerable increase in the work-hardening rate. Paterson (1955), working on solid copper crystals, found that an intermediate twist raised the flow stress but lowered the subsequent rate of work hardening in reverse testing. He also points out the disagreement with Paxton and Cottrell.

Diehl and Rebstock (1956) pointed out that the twisting experiments contradict Friedel's (1955) theory, which assumes that a single action of secondary slip is sufficient to give an increased coefficient of work hardening. In order to get such an increase (in the average) it is necessary to have repeated twists and therefore repeated action of secondary systems (Fig. 22). This of course is in line with the theory of continual formation of barriers in stage II.

A corollary of this formation of barriers throughout stage II is that the slip distance of the dislocations in the primary glide system must

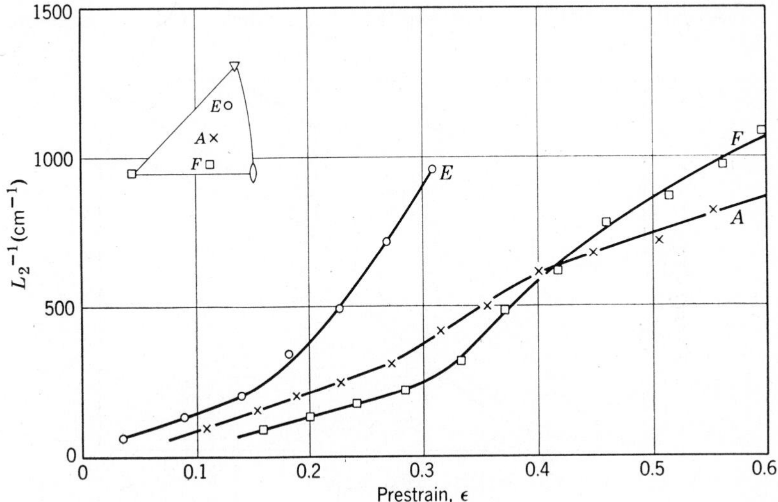

Fig. 22. Reciprocal of active length of slip lines L_2 on top surface of copper single crystals as a function of prestrain in tensile test at room temperature. Orientations of the crystals as indicated in the stereographic triangle. Strain increment after polishing $\Delta\epsilon = 0.05$.

decrease with increasing plastic deformation. The slip distance can be measured by observing the length of slip lines that are formed at a certain strain. This has been done for one copper crystal by Blewitt, Coltman, and Redman (1955), who polished the crystal after a prestrain ϵ and observed the length of the slip lines after an additional strain increment. (We call this the active length of slip lines at strain ϵ.) A more detailed investigation on copper crystals deformed at room temperature was carried out by Rebstock (1957) and Seeger, Diehl, Mader, and Rebstock (1957) (Figs. 22 and 23). Figure 22 gives the active length of slip lines for three different crystals A, E, and F, and Fig. 23 the corresponding stress-strain curves. It can be seen that in stage II the following relation between the slip distance L_2 of screw dislocations and the shear strain ϵ obtains:

$$L_2 = \frac{\Lambda_2}{\epsilon - \epsilon^*} \tag{25}$$

ϵ^* is somewhat smaller than ϵ_2, the shear strain at the end of stage I. A typical value of Λ_2 for crystals in the middle of the stereographic triangle is $\Lambda_2 = 8 \times 10^{-4}$ cm.

Rebstock's (1957) observations of L_2 were obtained with an optical microscope in dark field illumination. We have to add some comments on the relation of the "active lengths of slip lines" that are measured

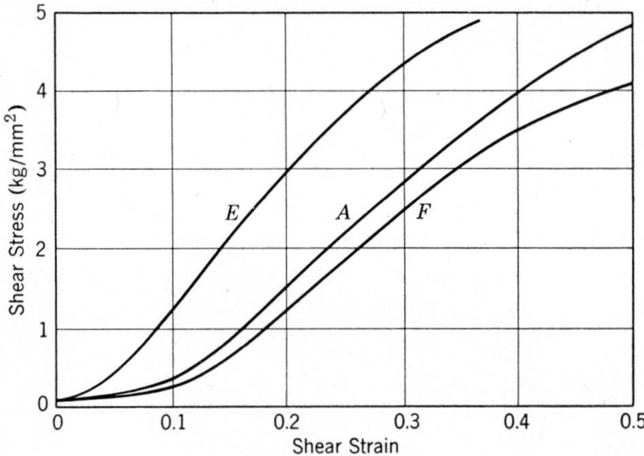

Fig. 23. Shear stress-shear strain curves of the single crystals *A, E, F* shown in Fig. 22.

under these conditions to the actual length of the individual slip lines that are observed with the electron microscope. Mader (1957) has recently succeeded in obtaining dark field illumination photographs and electron micrographs of the same areas on the crystal surface. Using essentially the same polishing technique as Rebstock, he found that the lines visible in stage III in the electron microscope are "slip bands" (see § 8), and that the lengths of the lines as observed in the optical microscope and in the electron microscope are the same. In stage II there are no slip bands but only individual lines. They are visible with the dark field illumination technique only if the lines are grouped together favorably. The length of the individual lines is smaller than the length of such a group as visible in the optical microscope. The exact ratio of these two lengths is not yet known. Preliminary results show that it is of the order one-half. This is in agreement with the $1/L_2$ data as extrapolated from stage III (Fig. 22). In quantitative discussion we shall therefore employ the value $\Lambda_2 = 4 \times 10^{-4}$ cm instead of the value given above.

A relation corresponding to eq. 25 applies to the observations on the side surface where the slip distance L_1 of the edge dislocations can be measured. It reads

$$L_1 = \frac{\Lambda_1}{\epsilon - \epsilon^*} \tag{26}$$

Rebstock finds experimentally [in agreement with the experiments of Müller and Leibfried (1955) on aluminum]

$$\Lambda_1 \approx 2\Lambda_2 \tag{27}$$

We shall now show how the decrease of the slip distance according to eqs. 25 and 26 is related to the linear law of work hardening in stage II. Since the hardening due to the change in τ_S is negligible for the present purpose, we shall only be concerned with

$$\theta_G = d\tau_G/d\epsilon \tag{28}$$

We use the following model for the calculation of θ_G: N dislocation rings per unit volume lie in the slip plane. Since these rings are held up by Lomer-Cottrell dislocations lying along the three [110]-directions in the slip plane, we expect the shape of these rings to be hexagon-like. Such hexagons can be seen in the infrared studies of Dash (1956) on silicon crystals. They could be interpreted in terms of Lomer-Cottrell dislocations, since the Bravais lattice of silicon is face-centered cubic.

These dislocation rings are supposed to be grouped together in groups of n rings, which presumably have come from the same Frank-Read source and which have been held up by a Lomer-Cottrell dislocation in or near to their glide plane. These groups of rings are assumed to be distributed more or less at random throughout the crystal volume. The shear stress oppossing dislocation movement in the primary glide system will then be inversely proportional to the mean distance between the groups.†

To simplify the discussion we consider the dislocation rings as being made up of screw and edge dislocations only. We shall see that the hardening due to edges and screws is about the same. We conclude that the exact shape of the dislocation rings is not important.

† Under all practical conditions the diameter of the rings is large compared with the distance of neighboring groups of different rings. It is therefore justified to treat the dislocations as being straight and infinitely long.

Since N/n is the number of piled-up groups per unit volume, the mean distance between the groups of screw dislocation is $(NL_1)^{-1/2}$ and that between the groups of edge dislocations is $(NL_2)^{-1/2}$, apart from a factor of the order unity. Each group acts like a dislocation of strength nb. The stress τ_G due to screw dislocations can therefore be written also

$$\tau_G = \alpha_2 Gnb\sqrt{NL_1/n} \tag{29}$$

a corresponding equation with suffixes 1 and 2 interchanged holding for edge dislocations.* The parameters α_1 and α_2 take care of the factors which come in through the details of the geometry. If it is justified to neglect the differences in the geometry of the stress fields of edge and screw dislocations, the ratio of these parameters will be determined by Poisson's ratio ν, and will be given by

$$\alpha_2/\alpha_1 = 1 - \nu \tag{30}$$

If the dislocation groups are arranged at random (say in a pattern similar to the individual dislocation lines in a planar section of the undeform crystal), α_2 will be of the order $1/5$ (Seeger, 1954a). If we have large deviations from such an arrangement, e.g., a concentration of dislocation groups on a few planes with very few dislocations in between, we should use smaller parameters α_1 and α_2. This means that the numerical considerations based on $\alpha_2 = 1/5$ underestimate the number n of dislocations if we try to deduce this from eq. 29.

Again apart from a factor of the order unity the strain increment due to dN dislocations per unit volume moving through slip distances L_1 (screws) and L_2 (edges) is

$$d\epsilon = bL_1L_2\, dN \tag{31}$$

Combining eqs. 29, 31, and 25 with each other, we obtain the following differential equation for the stress τ_G due to the screw dislocations:

$$\frac{d\tau_G}{d\epsilon} = \frac{\alpha_2{}^2G^2bn}{2\Lambda_2}\frac{\epsilon - \epsilon^*}{\tau_G} - \frac{1}{2}\frac{\tau}{\epsilon - \epsilon^*} \tag{32}$$

The particular integral of this equation which is of interest to us is (Seeger, Diehl, Mader, Rebstock, 1957)

$$\theta_G = \alpha_2 G\sqrt{\frac{bn}{3\Lambda_2}} \tag{33a}$$

* Screw and edge dislocations of the same glide system do not interact elastically with each other.

The solution of the corresponding equation for edge dislocations is

$$\theta_G = \alpha_1 G \sqrt{\frac{bn}{3\Lambda_1}} \tag{33b}$$

The differences between L_1 and L_2 (eq. 27) on the one hand and between α_1 and α_2 (eq. 30) on the other hand compensate each other. For practical purposes eqs. 33(a) and 33(b) therefore give the same results.* This confirms that the detailed shape of the dislocations rings presumably does not matter. Inserting the experimental values $\theta/G = 4 \times 10^{-3}$ and $\Lambda_2 = 4 \times 10^{-4}$ cm into these equations and keeping in mind our previous remarks about the nature of our approximations, we find

$$n \gtrsim 25 \tag{34}$$

In § 7 we shall produce an upper estimate for n from the experimental data on the end of stage II at very low temperatures, which will show that n cannot be larger than about 25. Another upper estimate can be obtained in the following way: The groups of dislocations of opposite sign which exist at the ends of slip lines tend to attract and annihilate each other in the very first moment after their formation, before they are stabilized by subsequent slip in their surroundings. The stress preventing them from doing so can at best be equal to the applied resolved shear stress τ, but is presumably slightly smaller since the internal stresses in the crystal have on the average an opposing effect. Leibfried (1954) has treated the problem of a large number n of dislocations pressed against a barrier of circular shape (radius R) in their glide plane by an applied shear stress τ. Since he assumed Poisson's ratio to be zero, a good approximation to the present problem should be to put $L_2 = 2R$.. We obtain from Leibfried's equations:

$$n = \frac{4\tau R}{\pi b G} = \frac{2\Lambda_2}{\pi b}\frac{\theta}{G} = \frac{2 \times 4 \times 10^{-4} \times 4 \times 10^{-3}}{\pi \times 2.56 \times 10^{-8}} = 40 \tag{35}$$

The value $n = 40$ found by this method is an upper limit to the actual value since we certainly have not underestimated the acting shear stress. This upper limit is in good agreement with our previous estimates.

In our derivation of the lower limit for n (eqs. 33 and 34) we have taken into account that the stress fields of groups of dislocations of opposite sign tend to cancel each other if they overlap. We have not allowed, however, for a possible "screening" of the stress field of one

* If we had used a two-dimensional model instead of a three-dimensional one, we would have obtained eq. 33(a) or 33(b), with the factor 3 replaced by 2.

such group by slip on secondary glide systems. If such screening took place the number N of dislocations entering the equation for the strain (eq. 31) would have to be larger than the number N of dislocations entering the equation for the stress (eq. 29). In order to obtain the experimental coefficient of work hardening we would have to increase the numerical value of n (eq. 34). This would contradict our estimates for the upper limit of n. We conclude that n is indeed of the order estimated above, and that screening is rather unimportant in stage II. The latter result is very satisfactory, since an effective screening requires about as many dislocations in secondary glide systems as there are in the primary system. Towards the end of stage II the slip distances are so short that the dislocations in secondary glide systems would produce a considerable contribution to the total shear that should be easily detectable by X-ray methods. Deviations of the order of only 1% from the shear on the primary glide system have been found so far. These deviations are too small to be connected with an appreciable amount of screening, but are sufficient to account for the contribution of the dislocations forming Lomer-Cottrell barriers.

The total number of dislocations in a work-hardened crystal as calculated from our assumptions is of the same order of magnitude as that deduced from X-ray data. We find that a total density (positive plus negative dislocations) $2N' = 10^{10}/\text{cm}^2$ corresponds to a flow stress $\tau = 0.3\theta$. This is in line with X-ray estimates [for details see Hirsch (1956)].

In conclusion, we contrast our picture with Friedel's (1955) theory. We concluded that in stage II the size of the dislocation groups is approximately strain-independent and equal to about 25 dislocations, or slightly less. The slip distance decreases with increasing strain; this is due to a continual formation of Lomer-Cottrell barriers by a small amount of glide on secondary systems. The geometrical arrangement of the groups is thought to be more or less statistical, in a pattern such that groups of opposite sign stabilize each other to some extent. As a consequence, the flow stress is proportional to the square root of the dislocation density (= number of dislocations penetrating a unit area perpendicular to the glide plane). In Friedel's theory the slip distance is assumed to be constant. No creation of barriers takes place during stage II. The deformed state is therefore not stable under unloading or reversed loading. The number of dislocations in each group is proportional to the stress. The same results hold for the total dislocation density.

The preceding discussion of experimental results has shown clearly that they fit far better into our theory than into Friedel's. We wish to point out that this agreement is not confined to copper crystals deformed at room temperature, where most observations were made, but also holds at liquid helium temperature, where the easy glide region extends to much higher stresses. The estimates which give as an upper limit $n = 25$ are based on experimental data obtained at liquid helium temperatures, as will be explained in § 7. This proves that even if stage II extends to very large stresses and strains, the number of dislocations per group does not grow larger than our theory demands. Another piece of experimental evidence pertaining both to room temperature and very low temperatures is the measurements of the electrical resistivity of deformed copper crystals as a function of flow stress by Blewitt, Coltman, and Redman (1955). Apart from small corrections the electrical resistivity due to dislocations should be proportional to the dislocation density. Blewitt *et al.* find that it is proportional to the square of the flow stress, both at room temperature in stage II and III, and at liquid helium temperature where stage II only is observed. These experiments therefore also support the view that our theory holds down to the lowest temperatures.

D. Latent Hardening and Bauschinger Effect

The picture that we have drawn for the hardening mechanism in face-centered cubic metals still lacks certain details. They can best be filled in by theoretical and experimental studies of additional properties of the deformed crystals. We first list a few properties on which experimental work has not yet been done, but which could be directly related to the data derived from stress-strain measurements, surface observations, and electrical data: stored energy, change in elastic moduli due to the cold work, change in density due to dislocations, small angle scattering of X rays. [For the theory of the two last-mentioned properties see Stehle and Seeger (1956) and Seeger (1956c).]

We shall confine our discussion to the questions of the *hardening of secondary slip systems* (latent hardening), and the *stability* or *instability of the deformed state* under reversed loading (Bauschinger effect), on which some experimental information is available. We have stated repeatedly that the increase in the flow stress, i.e., the *hardening of the primary slip systems,* is mainly due to an increase in τ_G, and not in τ_S. The reason for this is that during deformation many more dislocations are created lying in the glide plane than threading the glide plane. The situation, however, is just the reverse for dislocations with glide planes that intersect the primary one (so-called secondary glide planes). The large number of dislocations piled up in the primary plane should give rise to a large τ_S-contribution to the latent hardening of these secondary slip planes. We have mentioned this already in connection with the temperature dependence of the onset of stage II. Apart from this we do not know of existing experimental evidence for the rather pronounced temperature dependence of latent hardening of metal crystals predicted by the theory. It should not be too hard, however, to obtain such evidence by suitable experiments.

A conclusion from the character of τ_S of the latent hardening is that the latent hardening of secondary planes should depend on the ease with which the dislocations in these planes can intersect the dislocations of the primary system. A straight forward prediction of dislocation theory is that this intersecting should be easiest for the cross-slip system (Seeger, 1956b), since this requires jog formation neither in the dislocations of the primary system nor in those of the cross-slip system. This prediction is verified by observations of Garstone, Honeycombe, and Greetham (1956). They state that the first slip traces of secondary systems that can be observed in stage II are due to the cross-slip plane (see also the discussion in § 9 on cross slip in alpha-brass), other secondary planes coming into action later.

The discussion of *stability against unloading* in stage I is much the same as that given in § 5 for the hexagonal crystals. The conclusion is that the deformed state is not very stable and that we should expect a large Bauschinger effect, at least for the orientations of unperturbed easy glide. Contrary to this, we have two additional stabilizing mechanisms in stage II: Lomer-Cottrell dislocations will not only hold up dislocations on their way but will also form in the rear of piled-up groups, thus preventing the dislocations from slipping back when the load is reversed. The other stabilizing influence is the formation of piled-up groups at new sites. They will in general form in such a way that they are attracted elastically by already existing groups and will therefore possess a certain stability when the applied stress is removed.

These conclusions are in qualitative agreement (Seeger, Diehl, Mader, Rebstock, 1957) with the observations of Buckley and Entwistle (1956) on the Bauschinger effect of aluminum crystals deformed at room temperature. These authors find that the Bauschinger effect (measured by the "Bauschinger glide strain" $a_{3/4}$) increases in stage I approximately proportional to the work-hardening stress $(\tau - \tau_0)$, and remains constant at higher stresses.

7. DYNAMICAL RECOVERY AND WORK SOFTENING OF FACE-CENTERED METALS

In § 3 we have discussed the basic features of the dynamical recovery of face-centered cubic metals. We have particularly emphasized the stress dependence of the dynamical recovery which is quite different from that of the dynamical recovery of hexagonal metals. The general picture of the dynamical recovery occurring in stage III is this: In stage II a dislocation arrangement is built up that is essentially independent of the temperature and strain rate. At a sufficiently high stress and temperature the dislocations can undergo processes which at lower stresses and temperatures had been suppressed. They may, for example, allow the dislocations to circumvent obstacles that held them up in stage II and thus cause the coefficient of work hardening to be smaller than in stage II. Another possibility is that these processes enable some dislocations of opposite sign to annihiliate each other and to reduce the internal stress fields. Superimposed on the continuing hardening process, this also results in a reduction of the work-hardening coefficient.

Under these conditions the dislocated state of a crystal is no longer characterized to a good approximation by the stress or the strain, but depends markedly on the way in which a certain stress or strain at a certain temperature was reached. This is clearly illustrated by the phenomenon of "work softening" that was investigated by Cottrell and Stokes (1955) and others. Figure 24 shows schematically what happens if a crystal is deformed to the end of stage II at a low temperature T_1, unloaded, and reloaded at a higher temperature T_2. The work-hardened state reached at T_1 is unstable under the combined action of applied stress and temperature T_2. A catastrophic process sets in that tends to reduce the work hardening to what it would have been if the prestraining had been done at temperature T_2 (dashed curve in Fig. 24). There is general agreement that the mechanism of work softening and that of dynamical recovery in stage III are the same. The phenomenon of work softening can be used to define the beginning of stage III by the prestress at which the yield drop $\Delta\tau_y$ (Fig. 24) extrapolates to zero.

The processes responsible for work softening and dynamical recovery of face-centered cubic metals must satisfy the following requirements:

1. They must be possible in the face-centered cubic metals but not in the hexagonal metals, since in the latter the recovery characteristics are quite different (see § 5).

2. The energy of activation must be strongly stress-dependent.

3. This activation energy must be small for high stacking fault energy metals and large for low stacking fault energy metals (see the discussion of the difference in the empirical results on copper and aluminum in § 3).

So far only two processes have been proposed that satisfy these requirements: cross slip of screw dislocations (Seeger, 1955a; Diehl, Mader, and Seeger, 1955; Seeger, 1956a; Seeger, Diehl, Mader, and Rebstock, 1957) and collapse of Lomer-Cottrell dislocations (Cottrell and Stokes, 1955; Friedel, 1955; Cottrell, 1956; Stroh, 1956). Both processes have been discussed in § 3. The mathematical theory for the

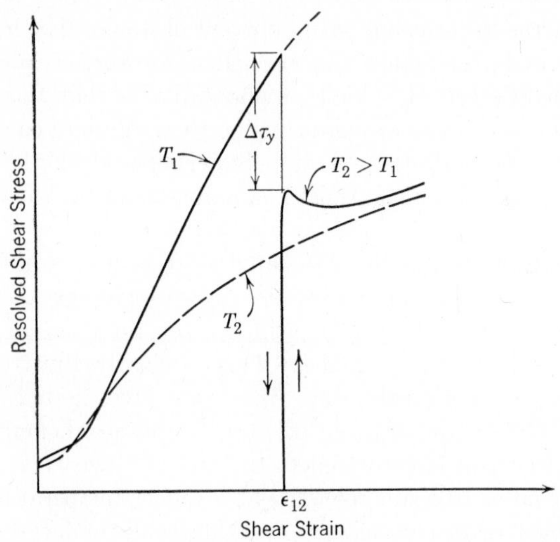

Fig. 24. Work softening of face-centered cubic metals. At a strain ϵ_{12} the temperature of deformation is changed from T_1 to T_2. If at the higher temperature T_2 the strain ϵ_{12} is already in stage II, the flow stress drops by $\Delta\tau_y$ to a lower value.

activation energies and for their stress dependence is very similar in both cases, and it is possible to say on quite general grounds that the activation energy of cross slip is always smaller than that for the collapse of the Lomer-Cottrell barrier acting as an obstacle for the screw dislocations.

Screw dislocations piled up against a Lomer-Cottrell barrier yield always by cross slip before the barrier breaks down. We conclude that the rate-determining process in dynamical recovery of face-centered cubic metals is cross slip and not the collapse of Lomer-Cottrell barriers. The only underlying assumption is that there *are* screw dislocations that are piled up against Lomer-Cottrell dislocations. The discussion in § 3 shows that such Lomer-Cottrell dislocations are possible and we believe that they are indeed formed in stage II.

There is very strong evidence from surface observations that the important mechanism in stage III *is* cross slip and not breakdown of Lomer-Cottrell dislocations. Some of this evidence will be discussed in § 8. We mention here only (see Fig. 22) that the active length of slip lines does not increase at the beginning of stage III as it should on the breakdown hypothesis, but continues to decrease with increasing strain.

Stage II begins at a stress τ_3 at which the frequency of thermally activated cross slip has become sufficiently large to be noticeable. In order to calculate the temperature dependence of τ_3 it is necessary to know the activation energy of the cross slip as a function of all relevant stress components. The same holds for a theoretical treatment of the dependence of τ_3 on the orientation of the tensile axis. Calculations are under way to supply the necessary information, but are not yet complete. At the moment we must confine ourselves to the discussion of very low stresses, where no pile-ups are present, and at very high stresses, where nearly all the energy necesary for cross slip is supplied by the applied stress.

The first case has already been mentioned in § 3. We have pointed out that the observations of cross slip in aluminum by Hirsch, Horne, and Whelan (1956) are in good agreement with the theoretical predictions. The theory accounts also for the very low stress at which stage III in Al begins at room temperature. Under these stresses little or no pile-up is required to give a sufficient rate of cross slip; it is therefore *not* possible to build up stage II with $n \sim 25$ dislocations per piled-up group. This is the reason why stage III begins before stage II is fully developed. The same explanation applies to lead crystals at room temperature.

The very marked difference in the beginning of stage III between these high stacking fault energy metals and the low stacking fault energy metals such as copper or nickel is also explained with the cross-slip mechanism. The activation energy of cross slip in low stacking fault energy metals is so high that both a rather large applied stress and the stress concentrations of pile-ups are necessary to give a noticeable rate of cross slip at room temperature. Since the dislocation arrangement in stage II and therefore also the size of the piled-up groups are essentially independent of the temperature of deformation, the lowering of the activation energy with decreasing temperature is brought about by an increase in τ_3. The lowest temperature at which experimental data on τ_3 is available is the temperature of liquid helium (4.2°K). If we assume that at that temperature thermal and quantum mechanical activation can be neglected in comparison with the work done by the applied stress, we can obtain a close upper bound for the product $n\tau_3$.

We have to identify τ in eq. 5 either with the stress τ_3 at very low temperatures or with the highest stress observed, if stage III is not reached (as is the case in the published experiments on copper). In copper we have $\gamma/Gb \approx 0.004$. Inserting this into eq. 5, the inequality for n takes the form

$$n \lesssim \frac{G}{10\tau_3} \tag{36}$$

For τ_3 we use the highest stage II stresses that were observed in a series of copper crystals (Blewitt, Coltman, and Redman, 1955) namely $\tau_3 = 16$ kg/mm^2. The shear modulus G in the (111)-plane is smaller for anisotropic face-centered cubic metals like Cu, Au, Ni, and Pb than the shear modulus of polycrystalline material. On the other hand, G at 4.2°K is larger than the room temperature value. Inserting for copper $G = 4100$ kg/mm^2 we obtain

$$n \lesssim 26 \tag{36a}$$

Equation 36(a) can be arrived at by another way of reasoning: If τ is the applied resolved shear stress, $n\tau$ is the shear stress at the head of the dislocation pile-up. This stress cannot exceed the theoretical shear strength very much without giving rise to some sort of catastrophic process, e.g., the spontaneous generation of dislocations just beyond the sessile dislocations holding up the piled-up groups. Such events should give rise to irregularities in the stress-strain curves, possibly of the types observed as discontinuous glide at very high stresses on copper (Blewitt, Coltman, and Redman paper in Part II of this volume) and nickel (Haasen, 1957). We think that in order to avoid such processes the applied stress τ must satisfy an equality $\tau = G/10n$. Inserting the highest stresses for which no serrations of the stress-strain curves are observed gives essentially the same estimate as eq. 36(b).

Turning now to lead single crystals, we are in the fortunate position of knowing experimentally the stress τ_3 at liquid helium temperature. Redman (1957) has observed that the stress-strain curve bends over at a stress $\tau_3 = 1.8$ kg/mm^2. We attribute to γ/Gb in lead the same value as in aluminum, namely 0.026, and put $G = 800$ kg/mm^2. Inserting this into eq. 5 leads us to the inequality

$$n \lesssim 0.06G/\tau_3 = 25 \tag{36b}$$

Estimates on aluminum give similar numerical results.

These considerations show that the cross-slip hypothesis accounts also for the behavior of single crystals at very low temperatures. They confirm that our picture of a temperature-independent dislocation structure in stage II is self-consistent and leads to reasonable orders of magnitude.

We have discussed dynamical recovery of face-centered cubic metals in terms of cross slip. An essential feature is that it can be introduced at any temperature provided the crystals are able to withstand sufficiently high stresses τ_3 without fracturing. It should be pointed out, however, that at those temperatures which are high enough for static recovery to occur the mechanism of static recovery should also contribute to dynamical recovery. We presume that the corresponding dislocation mechanism is the same as in the hexagonal metals, namely dislocation climb. In aluminum, climb should be of importance in tensile tests carried out at temperatures about or above 100°C, whereas in low stacking fault energy metals it should be of less importance. So far there are very few stress-strain data on face-centered cubic single crystals available that would form a suitable basis for a discussion of the climbing effects, with the possible exception of lead, where climbing might be important at temperatures as low as room temperature. On the whole, the dislocation climb mechanism manifests itself much more clearly in creep tests at high temperature than in tensile tests. We therefore postpone a more detailed discussion until § 10.

8. FORMATION OF SLIP BANDS AND CELL BOUNDARIES

Observations of slip markings on the surfaces of deformed crystals have for a long time been carried out in studies of the plasticity of crystals (see Schmid and Boas, 1935; for a more complete survey of the classic literature on slip markings see Kuhlmann, 1950). Starting with the investigation of Heidenreich and Shockley (1948), the electron microscope has become a tool of increasing importance. Heidenreich and Shockley showed that what appeared in the optical microscope as a single line on an aluminum crystal deformed at room temperature is a "slip band" built up of a cluster of narrowly spaced individual lines. Later Wilsdorf and Kuhlmann-Wilsdorf (1951) and Brown and Honeycombe (1951) discovered at small strains "microslip" which consisted of slip lines which were not clustered into bands. Wilsdorf and Kuhlmann-Wilsdorf called this surface pattern "elementary structure," since it was thought that the slip bands develop at larger strains. Brown (1951) showed (also on aluminum) that the number of individual slip lines clustered in one band increases with strain and with increasing temperature of deformation. In addition to a thorough electron microscope investigation of the slip markings on aluminum deformed at room temperature (Wilsdorf and Kuhlmann-Wilsdorf,

1952a, b, c), observations on copper, silver, and alpha-brass were carried out (Kuhlmann-Wilsdorf and Wilsdorf, 1953).

More recently a series of investigations with the electron microscope was started with the special objective of relating the surface markings

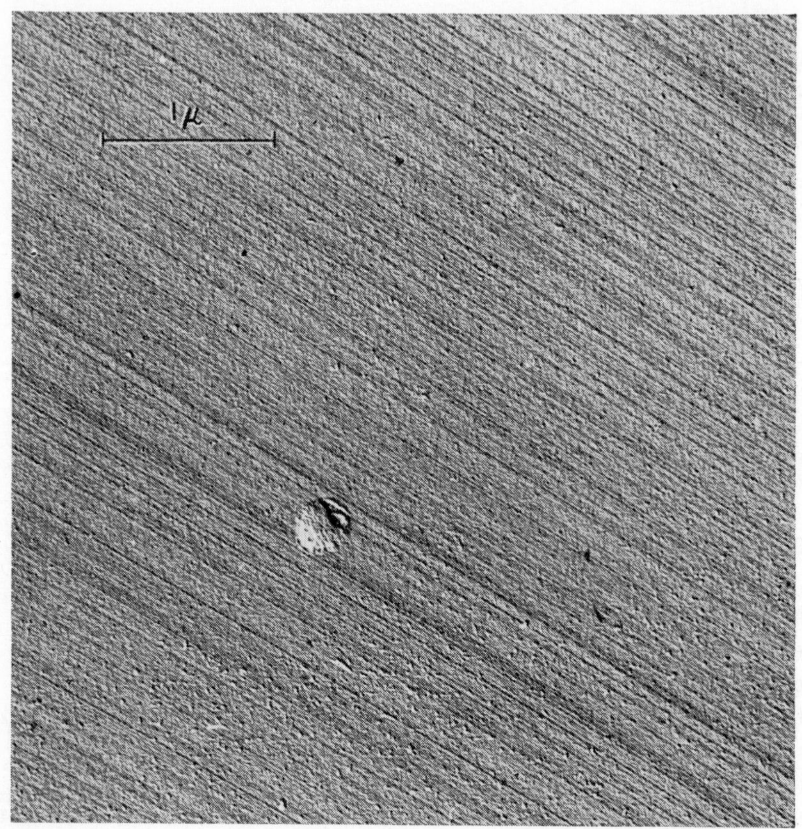

Fig. 25. Electron micrograph of slip lines at the end of stage I. Copper single crystal C 14 (see Fig. 11), strained 8% (shear strain) at room temperature.

to stages I, II, and III of the work-hardening curve of face-centered cubic metals and to the differences in the stacking fault energy of various metals (Diehl, Mader, and Seeger, 1955; Seeger, Diehl, Mader, Rebstock, 1957; Mader, 1957). We shall not repeat here the detailed results but confine ourselves to a brief discussion of the main findings. It was found that metals with high and low stacking fault energies (say aluminum and copper) give essentially the same surface patterns if they are deformed in the same stage. The characteristic features of each stage which were obtained by polishing off the markings due to prestraining are as follows:

Stage I: Slip lines are visible in the optical microscope (dark field illumination) only under very favorable conditions of illumination.

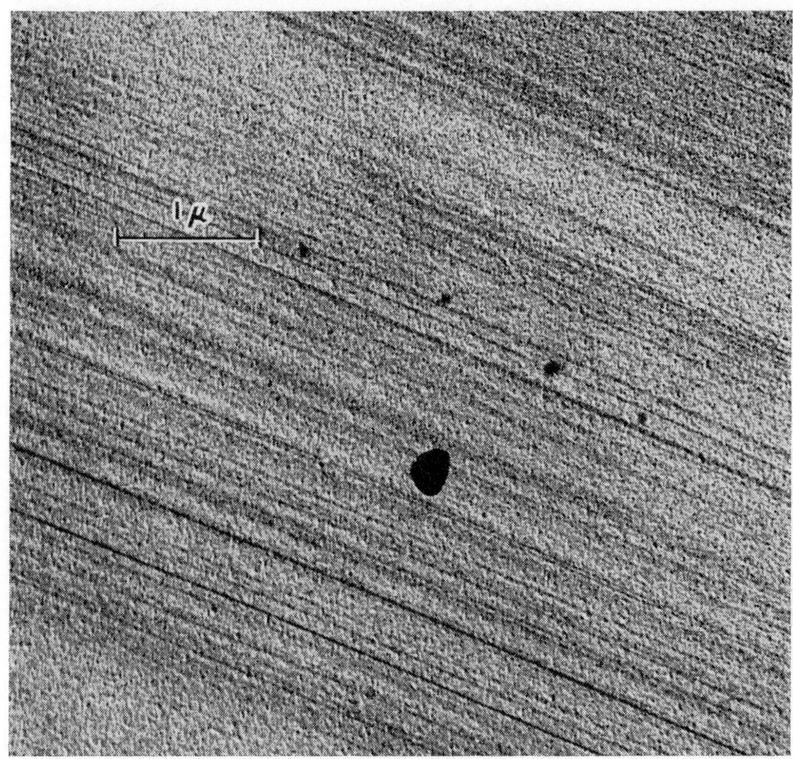

Fig. 26. Electron micrograph of slip lines generated in stage II, during a shear strain increment of 8%. Copper single crystal C 14 deformed at room temperature, prestrained 20%, repolished, additional strain 8% (shear strains).

The electron microscope reveals very long individual slip lines (length of the order 1 mm) of rather small step height (order of magnitude 50–100 A) which are very uniformly spaced (Fig. 25). The lines are much longer than those of the "elementary structure."

Stage II: Dark field illumination with the optical microscope reveals slip lines, the lengths of which decrease with increasing strain as shown in Fig. 22. With the electron microscope individual lines of varying step heights are visible. On the average they are stronger, shorter, and less regularly spaced than those of stage I (Fig. 26).

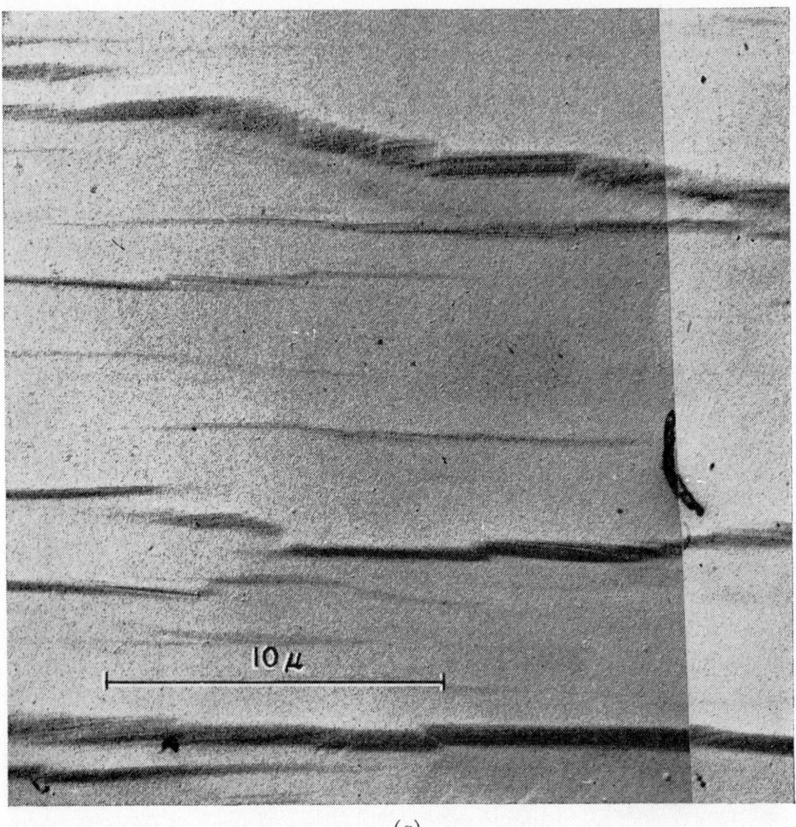

(*a*)

Fig. 27. Electron micrograph of slip bands, fragmentation, cross slip, and traces of a secondary glide system in stage III. Copper crystal C 17, repolished after a prestrain $\epsilon = 0.6$ at room temperature. (*a*) Slip pattern after a shear strain increment $\Delta\epsilon = 0.05$. (*b*) Same site as (*a*), but after an additional shear strain increment of 0.05, thus showing a total increment of 10% shear strain.

Their relation to "lines" visible with the dark field illumination technique has been discussed in § 6.

Stage III: In stage III slip bands (clusters of closely spaced strong slip lines) appear. Their lengths vary with prestrain as shown in Fig. 22 (the "lines" visible in this stage with the optical microscope are slip bands). If the straining is carried sufficiently far into stage III slip between bands ceases completely; the total slip seems to be concentrated into the bands (Fig. 27). The ends of the slip bands show the phenomenon of fragmentation (Blewitt, Coltman, and Red-

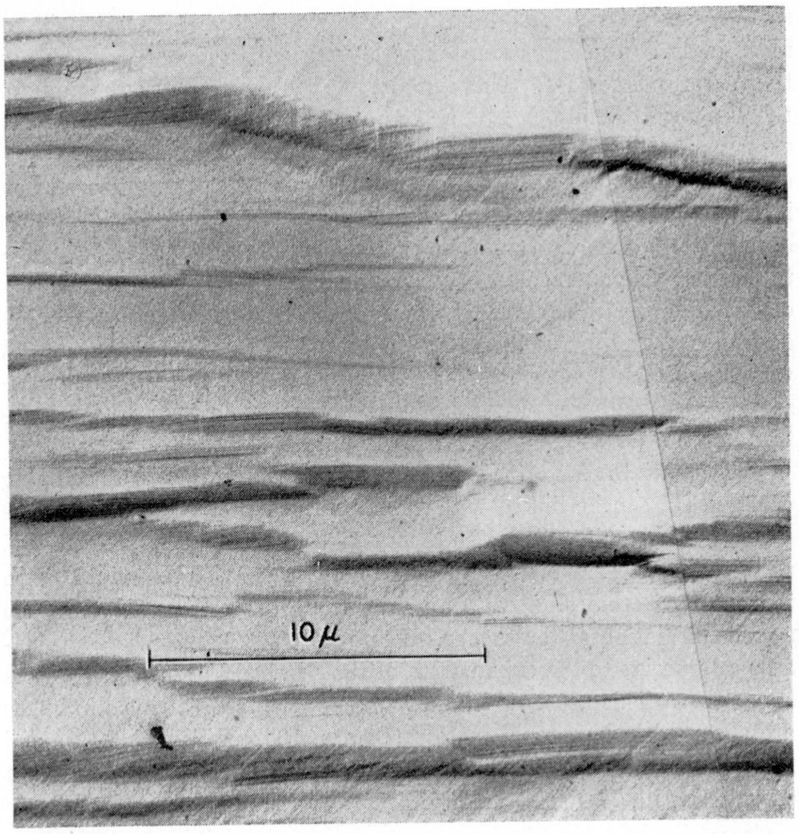

(b)

Fig. 27 (continued).

man, 1955); it has been resolved by the electron microscope into cross slip connecting the ends of slip bands with each other (Seeger, Diehl, Mader, Rebstock, 1957). The fragmentation cross-slip phenomenon which has been shown to occur in stage III only is presumably the same phenomenon as the cross slip on aluminum crystals discovered by Ogilvie and Boas (1948), studied in detail by Cahn (1951), and resolved by the electron microscope by Wilsdorf and Kuhlmann-Wilsdorf (1952b).*

These very different surface patterns associated with the various stages of the stress-strain curve explain at once the observations that have previously been made without the repolishing technique. The

* The mechanism of "cross slip" in alpha-brass is thought to be different. See § 9.

surface markings of aluminum crystals which have been strongly or moderately strained at room temperature are determined by processes that occur in stage III. This explains why in the studies on aluminum the slip bands dominated. The temperature dependence of stage III explains the observation that the cross slip visible with the optical microscope on aluminum crystals is more pronounced if the deformation is carried out at higher temperatures (Cahn, 1951). On the other hand, after moderate deformation of copper crystals at room temperature or lower temperatures, or of aluminum crystals at or below liquid oxygen temperature, stage II determines the surface appearance in agreement with the statements by Koehler (1953). We thus understand why the slip line pattern on such crystals as seen by the electron microscope looks so different from the well-known aluminum room temperature pattern (Diehl, Mader, Seeger, 1955).

The essential point of the preceding discussion is that the beginning of stage III can be linked with two types of surface markings: cross slip and slip bands. Since the theory presented in § 7 has already led us to the conclusion that the beginning of stage III is associated with the onset of cross slip, we may take the observations on cross slip as a confirmation of the theory. There does not seem to be a reasonable alternative to the explanation of the slip band formation by cross slip, either. This accounts in particular for the fact that no slip bands are observed in hexagonal metals (Brown, 1952; Wilsdorf, 1954) and for the correlation between slip band formation and stacking fault energy (Diehl, Mader, Seeger, 1955).

Cross slip had already been proposed as a possible mechanism of slip band formation by Koehler (1952a, b) (mainly on the basis of the temperature dependence of the slip band formation on aluminum) and by Leibfried and Haasen (1954). The mechanism considered by these authors is what has been termed double cross slip (Diehl, Mader, and Seeger, 1955): An extended screw dislocation has been held up in its glide plane [say the $(\bar{1}11)$-plane] by an obstacle or by a region of adverse internal stress. It changes its glide plane to a $(1\bar{1}1)$-plane by the cross-slip mechanism discussed in § 2 (Fig. 6). When the dislocation has slipped out of the range of the obstacle, it tends to return to the original $(\bar{1}11)$-plane under the action of the applied stress τ. In the $(1\bar{1}1)$ cross-slip plane there remain only two short pieces of the dislocation line (Fig. 28). Since the resolved shear stress on the cross-slip plane is less than on the main glide plane, the two pieces will eventually get stuck. That part of the dislocation line that has undergone cross slip twice is able to act as a Frank-Read source and to produce a slip line parallel to the original one from which the screw dislocations have emerged. If the situation is such that the two slip lines are close together * (separated by the typical width of lamellae in slip bands, 200 A) and the process can be repeated, we obtain a slip band. We believe that this is the mechanism of slip band formation in crystals that have undergone very little work hardening before stage III was reached, e.g., in aluminum and lead crystals at high and moderate temperatures.

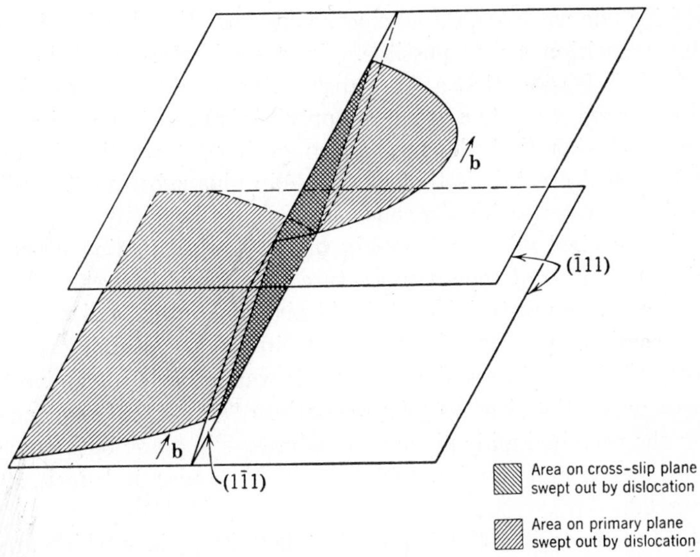

Fig. 28. Double cross slip of a screw dislocation. The dislocation leaves its original plane by cross slip and returns to a parallel plane by another cross-slip process.

It is perhaps unnecessary to stress that it is just under these conditions that "double cross slip" has been observed by Hirsch, Horne, and Whelan (1956).

If stage III is preceded by a well-developed stage II with a large number of piled-up groups in the crystal, cross slip can lead to band formation by another mechanism (Seeger, 1956a; Seeger, Diehl, Mader, Rebstock, 1957). In such a work-hardened material the screw dislocations leaving a piled-up group by cross slip will meet other groups and will be attracted by those of opposite sign. Annihilation takes place, and the annihilated dislocations will be replaced, partly at least, from the original source. By this mechanism weak slip lines may grow

* This should occur quite frequently since the screw dislocations tend to return to their original planes as soon as the configuration of internal stresses allows.

into strong ones. If this process is repeated it also leads to slip band formation.

The two mechanisms for slip band formation just discussed have in common that the dislocations circumvent the obstacles in their glide plane by cross slip, and that they do not break through these barriers. Between these two mechanisms for the limiting cases of lightly work-hardened crystals on the one hand and highly work-hardened crystals (which include work-softening experiments) on the other hand, a continuous transition seems possible. In a moderately work-hardened material it is feasible that a screw dislocation undergoes cross slip several times until it meets a group of opposite sign and is annihilated.

The conclusion that the mechanism of band formation in highly work-hardened crystals is that of cross slip plus subsequent annihilation is in agreement with the conclusions drawn by Kelly (1956) from a detailed optical microscope study of the work-softening process in aluminum crystals at room temperature. He found that crystals electropolished after prestraining at liquid air temperature and work-softened at room temperature showed wavy slip bands containing cross slip of the type observed by Cahn (1951). It was possible to resolve these patterns under the electron microscope into "stair-case" sequences of slip on the principal glide plane and the cross-slip plane both on work-softened copper and aluminum (Seeger, Diehl, Mader, Rebstock, 1956). See Fig. 29.

Let us now consider the fate of the edge dislocations which are left behind in the cross-slip plane. If the screw dislocations are "extracted" from the pile-up by another group of opposite sign, it is very likely that not only the leading dislocation of the pile-up leaves its original glide plane but also that the following screw dislocations undergo cross slip. A situation like that shown schematically in Fig. 30 will then arise. Left behind in the original glide plane $(\bar{1}11)$ are piled-up dislocation groups with predominant edge components. Together with similar groups on parallel planes they may later on form deformation bands. In the $(1\bar{1}1)$ cross-slip plane there are two groups of edge dislocations. Their elastic interactions tend to align them in the well-known manner of polygon boundaries. How well they can do so depends on the length of these dislocation pieces. The longer they are the smaller is the influence of the dislocations surrounding them and the better they can take up the structure of a small angle tilt boundary.

A cell structure of subgrains formed in cold work, in particular of polycrystalline metals, has been observed by a large number of investigators employing a variety of techniques (see Hirsch, 1956). A correlation of the degree in which this cell structure is developed in differ-

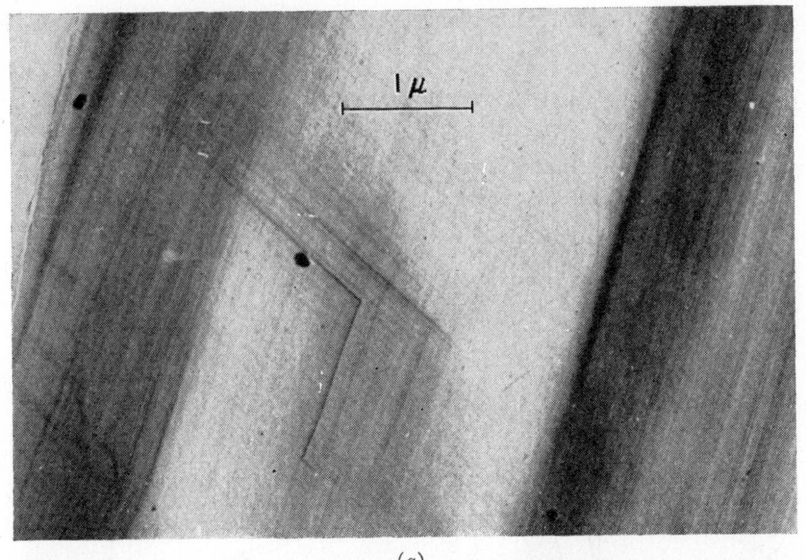

(a)

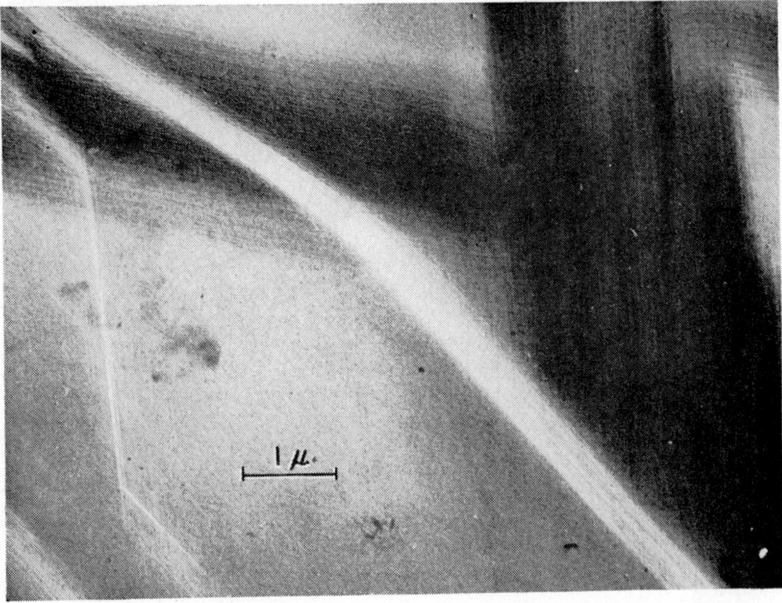

(b)

Fig. 29. Work softening of aluminum crystal. Shear strain $\epsilon = 0.35$ at 90°K, repolished, and work-softened at room temperature. (a) "Stair-case" of slip on cross-slip plane and primary plane between two slip bands. (b) Different site on same crystal, showing slip on the primary system (black slip markings) and on the conjugate system (white slip markings). The cross-slip systems of the primary and the conjugate slip systems possess the same glide plane, but different glide directions. The traces of the respective cross-slip lines are therefore parallel, but of different color, due to different shadowing conditions.

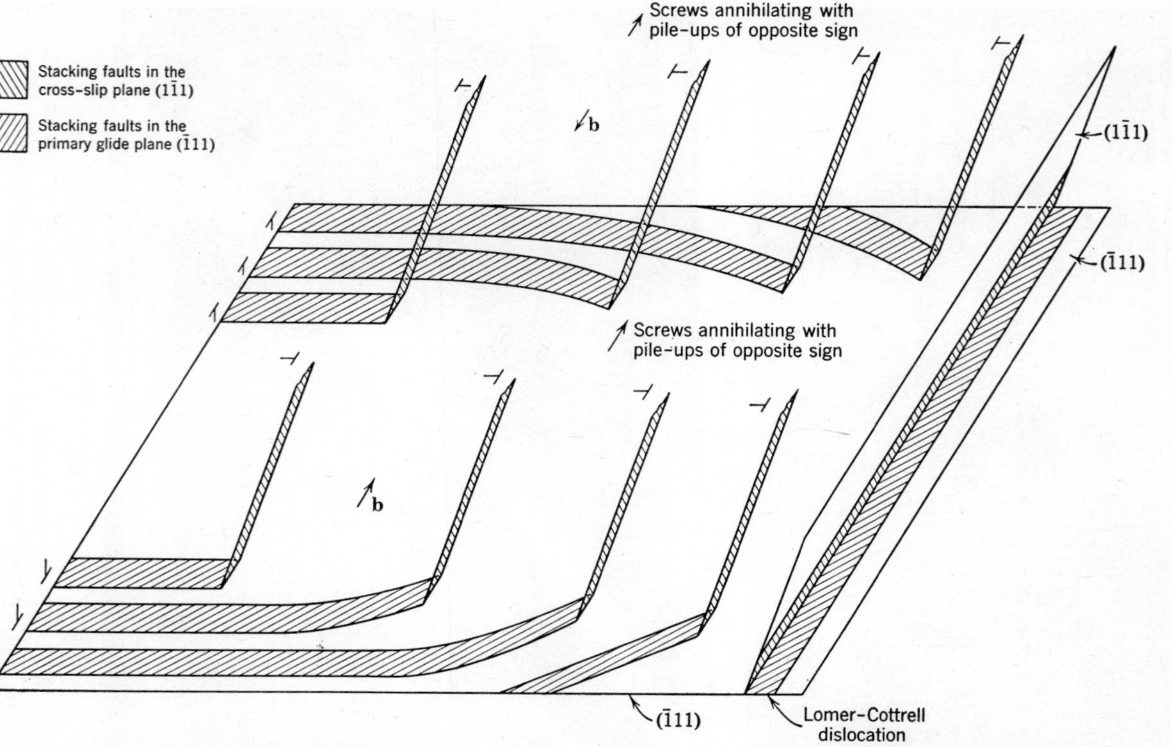

Fig. 30. Formation of arrays of edge dislocations in the cross-slip plane, which are approximately tilt subgrain boundaries, by cross slip of piled-up screw dislocations.

ent face-centered cubic metals deformed at various temperatures with the ease of cross slip has been mentioned and discussed earlier (Seeger, 1956a). In that paper no mechanism connected with cross slip for the formation of tilt boundaries (which, contrary to twist boundaries, do not involve screw dislocation) was suggested. We believe the mechanism outlined above to be the dominating one in face-centered cubic metals at temperatures at which climbing of edge dislocations is a slow process. It accounts for the observation (Gay, Hirsch, and Kelly, 1954) that the ultimate particle size (average diameter of the subgrains after very large deformation) is about the same as the minimum spacing of the slip bands. It also explains why the particle site shows the same dependence on strain (Kelly, 1954) as the active length of slip lines.

The experimental evidence for the correlation of cross slip and subgrain formation is as follows: If a metal recovers easily at the temperature of deformation (e.g., Cd, Zn, Sn, Pb deformed at room temperature) the microbeam technique shows the cell boundaries to be rather sharp (Gay and Kelly, 1953b). This is most easily explained by the ability of the dislocations to climb readily under these conditions, and to take up a sort of polygonized structure somewhat in the manner discussed for aluminum by Heidenreich (1951) and Hirsch (1952). Metals with a well-developed stage II at the temperature of deformation [aluminum deformed at liquid oxygen temperature (Kelly and Roberts, 1955); copper and nickel deformed at room temperature (Gay and Kelly, 1953a)] show a much less developed cell structure with broad transitions between the subgrains. This could be attributed to small rates of both dislocation climb and cross slip. Aluminum and alpha-iron deformed at room temperature occupy a sort of intermediate position (Hirsch, 1952; Gay and Kelly, 1953a; Kelly, 1954). Since dislocations in aluminum are unlikely to climb readily even at room temperature, the difference to the preceding group can best be understood in terms of the differences of the activation energies of cross slip. A rather decisive argument in favor of such an explanation, as pointed out by P. B. Hirsch (private communication), is the similarity of aluminum and alpha-iron. From a naïve point of view α-Fe would be expected to be in the same group as the other high melting point metals Cu and Ni. In view of the high energy of self-diffusion, dislocation climb should be an extremely slow process at room temperature. The activation energy for cross slip, however, should be of the same order of magnitude in alpha-iron as in aluminum, since the larger shear modulus of iron is balanced by the lesser degree of extension of the dislocations in the b.c.c. lattice.

9. INFLUENCE OF ALLOYING ELEMENTS ON WORK HARDENING AND WORK SOFTENING

There are comparatively few single crystal data on the plastic deformation of close-packed alloys. We leave aside the hexagonal alloys (for the experimental result see Schmid and Boas, 1935). The main experimental results on face-centered cubic alloys with a wide range of composition (Cu-Ni, Osswald, 1933; Ag-Au, Sachs and Weerts, 1930; alpha-brass, see Fig. 31) refer to deformation at room temperature.

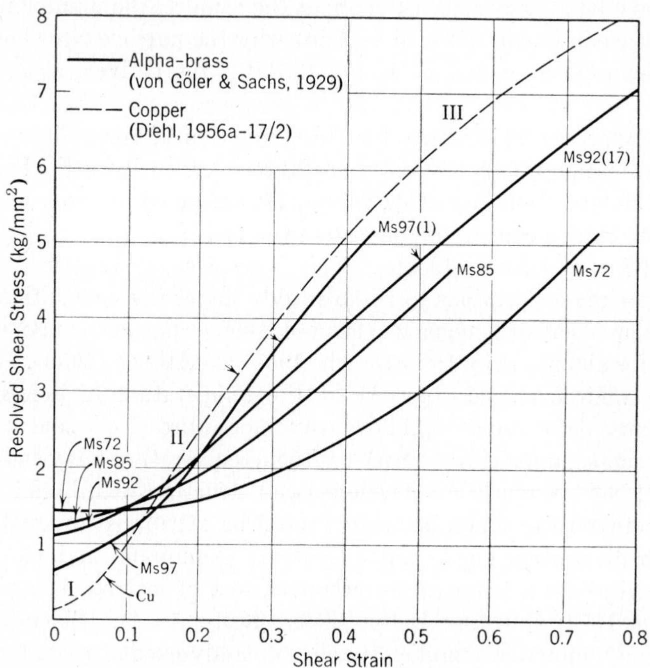

Fig. 31. Stress-strain curves of copper and alpha-brass single crystals of various compositions at room temperature. The arrows on the stress-strain curves indicate the beginning of stage III.

The two most striking features which distinguish the stress-strain curves of these alloys from those of the pure metals are a much larger critical shear stress and the phenomenon of "overshooting." The critical shear stress of alloys has been considered in great detail by Suzuki (see his paper in Part IV of this volume); for very small impurity concentrations see § 4 of the present paper. The overshooting of the tensile axis into the orientation region where the resolved critical shear stress in the conjugate slip systems is larger than that in the primary system has been discussed elsewhere in the spirit of this paper (Seeger, 1956b); we confine ourselves to the remark that although the degree of overshooting in metals and alloys seems to be influenced by the magnitude of the stacking fault energy, the situation in alloys is not yet quite clear.

Using as a criterion the work-hardening coefficient at room temperature, it is clear that the alloy stress-strain curves also exhibit stages I, II, and III. Stage III is thought to begin where the steep part of the stress-strain curve deviates markedly from linearity. Although there is evidence that θ/G in stage II is temperature-independent (Piercy, Cahn, and Cottrell, 1955, alpha-brass), no data are available on the temperature dependence of the deviation from linearity.

Turning to a discussion of stage I in alloys, we have to distinguish between two groups of alloys. Most of the alloy systems belonging to the first group (which includes all the alloys mentioned above) possess a wide range of primary solubility. In these the extension of the easy glide region (measured by ϵ_2 in Fig. 14) increases with increasing content of the alloying element. The work-hardening coefficient decreases with increasing alloying; it is virtually zero in heavily alloyed crystals. From our discussion of work hardening in stage I (§ 6) it appears to be obvious that such a small coefficient of work hardening and the associated propagation of Lüders band (Piercy, Cahn, and Cottrell, 1955) cannot be explained along the lines used for pure metals. It is presumably connected with typical alloy phenomena, in particular with the existence of a yield point in alpha-brass (Ardley and Cottrell, 1953). On the other hand, the beginning of stage II seems to be connected with the formation of Lomer-Cottrell dislocations in much the same way as in pure metals. Evidence in favor of this view has been deduced (Seeger, 1956b) from the observations of Burghoff (1940) on alpha-brass single crystals. It is in agreement with the experimental results of Piercy, Cahn, and Cottrell (1955), who have discussed the importance of conjugate slip in general terms.

The other group consists of primary alloys with a narrow solubility range, e.g., most aluminum alloys, the best investigated one being aluminum-silver (Haeszner and Schreiber, 1957.* It looks as if the primary solutions of copper-silver (Garstone, Honeycombe, and Greetham, 1956) belong also to this group. It is characterized by a slope of stage I which is either the same as or larger than that of the pure metal.

* For the orientation dependence of stress-strain curves of various aluminum alloys at room temperature (in particular Al-Cu) see Jaoul (1955) and Jaoul and Bricot (1955).

The explanation of the difference of these two groups is as follows: A wide solubility range indicates that the solute atoms can easily be accommodated by the matrix. There is therefore no reason why they should give rise to obstacles which could limit the slip distance of the dislocations once the critical shear stress has been applied. On the other hand, a narrow solubility range is usually connected with stress fields around the foreign atoms, tendency to cluster, and similar phe-

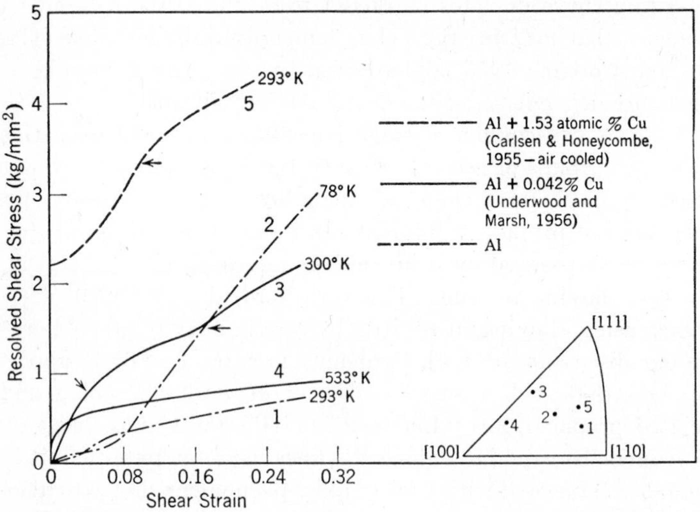

Fig. 32. Stress-strain curves of aluminum and aluminum-copper single crystals at various temperatures. The end of stage II has been indicated by arrows.

nomena, which are all capable of interfering with the dislocation movement. An extreme case is aluminum of so-called technical purity (99.5%), which certainly contains several kinds of precipitates and clusters (Diehl, 1956a). Here stage I is completely suppressed. The stress-strain curve of technical aluminum and its orientation and temperature dependence (Boas and Schmid, 1931) bears hardly any resemblance to the typical work-hardening curve of pure face-centered cubic metals.

The ratio of the work-hardening coefficient in stage II to the shear modulus seems to be the same in all alloys with a stress-strain curve similar to that of pure f.c.c. metals and a well-developed stage II. In addition to the binary alloys mentioned above, see Figs. 32 and 33 and the liquid-air temperature data on aluminum-silver alloys (Haeszner and Schreiber, 1957). Though detailed observations on the length of slip lines are not available, it appears that the work-hardening mechanism in stage II in these alloys is the same as in pure metals.

We have seen in § 8 how closely related slip band formation and the occurrence of stage III are. The influence of alloying on dynamical recovery (and work softening) and on slip band formation will therefore be discussed together as follows.

A straightforward way in which solute atoms can change the stage III characteristics is through the stacking fault energy (Seeger, 1956b).

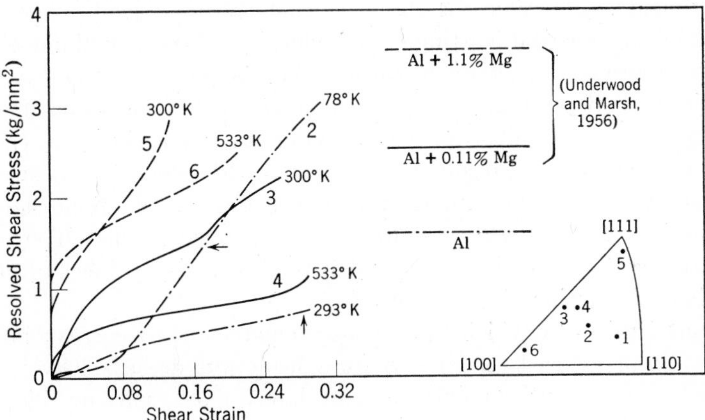

Fig. 33. Stress-strain curves of aluminum and aluminum-magnesium single crystals at various temperatures.

In § 2 we have seen that in alpha-brass there is strong evidence for a decrease of the stacking fault energy with increasing zinc content. Figure 31 shows that τ_3 (indicated by an arrow on the stress-strain curves) does indeed increase with increasing zinc content. This increase is so pronounced that in 72/28 brass stage III is not reached in tensile tests at room temperature. It is therefore not surprising that this alloy does not show any clustering of slip lines into bands (Kuhlmann-Wilsdorf and Wilsdorf, 1953). We expect, however, that deformation at higher temperatures gives rise to stage III and the associated slip pattern.

This "stacking fault energy mechanism" cannot be the only one responsible for the increase in τ_3 and the suppression of the slip band formation in alloys. Figures 32 and 33 show that single crystals of aluminum-copper and aluminum-magnesium alloys exhibit a well-developed stage II at room temperature with about the same slope as aluminum crystals deformed at liquid nitrogen temperature. In an electron microscope study of polycrystalline Al-Cu and Al-Mg alloys, Thomas and Nutting (1956) were able to show that after deformation at room temperature these alloys do not show the well-developed slip bands which are typical for pure aluminum. This is in line with the evidence from work-hardening curves mentioned above.

The solute concentrations in some of these experiments are rather low. Since the electron concentration in these alloys is not very different from that of pure aluminum, it seems unlikely that the stacking fault energy has been lowered to the extent necessary in order to explain the experiments. The clue for the resolution of this difficulty has been given by Thomas and Nutting (1956) who showed that aluminum-silver alloys deformed at room temperature exhibit slip bands at least as well developed as pure aluminum. They pointed out that the difference between additions of silver on the one hand and magnesium and copper on the other hand is presumably connected with effects of the sizes of atoms. Whereas silver atoms fit very well into the aluminum lattice, magnesium and copper atoms introduce mechanical strains. They suggested that these strains interfered with the cross-slip mechanism of slip band formation discussed in § 8.

A mechanism by which the strains around solute atoms can inhibit cross slip or at least render it more difficult was described by Seeger (1956b). Its essential point can be explained most easily by reference to Fig. 34. Whereas in pure metals and in alloys like aluminum-silver the screw dislocations pressed against a Lomer-Cottrell dislocation are straight, they will show deviations from straightness if solute atoms surrounded by stress fields are present. Cross slip is possible only if a dislocation is in an exact screw orientation. Straightening out the wavy dislocation lines in alloys like Al-Mg and Al-Cu requires the applied stress to do additional work and gives rise to an increase of the apparent activation energy for cross slip. This explanation of the difference between Al-Mg and Al-Cu alloys on the one hand and Al-Ag alloys on the other hand is in line with the data on work hardening of Al-Ag single crystals (Haeszner and Schreiber, 1957). They show that small additions of silver leave virtually unchanged the transition to stage III both at room temperature and liquid air temperature, in striking contrast to Figs. 32 and 33.

We conclude with two remarks on alpha-brass. First we wish to mention that although the "stacking fault energy effect" is certainly of great importance for the stage III properties of alpha-brass, there is the possibility that the "size-of-atoms effect" also contributes. (The possibility of both effects existing simultaneously exists in other alloy systems, too. In some cases an increase in stacking fault energy may even partially compensate the effects of the direct interaction between dislocations and foreign atoms.) The second remark refers to the frequent observation of "cross slip" on deformed alpha-brass (Maddin, Mathewson, and Hibbard, 1948, 1949; Kuhlmann-Wilsdorf and Wilsdorf, 1953), which might seem to contradict the statements made above about the inhibition of cross slip in alpha-brass. The cross slip

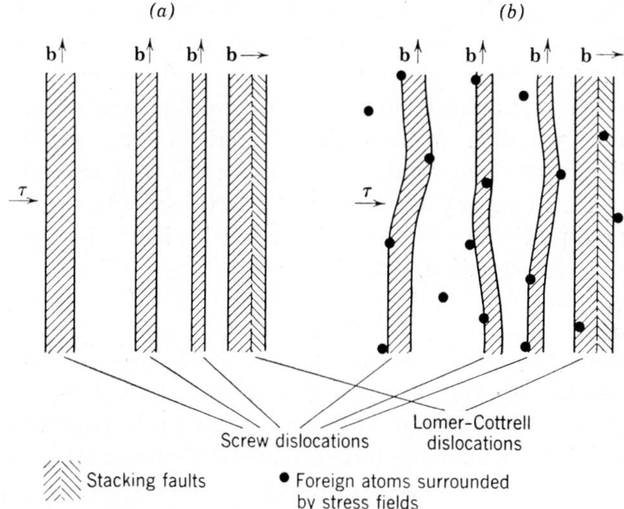

Fig. 34. The inhibition of cross slip by foreign atoms interacting with dislocations. (*a*) Screw dislocations piled up against a Lomer-Cottrell barrier in a pure material are straight. (*b*) The piled-up dislocations are wavy in a material containing foreign atoms which are surrounded by stress fields.

on alpha-brass observed by these authors and others, however, is not thermally activated but it is ordinary slip in a secondary glide system. The reason why such slip on secondary systems is particularly prominent on the cross-slip system (and on secondary systems with primary glide plane) is the same as for pure copper (see § 6.D): the latent hardening of these secondary slip systems is smaller than that of the other secondary systems, contrary to Al (Seeger, 1956b).

10. CREEP OF CLOSE-PACKED METALS

A survey of the modern theory of creep of metals has recently been given by Schoeck (1956), to which the reader is referred for details.* In the present paper we confine ourselves to a discussion of those aspects of creep of close-packed metals which are related to the

* For earlier surveys of creep see Orowan (1947) and Andrade (1952).

theories presented in the preceding paragraphs. This implies that we will not deal with grain boundary sliding. In the interest of conciseness we shall choose a theoretical approach rather than review the very large body of experimental evidence available.

Let us begin with the limiting case of very high temperatures, at which recovery proceeds rapidly. If the rate of recovery is sufficiently fast, it will balance the work-hardening rate. In an experiment with prescribed strain rate this means that the crystal deforms under a constant resolved shear stress. The situation is the same as in a creep test, the only difference being that in the creep experiment a constant shear stress is maintained and the steady-state strain rate is observed as a dependent variable. What we have described is the well-known recovery theory of steady-state creep. Since the recovery rate usually depends on the temperature T through a Boltzmann factor, it explains why the creep rate increases exponentially with increasing temperature according to the equation

$$\dot{\epsilon} = e^{-Q_c/kT}\dot{\epsilon}_\infty(\tau) \tag{37}$$

The magnitude of the activation energy of steady-state creep Q_c depends on the recovery mechanism involved. In metals like Zn and Cd, where the mechanism of dynamical recovery is dislocation climb, there is little doubt that the recovery mechanism causing steady-state creep is dislocation climb too (Mott, 1953). The situation is presumably similar in the low stacking fault energy metals aluminum and lead, which show steady-state creep in a temperature interval in which static recovery after deformation proceeds quite rapidly. There is strong evidence (e.g., polygonization) that the edge dislocations climb very easily under these conditions.

Low stacking fault energy metals like copper, nickel, etc., do not recover appreciably in the temperature range in which steady-state creep is observed. In spite of this we believe that in these metals the recovery in steady-state creep is due to a climbing mechanism too. This is supported by observations of Semmel and Machlin (1957) on silver. These authors were able to show by a thermal-etching technique that dislocations do not climb if a prestrained silver single crystal is annealed at about 500°C. They do climb in that temperature interval, however, if the crystal is stressed and undergoes creep. A similar observation is that of Franks and McLean (1956) who found that copper polygonizes to some extent during high temperature creep, though considerably more slowly than aluminum.

This difference between the low stacking fault energy metals and the high stacking fault energy metals is explained as follows (Seeger,

1955b): In the second of these two groups the energy of formation of jogs (Q_j) in edge dislocations is so low compared with the activation energy of self-diffusion (Q_d) that at temperatures at which self-diffusion is sufficiently rapid to give a noticeable rate of climb we have a rather large equilibrium concentration of jogs along the dislocation lines. They will suffice to maintain the equilibrium concentration of vacancies along the dislocation lines. (For definiteness we are assuming that self-diffusion proceeds by the migration of vacancies.) The rate-controlling factor is self-diffusion, in agreement with the experimental results of Dorn (1956b) and collaborators, who find

$$Q_c = Q_d \tag{38}$$

A theory of steady-state creep, based on dislocation climb and on the assumption of vacancy equilibrium along the dislocation lines, has been given by Weertman (1955). It derives the relation eq. 38 in more detail and compares well with the experimental data, in particular with regard to the stress dependence of $\dot{\epsilon}_\infty$.

Low stacking fault energy metals have such large jog energies Q_j that thermal formation of jogs is quite irrelevant at the temperatures of normal steady-state creep tests. The majority of the jogs participating in the climb process have been formed by the intersection of dislocation lines. Their concentration, therefore, does not directly depend on temperature. Under the conditions of static recovery the majority of jogs created during the gliding of the dislocations will soon be used up, and the recovery rate will be correspondingly small. Under creep conditions a more or less constant concentration of jogs is maintained by the cutting of gliding dislocations through the dislocation forest. The temperature dependence of the strain rate is determined by the rate of self-diffusion. Therefore eq. 38 holds again, in agreement with experimental data (Dorn, 1956b). The temperature-independent factor $\dot{\epsilon}_\infty$ and the creep rate are much smaller than for high stacking fault energy metals.

In the cases discussed above the jog energy did not appear in the expression for the activation energy Q_c of steady-state creep, contrary to the earlier formulation of the theory by Mott (1953), who arrived at

$$Q_c = Q_d + Q_j \tag{39}$$

There are intermediate cases in which Q_j does appear in the expression for Q_c. The conditions for this are: The concentration of jogs in thermal equilibrium is at least comparable with that of those jogs that had been created by intersection processes. Furthermore, it must be too small to maintain approximately the equilibrium concentration of vacancies at the dislocations during the creep process. The theory has not yet been worked out in this intermediate case. The relation between Q_c/Q_d and Q_j/Q_d given by Seeger (1955b) must be considered as tentative. It is clear, however, that Q_c can assume only values between the limits given by eqs. 38 and 39. Steady-state creep in silver bromide (Christy, 1954) appears to be an example for this intermediate situation. The activation energy for high-temperature creep is $Q_c =$ 69 kg-cal/mole. We shall now show by rough estimates that this value cannot be accounted for by self-diffusion alone but must contain a contribution from the jog energy. The effective activation energy of self-diffusion in climb of a binary compound is certainly not more than the sum of the self-diffusion activation energies of the constituents and therefore less than twice the activation energy of the constituent with the higher activation energy. The self-diffusion rate of Ag is greater than that of Br. The activation energy for the self-diffusion of Br in AgBr has been found to be 24 kg-cal/mole (Murin, 1954, quoted according to Tannhauser, 1955). We obtain 48 kg-cal/mole as an upper limit to Q_c. There is therefore a difference * of at least about 1 ev between Q_d and Q_c, which we attribute to the energy of jog formation.

The preceding discussion shows that though the magnitude of the energy of jog formation determines the absolute magnitude of the creep rate it usually does not show up in a simple way. For metals with high stacking fault energies it is possible to deduce reliable values of Q_j from flow stress measurements, in particular from T_0 and its variation with strain rate (eq. 12). In low stacking fault energy metals Q_j is too large to be obtained accurately in that way. A possible way of determining the energy of a jog in an edge dislocation in a low stacking fault energy metal is the following one: Brenner and Morelock (1956) have reported that copper whiskers dekink at temperatures above 1000°C with an observable rate. We believe that the mechanism of this dekinking process is essentially the same as that of high temperature creep, namely dislocation climb. The difference in the temperature intervals involved is interpreted by the reasonable assumption that the edge dislocations in a kinked copper whisker do not contain jogs save for those present in thermal equilibrium.

In this case the activation energy for climbing is about equal to the sum of the activation energies Q_j and Q_d. This interpretation is supported by the fact that the dekinking of sodium chloride whiskers (Gyulai, 1954) and of alpha-iron whiskers (S. Brenner, private communication) occurs at considerably lower temperatures than in copper.

* Attention to this big difference was called by J. Weertman at the ASM seminar, Cleveland, 1956.

NaCl and alpha-iron should have considerably smaller Q_j values than copper.

In the literature quite frequently a value of about 4 ev for the jog energy of edge dislocations in copper is employed. It was derived by a rather lengthy calculation from the stacking fault energy given in § 2 (Schoeck and Seeger, 1955) and is therefore not too certain. If the interpretation for the dekinking experiments given above is correct, this value appears to be somewhat too large. The correct value might be around 3 ev.

Our discussion of the steady-state creep of face-centered cubic metals has been based on the mechanism of static recovery dislocation climb. We have now to deal with the dynamical recovery by cross slip of screw dislocations. We do not know of any experimental evidence that this type of dynamical recovery gives rise to *steady-state creep,* nor is it known whether the recovery rate by cross slip can ever completely balance the work-hardening rate. There is, however, considerable evidence that cross slip can be the rate-controlling factor in *transient creep,* as will be shown below.

Transient creep is characterized by a creep rate that decreases with time (under a constant shear stress). As is the case with any creep process, transient creep is connected with either thermal or quantum mechanical activation. From a theoretical point of view we may divide it into beta-creep and alpha-creep, depending on whether recovery occurs during the creep process or not. In alpha-creep an equation of state in the sense discussed by Wyatt (1953) holds, whereas in beta-creep an equation of state cannot hold because of the recovery during flow.

The simplest form of alpha-creep is the so-called logarithmic creep

$$\epsilon = \alpha \log \nu_1 t \tag{40}$$

where t = time, and ν_1 is a frequency factor. Sometimes creep laws are observed with strain rates

$$\dot{\epsilon} = Ct^{-m} \tag{41}$$

where the exponent m does not have the value 1 corresponding to logarithmic creep, but is in general larger (hyperbolic creep) and occasionally slightly smaller (parabolic creep). For our purpose we need not consider these refinements. Cottrell (1952) and Mott (1953) have shown that eq. 40 can be derived on the assumption that the thermally activated process in creep is the cutting through the dislocation forest by gliding dislocations as discussed in § 5. Seeger (1954a) has pointed out that in such a process the parameter α in eq. 40

and the slope θ of the stress-strain curve are related to the quantities which we have introduced in § 5 in order to characterize the forest, by the equation

$$bdl_0' = \frac{kT}{\alpha\theta} \tag{42}$$

The work-hardening coefficient θ can be measured in creep experiments by a method of step-wise loading (Haasen and Leibfried, 1952; Masing and Weik, 1954; Bauser and Dehlinger, 1954); under conditions where the left-hand side of eq. 42, in particular the distance l_0' between the trees of the forest, is constant, the right-hand side should be strain-independent. This is indeed the case for the easy glide region of aluminum single crystals deformed at room temperature, as shown by the data collected by Seeger (1954a) and by the experimental results of Thompson, Coogan, and Rider (1955).

The activation energy of logarithmic creep, which can be measured by change-in-temperature tests, is given by eq. 10. Due to the action of the applied stress it is usually considerably smaller than the activation energy U_0 in the absence of an applied stress. As pointed out by Friedel (private communication), it is therefore in general not possible to obtain U_0 from creep tests directly, contrary to statements in the literature (Cottrell, 1953, p. 206; Seeger, 1955d). The measured apparent activation energy U is determined very much by the conditions of the test; in particular by the creep rate which can conveniently be observed by the creep apparatus employed. The approximate proportionality of activation energy and absolute temperature (Boas, 1947, p. 89; Sherby, Lytton, and Dorn, 1957; Dorn, 1956b) may therefore have a quite trivial explanation.

The fact that zinc (and cadmium) crystals creeping at liquid air temperatures obey eq. 40 (Boas and Schmid, 1936; Seeger, 1956b) is in agreement with the statement that alpha-creep is observed when no recovery occurs. [At and above room temperature the creep of zinc crystals can be described as a superposition of beta-creep according to eq. 43 and steady-state creep (Cottrell and Aytekin, 1950).] The classic creep law for beta-creep is Andrade's equation

$$\epsilon = \beta t^{1/3} \tag{43}$$

which has been observed in many materials (see Andrade, 1952), sometimes with slight modifications. Mott (1953) has given a derivation of Andrade's creep equation (43) under the assumption that beta-creep is due to the same thermally activated process as steady-state creep, the difference between the two types of creep being that the strain rate in beta-creep has not yet decreased to the value corresponding to equal rates of recovery and work hardening. This is very likely to be the correct explanation for substances like zinc or cadmium where the mechanisms of static and dynamical recovery are the same. Mott's theory is, however, unlikely to apply in those cases in which the dynamical recovery process responsible for beta-creep is different from that governing steady-state creep. An example of this is face-centered cubic metals creeping in the stress-temperature region corresponding to stage III, but at temperatures too low for climb to be of importance. Wyatt (1953) has carried out creep experiments on polycrystalline copper and aluminum in that range. He found that the observed creep laws could be approximately represented by a superposition of eq. 40 and eq. 43 (plus an instantaneous extension immediately after loading). The beta term is larger the higher the temperature and the larger the applied stress. The stress-temperature relation at the beginning of a noticeable beta contribution is different in copper and aluminum (Wyatt, 1951, 1953) and corresponds in both cases approximately to the beginning of stage III (allowing for the difference of the stresses of single crystals and polycrystals). The influence of the stacking fault energy is therefore apparent in the creep test, too, and supports strongly the assertion that the beta-creep observed by Wyatt is due to cross slip (Seeger, 1956b).

REFERENCES

M. A. Adams and A. H. Cottrell (1955), *Phil. Mag.*, **46,** 1187.

E. N. da C. Andrade (1952), *J. Iron Steel Inst.* (*London*), **171,** 217.

E. N. da C. Andrade and C. Henderson (1951), *Phil. Trans., A,* **244,** 177.

G. W. Ardley and A. H. Cottrell (1953), *Proc. Roy. Soc.* (*London*), *A,* **219,** 177.

C. S. Barrett and T. Massalski (1956), *Symposium on the Mechanism of Phase Transformations,* Institute of Metals, London. (Metals Monograph and Report Series No. 18, p. 331.)

M. Bauser and U. Dehlinger (1954), *Z. Metallkunde,* **45,** 618.

T. H. Blewitt (1953), *Phys. Rev.,* **91,** 1115.

T. H. Blewitt, R. R. Coltman, and J. K. Redman (1955), *Report of a Conference on Defects in Solids,* Physical Society, London, p. 369.

W. Boas (1947), *An Introduction to the Physics of Metals and Alloys,* Melbourne University Press, Carlton (Vict.).

W. Boas and E. Schmid (1930), *Z. Physik,* **61,** 767.

W. Boas and E. Schmid (1931), *Z. Physik,* **71,** 703.

W. Boas and E. Schmid (1936), *Z. Physik,* **100,** 463.

S. S. Brenner and C. R. Morelock (1956), *Acta Met.,* **4,** 89.

A. F. Brown (1951), *J. Inst. Metals,* **80,** 115.

A. F. Brown (1952), *Advances in Phys.,* **1,** 427.

A. F. Brown and R. W. K. Honeycombe (1951), *Phil. Mag.*, **42**, 1146.
S. M. Buckley and K. M. Entwistle (1956), *Acta Met.*, **4**, 352.
H. L. Burghoff (1940), *Trans. AIME*, **137**, 214.
R. W. Cahn (1951), *J. Inst. Metals*, **79**, 129.
K. M. Carlsen and R. W. K. Honeycombe (1955), *J. Inst. Metals*, **83**, 449.
R. W. Christy (1954), *Acta Met.*, **2**, 284.
H. Conrad and W. D. Robertson (1957), *Trans. AIME*, **209**, 503.
A. H. Cottrell (1949), *Progr. Metal Phys.*, **1**, 77.
A. H. Cottrell (1952), *J. Mech. Phys. Solids*, **1**, 53.
A. H. Cottrell (1953), *Dislocations and Plastic Flow in Crystals*, Oxford University Press, Oxford.
A. H. Cottrell (1956), *Deformation and Flow of Solids*, Springer-Verlag, Berlin, p. 33.
A. H. Cottrell and V. Aytekin (1950), *J. Inst. Metals*, **77**, 389.
A. H. Cottrell and R. J. Stokes (1955), *Proc. Roy. Soc.* (*London*), *A*, **233**, 17.
W. C. Dash (1956), *J. Appl. Phys.*, **27**, 1193.
A. Deruyttère and G. B. Greenough (1956), *J. Inst. Metals*, **84**, 337.
J. Diehl (1954a), Meeting Max-Planck-Institut, Stuttgart.
J. Diehl (1954b), Plasticity Meeting, Stuttgart.
J. Diehl (1955), Thesis, Technischen Hochschule, Stuttgart.
J. Diehl (1956a), *Z. Metallkunde*, **47**, 331.
J. Diehl (1956b), *Z. Metallkunde*, **47**, 411.
J. Diehl and A. Kochendörfer (1952), *Z. angew. Phys.*, **4**, 241.
J. Diehl, S. Mader, and A. Seeger (1955), *Z. Metallkunde*, **46**, 650.
J. Diehl and H. Rebstock (1956), *Z. Naturforsch.*, **11a**, 169.
H. Dietrich and E. Kneller (1956), *Z. Metallkunde*, **47**, 672.
H. Donth (1955), private communication.
J. E. Dorn (1956a), *Creep and Fracture of Metals at High Temperature*, H.M. Stationery Office, London, p. 89.
J. E. Dorn (1956b), ASM Seminar, Cleveland.
R. Drouard, J. Washburn, and E. R. Parker (1953), *Trans. AIME*, **197**, 1226.
E. H. Edwards and J. Washburn (1954), *J. Metals*, **200**, 1239.
J. D. Eshelby, F. C. Frank, and F. R. N. Nabarro (1951), *Phil. Mag.*, **42**, 351.
W. Fahrenhorst and E. Schmid (1930), *Z. Physik*, **64**, 845.
P. Feltham and J. D. Meakin (1957), *Acta Met.* (in press).
F. C. Frank (1949), *Proc. Phys. Soc.* (*London*), *A*, **62**, 131.
A. Franks and D. McLean (1956), *Phil. Mag.*, **1**, 101.
J. Friedel (1955), *Phil. Mag.*, **46**, 1169.
J. Friedel (1956), *Les Dislocations. Gauthier-Villars*, Paris.
R. L. Fullman (1951), *J. Appl. Phys.*, **22**, 448.
J. Garstone, R. W. K. Honeycombe, and G. Greetham (1956), *Acta Met.*, **4**, 485.
P. Gay, P. B. Hirsch, and A. Kelly (1954), *Acta Cryst.*, **7**, 41.
P. Gay and A. Kelly (1953a), *Acta Cryst.*, **6**, 165.
P. Gay and A. Kelly (1953b), *Acta Cryst.*, **6**, 172.
K. F. von Göler and G. Sachs (1929), *Z. Physik*, **55**, 581.
Z. Gyulai (1954), *Z. Physik*, **138**, 317.
P. Haasen (1953), *Z. Physik*, **136**, 26.
P. Haasen (1956), private communication.
P. Haasen and G. Leibfried (1952), *Z. Metallkunde*, **43**, 317.
F. Haeszner and D. Schreiber (1957), *Z. Metallkunde*, **48**, 263.

R. D. Heidenreich (1951), *Bell System Tech. J.*, **30,** 867.
R. D. Heidenreich and W. Shockley (1948), *Report of a Conference on Strength of Solids,* Physical Society, London, p. 57.
P. B. Hirsch (1952), *Acta Cryst.*, **5,** 172.
P. B. Hirsch (1956), "Mosaic Structure," *Progr. Metal Phys.*, **6,** 236.
P. B. Hirsch, R. W. Horne, and M. J. Whelan (1956), *Phil. Mag.*, **1,** 677. (See also paper by these authors in Part I of this volume.)
B. Jaoul (1955), *Compt. Rend.*, **240,** 2532.
B. Jaoul and I. Bricot (1955), *Rev. mét.*, **52,** 629.
A. Kelly (1954), *Acta Cryst.*, **7,** 554.
A. Kelly (1956), *Phil. Mag.*, **1,** 835.
A. Kelly and W. T. Roberts (1955), *Acta Met.*, **3,** 96.
J. S. Koehler (1952a), discussion in *Imperfections in Nearly Perfect Crystals,* W. Shockley, J. H. Hollomon, R. Maurer, and F. Seitz, John Wiley & Sons, New York, pp. 146–147.
J. S. Koehler (1952b), *Phys. Rev.*, **86,** 52.
J. S. Koehler (1953), *Acta Met.*, **1,** 377.
D. Kuhlmann (1950), *Z. Metallkunde,* **41,** 129.
D. Kuhlmann-Wilsdorf and H. Wilsdorf (1953), *Acta Met.*, **1,** 394.
H. Lange and K. Lücke (1953), *Z. Metallkunde,* **44,** 183.
G. Leibfried (1954), *Z. angew. Phys.*, **6,** 251.
G. Leibfried and H.-D. Dietze (1951), *Z. Physik,* **131,** 113.
G. Leibfried and P. Haasen (1954), *Z. Physik,* **137,** 67.
K. Lücke and H. Lange (1952), *Z. Metallkunde,* **43,** 55.
K. Lücke, G. Masing, and K. Schröder (1955), *Z. Metallkunde,* **46,** 792.
R. Maddin, C. H. Mathewson, and W. R. Hibbard (1948), *Trans. AIME,* **175,** 86.
R. Maddin, C. H. Mathewson, and W. R. Hibbard (1949), *Trans. AIME,* **185,** 529.
S. Mader (1957), Thesis, Technischen Hochschule, Stuttgart; *Z. Physik,* **149,** 73.
G. Masing and J. Raffelsieper (1950), *Z. Metallkunde,* **41,** 65.
G. Masing and H. Weik (1954), *Z. Metallkunde,* **45,** 417
N. F. Mott (1952), *Phil. Mag.*, **43,** 1151.
N. F. Mott (1953), *Phil. Mag.*, **44,** 742.
H. Müller and G. Leibfried (1955), *Z. Physik,* **142,** 87.
A. Murin (1954), *Dokl. Akad. Nauk S.S.S.R.*, **99,** 529.
G. J. Ogilvie and W. Boas (1948), *Trans. AIME,* **175,** 102.
E. Orowan (1947), *J. West Scot. Iron Steel Inst.*, **54,** 45.
E. Osswald (1933), *Z. Physik,* **83,** 55.
M. S. Paterson (1955), *Acta Met.*, **3,** 491.
H. W. Paxton and A. H. Cottrell (1954), *Acta Met.*, **2,** 3.
G. R. Piercy, R. W. Cahn, and A. H. Cottrell (1955), *Acta Met.*, **3,** 331.
M. Polanyi and E. Schmid (1929), *Naturwissenschaften,* **17,** 301.
W. T. Read, Jr. (1953), *Dislocations in Crystals,* McGraw-Hill, New York.
H. Rebstock (1957), *Z. Metallkunde,* **48,** 206.
J. K. Redman (1957), private communication.
F. Röhm and J. Diehl (1952), *Z. Metallkunde,* **43,** 126.
F. D. Rosi (1954), *Trans. AIME,* **200,** 1009.
G. Sachs and J. Weerts (1930), *Z. Physik,* **62,** 473.
E. Schmid (1931), *Z. Elektrochem.*, **37,** 447.
E. Schmid and W. Boas (1935), *Kristallplastizität,* Springer-Verlag, Berlin.

G. Schoeck (1956), *Theory of Creep,* ASM Seminar, Cleveland, 1956.
G. Schoeck and A. Seeger (1955), *Report of a Conference on Defects in Crystalline Solids,* Physical Society, London, p. 340.
A. Seeger (1954a), *Z. Naturforsch.,* **9a,** 758.
A. Seeger (1954b), *Z. Naturforsch.,* **9a,** 856.
A. Seeger (1954c), *Z. Naturforsch.,* **9a,** 870.
A. Seeger (1955a), *Report of a Conference on Defects in Crystalline Solids,* Physical Society, London, p. 328.
A. Seeger (1955b), *Report of a Conference on Defects in Crystalline Solids,* Physical Society, London, p. 391.
A. Seeger (1955c), Les Electrons dans les Métaux in *Report of 10th Solvay Conference on Physics,* Stoops, Brussels, p. 329.
A. Seeger (1955d), *Phil. Mag.,* **46,** 1194.
A. Seeger (1955e), Theory of Lattice Defects in *Handbuch der Physik,* Springer, Berlin, Vol. VII/1.
A. Seeger (1956a), *Deformation and Flow of Solids,* Springer-Verlag, Berlin, p. 90
A. Seeger (1956b), *Z. Naturforsch.,* **11a,** 985.
A. Seeger (1956c), *Z. Naturforsch.,* **11a,** 724.
A. Seeger, J. Diehl, S. Mader, and R. Rebstock (1957), *Phil. Mag.,* **2,** 323.
A. Seeger and G. Schoeck (1953), *Acta Met.,* **1,** 519.
J. W. Semmel and E. S. Machlin (1957), *Acta Met.,* in press.
O. D. Sherby, J. L. Lytton, and J. E. Dorn (1957), *Acta Met.,* **5,** 219.
A. Sosin and J. S. Koehler (1956), *Phys. Rev.,* **101,** 972.
W. Staubwasser (1954), Thesis, University of Göttingen.
H. Stehle and A. Seeger (1956), *Z. Physik,* **146,** 217.
A. N. Stroh (1954), *Proc. Phys. Soc. (London), B,* **67,** 427.
A. N. Stroh (1956) *Phil. Mag.,* **1,** 489.
H. Suzuki, S. Ikeda, and S. Takeuchi (1956), *J. Phys. Soc. Japan,* **11,** 382. (See also paper by these authors in Part VI of this volume.)
D. S. Tannhauser (1955), *Eighth Annual Report on High Pressure Research,* Institute for the Study of Metals, Chicago, p. 65.
G. I. Taylor (1934), *Proc. Roy. Soc. (London), A,* **145,** 362.
G. Thomas and J. Nutting (1956), *J. Inst. Metals,* **85,** 1.
N. Thompson (1953), *Proc. Phys. Soc. (London), B,* **66,** 158.
N. Thompson, C. K. Coogan, and J. D. Rider (1955), *J. Inst. Metals,* **84,** 73.
E. E. Underwood and L. L. Marsh, Jr. (1956), *Trans. AIME,* **206,** 477.
B. E. Warren and E. P. Warekois (1955), *Acta Met.,* **3,** 473.
J. Weertman (1955), *J. Appl. Phys.,* **26,** 1213.
H. Wilsdorf (1954), *Z. Metallkunde,* **45,** 14.
H. Wilsdorf and D. Kuhlmann-Wilsdorf (1951), *Naturwissenschaften,* **38,** 502.
H. Wilsdorf and D. Kuhlmann-Wilsdorf (1952a), *Z. angew. Phys.,* **4,** 361.
H. Wilsdorf and D. Kuhlmann-Wilsdorf (1952b), *Z. angew. Phys.,* **4,** 409.
H. Wilsdorf and D. Kuhlmann-Wilsdorf (1952c), *Z. angew. Phys.,* **4,** 418.
O. H. Wyatt (1951), Thesis, University of Cambridge.
O. H. Wyatt (1953), *Proc. Phys. Soc. (London), B,* **66,** 459.

ACKNOWLEDGMENTS

It is a pleasure to thank Dr. J. Diehl, Dr. P. Haasen, Professor J. Keller, and Dr. S. Mader (who supplied the electron micrographs for this paper) for discussions and valuable suggestions. The author is also grateful to Professor U. Dehlinger for his continued interest and encouragement.

EDITOR'S NOTE

The above paper, which was written after the Conference, makes Dr. Seeger's presentation much more complete and detailed than time would allow at the Conference. Much of the original oral discussion is therefore no longer pertinent, so the discussion will not be presented here.

Regarding Seeger's Paper on Work Hardening

JACQUES FRIEDEL

Centre de Recherches Métallurgiques de L'Ecole Nationale Supérieure des Mines Paris, France

I would like to make two points concerning Seeger's paper.* The first is a small point regarding the crossing of a forest of dislocations on an intersecting glide plane. In Fig. 1 we see a dislocation which is held up by such a forest of dislocations. Under the action of a stress, the dislocation will cut through the forest by thermal activation, forming jogs, and the loop will be free to expand. From such considerations as this, Seeger obtained a stress versus temperature curve which was initially linear and then constant, as illustrated in Fig. 2. This curve was obtained by assuming that the average distance L between trees along the loop is of the order of the average distance between the trees in the forest, which is called l. I want to show that L must be larger than l and should, in fact, vary with the stress; and that in consequence the stress-temperature curve should look more like Fig. 3.

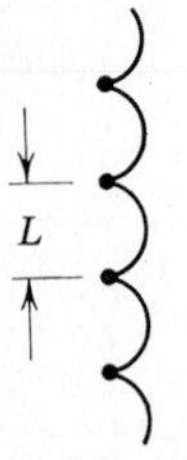

Fig. 1. Dislocation held up by a forest of dislocations.

The argument is as follows. The deformation is a steady-state process; therefore, each time a loop escapes from one of the trees T it must, in its table position, touch a new tree T' (Fig. 4). If it did not, the loops would grow to ever-increasing size, and the deformation

* The preceding paper in this volume.

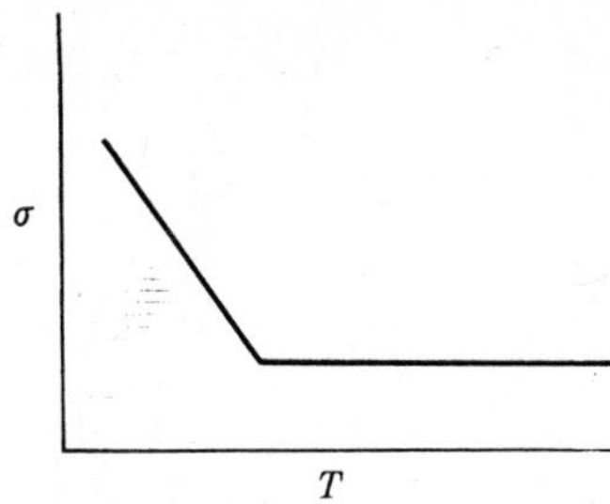

Fig. 2. Stress to force a dislocation through a forest versus temperature (according to Seeger).

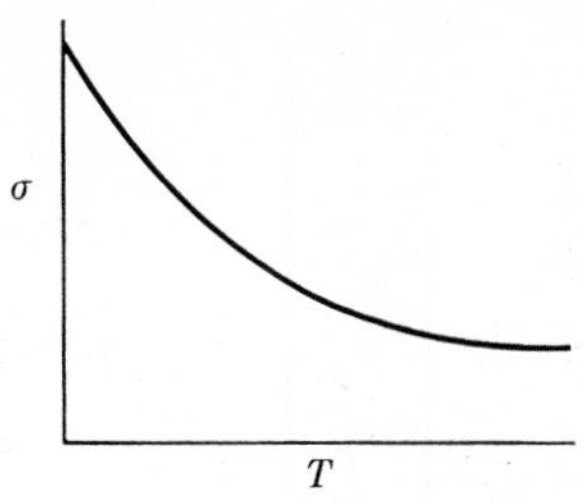

Fig. 3. Stress to force a dislocation through a forest versus temperature, when $L > l$ and L varies with stress.

would be accelerated. Thus, in a steady state, the area A described by a loop is roughly the area per tree in the forest; the product Ly (Fig. 4) must be a constant. Since y increases with the applied stress, L must decrease with increasing applied stress. As a result, the temperature versus stress curve must be a continuous hyperbolic type of curve as shown in Fig. 3. The curve in Fig. 3 fits the experiment approximately as well as the curve which Seeger has suggested. (For further details, cf. Friedel.[1])

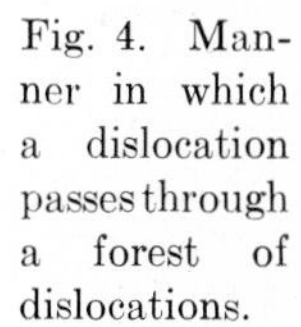

Fig. 4. Manner in which a dislocation passes through a forest of dislocations.

The second point of discussion concerns the variation with temperature of the beginning of stage III. This occurs at a stress σ_0 which varies as in eq. 1

$$\sigma_0 \propto T^{-m} \qquad \text{with } m \backsimeq \tfrac{1}{2} \text{ to } 1 \tag{1}$$

This is far from an exponential decrease, indicating that the activation energy U for cross-slip formation decreases markedly with increasing applied stress. I wish to emphasize (1) that this is evidence for regions of stress concentrations in the crystal (piled-up groups); and (2) that an exact determination of m for high applied stresses σ would distinguish between a picture such as Seeger's of piled-up groups with a constant number n of loops and the one I proposed previously with a size n increasing as σ.

As cross-slip formation may be described by the succession of events of Fig. 5, its activation energy U must be of the order of twice the energy of pinching. This is proportional to the width d of the extended dislocation. At the head of larger piled-up groups, this width is inversely proportional to the local stress, i.e., to $n\sigma$. Cross slip has a

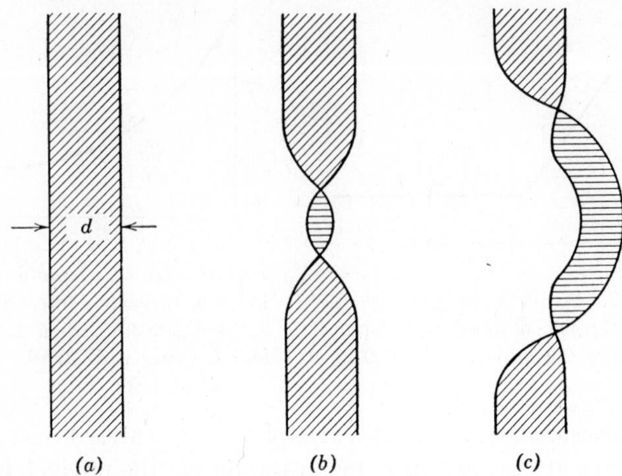

Fig. 5. Cross-slip formation at an extended dislocation. (*a*) Extended dislocation on original slip plane. (*b*) Dislocation has pinched off in the original slip plane, and started to extend on the cross-slip plane. (*c*) Portion that is extended on the cross-slip plane moves to give cross slip.

given probability to occur if U/kT is a constant, thus for $n\sigma \propto T^{-1}$. This gives eq. 1 with $m = 1$ in Seeger's model and $m = \frac{1}{2}$ in mine.

REFERENCE

1. J. Friedel, *Les Dislocations,* Gauthier-Villars, Paris (1956).

Lattice Defects in Plastically Deformed Metals

W. BOAS

Division of Tribophysics
Commonwealth Scientific and Industrial Research Organization
University of Melbourne, Australia

1. INTRODUCTION

For an understanding of the mechanism of plastic deformation and the nature of the cold-worked state of a crystal it is necessary to know the type of lattice defects present in the deformed crystal, their number, and their arrangement. To this end, several properties have been measured on metals which have been deformed to various extents and subsequently annealed at different temperatures. In this paper some results of such measurements will be discussed in relation to suggestions which have been made about the nature of the cold-worked state using current estimates of the properties of various types of lattice defects.

The discussion will be based mainly on the results obtained by Clarebrough, Hargreaves, Michell, and West,[1–4] who investigated the changes, on cold working and annealing, in the internal energy, density, electrical resistivity, hardness, and shape of X-ray diffraction lines. Particular attention should be drawn to the fact that the change in internal energy was measured as the energy liberated on annealing the deformed material at a constant rate of rise in temperature. The other properties were measured at room temperature.

The first results of this work showed that some properties are extremely sensitive to small concentrations of specific impurities. Therefore, the comparison of the behavior of different properties is only meaningful if all measurements are carried out on exactly the same material, on the same specimens or at least on specimens from the same bar.

It is convenient to start the discussion by considering Fig. 1 which gives typical results obtained with nickel of commercial purity (99.6%

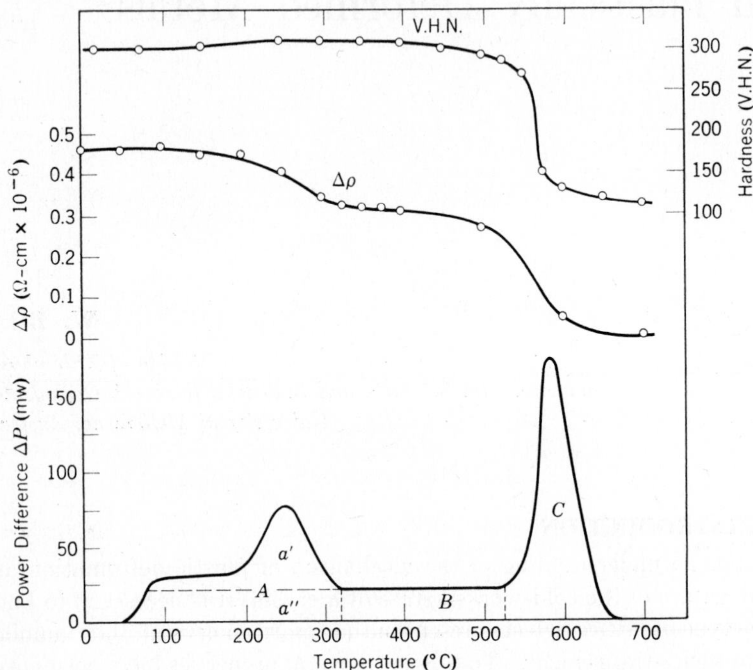

Fig. 1. Power difference (rate of release of stored energy), increment in electrical resistivity ($\Delta\rho$), and hardness for specimens of nickel (99.6% Ni) deformed in torsion to $nd/l = 2.34$. (After Clarebrough, Hargreaves, and West.[2])

Ni).[2] There are three stages of evolution of heat and, as different mechanisms are held to be responsible for the energy release in each of the stages, they will be examined in turn.

2. VACANCIES

The energy released in area a' is ascribed to the disappearance of vacancies into the dislocations forming subgrain boundaries. The evidence for this is as follows.

1. The energy release is associated with changes in density and electrical resistivity but no change in hardness.

2. There is no change in lattice parameter which could account for the change in density.

3. By ascribing to vacancies the total changes in density and resistivity in this range of temperature one can estimate the vacancy concentration in two independent ways. The increase in volume associated with the formation of a vacancy is taken to be 0.9 of an atomic volume and the resistivity change due to 1 at. % vacancies to be 4 $\mu\Omega$-cm.[5]

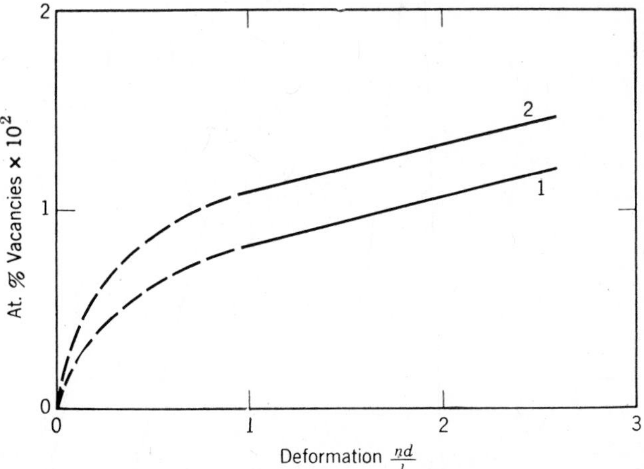

Fig. 2. Vacancy concentration (at. %) in nickel as a function of deformation by torsion. Curve **1**: from density measurements. Curve **2**: from measurements of electrical resistivity.

The concentrations of vacancies thus obtained are plotted in Fig. 2 and it is seen that they agree satisfactorily.*

4. The shape of the curve giving the energy release versus temperature for constant rate of heating has been calculated by Nicholas[6] assuming that point defects are distributed uniformly in spherical subgrains, that they move independently of each other by a thermally activated process, and that their energy is evolved when they reach the boundary of the subgrains. The activation energy for the migration was found from the change in temperature of the peak with change in heating rate to be 1.0 ev. Good agreement was obtained between experimental and calculated curves of energy release.

Although the above discussion was conducted in terms of vacancies, the possibility cannot be excluded that interstitial atoms are present

* If the energy of a vacancy in nickel were known, the measurements of the stored energy would provide a third independent way of calculating vacancy densities. Conversely, if the vacancy densities obtained from the measurements of macroscopic density are combined with those of stored energy, a value of 1.6 ev is obtained for the energy of a vacancy. This estimate is at present being refined.

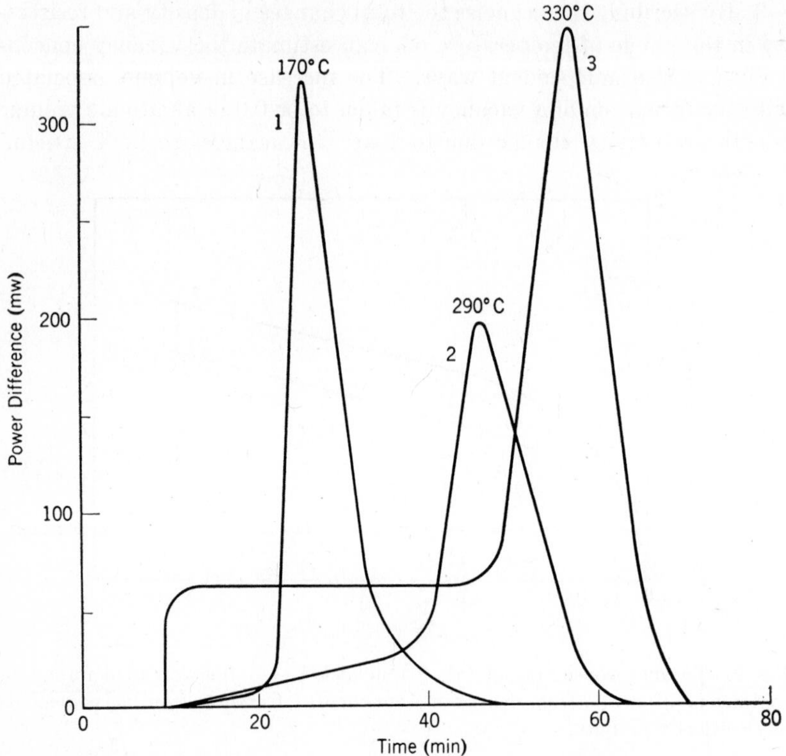

Fig. 3. Rate of release of stored energy for copper of three degrees of purity all deformed by torsion to the same extent. Curve 1: 99.98% Cu. Curve 2: 99.96% Cu. Curve 3: 99.6% Cu, 0.35% As. (After Clarebrough, Hargreaves, and West.[2])

and contribute to the effects, although it is difficult to explain the observed changes in density as being due to interstitials.

3. IMPURITIES

The peak (area C) at the end of the curve showing the release of stored energy (Fig. 1) corresponds to recrystallization and will be discussed in the next section. However, for both nickel and copper the temperature at which this recrystallization peak occurs is sensitive to purity, as shown in Fig. 3 and by comparison of Figs. 1 and 4. The three curves in Fig. 3 show the marked dependence of the recrystallization temperature on the purity for three types of copper deformed to the same extent. Similarly, the recrystallization peak for a purer grade of nickel, Fig. 4, occurs at a lower temperature than that in Fig.

1 for impure nickel, even though the purer nickel is much more lightly deformed.

Further, it can be seen that as the purity decreases there is an increase in the amount of energy released prior to the recrystallization. This is particularly evident for the arsenical copper (Fig. 3) and for the less pure nickel. The area B in Fig. 1 is absent for the purer nickel (Fig. 4). The processes responsible for this release of energy may be described, in general, as recovery.

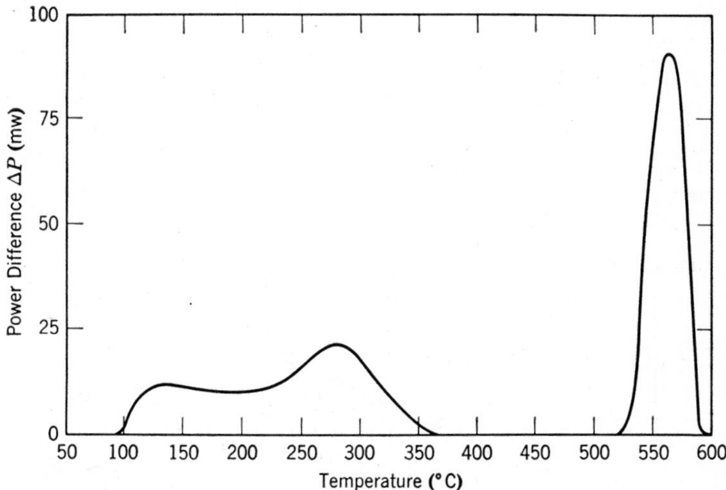

Fig. 4. Rate of release of stored energy for nickel (99.85% Ni) deformed 40% in compression. (Clarebrough, Hargreaves, and West, unpublished work.)

Thus it appears that in both recrystallization and recovery the mobility of dislocations under thermal activation is decreased by the presence of impurities. That this may be due to interaction between impurity atoms and dislocations has been demonstrated for arsenical copper by the observation that the material strain ages. Yield points are observed as shown in Fig. 5, and there is an accompanying change in electrical resistivity (Fig. 6). The anomalous rise in electrical resistivity during recovery observed for this material [2] is probably due to the movement of dislocations away from their atmospheres under thermal activation.

4. DISLOCATIONS

In all metals investigated, irrespective of the heating rate and of whether deformation occurs by tension, compression, or torsion, there is

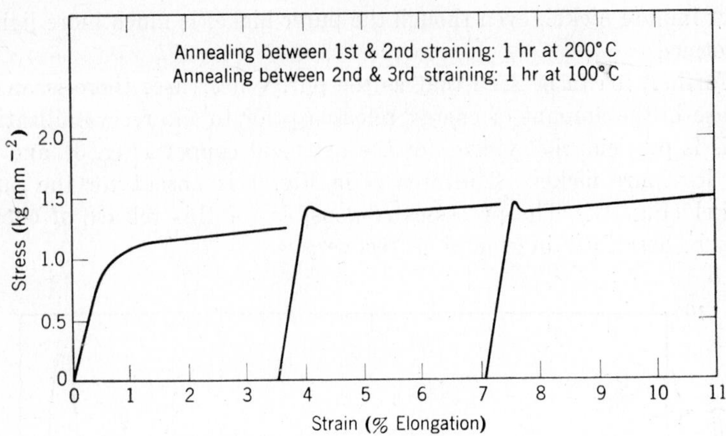

Fig. 5. Stress-strain curves for a single crystal of copper containing 0.4% As showing the development of yield points. (K. Schröder, unpublished work.)

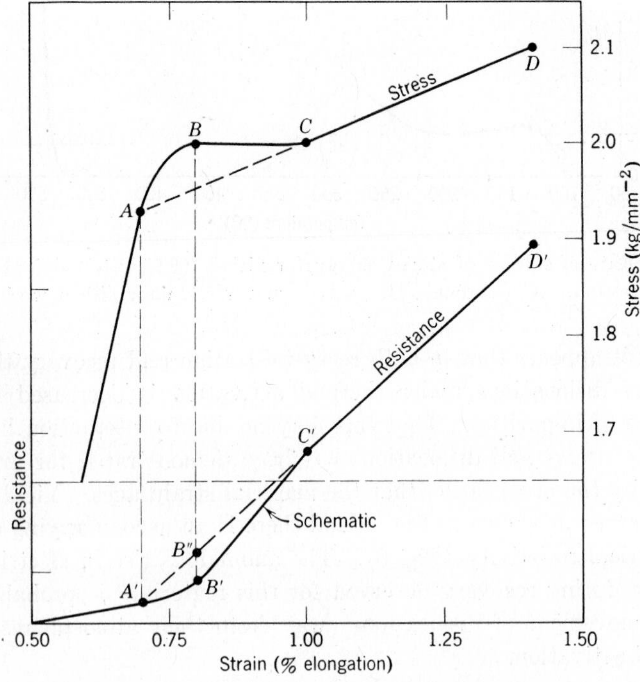

Fig. 6. Stress-strain and electrical resistance-strain curves for a single crystal of copper containing 0.4% As. (K. Schröder, unpublished work.)

a rapid evolution of energy at the high-temperature end of the curve showing the release of energy (peak C in Fig. 1). This energy release is always associated with recrystallization, as has been proved by metallographic and X-ray methods. It is accompanied by changes in hardness, density, and electrical resistivity. It is therefore likely that this energy is derived from the disappearance of the dislocations created by deformation.

Assuming that the energy released in stage C is the sum of the energies of individual dislocations and that no interaction energy is involved, dislocation densities can be calculated. These densities obviously depend critically on the energy assumed for a single dislocation. Following Cottrell[7] one obtains for nickel a value of 7×10^{-4} erg cm^{-1} and this has been used in plotting dislocation densities against deformation in Fig. 7, curve 1.

Further, it is likely that part of the energy released in areas a'' and B is also due to a decrease in dislocation density. If, therefore, the calculation of the density of dislocations, as independent dislocations, is based on the energy of the area $(a'' + B + C)$, too large a value will be obtained (Fig. 7, curve 2). However, the energy of a dislocation is somewhat arbitrary for in heavily cold-worked metals dislocations will occur in piled-up groups and, after some annealing, in subboundaries. In the first case the energy per dislocation is proportional to the number in the pile-up; in the second case the energy is considerably reduced. For the purposes of calculation the figure of 7×10^{-4} erg cm^{-1}, given above, has been used here as an average value. This gives dislocation densities of the same order as found by Gay, Hirsch, and Kelly[8] from X-ray diffraction data.

In spite of the uncertainty of the calculation, it is clear that the dislocation density will increase almost linearly with deformation.

Attempts to calculate dislocation densities can also be made in two other ways, i.e., by using the measurements of density[3] and those of electrical resistivity.[2] If the total change in density, apart from that attributed to vacancies, is due to a decrease in the number of dislocations, if an edge dislocation causes the same change in density as a row of vacancies of the same length, and if half of the dislocations are screw dislocations which do not contribute to the density change, the dislocation density becomes $4\sqrt{2}\delta/0.9a^2$ lines cm^{-2}, where δ is the fractional change in density and a the lattice parameter. Values so calculated are contained in Table 1.

Table 1 also gives dislocation densities calculated from the change in electrical resistivity associated with area $(a'' + B + C)$. It has been assumed that the value of the increase in resistivity due to a

TABLE 1. DISLOCATION DENSITIES CALCULATED ON VARIOUS ASSUMPTIONS IN NICKEL (IN LINES cm^{-2}) DEFORMED BY TORSION

nd/l	From Stored Energy	From Density	From Electrical Resistivity
0.94	1.6×10^{11}	1.0×10^{12}	0.9×10^{13}
1.87	2.7	1.9	1.5

random (isotropic) arrangement of edge dislocations in nickel is 1.8×10^{-14} $\mu\Omega$-cm per dislocation line. This is three times the value calculated by Hunter and Nabarro [9] for copper by analogy to the factor found for the resistivity of vacancies.[5]

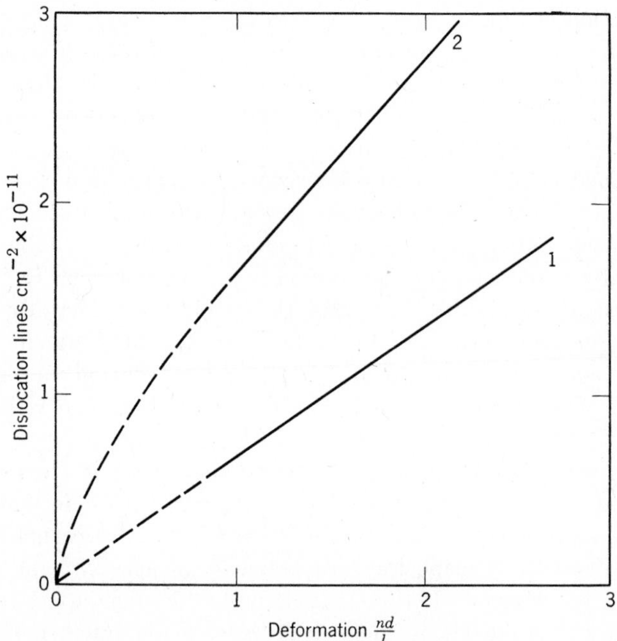

Fig. 7. Density of dislocations as a function of deformation calculated from stored-energy measurements assuming independent dislocations of energy 7×10^{-4} erg cm^{-1}. Curve 1: based on area C of Fig. 1. Curve 2: based on area $(a'' + B + C)$ of Fig. 1.

The dislocation densities thus calculated from measurements of density and electrical resistivity are considerably larger than those obtained from the measurements of the stored energy. The discrepancies are too large to be explained by uncertainties in the calculations and it is obvious that at least one of the assumptions made must be at fault. Two ways of resolving the difficulty have been suggested.

The first was made by Mott[10] and involves the formation of micro-cracks near a piled-up group of dislocations if the stress concentration is sufficiently great, i.e., of the order of the true fracture stress of the material, and if the formation of the crack leads to a decrease in energy of the system. If n dislocations are piled up or if there is a dislocation with the Burgers vector nb giving rise to a crack, this will, according to Stroh,[11] have a maximum width nb and a stable equilibrium length

$$c = n^2 \frac{b}{\pi} \mathrm{K}$$

where $\mathrm{K} = bG/8(1 - \nu)\gamma$, G being the rigidity modulus, ν Poisson's ratio, and γ the surface energy. For nickel, $\mathrm{K} = 2.04$.

Assuming that there are N such cracks cm^{-2}, Stroh * calculates[12] the relative change in density due to the cracks as $\delta = \frac{1}{2}nNbc$, and the relative change in specific resistivity as $\Delta\rho/\rho = (\pi/12)Nc^2$. Thus

$$n = \frac{6}{\mathrm{K}} \frac{\Delta\rho/\rho}{\delta}$$

From the experimental results N, n, and c may be found as functions of the deformation. For the case considered here, $n = 300$ and $c =$

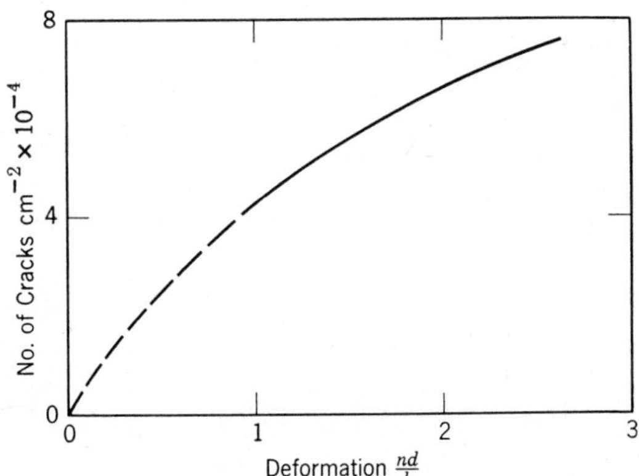

Fig. 8. Density of microcracks as a function of the deformation.

1.3×10^{-3} cm, independent of the deformation, while the variation of N is shown schematically in Fig. 8.

It can be seen that n is of the magnitude estimated by Stroh[11] as

* I wish to thank Dr. Stroh for letting me use his paper before publication.

satisfying the condition that the crack forms with a decrease of energy. The total density of dislocations in those piled-up groups which cause cracks increases with deformation and is of the order of 2×10^7 lines cm^{-2} for a deformation of $nd/l = 2$. This means that if about 0.01% of the dislocations pile up in groups and form cracks, the changes in density and electrical resistivity can be explained. Clearly, there will be piled-up groups of smaller n which will not give rise to cracks. The energy of the cracks is negligible compared with the measured stored energy. As the energy of a piled-up group is about n times higher than that of the same number of dislocations when dispersed, the total energy of the groups may be perhaps one-quarter of the total stored energy, but in view of the uncertainty of all these calculations it seems unnecessary to change the dislocation densities indicated in Fig. 7. No direct experimental evidence has yet been found for the existence of such cracks.

The other way of resolving the difficulty is provided by the suggestion that stacking faults have a large effect on resistivity.[13] Koehler[14] has estimated this effect by comparing the reflection probability of a vacancy σ_v with that of a stacking fault σ_F. The change in resistivity due to 1 at. % vacancies is

$\rho_v = c\sigma_v \times$ (number of vacancies cm^{-3}) $\times$ (cross-sectional area of vacancy)
$= c\sigma_v/50a$, where c is a constant of proportionality.

The change in resistivity due to stacking faults is then

$\rho_F = c\sigma_F \times$ (projected area of fault cm^{-3})
$= c\sigma_F Dw/3$, where D is the density of dislocations and w the width of the fault.

One thus obtains

$$\rho_F = \rho_v \frac{\sigma_F}{\sigma_v} \frac{50}{3} Dwa$$

The probability of occurrence of a stacking fault α is equal to the total area of stacking fault cm^{-3} divided by the total area of octahedral plane cm^{-3}, i.e., $\alpha = Dwa/4\sqrt{3}$, and hence

$$\rho_F = \rho_v \frac{\sigma_F}{\sigma_v} \alpha \frac{200}{\sqrt{3}}$$

If one assumes with Klemens[15] $\sigma_F = 0.5$, with Jongenburger[16] $\sigma_v = 0.4$, and with Seeger[5] $\rho_v = 4\ \mu\Omega\text{-cm}$, one obtains

$$\rho_F = 560\alpha \quad \mu\Omega\text{-cm}$$

Then, to account for the experimental values of resistivity, stacking fault probabilities of about 5×10^{-4} are needed. The way in which the probability depends on deformation is indicated in Fig. 9.

Using X-ray diffraction, Michell[4] has looked for stacking faults in filed nickel powder. He found no effect and, in view of the sensitivity

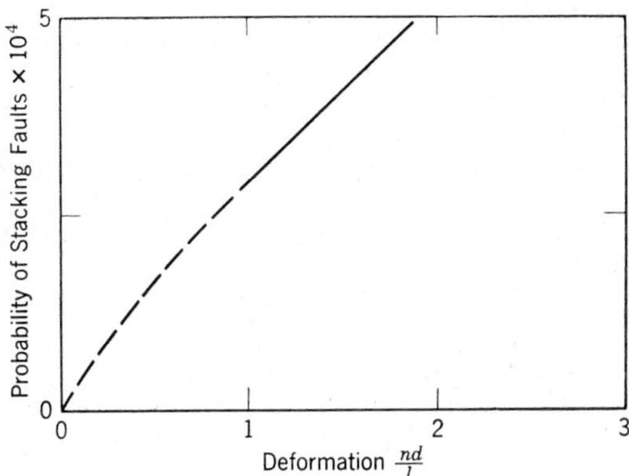

Fig. 9. Probability of stacking faults as a function of the deformation.

of the experiments, estimated that α could not be greater than 10^{-3}. Thus it appears that stacking faults sufficient to account for the change in resistivity may exist and escape detection.

Seeger[17] has suggested that stacking faults should have a low energy in nickel, i.e., w should be relatively large. Therefore, w will be taken equal to twice the value given by Cottrell[18] for copper, i.e., $w_{\text{Ni}} = 6 \times 10^{-7}$ cm. Then for $nd/l = 1.87$, $\alpha = 5 \times 10^{-4}$, which corresponds to $D = 1.6 \times 10^{11}$, i.e., most of the dislocations need to be extended to account for the resistivity change but our estimates of dislocation density from the stored energy need not be altered.

Clearly, the presence of stacking faults cannot explain the density changes and the existence of some type of void must be invoked. One such possibility is provided by the *cavités* postulated by Blin[19] on the basis of low-angle X-ray scattering experiments.

5. CONCLUSIONS

The above discussion has shown what type of conclusions may be drawn from the experimental results. These conclusions are not fully satisfactory and appear, in some cases, to be mere speculations. To the author the situation seems to be this: Reliable experimental data are now available but the theoretical ideas have not yet been worked out in sufficient detail and any quantitative conclusion is still open to considerable doubt. At present it is not possible to decide between the various suggestions made to interpret the experimental results.

REFERENCES

1. L. M. Clarebrough, M. E. Hargreaves, D. Michell, and G. W. West, *Proc. Roy. Soc. (London), A,* **215,** 507 (1952).
2. L. M. Clarebrough, M. E. Hargreaves, and G. W. West, *Proc. Roy. Soc. (London), A,* **232,** 252 (1955).
3. L. M. Clarebrough, M. E. Hargreaves, and G. W. West, *Phil. Mag.,* **1,** 528 (1956).
4. D. Michell, *Phil. Mag.,* **1,** 584 (1956); D. Michell and F. D. Haig, *ibid.*
5. A Seeger, *Z. Physik,* **144,** 637 (1956).
6. J. F. Nicholas, *Phil. Mag.,* **46,** 87 (1955).
7. A. H. Cottrell, *Dislocations and Plastic Flow in Crystals.* Oxford University Press, Oxford, p. 38 (1953).
8. P. Gay, P. B. Hirsch, and A. Kelly, *Acta Met.,* **1,** 315 (1953).
9. S. C. Hunter and F. R. N. Nabarro, *Proc. Roy. Soc. (London), A,* **220,** 543 (1953).
10. N. F. Mott, oral communication (May 1956).
11. A. N. Stroh, *Proc. Roy. Soc. (London), A,* **223,** 404 (1954); *ibid.,* **232,** 548 (1955).
12. A. N. Stroh, *Phil. Mag.,* **2,** 1 (1957).
13. T. Broom, *Proc. Phys. Soc. (London), B,* **65,** 871 (1952).
14. J. S. Koehler, in *Impurities and Imperfections,* A.S.M., Cleveland, pp. 162–169 (1955).
15. P. G. Klemens, *Australian J. Phys.,* **6,** 122 (1953).
16. P. Jongenburger, *Appl. Sci. Research, B,* **3,** 237 (1953).
17. A. Seeger, *Phil. Mag.,* **46,** 1194 (1955).
18. A. H. Cottrell, *op. cit.,* p. 74.
19. J. Blin, Thesis, University of Paris (1954).

ACKNOWLEDGMENT

The author wishes to express his most sincere thanks to his colleagues at the Division of Tribophysics for many discussions, and for their help in preparing this paper and allowing him to use unpublished data.

DISCUSSION

LÜCKE asked if the long plateau observed in the energy plot could possibly be due to the solution of arsenic into the copper. It had been found by calorimetric measurements that these effects are sometimes very large in such alloys. BOAS said that the heat of solution of arsenic in copper would not be measured by their differential technique because the solution would occur in the same way in both the deformed and undeformed specimen. A difference in the rate of solution in the two specimens would show up in the second run, which is made to be sure the two specimens are identical after the first run has been made. Since no difference is observed on the second run, the solution must occur in the same way in the deformed and undeformed specimens. LÜCKE expressed the opinion that the deformation could give a forced precipitation so that the state of the precipitate could be different in the deformed and undeformed specimens. This difference would disappear during the first recrystallization so that nothing is seen during the second run. Therefore, one cannot rule out the possibility that the heat of solution is entering.

Written comment by BOAS:

According to Merz and Mathewson,[1] the solid solubility of As in Cu is about 7.9 wt. % As at 680° and it decreases slowly and approximately linearly to about 7.5 wt. % at 300°C. Owen and Rowlands[2] give the solubility at 215°C as 6.0 at % As. These data have been confirmed again by Owen and Morris.[3] There do not appear to be any more recent determinations of the solubility of As in Cu. It appears, therefore, that the measurements of stored energy in arsenical copper are not complicated by precipitation or solution processes.

LÜCKE asked if the density change due to the spread-out nature of the dislocation core discussed by Seeger would not show up as a change in the lattice parameter. BOAS answered that the change in lattice parameter is too small to account for the macroscopic density change observed. SEEGER said that a change in lattice parameter should certainly be observable in principle, although it would not necessarily be the same for all Debye-Scherrer rings.

1 J. C. Merz and C. H. Mathewson, *Trans. AIME,* **124,** 59 (1937).

2 E. A. Owen and V. W. Rowlands, *J. Inst. Metals,* **66,** 361 (1940).

3 E. A. Owen and D. T. Morris, *J. Inst. Metals,* **76,** 145 (1949/50).

Written comment by SEEGER:

The practical difficulty is that the linear strains around dislocations, which are much larger than the nonlinear ones leading to the change in lattice parameter, are so large that they give rise to a considerable broadening of Debye-Scherrer rings or Laue spots as shown by the calculations of Wilson [4, 5] and Suzuki.[6] It might therefore be difficult to observe the shift in the positions of these broadened rings. Crussard and Aubertin [7] have observed (by a back reflection technique) a decrease in the lattice parameter of cold-worked copper on recrystallization. It seems that this decrease is due to the effect we have been discussing.

COTTRELL pointed out that X-ray work on heavily cold-worked copper indicates that one atom in 300 is in a stacking fault; and he asked if the present work agreed with this. BOAS said that a stacking fault probability of 5×10^{-4} would be needed to explain the resistivity change in nickel. They had not found positive exidence for stacking faults in nickel, but the sensitivity of their experiments would not allow the detection of such a small density of stacking faults.

HART questioned whether the microcracks due to dislocation pile-ups were pertinent in explaining the density change unless they could be shown to be stable upon removal of the stress. MOTT said that the material does eventually show ductile fracture and if this is due to such cracks, there must be some stabilizing mechanism that was not treated in Stroh's paper.

FRIEDEL, commenting on the slowing down of recovery by impurities, said he found it hard to believe that it was because of Cottrell clouds, since the clouds would diffuse at least as readily as the dislocations. He asked if it could be due to the influence of the impurity atoms on the jog energy of split dislocations. LOMER asked why the argument should differ from that used in discussing the change in yield point, as recovery is due to movement of dislocations under their mutual stresses. HONEYCOMBE commented that the 0.3% arsenic would certainly have an effect and asked if microcracks which were stable would not show a permanent effect on the resistivity after annealing. BOAS said that the piled-up dislocations disperse and the cracks close on annealing since there is no gas inside the material to prevent their collapse.

[4] A. J. C. Wilson, *Acta Cryst.*, **5**, 318 (1952).

[5] A. J. C. Wilson, *Nuovo cimento,* **1**, 277 (1955).

[6] T. Suzuki, *J. Phys. and Chem. of Solids,* to be published.

[7] C. Crussard and F. Aubertin, *Rev. Met.*, **46**, 354 (1949).

Stored Energy and Resistivity Changes in Cold-Worked Metals

ALFRED SEEGER

Max Planck Institut für Metallforschung and Institut für theoretische und angewandte Physik der Technischen Hochschule Stuttgart, Germany

I cannot be so pessimistic about the state of the stored-energy measurements and resistivity change measurements as Dr. Boas is. I also believe that we have to rule out the possibility of microcracks, as he has already indicated. Let me start off with Boas' results in the following table, as they have stimulated us to look a little closer at the problem and to do certain calculations. The results of some of these calculations are presented in Part VI of this volume. I will take over Boas' results for this discussion with the one exception of the change in density which you will note in Table 1.

TABLE 1. DISLOCATION DENSITIES IN COLD-WORKED NICKEL ($nd/l = 1.87$) CALCULATED BY VARIOUS METHODS FROM THE DATA OF BOAS AND CO-WORKERS

Calculated from	Calc. by Boas	Calc. by Seeger and Stehle
Stored energy	$2.7 \times 10^{11}/\text{cm}^2$	
Density change	$1.9 \times 10^{12}/\text{cm}^2$	$5 \times 10^{11}/\text{cm}^2$
Resistivity	$1.5 \times 10^{13}/\text{cm}^2$	

You will note that in pages 504–506 I have suggested that the volume change induced in a crystal by a dislocation is about 1.5 atoms per unit Burgers vector length along the dislocation. This value gives a very nice agreement between the stored energy and the change in density. The agreement with resistivity calculations is very bad indeed. We need an additional factor of the order of 40 in the dislocation scattering of electrons to bring about an agreement. Thus, we need a defect which gives no change in density, which does not change the energy particularly, but which does contribute considerable electrical resistivity. The stacking faults in the extended dislocations of nickel and copper are ideally suited for doing just these things. The only difficulty is that the resistivity effect must be very large indeed. Stehle and I have been trying to calculate this resistivity from first principles. We believe that the width of the stacking fault in a dislocation in copper is given by the value which has been rather successfully used over the past 3 or 4 years, namely $5b$ for screws and $12b$ for edges,[1] (b = modulus of Burgers vector). We have calculated what we believe to be upper and lower limits of the resistivity change to be expected.[2] The experimental value lies between the theoretical limits, and I believe a more refined value should give more complete agreement. The results of the calculations and the comparison with experiment show that about $^{39}\!/_{40}$ of the dislocation resistivity in both nickel and copper is due to the stacking faults, and $^{1}\!/_{40}$ of the total resistivity is due to the scattering of the dislocation line itself. The results of some of the calculations are displayed in Table 2.

Table 2. Resistivity Change Due to Vacancies and Dislocations
Microhm-centimeters per 1% density change due to the defect

	Vacancies (theoretical)	Vacancies (experimental)	Screw Disl. (theor.)	Isotropic Disl. (theor.)	Disl. (experimental)
Cu	1.67	...	0.1	0.06	2.5
Ni	4	5–6	(0.3)	(0.18)	10

All of the data in Table 2 are in microhm-centimeters per 1% change in density. In the calculations we have used the change in density to calibrate the whole calculation. The column headed "Isotropic Dislocations" is meant to show the scattering by an essentially random distribution of dislocations without stacking faults with all types of slip planes and all variations from edge dislocation to screw. Note that the scattering due to vacancies which we report[3] is slightly larger than that which other people have found. Note also the large value in the case of nickel. The approximations that were made in the calculations for nickel[4] were such that the value of 4 is the lower limit, and actually the value for the vacancy scattering may be as large as 4.5 to 5.5. We have no experimental values in the copper case, but the experimental values for nickel are those given by Boas and collaborators and we see that the agreement is reasonable. The values for screw dislocations and isotropic dislocations for nickel were not calculated specifically for this case but were extrapolated from the results in copper. These figures have been put in parentheses in the table. The conclusion is that if the appropriate change in density due to the dislocations is used and if the stacking faults are taken into account, the determination of dislocation densities from stored energy, change in density, and electrical resistivity fit well together.

REFERENCES

1. A. Seeger and G. Schoeck, *Acta Met.,* **1,** 519 (1953).
2. A. Seeger, Ottawa Conference, *Can. J. Phys.,* **34,** 1219 (1956).
3. H. Stehle and A. Seeger, to be published.
4. A. Seeger, *Z. Physik,* **144,** 637 (1956).

Effect of Impurities on Dislocation Climb

N. F. MOTT

Cavendish Laboratory
University of Cambridge
Cambridge, England

Boas has pointed out (Part III of this volume) that impurities in nickel raise the temperature of recovery (prior to recrystallization), and hence presumably impede the climb of dislocations. We now know several mechanisms by which impurities can make slip more difficult but it is less easy to see how they do this for climb, because the rate of diffusion of most impurities exceeds that of self-diffusion. I would like to make a suggestion about how this can occur.

Climb depends on the presence of jogs. Let us consider a network in which the dislocations are a distance l apart; so long as the distance between jogs is small compared with l, the number of jogs will not affect the rate of climb which will depend on the coefficient of self-diffusion only. But if the number of jogs capable of omitting or absorbing vacancies is small so that the distance between them is great compared with l, climb will be slowed down. The assumption made here is that impurities—or at any rate some impurities—will be strongly bound to jogs, more strongly than they are bound to the rest of the dislocation by the Cottrell mechanism. Thus, when jogs are formed on a dislocation, they will rapidly acquire an impurity atom adsorbed to them, as shown in Fig. 1. This will increase the activation energy for the formation of vacancies. For to form a vacancy at this site, one either has to move an atom from a neighboring site to B, thus leaving one impurity atom at an unjogged site, or move it to A and at the same time move the impurity atom to B. If this process has a higher activation energy than that for the movement of a vacancy in the body of the lattice, as seems likely, the climb process will be slowed down.

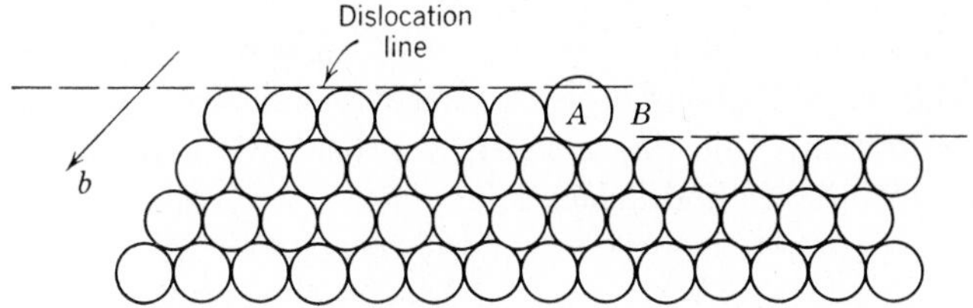

Fig. 1. Extra half plane that defines an edge dislocation with a jog. The adsorbed impurity atom, A, is at the jog.

DISCUSSION

SEEGER said that provided self-diffusion occurs by vacancy migration, a vacancy would diffuse to the position occupied by the atom adjacent to the impurity. The energy gained in doing so should be large enough to allow the impurity to jump into the vacant position almost instantaneously, thereby moving the jog by one atomic distance just as readily as if the impurity atom were not there. The situation is analogous to the evaporation of crystals loaded with impurity atoms, and not to their growth from the vapor. Experimentally (according to experiments on copper by Young and Cabrera *) dislocations in impure copper do climb to some extent at sufficiently high temperatures, whereas they do not in high purity copper. MOTT answered that this would be the nucleation of a new jog, but SEEGER did not agree. MOTT said that one would have to have a strong adsorption for an impurity and that is the last point where it would occur. SHOCKLEY said a jog-pinning process of this sort could occur in a diamond-type crystal, where the jog might have two dangling bonds which would hold a monovalent impurity stronger than would the dislocation line with one row of dangling bonds. SHOCKLEY added that he had difficulty visualizing such a process in a metal.

* F. W. Young, Jr. and N. Cabrera, *J. Appl. Phys.*, **28**, 787 (1957).

AMELINCKX asked if the blocking of dislocation nodes would not be sufficient to inhibit climb. He pointed out that precipitation is observed to start at the nodal points.

SHOCKLEY asked if an extended dislocation structure could climb. SEEGER answered that an extended dislocation would have difficulty climbing without enough jogs in it, and that jogs are difficult to form. MOTT pointed out that the two halves of an extended dislocation are supposed to come together at a jog. SEEGER, in answer to another question by SHOCKLEY, said that an extended dislocation should inhibit the climb of an intersecting dislocation.

The Nature and Effect of Substructure in Polycrystalline Aluminum*

C. J. BALL

Cavendish Laboratory
University of Cambridge
Cambridge, England

When polycrystalline aluminum is deformed a substructure is formed, the subgrain size decreasing with increasing deformation and approaching a limiting value which increases linearly with the temperature of deformation.

It has been possible to determine the axis of misorientation across some subgrain boundaries. The results of these determinations are shown in Fig. 1. Notice that most of the rotation axes are clustered around the [100] and [111] directions, while there are two which are not near [100] or [111].

The types of stress-free low-angle boundary that can be formed without climb with dislocations of one, two, or three systems have been calculated. If dislocations of only one or two systems are present the possible rotation axes are [100], [111], and in the plane (110). If dislocations of three systems are present the rotation axes can lie on loci which traverse the middle of the unit triangle. It does seem as if the rotation axes which have been observed correspond to boundaries formed with dislocations of only two systems. In this connection the electron optical experiments on aluminum foils which were described previously (in Part I of this volume by Hirsch, Horne, and Whelan)

* Presented by P. B. Hirsch.

also indicate that networks often occur and that many of these networks appear to be explicable in terms of two- or three-system networks. We have not determined the boundary planes, and this should be done. However, we are confident that these boundaries are reasonably stress-free, and we suppose that they have the theoretically expected boundary planes for two system boundaries with the observed rotation axes. As these boundaries are not, in many cases, parallel to (111) planes, we do not now believe that subgrain boundaries are to be

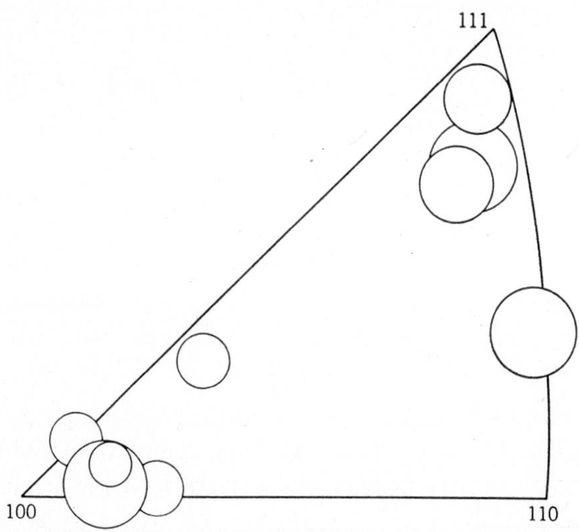

Fig. 1. Rotation axes of the substructure in polycrystalline aluminum.

identified with slip bands. In particular, the rotation axis common to a number of subgrains has been found to be [100] in a region showing double slip. The substructure is probably in the form of lamellae whose boundary planes are twist boundaries on (100), and certainly the boundaries will not be parallel to the slip planes.

The next question is, how does this substructure affect the flow stress? A series of polycrystals with different substructures were prepared. These substructures differ in the size of the subgrains and the magnitude of the misorientations. The specimens were annealed so that any residual dislocations left behind inside the subgrains would go to the boundaries.

A plot of log (flow stress σ) versus log (subgrain size, t), Fig. 2, gives a straight line of slope very nearly $-\frac{1}{2}$, indicating a straight line relationship between flow stress and (subgrain size)$^{-1/2}$. The subgrain size varies from about 1 to 50 μ.

We believe that this is good evidence that subgrain boundaries account for the strength of these crystals. We have the tentative idea that sources within the subgrains operate so that dislocations pile up against the boundary. The stress against the boundary is $N\sigma$, where N is the number of dislocations piled up. Yielding occurs when $N\sigma = \sigma_B$, where σ_B is a constant, and as $N \propto \sigma t$, we get a relationship of the form $\sigma \propto t^{-1/2}$, as observed.

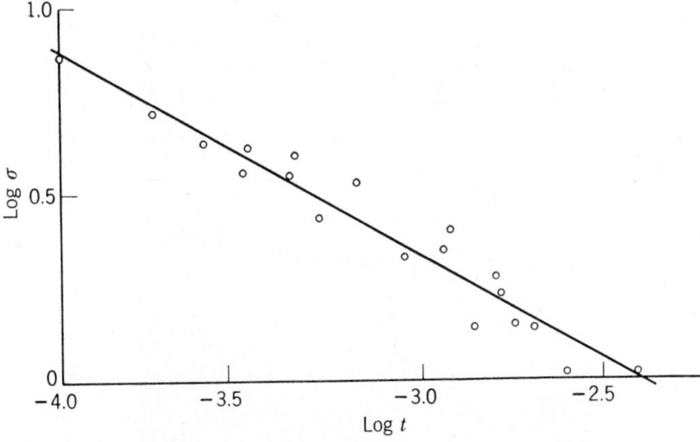

Fig. 2. Logarithm of flow stress versus logarithm of subgrain size.

We cannot explain the strength of the boundaries. Elastic interaction, though giving strengths of the right order of magnitude, is unsatisfactory as there does not seem to be any dependence of boundary strength on angle. Another possibility is that the leading dislocation of the pile-up forms a Cottrell-Lomer lock with one of the dislocations in the boundary, and that the strength of the boundary is the strength of this lock. According to Stroh's calculations,[1] such a lock should have a strength at room temperature very close to the observed strength, but the strength is temperature-dependent. The variation of flow stress with temperature has been determined, and in the range 0–200°C it is no more than can be accounted for by the change in elastic constants.

REFERENCE

1. A. N. Stroh, *Phil. Mag.*, **1**, 489 (1956).

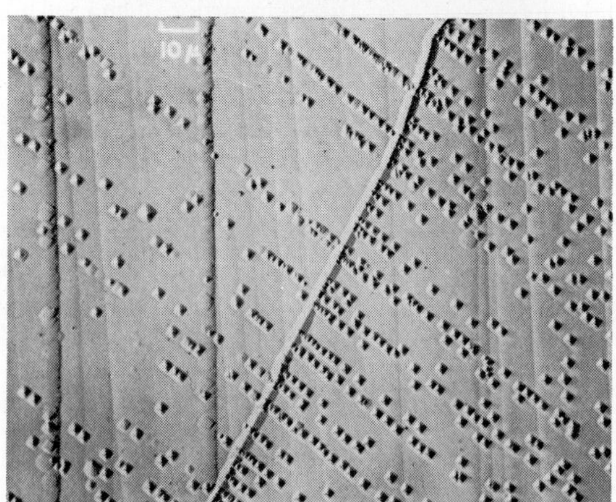

Fig. D1. Examples of edge dislocations being blocked by subboundaries in LiF crystals.

DISCUSSION

GILMAN and JOHNSTON presented two slides showing the interaction of glide dislocations with substructure in LiF. Figure D1 shows edge dislocations piled up at subboundaries. Most subboundaries do not present obstacles to dislocation movements. A type of boundary that seems to be particularly effective is one in which the boundary surface is roughly parallel to a (110) plane. Figure D2 shows edge dislocations and screw dislocations piled up against bands of edge dislocations. Heavy slip bands are obstacles to the movement of dislocations on intersecting slip systems.

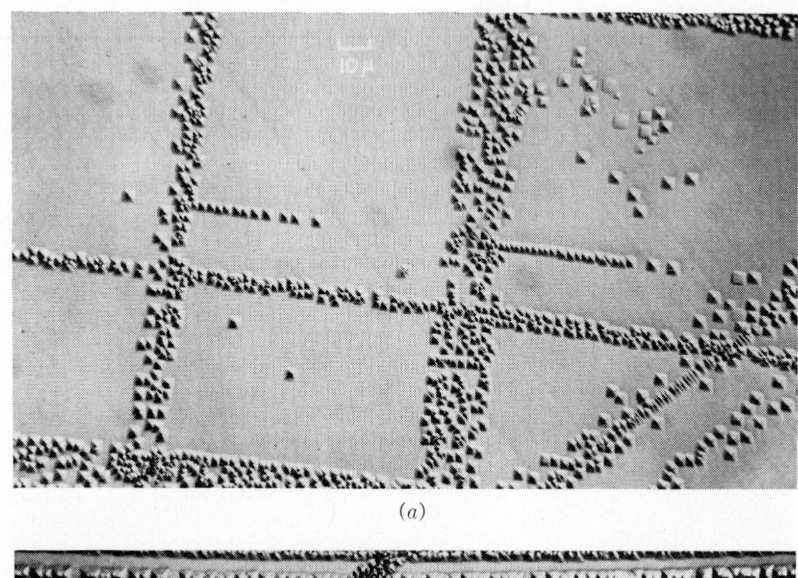

(*a*)

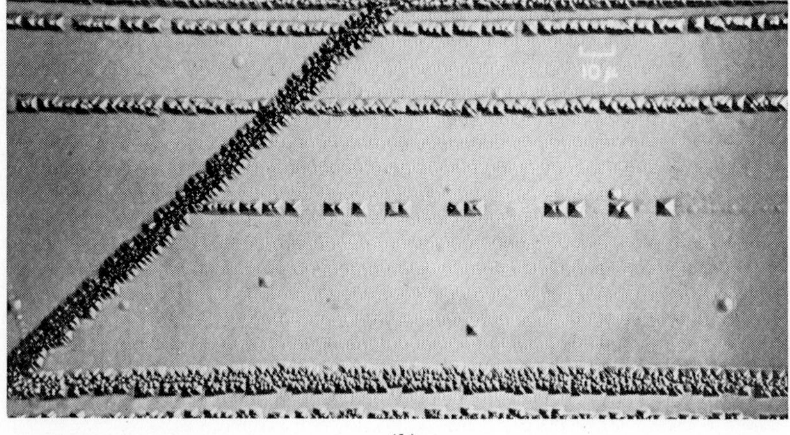

(*b*)

Fig. D2. Mutual blocking of glide bands in LiF crystals. (*a*) Edge dislocations blocked by bands of edge dislocations. Etch "A." (*b*) Screw dislocations blocked by a band of edge dislocations. Etch "W." See paper by Gilman and Johnston in Part I of this volume for a description of the etchants.

IV ALLOY CRYSTALS, IMPURITIES, YIELD POINT PHENOMENA

The Yield Strength of Binary Alloys

HIDEJI SUZUKI

Research Institute for Iron,
Steel, and Other Metals
Tohoku University
Sendai, Japan

1. INTRODUCTION

It must be possible to evaluate the strength of metals and alloys in terms of properties of constituent atoms, if the theory of strength is correctly established. Dislocation theory has contributed to this subject enormously, especially the theory of precipitation hardening by Mott and Nabarro,[1] the theory of hardening due to segregation of solute atoms around a dislocation by elastic interaction proposed by Cottrell,[2] the model of hardening due to segregation of solute atoms at a stacking fault by chemical interaction proposed by Suzuki,[3] and short-range order hardening proposed by Fisher.[4] On these contributions we have excellent review articles by Cottrell,[5] and by Parker and Hazlett.[6]

The investigations performed previously, however, paid little attention to the interrelations between various mechanisms proposed by other authors, nor did they attempt quantitative comparison between the calculated strength and observed one. The external force required to move a single dislocation locked in the crystal by any means will not be equal to the observed yield strength, because the usual yield strength must be related to the motion of many dislocations, which interact with each other. It is intended in this report to develop theories to evaluate yield strength under various conditions and to compare them with observations.

The precipitation hardening has been treated in detail by Mott and Nabarro, and the present author has nothing to add to their work. Solution hardening will be discussed first, then the relation between the locking force and yield strength in single crystals will be considered.

2. HARDENING DUE TO ELASTIC INTERACTION BETWEEN SOLUTE ATOMS AND DISLOCATIONS (COTTRELL EFFECT)

A. Equilibrium Distribution of Solute Atoms

Cottrell first pointed out that a substitutional solute atom with different atomic radius or an interstitial solute atom interacts with the dilatational stress field round a dislocation and the solute atoms form an atmosphere. Cottrell and Bilby [7] discussed in detail the yield strength of steel, its temperature dependence, and the rate of formation of the atmosphere. For simplicity they assumed that a carbon atmosphere in iron tends to condense into a line of carbon atoms. This assumption cannot be applied to substitutional alloys; therefore, we must first consider the distribution of solute atoms around a dislocation.

Let us suppose a dislocation along the z-axis with a Burgers vector parallel to the xz plane in a substitutional alloy crystal of large dimensions. Since the change in concentration produces a homogeneous expansion or contraction in a substitutional alloy, the Gibbs free energy per mole, G, is given by the expression

$$G = F + \frac{W}{2}\left[\left(\frac{\partial c}{\partial x}\right)^2 + \left(\frac{\partial c}{\partial y}\right)^2\right] b^2 + \left[P_0(x, y) - \frac{K}{2}\frac{1}{v}\left(\frac{\partial v}{\partial c}\right)(c - c_0)\right]\left(\frac{\partial v}{\partial c}\right)(c - c_0) \quad (1)$$

where F is the free energy of Helmholtz, W the energy of mixing defined by the relation $W = ZN[\chi_{AB} - (\chi_{AA} + \chi_{BB})/2]$, b the strength of the dislocation, K the bulk modulus, v the volume of the alloy per mole, c the concentration of the solute, c_0 the average concentration, and $P_0(x, y)$ the dilatational stress field around the dislocation, given by the expression

$$P_0(x, y) = \frac{\mu b_e}{3\pi}\left(\frac{1 + \nu}{1 - \nu}\right)\frac{y}{x^2 + y^2} \quad (2)$$

In the definition of W, Z is the number of the nearest neighbors; N is

Avogadro's number, χ_{AB}, χ_{AA}, and χ_{BB} are the potential energies of atomic pairs A-B, A-A, and B-B respectively. In the definition of $P_0(x, y)$, μ is the shear modulus, b_e the edge component of the Burgers vector, ν Poisson's ratio.

For binary alloys we may assume the free energy to be

$$F = (1 - c)F_a + cF_b + RT[c \ln c + (1 - c) \ln (1 - c)] + c(1 - c)W$$

where F_a and F_b are the free energy of pure metals composed of A and B atoms respectively.

Thermal equilibrium will be established when total Gibbs free energy of the alloy crystal is a minimum, namely

$$\delta \iint G \, dx \, dy = 0$$

Then taking into account that the numbers of A and B atoms are constant, we have the equation

$$Wb^2 \left(\frac{\partial^2 c}{\partial x^2} + \frac{\partial^2 c}{\partial y^2} \right) + 2W(c - c_0) + RT \ln \frac{c_0(1 - c)}{c(1 - c_0)} + \left[P_0(x, y) - \frac{K}{v} \left(\frac{\partial v}{\partial c} \right) (c - c_0) \right] \left(\frac{\partial v}{\partial c} \right) = 0 \quad (3)$$

Since we cannot assume any change in concentration in a distance less than b, the relation

$$\left| Wb^2 \left(\frac{\partial^2 c}{\partial x^2} + \frac{\partial^2 c}{\partial y^2} \right) \right| \ll \left| 2W(c - c_0) \right|$$

holds in the crystal except in the core of the dislocation. Then, neglecting the first term in eq. 3, we have

$$c/c_0 = [(1 - c_0)e^{-\lambda} + c_0]^{-1}$$

where

$$\lambda = \frac{1}{RT} \left[P_0(x, y) - K \frac{1}{v} \left(\frac{\partial v}{\partial c} \right) (c - c_0) \right] \left(\frac{\partial v}{\partial c} \right) + \frac{2W}{RT} (c - c_0) \quad (4)$$

When $\lambda \ll 1$, eqs. 4 become

$$c - c_0 = \frac{\dfrac{P_0(x, y)}{RT} \left(\dfrac{\partial v}{\partial c} \right) c_0(1 - c_0)}{1 + \dfrac{1}{RT} \left[\dfrac{K}{v} \left(\dfrac{\partial v}{\partial c} \right)^2 - 2W \right] c_0(1 - c_0)} \quad (5)$$

B. The Locking Force

The resisting force, f, against the motion of the dislocation due to the atmosphere of solute atoms is given by

$$f = \frac{\partial}{\partial \xi} \int_x \int_y \left(\int_{v_0}^{v} P \, dv \right) dx \, dy \tag{6}$$

Here ξ is the co-ordinate of dislocation line and

$$\int_{v_0}^{v} P \, dv = \frac{P_0 + P_f}{2} \frac{1}{v} \frac{\partial v}{\partial c} (c - c_0),$$

where P_0 is the dilatational stress field due to the dislocation, and P_f is the stress field relaxed by the formation of the atmosphere, and has the expression

$$P_f(x, \xi, y) = P_0(x - \xi, y) - \frac{K}{2} \frac{1}{v} \frac{\partial v}{\partial c} (c - c_0)$$

Since the second term on the right side of the above equation is independent of ξ, eq. 6 becomes

$$f = \frac{1}{v} \frac{\partial v}{\partial c} \int_x \int_y \frac{\partial P_0(x - \xi, y)}{\partial \xi} (c - c_0) \, dx \, dy \tag{7}$$

Substituting eqs. 2 and 5 into eq. 7 we have

$$f = A/\xi$$

where

$$A = \frac{\dfrac{\mu^2 b_e^2}{9\pi} \dfrac{1}{RT} \left(\dfrac{1 + \nu}{1 - \nu} \right)^2 \dfrac{1}{v} \left(\dfrac{\partial v}{\partial c} \right)^2 c_0(1 - c_0)}{1 + \dfrac{1}{RT} \left[\dfrac{K}{v} \left(\dfrac{\partial v}{\partial c} \right)^2 - 2W \right] c_0(1 - c_0)} \tag{8}$$

or

$$V = A \ln |\xi|$$

Here V is the potential energy of the dislocation due to the Cottrell atmosphere. The above consideration is based on the assumption that Hooke's law holds even in the core of the dislocation, which is not correct. In order to take into account the failure of Hooke's law in the core, it is simplest to cut off the potential at an appropriate radius, r_0. Then the force is given by eqs. 8 when ξ is greater than r_0, and it becomes zero for smaller values than this. We will refer to this potential as the cutoff potential. An alternate and more reasonable way to take into account the deviation from Hooke's law in the core may be the following: f must be zero when $\xi = 0$, and it becomes larger with increasing ξ, reaches a maximum, and then decreases. It may thus be a reasonable approximation to replace $1/\xi$ by $\xi/(\xi^2 + r_0^2)$, where r_0 may be assumed to be the distance between the nearest neighboring atoms. We will refer to this potential as a smoothed potential.

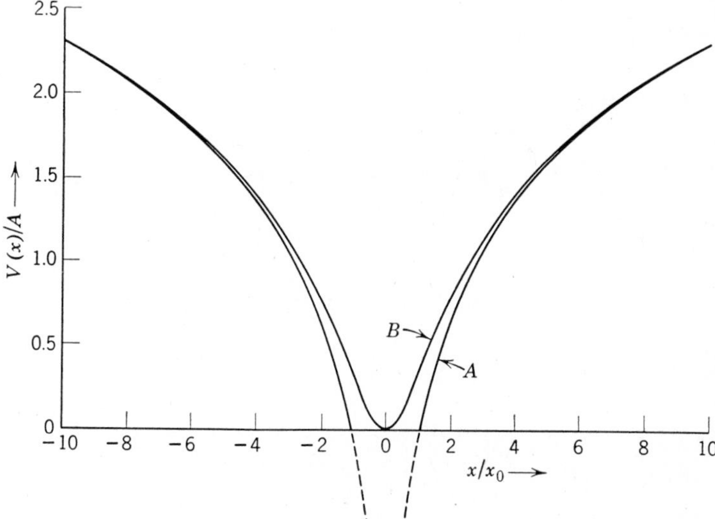

Fig. 1. Potential energy of a dislocation resulting from a Cottrell atmosphere.

The maximum resisting force in the smoothed potential is just one-half of the corresponding force in the cutoff potential, namely

$$\sigma_0 b = A/2r_0$$

In Fig. 1 the potential energy is plotted against the position of the dislocation for both types of potentials described above.

C. The Activation Energy Required for a Dislocation to Escape from Its Locked Site

At temperatures above 0°K, thermal fluctuations help the external forces to tear a dislocation from its atmosphere. The activation energy required for this process becomes a minimum when the dislocation is bent so far that it is in a metastable equilibrium. Assuming that the line tension of a dislocation is a constant independent of direction, the metastable dislocation loop will satisfy the relation

$$T \frac{d^2x}{dz^2} = \frac{dV(x)}{dx} - \sigma b \tag{9}$$

where T is the line tension of the dislocation line, σ the resolved shear stress applied to the crystal, and $V(x)$ is the potential energy due to the atmosphere when the entire dislocation moves to x. In the case of the simple cutoff potential from eqs. 8:

$$V(x) = A \ln | x/r_0 |, \qquad \text{for } | x | \geq r_0 \tag{10}$$

and

$$\sigma_0 b = A/r_0$$

The activation energy, U, is then

$$U = 2\int_0^{z_0} A \left[1 + \left(\frac{dx}{dz}\right)^2\right]^{1/2} \ln \frac{x}{r_0}\, dx - 2\sigma b \int_0^{z_0} (x - r_0)\, dz + 2T \int_0^{z_0} \left\{\left[1 + \left(\frac{dx}{dz}\right)^2\right]^{1/2} - 1\right\} dz \tag{11}$$

where $\left(\frac{dx}{dz}\right)_{z=z_0} = 0$, or

$$U = \frac{\beta}{x_0'} \int_0^{z_0'} \left\{\left[1 + \alpha \left(\frac{dx'}{dz'}\right)^2\right]^{1/2} \ln \frac{x'}{x_0'} - (x' - x_0') + \alpha \left[1 + \alpha \left(\frac{dx'}{dz'}\right)^2\right]^{1/2} - \alpha\right\} dz' \tag{12}$$

where $\left(\frac{dx'}{dz'}\right)_{z'=z_0'} = 0, \qquad x_0' = \sigma/\sigma_0$

$$\alpha = 2\sigma_0 r_0/\mu b_e, \quad \beta = (2\mu\sigma_0 r_0^3 b e^3)^{1/2}$$

After numerical solution of eqs. 9, 10, and 11, we obtain the relation between applied stress and activation energy, which is represented in Fig. 2.

The activation energy shown in Fig. 2 decreases very rapidly with increasing σ/σ_0 and it is nearly proportional to $(1 - \sigma/\sigma_0)^{2.2}$. This may be caused by the special form of the potential energy valley as indicated by curve A in Fig. 1. If we use the smoothed potential of Fig. 1 (curve B), σ_0 decreases to one-half of the former case for the same depth of the potential energy valley. Since the difference between the former and the latter is significant only in the vicinity of $x = r_0$, the activation energies in both cases may be nearly equal for small values of σ/σ_0 and it is reasonable to suppose that the activation energy for the smoothed potential is represented by the dashed curves in Fig. 2.

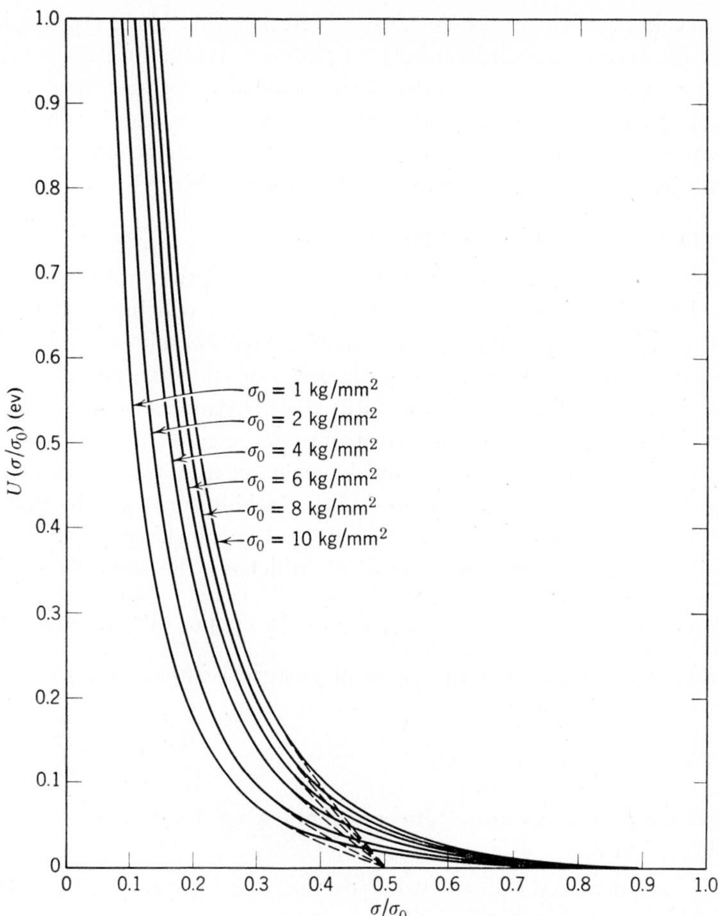

Fig. 2. Activation energy required to tear the dislocation from a locked site in the case of Cottrell effect. Cu-alloys with $b_0 = 2.55 \times 10^{-8}$ cm and $\mu = 4.6 \times 10^{11}$ dynes/cm^2.

D. The Character of the Locking Force in the Cottrell Effect

The locking force by means of the Cottrell effect at 0°K is very large even in usual substitutional face-centered cubic alloys, as will be shown in § 7. The locking force depends strongly upon the concentration, if the difference in atomic radius between solute and solvent is not too large. At 0°K the locking force is proportional to $c(1 - c)$ in a fair approximation, and at high temperatures it decreases considerably, because thermal motions help the external forces to tear the dislocation from its atmosphere.

A well-known feature of the Cottrell effect is the strong dependence of locking force on the angle between Burgers vector and dislocation line. In the case of an extended dislocation in a face-centered cubic crystal, the ratio of the locking forces for the screw and for the edge dislocation is about 1 to 3. This situation seems to be important to explain the strength of alloys, as will be discussed in § 7.

3. ELECTRICAL INTERACTION

Cottrell, Hunter, and Nabarro [8] pointed out that the charge potential around a dislocation due to the dilatational field will interact with a solute atom which has a different valency than the solvent and which carries an effective charge. They showed that in some copper alloys at least, the elastic interaction with a dislocation is some three to seven times larger than the electrical interaction.

Since the electrical interaction depends on the dilatational field around a dislocation, the character of the locking force due to this interaction is similar to the Cottrell effect. The locking force due to both interactions, elastic and electrical, will have the same expression (8) replacing $\frac{1}{v}\left(\frac{\partial v}{\partial c}\right)^2$ by $\frac{1}{v}\left(\frac{\partial v}{\partial c}\right)\Phi(J-1)$ in copper alloys, where Φ is a constant depending on the ratio of electrical interaction to elastic interaction. J is the valency of the solute atom.

4. CHEMICAL INTERACTION

A. Chemical Interaction Between a Stacking Fault and Solute Atoms

In a face-centered cubic crystal, ordinary dislocations are unstable and split into two half dislocations. In the region between the half dislocations there is a layer of a stacking fault, i.e., a layer about two atoms in thickness where the crystal structure is close-packed hexagonal.[9] Since the cohesive energy between atoms in the stacking fault differs from that in face-centered cubic material, it is thermodynamically evident that the concentration of the solute atoms in the stacking fault will differ from the average, if the region is in equilibrium with the surrounding face-centered cubic phase. Then the heterogeneous distribution of solute atoms will play the same role as a Cottrell atmosphere in resisting the motion of the dislocation, although the two effects are different in nature from each other.

It is obvious that the thickness of the stacking fault is too small to be considered a bulk phase. When the width of the stacking fault is sufficiently large in comparison with its thickness, the energy of a stacking fault will be proportional to its area. The energy of the stacking fault will consist of the energy of pairs of nearest neighboring ions, such as ion-ion repulsive force, and of energy change due to the reflection of electrons at the stacking fault. The energy of the first kind will be calculated under the usual nearest neighbor assumption, and the energy of the second kind seems to be proportional to the coefficient of reflection of electrons which may be assumed to depend linearly on the concentration.

If $W \leq 0$, the concentration is nearly equal to the average except for only the two atomic planes of the stacking fault.[10] Then we may assume the free energy of the two atomic planes of the stacking fault to be

$$\epsilon = (2h/v)\{F_a{}^s(1 - c) + F_b{}^s c + RT[c \ln c + (1 - c) \ln (1 - c)] + W[c(1 - 2c_0) + c_0{}^2]\} \quad (13)$$

The concentration in the stacking fault, c_1, satisfies the relation

$$\left(\frac{\partial F^f}{\partial c}\right)_{c_0} = \frac{v}{2h}\left(\frac{\partial \epsilon}{\partial c}\right)_{c_1} \quad (14)$$

neglecting the concentration dependence of the lattice parameter, where F^f is the free energy per mole of a face-centered cubic crystal which is given by the expression

$$F^f = F_a{}^f(1 - c) + F_b{}^f c + RT[c \ln c + (1 - c) \ln (1 - c)] + Wc(1 - c) \quad (15)$$

in the same approximation as eq. 13.

B. The Force Resisting the Motion of a Dislocation

Let us suppose that two half dislocations a and b are at x_1 and x_2 in their equilibrium separation associated with the stacking fault. Under a shearing stress $\mathbf{f}$ in the slip plane, a and b proceed to x_1' and to x_2' respectively. The force acting on the half dislocation a per unit length will be given by the sum of the following terms:

1. The repulsion by the half dislocation b

$$D/(x_2' - x_1') \quad (16)$$

2. The tension of the stacking fault

$$-\left(\epsilon - \frac{2h}{v} F^f\right)_{c0} \qquad \text{for } x_1' < x_1 \quad \text{or} \quad x_1' > x_2 \tag{17}$$

$$-\left(\epsilon - \frac{2h}{v} F^f\right)_{c1} \qquad \text{for } x_1 < x_1' < x_2$$

(3) The force exerted by the external stress

$$\mathbf{f} \cdot \mathbf{b}_a \tag{18}$$

Here D is a constant depending on the angle between the resultant Burgers vector of the extended dislocation, $\mathbf{b}$; and the dislocation line, $\mathbf{b}_a$, is the Burgers vector of the half dislocation, a. For a quasistatical motion of the dislocation, the sum of the above three terms should vanish. Namely,

$$\frac{D}{x_2' - x_1'} \begin{cases} = \left(\epsilon - \frac{2h}{v} F^f\right)_{c0} - \mathbf{f} \cdot \mathbf{b}_a & \text{for } x_1' < x_1 \quad \text{or} \quad x_1' > x_2 \\ = \left(\epsilon - \frac{2h}{v} F^f\right)_{c1} - \mathbf{f} \cdot \mathbf{b}_a & \text{for } x_1 < x_1' < x_2 \end{cases} \tag{19}$$

$$\left(\epsilon - \frac{2h}{v} F^f\right)_{c1} - \mathbf{f} \cdot \mathbf{b}_a < \frac{D}{x_2' - x_1'} < \left(\epsilon - \frac{2h}{v} F^f\right)_{c0} - \mathbf{f} \cdot \mathbf{b}_a$$

$$\text{for } x_1' = x_1$$

For the half dislocation b, similar equations will also be obtained:

$$\frac{D}{x_2' - x_1'} \begin{cases} = \left(\epsilon - \frac{2h}{v} F^f\right)_{c0} + \mathbf{f} \cdot \mathbf{b}_b & \text{for } x_2 < x_2' \quad \text{or} \quad x_2' < x_1 \\ = \left(\epsilon - \frac{2h}{v} F^f\right)_{c1} + \mathbf{f} \cdot \mathbf{b}_b & \text{for } x_1 < x_2' < x_2 \end{cases} \tag{20}$$

$$\left(\epsilon - \frac{2h}{v} F^f\right)_{c1} + \mathbf{f} \cdot \mathbf{b}_b < \frac{D}{x_2' - x_1'} < \left(\epsilon - \frac{2h}{v} F^f\right)_{c0} + \mathbf{f} \cdot \mathbf{b}_b$$

$$\text{for } x_2' = x_2$$

Remembering that the following relations exist

$$\mathbf{b}_a + \mathbf{b}_b = \mathbf{b}$$

$$\mathbf{f} \cdot \mathbf{b}_a + \mathbf{f} \cdot \mathbf{b}_b = \mathbf{f} \cdot \mathbf{b} \tag{21}$$

and $$x_2 - x_1 \geq x_2' - x_1' > 0$$

eqs. 20 and 21 yield the relation

$$
f \begin{cases}
= \dfrac{1}{b}\left[\left(\epsilon - \dfrac{2h}{v}F^f\right)_{c0} - \left(\epsilon - \dfrac{2h}{v}F^f\right)_{c1}\right] & \text{for } x_1 < x_2' < x_2'' \\
= -\dfrac{1}{b}\left[\left(\epsilon - \dfrac{2h}{v}F^f\right)_{c0} - \left(\epsilon - \dfrac{2h}{v}F^f\right)_{c1}\right] & \text{for } x_1'' < x_1' < x_2 \\
= 0 & \text{for } x_2' < x_1 \quad \text{or} \\
 & \qquad x_1' > x_2 \\
= \Lambda_a\left[\left(\epsilon - \dfrac{2h}{v}F^f\right)_{c1} - \dfrac{D}{x_2' - x_1'}\right] & \text{for } x_2'' < x_2' < x_2 \\
= -\Lambda_b\left[\left(\epsilon - \dfrac{2h}{v}F^f\right)_{c1} - \dfrac{D}{x_2' - x_1'}\right] & \text{for } x_1 < x_1' < x_1''
\end{cases} \tag{22}
$$

Here Λ_a and Λ_b are defined by the relations $\Lambda_a = f/\mathbf{f}\cdot\mathbf{b}_a$, $\Lambda_b = f/\mathbf{f}\cdot\mathbf{b}_b$ respectively, and x_1'', x_2'' satisfy the relation

$$x_2 - x_1'' = x_2'' - x_1 = D\Big/\left(\epsilon - \frac{2h}{v}F^f\right)_{c0}$$

The differences between x_1 and x_1'' and between x_2 and x_2'' occur because of the decrease in the energy of stacking fault due to the change in concentration, as pointed out by Cottrell.[5]

The maximum locking force will then be given by

$$\sigma_0 = \frac{1}{b}\left|\left(\epsilon - \frac{2h}{v}F^f\right)_{c0} - \left(\epsilon - \frac{2h}{v}F^f\right)_{c1}\right| \tag{23}$$

Substituting eqs. 13 and 15 into eq. 23, we have

$$\sigma_0 = \frac{2h}{vb}Hc_0(1 - c_0)\frac{1 - \exp(-H/RT)}{1 - c_0[1 - \exp(-H/RT)]} \tag{24}$$

where
$$H = (F_a^f - F_a^s) - (F_b^f - F_b^s)$$

or
$$H = \frac{v}{2h}(\gamma_b - \gamma_a)$$

Here γ_a and γ_b are the energies of stacking faults in a and b metals respectively. Therefore H hardly depends on temperature.

If the main part of the stacking fault energy is due to overlap, γ will be about twice the coherent twin boundary energy, whereas if the energy change due to the reflection of electrons by the stacking fault is important, γ may have about the same magnitude as the twin boundary energy.

C. The Effect of the Strain Energy Caused by the Segregation of Solute Atoms in the Stacking Fault

Usually the radius of solute atoms differs from that of solvent, so that the segregation of solute or solvent atoms in the stacking fault results in an increase of strain energy. The value of c_1 should, therefore, be less than that calculated from expressions 17.

If the width of the stacking fault is sufficiently large compared to its thickness, the normal stress in the direction of the thickness of the stacking fault may be negligible. Then the strain energy is about

$$\frac{2\mu}{9}\left(\frac{1+\nu}{1-\nu}\right)\left(\frac{1}{v}\frac{\partial v}{\partial c}\right)^2 (c_1 - c_0)^2$$

per unit volume. The relation 17 then becomes

$$\left(\frac{\partial F^f}{\partial c}\right)_{c_0} = \frac{v}{2h}\left(\frac{\partial \epsilon}{\partial c}\right)_{c_1} + \frac{4\mu}{9}\left(\frac{1+\nu}{1-\nu}\right)\frac{1}{v}\left(\frac{\partial v}{\partial c}\right)^2 (c_1 - c_0)$$

or $$RT \ln \frac{c_0(1-c_1)}{c_1(1-c_0)} = H + \frac{4\mu}{9}\left(\frac{1+\nu}{1-\nu}\right)\frac{1}{v}\left(\frac{\partial v}{\partial c}\right)^2 (c_1 - c_0) \tag{25}$$

and $$\sigma_0 = \frac{2h}{vb}(c_0 - c_1)H \tag{26}$$

D. The Activation Energy Required to Make a Dislocation Escape from the Atmosphere

By the method used in § 2.C we calculated the activation energy required to make a dislocation escape from the locked site in the case of chemical interaction. We assume that the extended dislocation will be bent in the same way as an unextended dislocation, and also that the locking force is zero when the half dislocation is in the region

$$x_2'' < x_2' < x_2$$

Then we have the following relations for the form of the metastable loop of a dislocation:

$$\begin{aligned} T\frac{d^2x}{dz^2} &= (\sigma_0 - \sigma_b) \qquad \Delta \leq x \leq l + \Delta \\ T\frac{d^2x}{dz^2} &= -\sigma b \qquad x > l + \Delta \quad \text{or} \quad x < \Delta \end{aligned} \tag{27}$$

where Δ is the increase in the width of the extended dislocation by the decrease in stacking fault energy due to segregation of solute atoms.

By straightforward calculation, the activation energy is given by the expression

$$U = \frac{T^2}{2\sigma_0 b}\left(\frac{1}{2}\eta^3 - \frac{1}{20}\eta^5 - \frac{1}{24}\eta^6 + \frac{1}{7}\eta^7 + \frac{27}{64}\eta^8 + \cdots\right)\frac{1}{\sigma/\sigma_0(1 - \sigma/\sigma_0)} \tag{28}$$

where
$$\eta = 2[(l\sigma_0 b/T)(1 - \sigma/\sigma_0)]^{1/2}$$

Since $\eta \ll 1$, we have

$$U = \frac{2[(\sigma_0 bTl^3)(1 - \sigma/\sigma_0)]^{1/2}}{\sigma/\sigma_0} \tag{29}$$

Expression 29 is the same as that obtained in a previous paper,[3] where a triangular loop was used for the calculation.

In Fig. 3 the activation energy is plotted against σ/σ_0 for a combination of constants.

E. The Character of the Locking Force by Chemical Interaction

The locking force by chemical interaction is considerably weaker in many alloys than that by the Cottrell effect, as is already known from the rough estimate in § 2.B. The locking force is of the order of 1 kg/mm^2 in the case of chemical interaction whereas it is of the order of 10 kg/mm^2 in the case of Cottrell effect. The effective locking force at high temperature, however, hardly decreases in the case of chemical interaction, but it decreases very rapidly in the case of Cottrell effect. Therefore, the locking force by chemical interaction becomes more important than Cottrell effect at a high temperature. The concentration dependence of the locking force due to chemical interaction is very similar to that due to Cottrell effect, as is easily seen from eqs. 24 and 8.

It must also be mentioned that the locking force due to chemical interaction is independent of the angle between the Burgers vector and dislocation line, whereas the Cottrell effect depends on the angle strongly, as already mentioned in § 2.D.

5. SHORT-RANGE ORDER HARDENING

Fisher[4] has pointed out that a dislocation in a crystal with short-range order is in stable equilibrium under zero stress, for its motion would destroy the equilibrium short-range order across the glide plane, producing a more random configuration of higher energy. Denoting the energy change due to such destruction of short-range order by ψ

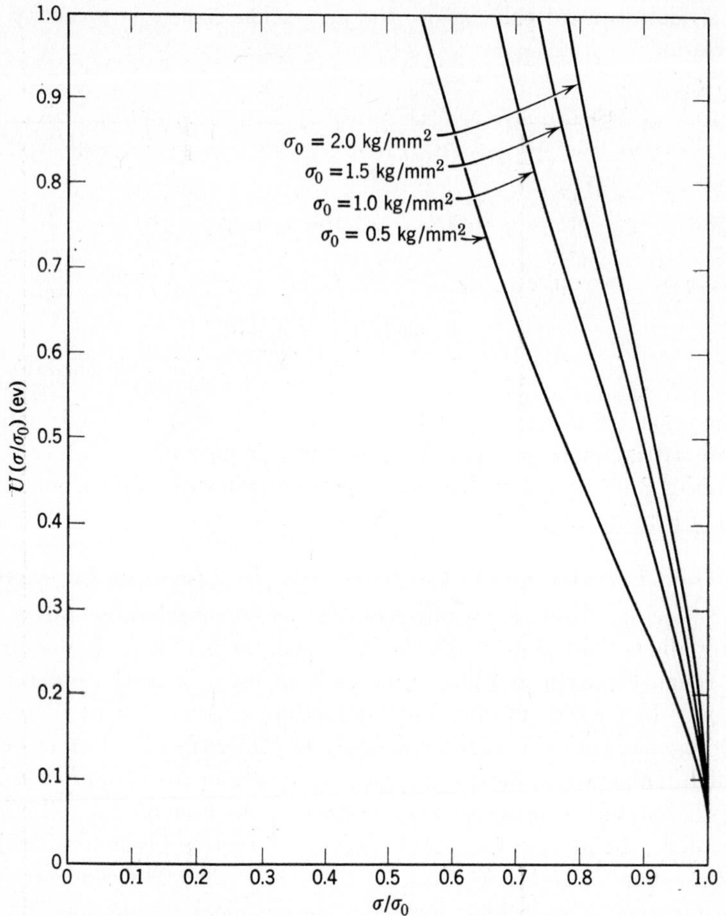

Fig. 3. Activation energy required to tear the dislocation from a locked site in the case of chemical interaction in Cu-alloys. $U = [(2\sigma_0 \mu b^3 l^3)(1 - \sigma/\sigma_0)]^{1/2}/(\sigma/\sigma_0)$, $b = 2.55 \times 10^{-8}$ cm, $\mu = 4.6 \times 10^{11}$ dynes/cm^2, and $l = 1.3 \times 10^{-7}$ cm.

per unit area, the shear stress required to move a dislocation in the crystal is given by the expression

$$\sigma_0 = \psi/b \tag{30}$$

The short-range order hardening thus depends only upon the magnitude of ψ. Assuming that there is only nearest neighbor interaction, the excess number of A-B pairs from a perfect disordered state decreases to one-third of the initial state, by glide of one atomic distance in a face-centered cubic crystal. Then we have

$$\psi = -\frac{2}{3}\frac{h}{v}(P_{AB} - P_{AB}{}^0)\frac{W}{12N} \tag{31}$$

where P_{AB} and $P_{AB}{}^0$ are the number of A-B pairs per mole of solution in the thermal equilibrium state and in the perfectly disordered state respectively. According to Takagi [11]

$$P_{AB} = 6N\frac{\{1 + 4c(1 - c)[\exp(W/6RT) - 1]\}^{1/2} - 1}{\exp(W/6RT) - 1}$$

while $\quad P_{AB}{}^0 = 12Nc(1 - c)$

If $W/6RT \ll 1$, eq. 31 is approximated by the expression

$$\psi = \frac{2}{3}\frac{h}{v}4c^2(1 - c)^2\frac{W^2}{12RT}$$

and

$$\sigma_0 = \frac{2}{9}\sqrt{\frac{2}{3}\frac{W^2}{vRT}}\,c^2(1 - c)^2 \tag{32}$$

σ_0, in short-range order hardening, is independent of the angle between the Burgers vector and the dislocation line. The dislocation experiences the resisting force, σ_0, as long as it moves through annealed crystal. Thermal fluctuations therefore cannot diminish the stress required to move a dislocation, unless atom migration does take place at a considerable frequency. The temperature dependence of short-range order hardening is caused by the change in ψ. The critical shear stress required to operate a Frank-Read source is therefore $\sigma_0 + \mu b/l$, where l is the length of the source.

6. RELATION BETWEEN THE SHEARING FORCE REQUIRED TO MOVE A DISLOCATION AND THE YIELD STRENGTH OF A SINGLE CRYSTAL

It is usually assumed that the shear stress required to move a dislocation, which is locked in the crystal by the mechanisms mentioned above, is identical with the critical shear stress of the crystal. However, it is evident that at the yield point not only one Frank-Read source operates but many sources should operate. Since such co-operative action of sources takes place as the result of interaction between them, the yield strength depends on the interaction force between sources as well as on the force required to tear a dislocation from its locked site. The yield strength determined in experiment is usually the transition point at which the tangent in a stress-strain curve decreases considerably. The yield strength in theory therefore is reasonably determined from the theoretical stress-strain curve.

The above-mentioned situation is very simple in the case of precipitation hardening and ordered hardening, because in these cases the resisting force is not limited in a small region but extends over the crystal, and all dislocations even multiplied from other sources are subjected to nearly the same resisting force. Therefore the yield strength is nearly equal to the stress required to move a dislocation.

In the case of short-range order hardening, the stress needed to move dislocations is large at first but becomes rapidly smaller as the glide proceeds in one atomic plane, as pointed out by Cottrell.[5] Another source will come into operation by the stress field of the dislocation group multiplied from the first source. The stress field must be the same over the distance $2l$; therefore the stress field due to a dislocation nearer than l cannot induce the operation of the source. The required stress to operate the source with length l is

$$\sigma_0 + \mu b/l \tag{33}$$

while the maximum stress concentration due to n dislocations with a separation of πl, situated on a slip plane and separated by l from the plane of the source, is about

$$\mu b \ln 2n/2\pi^2(1 - \nu)l$$

The resultant stress acting on the source is

$$f + \mu b \ln 2n/2\pi^2(1 - \nu)l \tag{34}$$

The second term in expression 34 is slightly smaller than the second term in 33; therefore, the cataclysmic action will not take place unless

$$f > \sigma_0 \tag{35}$$

This result suggests that the deformation takes place nearly in the same way as in the pure crystal, and without a sharp yield point.

A. Dislocations Locked by a Short-Range Force

When a dislocation is locked in a small potential energy valley, the co-operative action of Frank-Read sources become more important. In these cases the stress concentration is required only when the dislocation escapes from the locked site, if the length of the Frank-Read source is sufficiently large to produce a loop without stress concentration. There is the one restriction that the two dislocations can pass through each other. Then the relation is obtained:

$$\sigma_0 - f < \mu b/2\pi\alpha < f$$

Hence
$$\sigma_0 < 2f \tag{36}$$

In a real crystal σ_0 differs for each dislocation because of the Cottrell effect. Moreover, the Frank-Read source is not always sufficiently long to operate under the force f. Therefore, we must take into account the distribution of locking force and lengths of Frank-Read sources. The locking force is nearly constant in chemical interaction, and depends on the angle between the Burgers vector and dislocation line, and also on the temperature in the case of Cottrell effect. Let us denote by $N(\sigma)\,d\sigma$ the number of sources which can escape from the locking site by the shear stress between σ and $\sigma + d\sigma$, and by $M(l)\,dl$ the number of sources whose lengths are between l and $l + dl$. Then

$$\int_0^\infty N(\sigma)\,d\sigma = \int_0^\infty M(l)\,dl = N_0$$

It is reasonable to assume that the length of the Frank-Read source is independent of its locking force. For small strains, the shear under the force f will be given by

$$\delta = s\left[\int_0^f N(\sigma)\,d\sigma \int_{\mu b/f}^\infty \frac{M(l)}{N_0}\,dl + \int_{y_0}^L S \int_f^{f'(y)} N(\sigma)\,d\sigma\,dy \int_{\mu b/f}^\infty \frac{M(l)}{N_0}\,dl\right] \tag{37}$$

where s is the shear produced by the operation of a Frank-Read source, S is the area of slip plane swept by dislocations multiplied from a source, L is the length of the crystal, $f'(y)$ and y_0 are given by the relations

$$f = \mu b/4\pi y_0$$

$$f'(y) = f + \mu b/4\pi y$$

B. Lower Yield Stress

When the stress-strain curve shows a sharp yield point, the lower yield stress σ_y satisfies the relation

$$\int_{y_0}^L S \int_{\sigma_y}^{f'(y)} N(\sigma)\,d\sigma\,dy \int_{\mu b/\sigma_y}^\infty \frac{M(l)}{N_0}\,dl = 1 \tag{38}$$

When every source is locked by the same force, σ_0,

$$SN_0(y_1 - y_0)\int_{\mu b/\sigma_y}^\infty \frac{M(l)}{N_0}\,dl = 1$$

where
$$\sigma_0 = \sigma_y + \mu b/4\pi y_1$$
$$\sigma_0/2 = \mu b/4\pi y_0$$
$$N_0 \simeq \rho^{3/2}/12$$
$$S \simeq 200\ (\sigma_y/\mu b\rho)^2$$

Then
$$\left(\frac{4\sigma_y^{\ 2}}{\pi\mu b\sigma_0\rho^{1/2}}\right)\frac{(2\sigma_y - \sigma_0)}{(\sigma_0 - \sigma_y)}\int_{\mu b/\sigma_y}^{\infty}\frac{M(l)}{N_0}\,dl = 1$$

Putting $\sigma_y = 3 \times 10^8$ dynes/cm² and $\rho = 10^8/\text{cm}^2$, the quantity in the first parenthesis is of the order of 10; therefore, unless $\int_{\mu b/\sigma_y}^{\infty} M(l) / N_0\, dl$ is considerably less than unity, σ_y is nearly equal to $\sigma_0/2$, but when σ_0 decreases to one-tenth of this value, σ_y becomes nearly equal to σ_0.

Next we will examine the lower yield stress in the case of the Cottrell effect at 0°K. If the angle between the Burgers vector and dislocation line is perfectly random, the frequency function, $N(\sigma)$, is given by the expression

$$N(\sigma) = \frac{4N_0\sigma_0}{\pi[1 - (2 - \sigma/\sigma_0)^2]^{1/2}} \tag{39}$$

where σ_0 is the locking force for screw dislocation. It is easily seen from eq. 39 that $N(\sigma)$ is sufficiently large in the vicinity of σ_0, and since σ_0 is sufficiently large in usual crystals in comparison with $\mu b/l$, we have

$$\sigma_y \simeq \sigma_0/2$$

For temperatures higher than 0°K, the situation is very complicated, but it seems to be reasonable to write

$$\sigma_y = k\sigma'$$

where
$$\tfrac{1}{2} < k < 1$$

and
$$\frac{U(\sigma'/\sigma_0)}{RT} = \text{const}$$

7. COMPARISON OF THE CALCULATED CRITICAL SHEAR STRESS WITH THE OBSERVATION IN A SINGLE CRYSTAL

A. Cu-Ni Alloys

Figure 4 shows the yield strength of various Cu-Ni alloy crystals plotted against the temperature, as measured in our laboratory.[12]

The yield strength increases considerably below the room temperature and is almost constant above 600°K, except for the 50% and 70% Ni alloys. The rapid increase at low temperatures seems to be caused

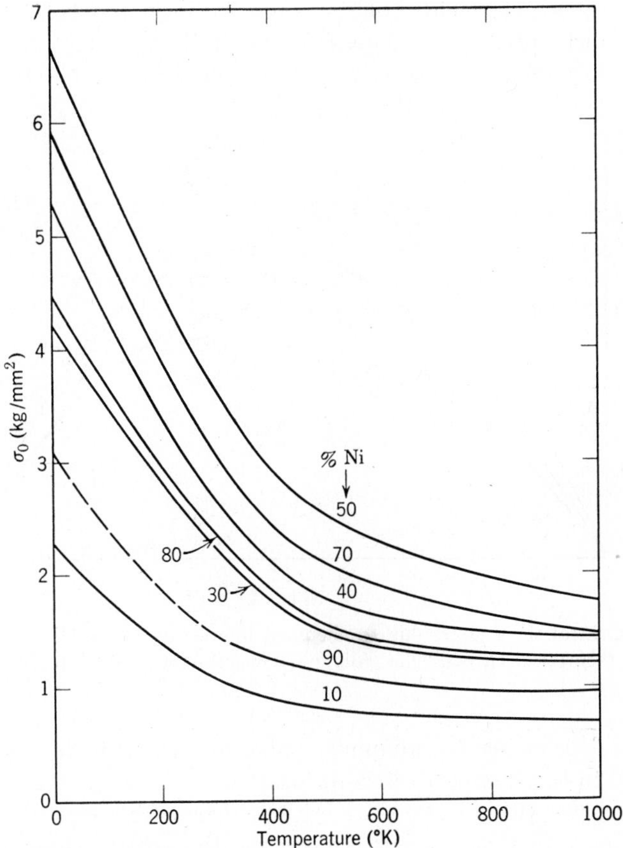

Fig. 4. Critical shear stress of Cu-Ni alloys plotted against temperature (Suzuki, Ikeda, and Takeuchi [12]).

by the Cottrell effect, and the flat part at high temperatures is due to chemical interaction or short-range order hardening.

Kachi [13] recently measured the activity of copper ions in Cu-Ni alloys electrochemically. According to his results, $-W$ is of the order of 1.3 kcal/mole. Then eq. 32 gives

$$\sigma_0 \simeq 0.6 \text{ kg/mm}^2$$

for c = 0.5 at 1000°K. This value is considerably smaller than the observed values.

When the Cottrell effect and chemical interaction coexist, both effects are not simply additive. As already mentioned, the chemical interaction is independent of the angle between the Burgers vector and the dislocation line, whereas the Cottrell effect depends strongly on it. According to the consideration in § 6, the observed yield

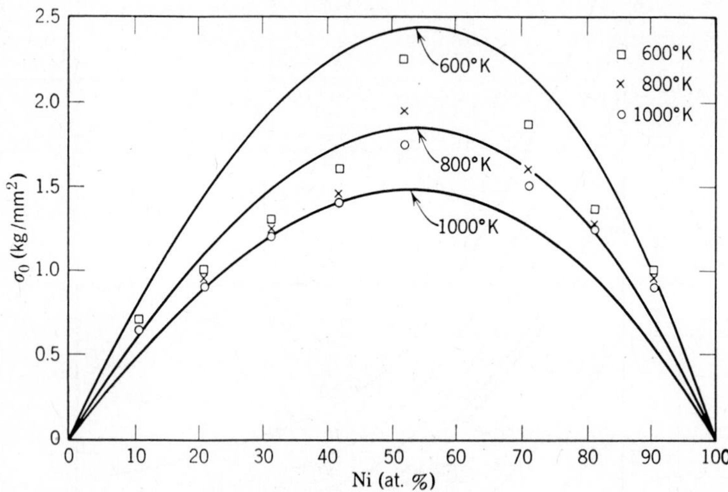

Fig. 5. Critical shear stress due to chemical interaction in Cu-Ni alloys. Solid lines are theoretical curves. The points are experimental values of critical shear stress.

strength depends on the minimum value of locking force, which corresponds to the case of a screw dislocation.

At first we will calculate the critical shear stress due to chemical interaction. In this estimate we assume the critical shear stress at 1000°K is due completely to chemical interaction. As is easily seen from eq. 24, when the value of H is given the critical shear stress due to chemical interaction is perfectly determined for the whole composition range at various temperatures. In Fig. 5 the calculated critical shear stress is plotted against the concentration of nickel, for 600, 800, and 1000°K, assuming $H = 1.42 \times 10^{10}$ ergs/mole, and the corresponding observed values are also plotted in the figure. The value of H seems to give a reasonable stacking fault energy for nickel. It is 126 ergs/cm², which is considerably smaller than in previous analyses and rather near the value accepted by Seeger.[14]

Though the observations scatter considerably, it is significant that the observed temperature dependence of critical shear stress is considerably smaller than the calculated value. Also, the observed critical shear stress is rather high on the nickel side in comparison

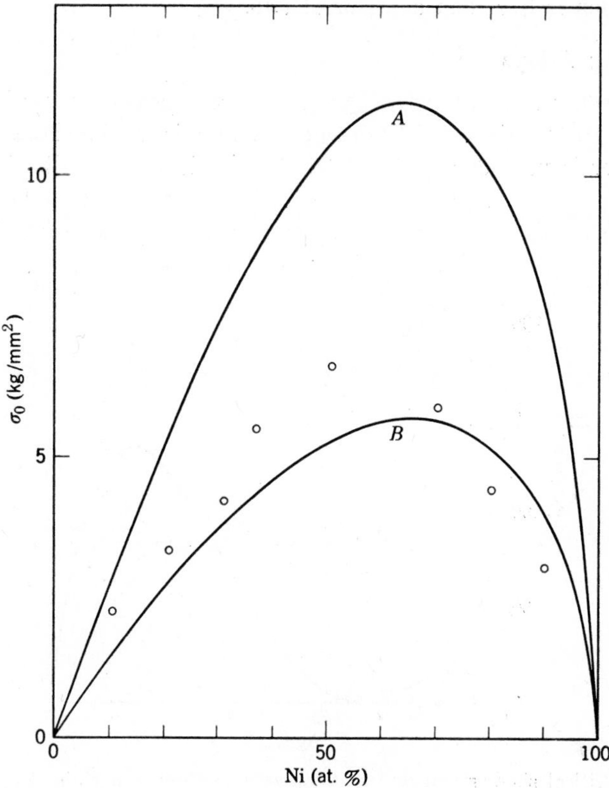

Fig. 6. Critical shear stress due to the Cottrell effect at 0°K in Cu-Ni alloys. Curve A is calculated for a cutoff potential and curve B is for a smoothed potential. The points are extrapolated from measurements at higher temperatures.

with calculated value. The first divergence might be removed by assuming that the atom migration is not so rapid as to establish equilibrium distribution of solute atoms in the stacking fault at temperatures lower than 1000°K.

In Fig. 6 the shear stress required to move a screw dislocation from the Cottrell atmosphere which is formed at 300°C is plotted against the concentration. Curve A is for the cutoff potential, B for the smoothed potential. Extrapolated values from the observed values to 0°K are also plotted. According to the discussion in § 6, the theoretical critical shear stress is about half of the calculated values in Fig. 6. Then the cutoff potential shows better agreement with the observation. At any rate the divergence between the calculation and observation is less than a factor of two.

B. Au-Ag Alloys

Concerning these alloys we know only the measurements by Sachs and Weerts.[15] Since the difference in atomic radius between gold and silver is very small, the Cottrell effect is very small. In Fig. 7

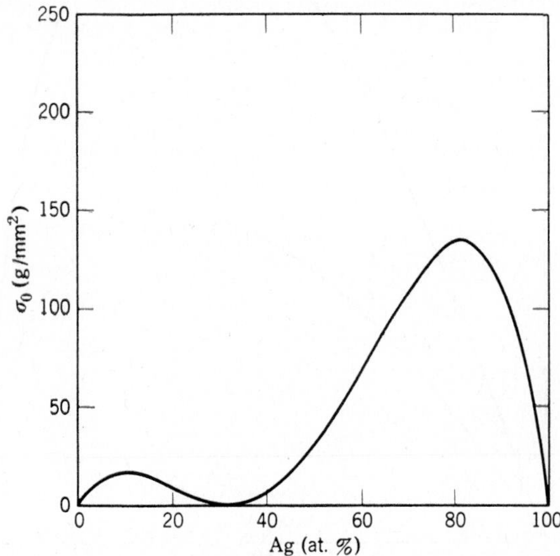

Fig. 7. Critical shear stress due to the Cottrell effect at 0°K in Au-Ag alloys.

the shear stress required at 0°K to move a screw dislocation from the Cottrell atmosphere which is formed at 300°C is plotted against the concentration. The hardening at room temperature is therefore due to short-range order hardening and chemical interaction and these two effects are simply additive.

The short-range order in Au-Ag alloys was measured directly by Norman and Warren [16] and their result shows fair agreement with the one calculated on the nearest neighbor assumption, using the cohesive energy obtained from electrochemical measurement by Kubaschewski and Huchler [17] and Schmahl.[18] Figure 8 shows the calculated critical shear stress for a degree of short-range order characteristic for 300°C plotted against the composition. Observed values by Sachs and Weerts are also plotted in the figure. The divergence between the calculation and observation is considerable.

The calculated shear stress due to chemical interaction is of the

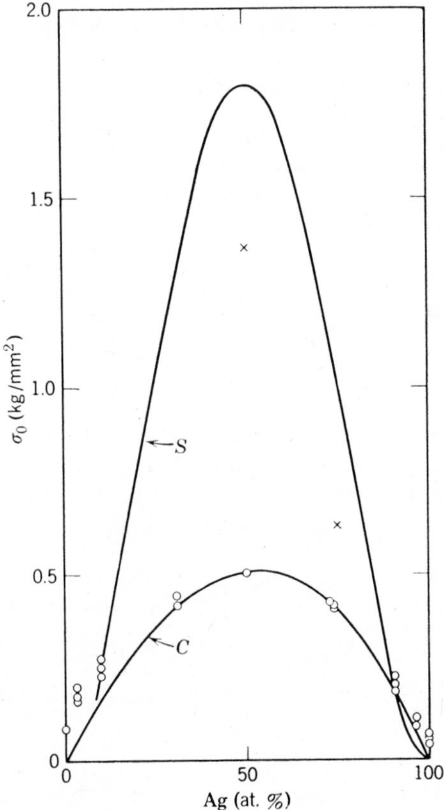

Fig. 8. Critical shear stress due to short-range order, S, and chemical interaction, C, in Au-Ag alloys. The circles are the measured values. The crosses represent the calculated critical shear stress using the degree of short-range order obtained from X-ray measurements.

order of the observed value as shown by curve C in Fig. 8, if we assume the difference in stacking fault energy between gold and silver as 25 ergs/cm^2. This value of energy is reasonable in comparison with the value in copper and nickel. Although there is an evidence for chemical interaction in Au-Ag alloys, which was pointed out by Cottrell,[5] it may be that the contribution of chemical interaction to the hardening in Au-Ag alloys is negligible. The difference between theory and observation is a factor of three in this alloy at present.

C. Cu-Zn Alloys

Recently Jamison and Sherrill [19] observed the critical shear stress in alpha-brass as a function of zinc concentration and temperature. Their results are reproduced in Fig. 9, and results from our laboratory [12] are also plotted in the figure. The critical shear stress increases rapidly

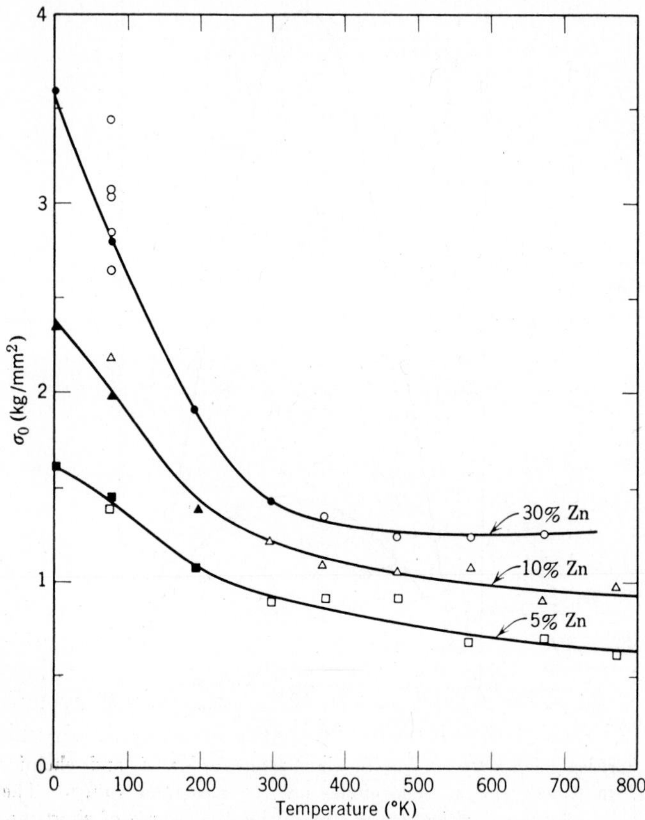

Fig. 9. Critical shear stress of Cu-Zn alloys plotted against temperature.

at low temperatures as in the case of Cu-Ni alloys. The critical shear stress extrapolated to 0°K is plotted against the concentration of zinc in Fig. 10. The curve shows the calculated value, which is half the shear stress required to tear a screw dislocation from Cottrell atmosphere formed at 300°C, assuming a smooth potential. The magnitude of the absolute value shows good agreement, but in the case of Cu-Ni alloys calculations and observations show good agreement only when we assume a cutoff potential or neglect the decrease in critical shear stress by co-operative operation, namely, when the theoretical value is assumed to be twice the present case. At any rate, when we use elasticity, thermodynamics, and crystallography, the calculated value of the Cottrell effect differs from observations only by a factor of two. This divergence seems to be removed by taking into account the electrical interaction between dislocation and solute atoms.

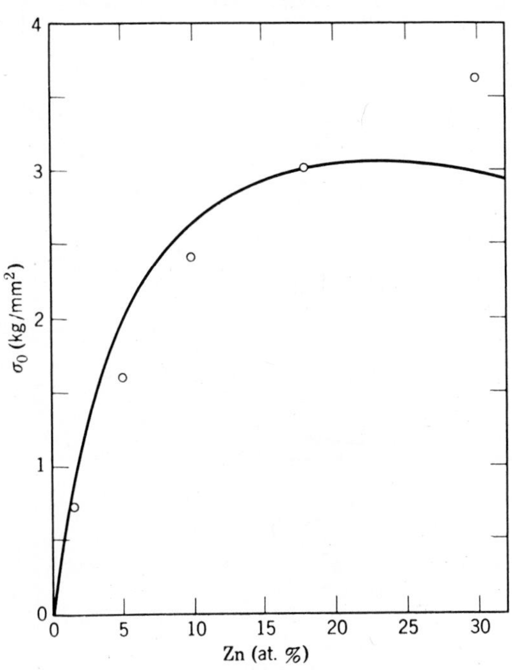

Fig. 10. Critical shear stress due to Cottrell effect at 0°K in Cu-Zn alloys. Calculated values shown by curve. The points are extrapolations from higher temperature measurements.

The short-range order in alpha-brass was studied by Keating [20] using neutron diffraction. He used an alpha-brass crystal annealed at 190°C for 6 weeks, but he could not detect any definite amount of diffuse scattering due to short-range order. From the sensitivity of the experiment, he concluded that the maximum amount of short-range order in alpha brass at 190°C is roughly that corresponding to a temperature 1.26 or more times the critical temperature of long-range order. From this one would predict a critical temperature of about 95°C or lower.

According to Cowley,[21] the critical temperature in an A_3B superlattice satisfies the relation

$$-W/RT_c = 1/0.274$$

Hence $$-W < 2680 \text{ cal/mole}$$

In Fig. 11 the critical shear stress due to short-range order hardening at 600°K is plotted against zinc concentration for $-W = 2680$

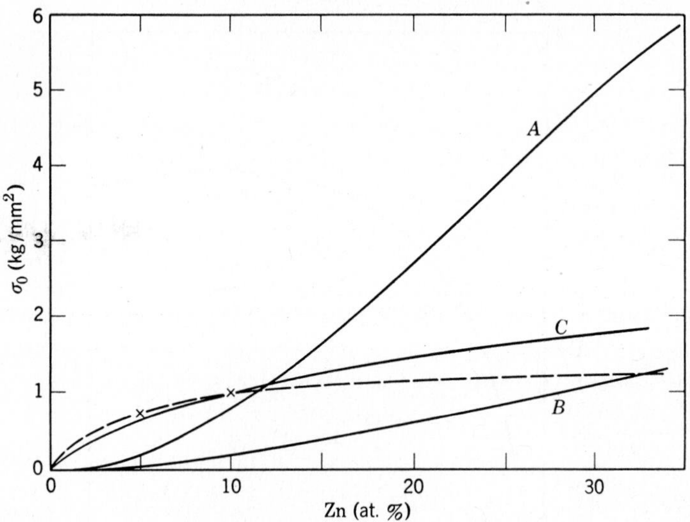

Fig. 11. Critical shear stress of Cu-Zn alloys at 600°K. Curves A and B are calculated curves for short-range order hardening (see text). Curve C is calculated hardening due to chemical interaction. Observed values are shown by the dashed curve.

cal/mole (curve A), which is the maximum value allowed by neutron diffraction experiment. The observed values are also plotted in the figure. It is evident that the calculated value cannot be greater than the observation, so we must use a smaller value for $-W$ than this. The calculated curve for the maximum value of $-W$ under this restriction is denoted by curve B. The difference between the observation and calculation is significant, so we must suppose that another mechanism of hardening such as chemical interaction is also contributing.

In Fig. 11 the shear stress required to move a dislocation from potential valley due to chemical interaction is plotted against the concentration of zinc. In this calculation we used eqs. 25 and 26, because the difference in atomic radii between copper and zinc cannot be neglected. The energy of stacking fault was assumed as

$$\gamma_{\mathrm{Cu}} = 40 \text{ ergs/cm}^2$$

$$\gamma_{\mathrm{Zn}} = -50 \text{ ergs/cm}^2$$

The calculated values show better agreement with the observation than short-range order hardening, because the theoretical critical shear stress decreases to half of σ_0, when σ_0 is sufficiently large in comparison with the frictional force due to intersecting dislocations.

The remarkable yield strain in alpha-brass [22] must be explained in connection with the locking mechanism of a dislocation. Any locking mechanism seems to give a reasonable explanation for this behavior, because the number of sources that operate becomes small in these cases and the chance of dislocation reaction decreases. The chemical interaction, however, seems to give the most favorable explanation for the following reasons. At low temperature the locking force in a low alloy reaches the same value as the 30% Zn alloy at room temperature, but the yield behavior differs considerably from that of the 30% Zn alloy at room temperature. This means the Cottrell effect is not responsible for the large yield strain. On the other hand, short-range order hardening cannot show such a sharp yield point as observed by Ardley and Cottrell [23] in alpha-brass.

REFERENCES

1. N. F. Mott and F. R. N. Nabarro, *Report of a Conference on Strength of Solids,* Physical Society, London, p. 1 (1948).
2. A. H. Cottrell, *Report of a Conference on Strength of Solids,* Physical Society, London, p. 30 (1948).
3. H. Suzuki, *Sci. Rep. Res. Inst. Tohoku Univ., A,* **4,** 455 (1952).
4. J. C. Fisher, *Acta Met.,* **2,** 9 (1954).
5. A. H. Cottrell, *Relation of Properties of Microstructure,* A.S.M., Cleveland, p. 131 (1954).
6. E. R. Parker and T. H. Hazlett, *Relation of Properties to Microstructure,* A.S.M., Cleveland, p. 30 (1954).
7. A. H. Cottrell and B. A. Bilby, *Proc. Phys. Soc. (London), A,* **62,** 49 (1949).
8. A. H. Cottrell, S. C. Hunter, and F. R. N. Nabarro, *Phil. Mag.,* **44,** 1064 (1953).
9. R. D. Heidenreich and W. Shockley, *Report of a Conference on Strength of Solids,* Physical Society, London, p. 57 (1948).
10. H. Suzuki, *Sci. Rep. Res. Inst. Tohoku Univ., A,* **7,** 194 (1955).
11. Y. Takagi, *Proc. Phys.-Math. Soc. Japan,* **23,** 44 (1941).
12. H. Suzuki, S. Ikeda, and S. Takeuchi, unpublished.
13. S. Kachi, unpublished.
14. A. Seeger, *Phil. Mag.,* **45,** 1194 (1954).
15. G. Sachs and J. Weerts, *Z. Physik,* **62,** 473 (1930).

16. N. Norman and B. E. Warren, *J. Appl. Phys.*, **22,** 483 (1951).
17. O. Kubaschewski and O. Huchler, *Z. Elektrochem.*, **52,** 170 (1948).
18. N. G. Schmahl, *Z. anorg. u. allgem. Chem.*, **266,** 1 (1951).
19. R. E. Jamison and F. A. Sherrill, *Acta Met.*, **4,** 197 (1956).
20. D. T. Keating, *Acta Met.*, **2,** 885 (1954).
21. J. M. Cowley, *Phys. Rev.*, **77,** 669 (1950).
22. F. von Göler and G. Sachs, *Z. Physik*, **55,** 581 (1929).
23. G. Ardley and A. H. Cottrell, *Proc. Roy. Soc.* (*London*), *A,* **219,** 328 (1953).

ACKNOWLEDGMENTS

The author wishes to express his hearty thanks to Professor Sakae Takeuchi for his interest and support, and also to Dr. P. Haasen, Institute for the Study of Metals, University of Chicago, who read through the manuscript and gave valuable comments.

DISCUSSION

SEEGER reported the results of a refined calculation of the short-range order hardening carried out in collaboration with R. Ranzinger.[1] They did not use the quasi-chemical theory and did not assume the complete destruction of short-range order, but worked explicitly with the interaction potentials between neighboring atoms, next nearest neighbors, etc., and with the displacements of atoms. The resolved shear stress necessary to move a single dislocation in an octahedral glide system through a short-range ordered f.c.c. binary alloy was found to be

$$\tau = \sqrt{\frac{4}{3}}\frac{2(m_a m_b)}{b^3}\{V_1[\alpha_2 - 2\alpha_1 + \alpha_1(-\tfrac{1}{2}\alpha_1 - \tfrac{1}{2}\alpha_2)] + V_2[\alpha_1 - 2\alpha_2 + \alpha_1(\alpha_2 - 2\alpha_1)]\} \quad (1)$$

plus entropy terms corresponding to those degrees of freedom which are not frozen in at the temperature of deformation. In eq. 1 b is the dislocation strength, m_a and m_b are the concentrations of the two constituents, and V_1 and V_2 are the interaction potentials between nearest and next nearest neighbors [as usual $V = \frac{1}{2}(V_{aa} + V_{bb} - 2V_{ab}]$. α_i is related to the coefficients of the Fourier expansion of the

[1] R. Ranzinger, Diplomarbeit, Technischen Hochschule, Stuttgart, 1955.

scattering power of the alloy in reciprocal space, and also to the probability of finding an a-atom in the ith sphere around a b-atom. More terms than are given in eq. 1 can be found in ref. 1.

In order to check the theory, the short-range order (i.e., the parameters α_i and the potentials V_i) and the critical shear stress τ_0 must be known. These quantities have not yet been measured on the same specimens. Short-range order data are available on Ag-Au and Ag_3Au.[2] The critical shear stress in the binary system Ag-Au has been measured at room temperature.[3] Combining this information, it is found that the shear stress τ obtained from eq. 1 is larger by a factor of about 1.5 than the experimental value τ_0 (corrected for contributions which are not due to the alloying). One cannot say whether this slight discrepancy is due to the comparison of specimens with different heat treatments or whether the dislocations move in pairs, the second one pushing the first one through the alloy. At any rate it appears that the short-range order accounts for the critical shear stress of Ag-Au at room temperature. Unfortunately no data are available on the temperature dependence of these alloys. SEEGER said that their theory predicts a slight increase in the critical shear stress with decreasing temperature because of a corresponding increase in the V_i. If one applies the X-ray data on Cu_3Au,[4] it is found by analogy that this effect gives a 20% increase in the critical shear stress when going from 300°C to room temperature. A further increase of the same order of magnitude is expected when going to liquid-helium temperature.

NABARRO brought up the question of the existence of a yield point in an alloy such as Cu_3Au which has short-range order hardening. The crystal has short-range order prior to deformation. The first dislocation that passes over the glide plane should raise the energy by greatly reducing the short-range order at that plane. The following dislocations that pass over that glide plane will cause less and less change in short-range order since they will be passing through a region that is already disordered. NABARRO said H. J. Logie had pointed out that this should lead to a yield point, but that such a yield point has not been found in Cu_3Au.

FISHER commented that Ardley and Cottrell have found yield points in alpha-brass.

[2] N. Norman and B. E. Warren, *J. Appl. Phys.,* **22,** 483 (1951).
[3] G. Sachs and J. Weerts, *Z. Physik,* **62,** 473 (1930).
[4] J. M. Cowley, *J. Appl. Phys.,* **21,** 24 (1950).

SEITZ inquired whether one would not expect an upper yield point to occur if Cottrell locking is the principal factor in determining the critical resolved shear stress. He asked if an upper yield point is found in such alloys. SUZUKI replied that, at least in a face-centered cubic crystal, an upper yield point is expected to occur, and it has already been observed in alpha-brass crystals at liquid N_2 temperature, where Cottrell locking is predominant. If there is no stress concentration, the stress required to initiate the slip is equal to the external stress required to move a screw dislocation, σ_0; the stress required to continue the slip is about $\sigma_0/2$. Thus, in such a case a sharp yield point must be expected. Of course, the upper yield point might be lowered by stress concentration due to the grip, uneven surfaces, etc. Therefore, the upper yield point might be considerably lower than σ_0 and this was observed when a crystal was deformed with care.

The Deformation of Alloy Single Crystals

* J. GARSTONE

R. W. K. HONEYCOMBE

Department of Metallurgy
University of Sheffield
Sheffield, England

1. INTRODUCTION

The hardening of metals by adding solute elements in solid solution is of great practical importance, yet despite extensive research the basic principles of solution hardening have not been fully elucidated. It is convenient to make a distinction between the effect of alloying elements on the stress necessary for plastic deformation to commence, i.e., the yield stress, and on the subsequent work hardening of the alloy.

In recent years there have been substantial contributions to the theory of the yield point, with the result that there are now several feasible theories of solution hardening which depend essentially on the interaction of solute atoms with dislocations. However, there is still only limited information on the effects of different solute elements on the yield stress of various metals, and there is no general agreement on the relative role of such factors as atomic size, lattice distortion, and relative valencies. Most of the experimental work has been done on polycrystalline alloys using either hardness or tensile tests, whereas the critical resolved shear stress for glide of a single crystal is clearly a more fundamental property. For this reason the present paper is

* Now at Atomic Energy Research Establishment, Harwell, England.

restricted to the measurements of critical resolved shear stress obtained on single crystals.

As far as the contributions of alloying elements to work hardening is concerned, it is essential that single crystal studies should be made. Here again, there is a paucity of experimental data except on brass crystals, the behavior of which appears not to be typical of all alloy crystals.

2. EARLY WORK ON THE CRITICAL SHEAR STRESSES OF ALLOY CRYSTALS

Von Göler and Sachs [1] studied the deformation of copper-zinc alloy crystals of increasing zinc content and found that for dilute alloys the critical shear stress S_c increased almost linearly with concentration. They also determined the stress-strain curves which revealed, particularly in the higher zinc alloys, practically no work hardening to strains of 20% or more. This is often referred to as "easy glide," but it is not yet certain that it is the same phenomenon which gives a region of low linear hardening in pure metal crystals.

Schmid and Seliger [2] also found that with magnesium-aluminum and magnesium-zinc crystals, S_c varied linearly with concentration. With gold-silver alloys, Sachs and Weerts [3] obtained a linear relationship at low concentrations, but over the whole range of compositions a curve symmetrical about 50 at. % concentration was obtained. Osswald [4] obtained a similar curve for copper-nickel solid solutions with a maximum of S_c at 60 at. % nickel. Greenland [5] found that the S_c of mercury crystals was very much altered by extremely small additions of silver, and obtained a nearly linear plot of S_c against the log of the impurity content.

3. RECENT WORK ON THE CRITICAL SHEAR STRESSES OF ALLOY CRYSTALS

In the last few years, Linde and co-workers [6] have published results showing the variation of the critical shear stress of copper when alloyed with tin, antimony, indium, germanium, silicon, nickel, and gold. These workers found a relationship between the slope of the linear S_c composition plot and the rate of change of lattice parameter with composition

$$\frac{dS_c}{dc} = K\epsilon^n \tag{1}$$

where S_c = critical resolved shear stress

c = atomic concentration

$\epsilon = \frac{1}{a}\frac{da}{dc}$, where a = lattice parameter

$n \simeq 2$ from experiments

If Linde's results are plotted logarithmically (Fig. 1), a straight line of slope unity is obtained, not 2 as he claimed. However, the re-

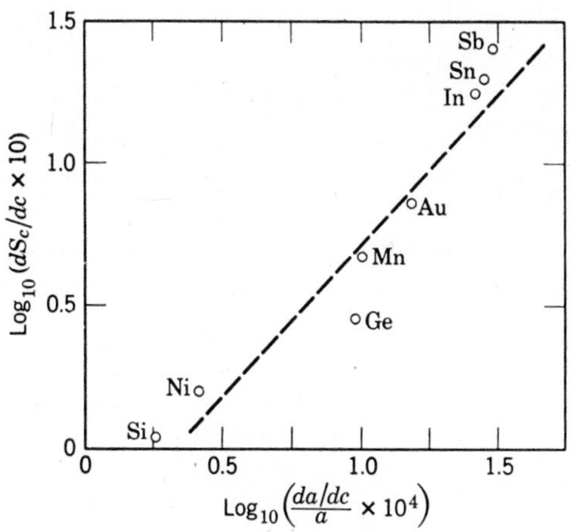

Fig. 1. Log-log plot of the data of Linde and co-workers [6] for copper alloys. S_c = critical resolved shear stress, c = concentration of solute, and a = lattice parameter.

sult for nickel is based only on one crystal, and can thus be regarded as uncertain, whereas both Norbury [7] and Brick *et al.*[8] have obtained anomalous results with polycrystalline copper-silicon alloys. If a line is drawn through the remainder of the plot for Ge, Mn, An, In, Sn, and Sb, a straight line of slope 1.9 is obtained which more closely fits Linde's equation.

Alternatively, dS_c/dc can be plotted against the difference in Goldschmidt's atomic diameter between solute and solvent atoms. Although the use of these atomic diameters may be hard to justify, when those which can be determined with any degree of accuracy are plotted, a straight line of slope 1.85 is obtained (Fig. 2) which again fits eq. 1.

It is relevant to recall that Mott and Nabarro,[9] using a dislocation model, derived the following relationship

$$S = G\epsilon^2 c \tag{2}$$

where G is the shear modulus and c is the atomic concentration of solute. However, Mott[10] subsequently revised the theory which then gave the solution hardening proportional to $\epsilon^{4/3}c$.

More recently the present authors[11] have studied the effect of small concentrations of silver, gold, and germanium on the critical shear stress of pure copper. The critical shear stress S_c was determined at 290°K for crystals made from copper-silver and copper-gold alloys of several concentrations. Segregation difficulties limited the work to alloys of low concentration and even then the compositions are only very approximate as they vary along the length of the crystal. The silver alloys contained approximately 0.15, 0.3, and 0.5 at. % of silver; the gold alloys contained 0.15, 0.3, and 0.6 at. % of gold.

When the critical shear stresses were plotted against the atomic concentration of solute metal, a near linear relation was obtained in the silver, gold, and germanium alloys over the small range of composition examined (Fig. 3). From such graphs were obtained values for dS_c/dc which are listed in Table 1, together with the difference in Goldschmidt diameter (ΔD).

TABLE 1. RELATIVE HARDENING OF COPPER BY SILVER, GOLD, AND GERMANIUM

Solute	$\frac{dS_c}{dc}$ at 290°K (g/mm²/%)	ΔD (KX units)
Ag	1240	0.332
Au	1126	0.327
Ge	667.5	0.237

The values are shown plotted logarithmically in Fig. 4. A straight line can be drawn through the points, assuming that a relation of the type $ds/dc = K(\Delta D)^n$ holds. The value of n, the slope of the curve, is 1.7. It thus appears from these results, as well as those of Linde, that the model of Mott and Nabarro for solution hardening has some experimental support. However, the situation is not quite so satisfactory when the temperature dependence of the critical resolved shear stress is examined.

4. TEMPERATURE DEPENDENCE OF S_c IN ALLOY CRYSTALS

The present authors[11] have investigated the temperature dependence of S_c for pure copper crystals, and a number of crystals of two copper-silver alloys (0.15 and 0.3 at. % Ag) and of one copper-germanium alloy (0.35 at. % Ge). The results for the copper-silver alloy crystals are shown in Fig. 5 for three temperatures: 77°K, 196°K, and 290°K.

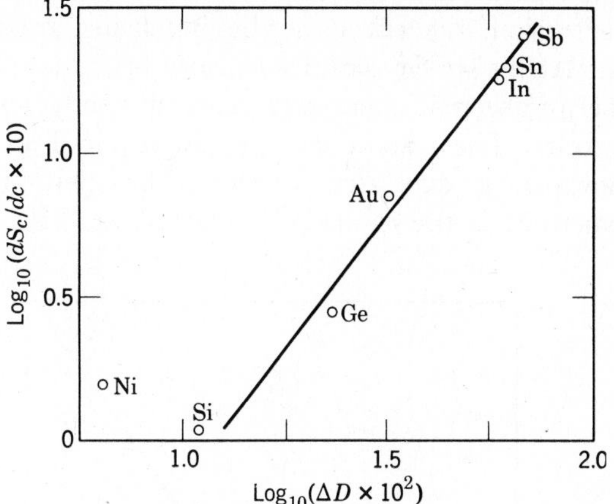

Fig. 2. Log-log plot of data of Linde and co-workers [6] versus difference in Goldschmidt's atomic diameter (ΔD) between solvent and solute atoms.

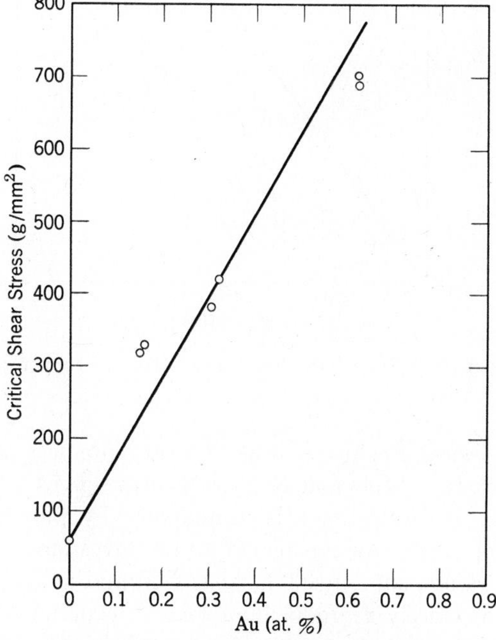

Fig. 3. Critical resolved shear stress of copper-gold alloy single crystals with low gold concentration.

In all cases the critical shear stress increases more or less linearly with atomic concentration, the effect of alloying being greater at lower temperatures. At higher concentrations S_0 is beginning to fall below the linear plot, an observation already made by von Göler and Sachs [1] on brass crystals. The results are summarized in Fig. 6 where all the curves shown can be expressed in terms of the equation $170[(S_0/S_c) - 1] = T$, where S_0 is the critical shear stress at 0°K.

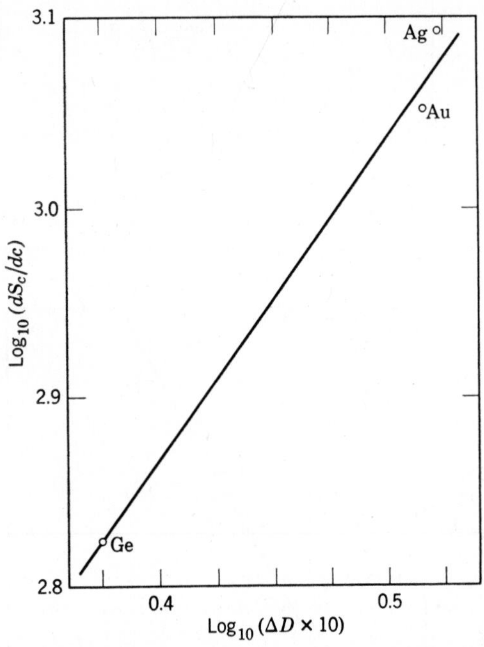

Fig. 4. Log-log plot of critical resolved shear stress of copper-gold alloys with low gold concentration.

Now the classical Becker-Orowan [12] theory predicts that S_c should vary as $T^{1/2}$, whereas Mott and Nabarro's theory gives a $T^{2/3}$ variation. The experimental results have been analyzed by plotting S_c against various powers of T. As the temperatures investigated were over a fairly narrow range, namely, 83°K to 273°K, and as the critical shear stresses are not closely reproducible owing to experimental difficulties such as segregation, it was not possible to deduce the precise temperature dependence. However, the most likely power of the temperature seems to be between 0.25 and 0.50. Further results at lower temperatures are needed before this can be satisfactorily established.

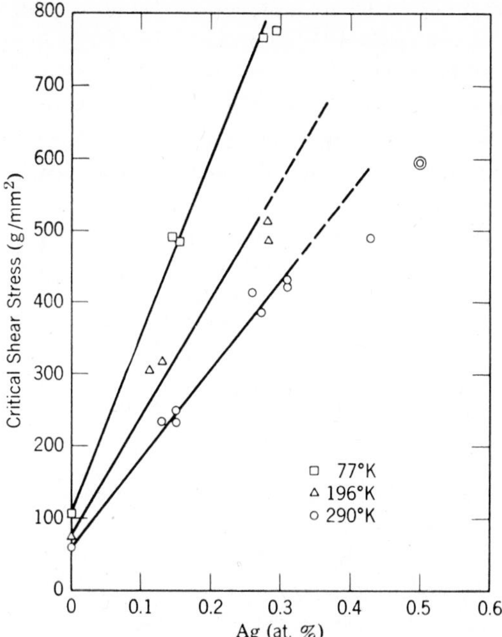

Fig. 5. Critical resolved shear stress of copper-silver single crystals.

5. EASY GLIDE IN ALLOY CRYSTALS

It is now well established that pure face-centered cubic metal crystals of aluminum, copper, gold, and silver exhibit an almost linear region in the early part of the plastic range of the stress-strain curve when suitable orientations are chosen. The recent work of Rosi [13] and of Garstone, Honeycombe, and Greetham [14] has shown that the end of the easy glide range in copper is characterized by a constant value of the ratio S/S_c, where S is the critical shear stress at the end of easy glide. The present authors have extended the study to the dilute copper-alloy crystals used in the critical shear stress determinations discussed in the previous sections.

Several crystals whose orientations were towards the center of the stereographic triangle were tested for each alloy. A typical group of curves for one silver alloy ($\sim$0.3 at. %) is shown in Fig. 7. The orientations are all fairly similar. Figure 8 shows typical shear stress-strain curves for increasing silver contents, namely, 0.13, 0.27, and 0.50 at. % silver. Not only is the critical shear stress for glide increased by alloying but so is the range of easy glide, reaching as much as 60% for the 0.50% silver alloy, which has an S_c of approximately 600 g/mm². A pure copper crystal of similar orientation would possess an S_c of approximately 60 g/mm^2, while the easy glide range would be about 6%, so the critical shear stress is increased in the same ratio as is the easy glide.

The copper-gold alloys behaved in a similar way to the copper-silver alloys. Some shear stress-strain curves are shown in Fig. 9 which make it clear that the crystals of the three compositions used form

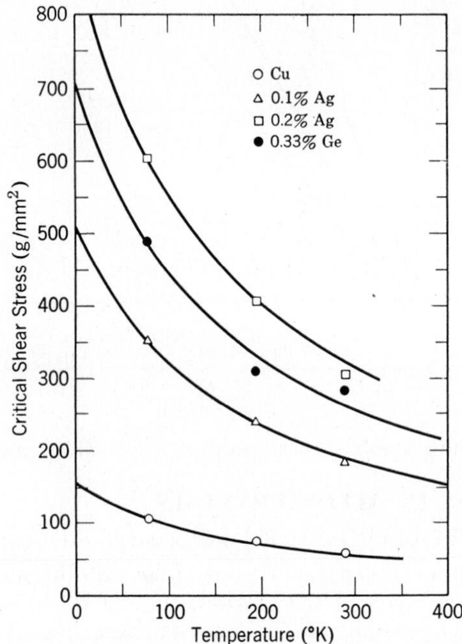

Fig. 6. Temperature dependence of critical resolved shear stress of copper and copper-alloy single crystals. The data for the selected compositions 0.1 and 0.2 at. % Ag have been taken from the curves in Fig. 5.

three fairly well defined groups (except crystal 4G), the linear region of hardening again varying markedly with the solute concentration.

When a further comparison is made with the behavior of pure copper crystals, it is found that the alloying additions have little effect on the rate of hardening during easy glide, the slope scarcely changing with increasing alloy content. At present we have insufficient data to determine the effect of orientation on the extent of easy glide in the alloy crystals.

Microscopic examination of the deformed crystals revealed that although sporadic secondary slip occurred at surface pits and scratches during easy glide, general secondary slip was only detected when the crystals began to harden rapidly. During easy glide, coarse kink bands were detected which were more pronounced than those occurring in pure copper crystals. If the surface of a crystal was scratched, a very coarse kink band would often develop from it. Although the slip appeared to be very fine in the early stages of deformation, it was evident that

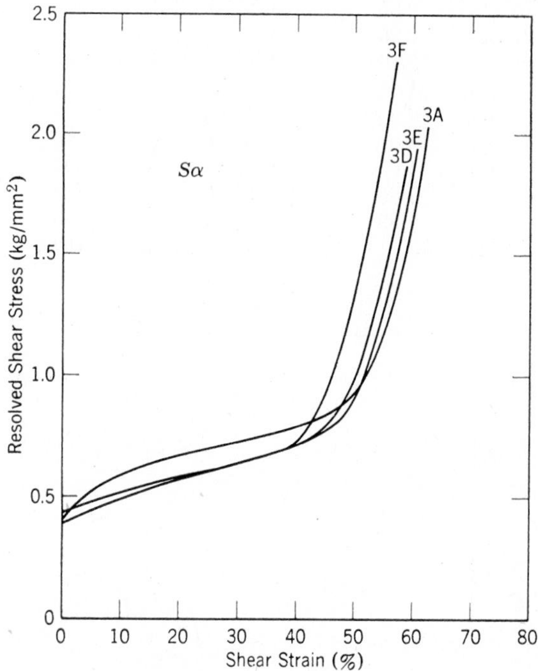

Fig. 7. Shear stress–shear strain curves for copper-silver single crystals containing approximately 0.3 at. % silver.

coarser slip bands were formed towards the end of the extensive easy glide range.

6. THE EXTENT OF THE EASY GLIDE RANGE

Data from both copper and copper-alloy single crystals have been examined, and it has been found that the ratio S/S_c, where S is the critical shear stress at the *end* of the easy glide range, is approximately constant. The value of S is taken as the intersection of the extrapolations of the two parts of the stress-strain curve, and thus corresponds to the S_{II} value used by Rosi. Table 2 shows the results for a large number of copper and alloy crystals from which it can be seen that the stress increment to the end of the easy glide range is approximately equal to S_c.

TABLE 2. THE RATIO S/S_c FOR SOME COPPER AND COPPER-ALLOY SINGLE CRYSTALS

Crystal	S_c (g/mm²)	S (g/mm²)	$\frac{S}{S_c}$	Crystal	S_c (g/mm²)	S (g/mm²)	$\frac{S}{S_c}$
Cu 35	57	134	2.35	0.15 at. % Ag	247	508	2.06
Cu 38	53	120	2.26	0.15 at. % Ag	232	485	2.09
Cu 40	57	123	2.16	0.15 at. % Ag	233	490	2.10
Cu 42	65	127	1.95	0.3 at. % Ag	415	900	2.17
Cu 43	59	136	2.30	0.3 at. % Ag	426	780	1.83
Cu 45	50	100	2.00	0.3 at. % Ag	386	770	2.00
Cu 49	86	142	1.65	0.5 at. % Ag	595	1230	2.07
Cu 51	58	108	1.86	0.15 at. % Au	320	585	1.83
Cu 53	64	121	1.89	0.17 at. % Au	330	790	2.39
Cu 55	53	117	2.21	0.30 at. % Au	409	790	1.93

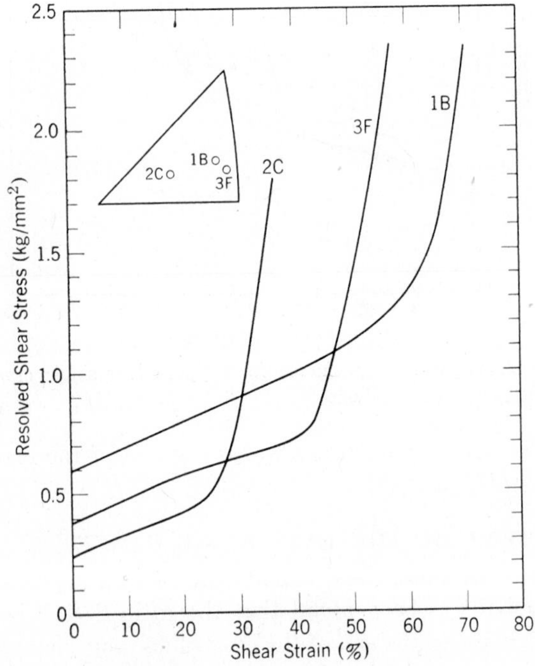

Fig. 8. Typical shear stress–shear strain curves of copper-silver single crystals at 290°K. Crystal 2C: 0.13 at. % Ag. Crystal 3F: 0.27 at. % Ag. Crystal 1B: 0.50 at. % Ag.

It is now widely agreed that easy glide ends when numerous localized patches of secondary slip occur. In pure metals this may take place unpredicted, long before the macroscopic shear stress on the secondary plane has reached a sufficiently high value. In many alloy crystals secondary slip is delayed much longer, and may in fact occur at a

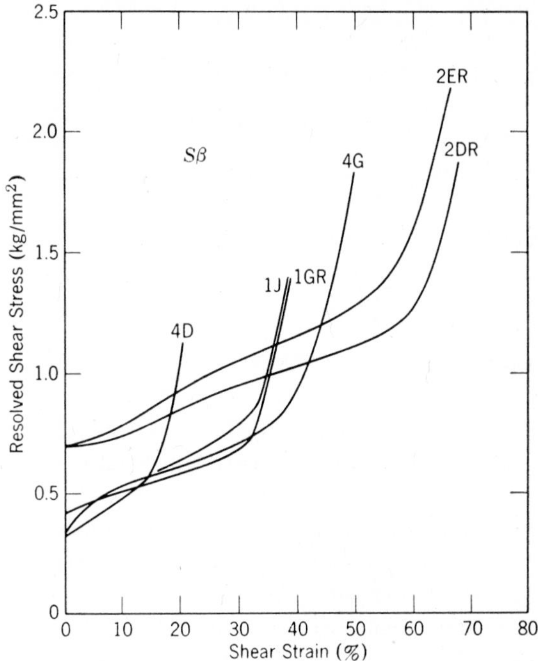

Fig. 9. Shear stress–shear strain curves of copper-gold alloys. Crystals 4D and 4G contain 0.16 at. % Au. Crystals 1J and 1GR contain 0.31 at. % Au. Crystals 2ER and 2DR contain 0.62 at. % Au.

later stage than predicted, thus resulting in the phenomenon of "overshooting."

Calculation of the macroscopic resolved shear stress on the operative secondary slip planes shows that in most cases it is very small, so it must be the shear stress on the primary system which is the controlling factor in initiating secondary slip. The experimental evidence for pure metals and for alloy crystals is that easy glide ends at an approximately constant value of S_c. It is a logical step to suppose that stress concentrations exist on the primary planes so that locally the shear stress can be raised sufficiently to cause slip on the secondary planes. Dislocation pile-ups appear to be the most likely stress concentrators in single crystals. Stroh's [15] work on the stress fields around dislocation pile-ups has shown that there is a maximum in the shear stress in the primary slip direction which would thus tend to activate other slip systems containing this direction, e.g., the classical cross-slip plane. So once a pile-up of dislocations has formed it will promote both further primary slip and cross slip in its vicinity.

It would be expected that any factor which raises the critical resolved shear stress S_c will thus increase the extent of easy glide. Andrade and Henderson [16] and Garstone, Honeycombe, and Greetham [14] have shown that the easy glide range of pure metal crystals is greater at lower temperatures. The present experiments reveal that elevation of S_c by alloying also extends the easy glide range in the same proportion, for the local stress in the vicinity of the pile-up must build up to a value approaching that of $(S_c)_{\text{alloy}}$. Recently, Jaoul and Bricot [17] have shown that silicon and copper in solid solution extend the easy glide range of aluminum crystals.

7. ALLOY CRYSTALS CONTAINING A DISPERSED SECOND PHASE

The present experiments show conclusively that alloying additions which enter into solid solution increase the length of the easy glide region. However, as Rosi [13] has pointed out, the effects of impurities on easy glide as reported in the literature are rather ambiguous. It appears that the confusion arises from the lack of distinction between impurities present as a second phase and impurities present in solid solution. For example, commercial purity aluminum (99.8%) crystals show less easy glide than crystals 99.99% pure. This situation results because the impurities are largely present as a finely dispersed second phase. The dislocation pile-up would then tend to occur in the vicinity of these particles at an early stage of the deformation, thus leading to rapid hardening.

This distinction is more clearly brought out in work with age-hardening crystals, e.g., Al-3.5% Cu. Carlsen and Honeycombe [18] have shown that with Al-3.5% Cu crystals, easy glide only occurs in the supersaturated solid solution when deformed at a low temperature, so that aging does not take place during the deformation. If the crystals are aged to peak hardness, or overaged, before deformation, then the subsequent stress-strain curve shows normal parabolic hardening. The view that dislocation pile-ups are more numerous and involve fewer dislocations as they occur in the vicinity of precipitate particles is confirmed by the complete absence of visible slip bands in the fully aged alloys, and their development at a relatively later stage of the deformation in overaged alloys.

REFERENCES

1. F. von Göler and G. Sachs, *Z. Physik,* **55,** 581 (1929).
2. E. Schmid and H. Seliger, *Metallwirtschaft,* **31,** 421 (1932).
3. G. Sachs and J. Weerts, *Z. Physik,* **62,** 473 (1930).
4. E. Osswald, *Z. Physik,* **83,** 55 (1933).
5. H. M. Greenland, *Proc. Roy. Soc.* (*London*), *A,* **163,** 34 (1937).
6. J. O. Linde, B. Lindell, and C. H. Stade, *Arkiv Physik,* **2,** 89 (1950).
   J. O. Linde and S. Edwards, *Arkiv Physik,* **8,** 511 (1954).
7. A. L. Norbury, *J. Inst. Metals,* **29,** 423 (1923).
8. R. M. Brick, D. L. Martin, and R. P. Angier, *Trans. A.S.M.,* **31,** 675 (1943).
9. N. F. Mott and F. R. N. Nabarro, *Report of a Conference on Strength of Solids,* Physical Society, London, p. 1 (1948).
10. N. F. Mott, Chap. 6 in *Imperfections in Nearly Perfect Crystals,* W. Shockley, J. H. Hollomon, R. Maurer, and F. Seitz, John Wiley & Sons, New York (1952).
11. J. Garstone and R. W. K. Honeycombe, unpublished work.
12 R. Becker, *Phys. Z.,* **26,** 919 (1925).
   E. Orowan, *Z. Physik,* **89,** 605 (1934).
13. F. D. Rosi, *Trans. AIME,* **200,** 1009 (1954).
14. J. Garstone, R. W. K. Honeycombe, and G. Greetham, *Acta Met.,* **4,** 485 (1956).
15. A. N. Stroh, *Proc. Roy. Soc.* (*London*), *A,* **223,** 404 (1954).
16. E. N. da C. Andrade and C. Henderson, *Phil. Trans., A,* **244,** 177 (1951).
17. B. Jaoul and J. Bricot, *Rev. mét.,* **52,** 629 (1955).
18. K. M. Carlsen and R. W. K. Honeycombe, *J. Inst. Metals,* **83,** 449 (1955).

DISCUSSION

LÜCKE, discussing the interpretation of the critical shear stress of solid solutions, presented the damping versus strain amplitude curves shown in Fig. 6 of the paper by Lücke and Granato (in Part V of this volume). The curves for higher impurity content show an abrupt increase of damping with strain amplitude which was attributed to the breakaway of a large number of dislocations from solute atoms. The stress level, σ_b, corresponding to this breakaway strain can be plotted as a function of solute concentration. The plot is a straight line, agreeing with the theory given in the paper of Lücke and Granato; and the measurements of critical resolved shear stress of Linde and co-workers fall on the same straight line, if one considers the different shear modulus and misfit parameter adequately. In this way one obtains an interpretation of the critical shear stress of solid solutions which is somewhat different from that of Mott and Nabarro, and which is explained by the use of Fig. D1. Curve (*a*) shows the yield stress

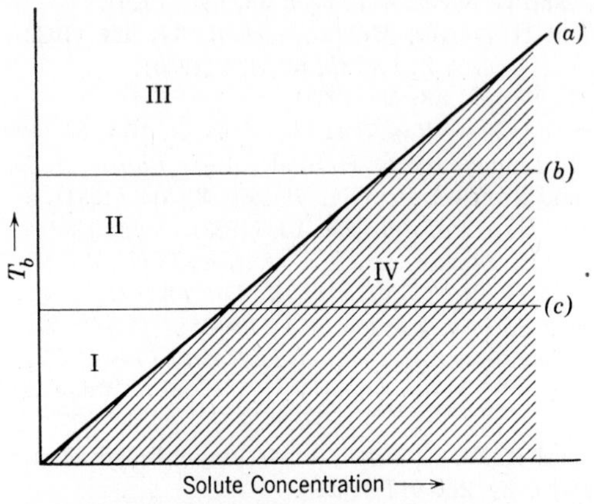

Fig. D1. Yield stress versus solute concentration. (*a*) Yield stress necessary for the breakaway from foreign atoms. (*b*) Yield stress required for dislocations to cut through each other. (*c*) Yield stress required to start a Frank-Read source.

necessary for the breakaway from foreign atoms as a function of concentration; curve (*b*) is the yield stress required for dislocations to cut through each other; and curve (*c*) is the yield stress required to start a Frank-Read source. All three of these stresses must be exceeded if plastic flow is to take place. Thus, the stress level must be in region III to bring plastic flow. In region II Frank-Read sources operate, but this dislocation motion will be observable only by such methods as damping. In region I one finds only strain amplitude dependent damping, and in region IV the dislocations are not able to leave the foreign atoms.

COTTRELL, discussing the solute strengthening effect predicted by the Mott-Nabarro formula, said that the dimensional aspects compared satisfactorily with the experimental results but that the theory predicts a greater solution hardening than is observed by about a factor of ten. COTTRELL had attributed this discrepancy to temperature effects, and he remarked that the data presented by Honeycombe did show that all the strengths do go up very considerably at low temperatures. HONEYCOMBE replied that the calculation had not been checked using the low-temperature data.

HONEYCOMBE said that the raising of the critical shear stress was interpreted as due mainly to the locking of the dislocations rather than to a hardening of the whole lattice. He added that no substantial yield point had been detected in his samples.

LOMER asked if the temperature dependence of the critical stress followed a $T^{1/2}$ relation as observed by Blewitt in irradiated crystals. HONEYCOMBE answered that the critical shear stress does go approximately with the half power of the temperature.

Written comment by HONEYCOMBE:

> Recently the results have been re-examined, and we find that it is difficult to say precisely what the temperature dependence is. It seems that the temperature dependency is between $T^{1/4}$ and $T^{1/2}$, but further work at lower temperatures is needed to settle this point.

Similar experiments for aluminum alloys by Jaoul, in Paris, were discussed by FRIEDEL. A yield point, observed at the beginning of flow in these experiments, was believed by FRIEDEL to be due to Cottrell-Lomer locking.

SEEGER was of the opinion that one should be careful in comparing impurity effects in crystals of copper, silver, gold, etc., because a variation of the dislocation density of as-grown crystals with impurity content must be taken into account in order to get out the intrinsic impurity effect. This is explained in more detail in § 4 of Seeger's paper (pages 271–277 in this volume).

LEIBFRIED asked if all of the solute atoms were going to dislocations, or if part of them were distributed in the lattice. HONEYCOMBE commented that the critical stress is still going up with solute concentration for very high concentrations, and wondered how much solute was required to give the maximum effect. MACHLIN presented some data from internal friction tests which bore on this question. Copper-base alloys with aluminum and silicon solute were quenched from a preanneal temperature. The breakaway stress was found to decrease as the preanneal temperature was increased, which indicated Cottrell locking. H. SUZUKI said that the yield strength and the appearance of easy glide observed by Honeycombe could be explained by the Cottrell effect as he reported in his presentation (preceding paper in this volume).

Color Change in Metals upon Plastic Deformation

W. BOAS

Division of Tribophysics
Commonwealth Scientific and Industrial Research Organization
University of Melbourne, Australia

This paper concerns one contribution to the core energy of a dislocation. The quantity in point is relatively small but should be considered.

Fumi [1] has shown that the main contribution to the energy to form a vacancy comes from the change in energy of the conduction electrons which is related to a change in the Fermi energy of the metal. A somewhat smaller but similar change in the Fermi energy will occur at the core of an edge dislocation.

As the Fermi energy influences the position of the absorption band, this position might be expected to change on plastic deformation whereby more dislocations are introduced. Indeed, such an effect has recently been observed in germanium.[2] For a metal with an absorption band in the visible region an observable change in color might result. Such a change in color was reported by Tammann [3] almost 40 years ago. He claimed that whitish-green silver-gold alloys become yellowish on heavy cold rolling and that the effect is more pronounced with some ternary copper-silver-gold alloys, the change in color increasing with the extent of deformation.

Since no further observations seem to have been made after those by Tammann, we have, during the last few weeks, prepared an alloy of about 52 wt. % gold, 22 wt. % silver, and 26 wt. % copper. The alloy has a definite reddish tint in the fully annealed state. An ingot of this alloy was cold-rolled from 3 mm to 0.25 mm and a part of it was then annealed in nitrogen for ½ hr at 450°C. Visual observation showed that the annealed and the rolled strips have different colors, the rolled specimen being more yellow than the annealed one. An attempt to make a color slide showing this difference was not successful.

We plan to use a spectrophotometer to observe the color change quantitatively, and by annealing to various temperatures to determine whether vacancies or dislocations are responsible for the change.

REFERENCES

1. F. G. Fumi, *Phil. Mag.*, **46,** 1007 (1955).
2. H. G. Lipson, E. Burstein, and P. L. Smith, *Phys. Rev.*, **99,** 444 (1955).
3. G. Tammann, *Z. anorg. u. allgem. Chem.*, **107,** 1 (1919); see particularly pp. 115–117.

DISCUSSION

SHOCKLEY inquired if there was a chance that the color change resulted from an order-disorder reaction and if quenching the alloy would produce the color change. BOAS answered that he did not know if the effect was due to an order-disorder reaction since the experimental work had not been completed.

Written comment by BOAS:

Measurements have shown that the reflectances of annealed and deformed specimens are different but the possible effect of surface films has still to be investigated. X-ray diffraction diagrams have shown that there is no order-disorder transformation. The alloy consists of two face-centered cubic phases, indicating the existence of a miscibility gap.

The Diffusion of Copper in Germanium

F. C. FRANK
University of Bristol
Bristol, England

The diffusion of copper in germanium involves an interaction between point defects and dislocations which is quite different from what it first appears to be. The general behavior of copper diffusion in germanium can be described in terms of an experiment in which one diffuses copper into n-type germanium. When the copper concentration reaches 50% of saturation, the n-type changes to p-type so that the 50% concentration contour is a p-n junction. The p-n junction can be made visible when the specimen is sectioned and examined under a microscope.

The above experiment has been performed by Tweet and Gallagher [1] and what they observe is depicted in Fig. 1. The 50% concentration contour runs parallel to the surface to a depth, X, which depends on diffusion time. There are also spikes of diameter $2X$ that run in from the surface, and it can be established that these spikes are along dislocations. In addition, there are isolated regions of size about $2X$ with a high copper concentration. It appears that there is a slow diffusion normal to the surface in the good region of the crystal and a very fast piping along the dislocations with slow diffusion outward from the dislocations. The diffusion coefficient outward from the dislocations can be calculated as:

$$D = \frac{X^2}{t}$$

For $t = 10^3$ sec one finds that $X = 40\ \mu$ at 750°C so that

$$D = 1.6 \times 10^{-8}\ \text{cm}^2\ \text{sec}^{-1}$$

The gross diffusion coefficient of copper in germanium has been measured by Fuller *et al.*[2] who found that in the range of 700 to 900°C the

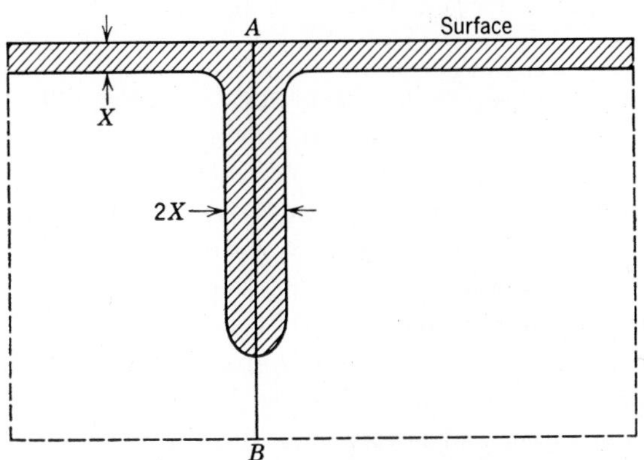

Fig. 1. Section of a Ge crystal into which copper has diffused from the surface. There is a copper-rich layer at the surface, and a spike along the dislocation, *AB*. (After Tweet and Gallagher.[1])

diffusivity is about 3×10^{-5} cm^2 sec^{-1}, and it is practically independent of temperature. The penetration curve that was found had a deep tail that increased with time, and the curve could be considered as being due to two superposed diffusion effects. One has a diffusion coefficient on the order of 10^{-5} cm^2 sec^{-1} and the other is on the order of 10^{-3} cm^2 sec^{-1}.

One cannot explain the gross diffusivity as measured by Fuller *et al.* as due to the fast piping of copper along the dislocation lines, which it first appears to be. The value of 10^{-5} cm^2 sec^{-1} is characteristic of a crystal with about 10^6 dislocations cm^{-2}. If one uses a reasonable cross-sectional area through which the copper is piped along the dislocation, then the diffusion coefficient in this area comes out enormously high, on the order of thousands. Alternatively, if the diffusion coefficient is given an acceptable value, then the dislocation must raise the diffusion coefficient to this value over an incredibly large area.

An interpretation [3] that seems to explain the experimental facts is that the copper is much more mobile interstitially than substitutionally although the substitutional solubility is much higher. Only about 1% of the dissolved copper is interstitial. It turns out that the diffusion coefficient for the interstitial copper, D_i, is about 10^{-3} cm² sec⁻¹, which explains the deep tail penetration. In a region which has many dislocations the equilibrium between the interstitial copper and the substitutional copper concentration is maintained. Therefore the effective diffusion coefficient is:

$$D_{\text{eff}} \doteq D_i \frac{C_i}{C_s} \approx 10^{-5}$$

which is what one observes in measurement of gross diffusivity. The reason why spikes of copper appear along dislocations is apparent. The copper penetrates rapidly as interstitial copper, but it can change to substitutional copper only where there are vacancies available. The dislocations provide the necessary vacancies so that the substitutional concentration builds up near the dislocations. This mechanism predicts that the substitutional copper concentration should build up also at those dislocations that have no connection with the surface from which the copper is diffusing. This has been verified by Tweet and Gallagher [4] and Fuller and Ditzenberger.[5]

The rate at which substitutional copper diffuses from the dislocation lines or in from the surface in a good region of the crystal, as calculated above, is much too fast to be due to normal substitutional diffusion. The normal diffusion of substitutional copper should be approximately the same as the self-diffusion coefficient of germanium, which is about 6×10^{-15} cm² sec⁻¹ at 750°C. However, the substitutional copper should diffuse faster than that, because part of the time it is dissociated into a vacancy and an interstitial copper which diffuse independently. The diffusion by this dissociative mechanism is controlled by the slower moving species which is the vacancy, and it is given by the vacancy diffusivity times a factor which represents the proportion of time that the vacancies are free from combination with copper.

$$D_s = D_v \frac{C_v}{C_v + C_s}$$

C_v, the concentration of vacancies, can be neglected in comparison with the concentration of substitutional copper, which is 10^{-7}. The product $D_v C_v$ is the self-diffusion coefficient of Ge which is known.

$$D_s = \frac{D_{Ge}}{C_s} = \frac{6 \times 10^{-15}}{10^{-7}} = 6 \times 10^{-8} \text{ cm}^2 \text{ sec}^{-1}$$

The proposed mechanism therefore accounts for three vastly different diffusion coefficients in the same system.

REFERENCES

1. A. G. Tweet and C. J. Gallagher, *Phys. Rev.*, **103,** 828 (1956), and General Electric Research Laboratory Report, RL-1685.
2. C. S. Fuller, J. D. Struthers, J. A. Ditzenberger, and K. B. Wolfstirn, *Phys. Rev.*, **93,** 1182 (1954).
3. F. C. Frank and D. Turnbull, *Phys. Rev.*, **104,** 617 (1956).
4. A. G. Tweet and C. J. Gallagher, private communication.
5. C. S. Fuller and J. A. Ditzenberger, *J. Appl. Phys.*, **28,** 40 (1957).

DISCUSSION

READ recalled the work of Van der Maesen and Brenkman,[1] who had measured the penetration curve of copper into germanium, and had plotted the copper concentration as a function of $X/\sqrt{t}$ in the usual manner. They found that the copper concentration was not an error function of $X/\sqrt{t}$, but that the observed curve lay below the error function curve for short times, and approached the error function curve for longer diffusion times.

READ pointed out that if one assumes that there is a constant equilibrium concentration of vacancies, and that the diffusion is by fast interstitials which then combine with vacancies, then the time for the penetration curve to approach the error function curve should be too small to measure. Since the time is not small, READ concluded that the copper was going in rapidly, and using up the available vacancy supply quickly, so that the limiting reaction in early times was the vacancies being supplied by dislocations. Fuller and Ditzenberger [2] tested this hypothesis by measuring the rates of approach to saturation with copper in a thin flat plate of germanium and in a similar plate which had been bent so as to introduce many dislocations. The copper content was determined by measuring the electrical conductivity. In the case of the bent crystal, Fuller and Ditzenberger found a much faster approach to saturation than for the unbent crystal. This agreed with

[1] F. van der Maesen and J. A. Brenkman, *J. Electrochem. Soc.*, **102**, 229 (1955).
[2] C. S. Fuller and J. A. Ditzenberger, *J. Appl. Phys.*, **28,** 40 (1957).

the idea that when many dislocations are present the vacancies are replenished rapidly, and the approach to saturation is quicker. READ added that a further piece of evidence that the diffusion of copper does not take place principally along dislocation "pipes" is that in a bent specimen with all the dislocations running in one direction the diffusion appears isotropic.

SEITZ pointed out that although the vacancy mechanism for self-diffusion in germanium was assumed in the remarks by Frank and by Read, the vacancy mechanism is not a unique model. SEITZ said that one could build other models, such as an interstitialcy model, in which all the same kinetics could be obtained and thus give an alternative explanation of the process. The vacancy mechanism for self-diffusion is not established on the basis of the interpretation of the copper diffusion experiments. SEITZ said that there is additional evidence that seems to eliminate mechanisms other than the vacancy mechanism. There is now firm evidence [3] that monovalent noble metals when added to germanium tend to act as acceptors of three electrons. This would seem reasonable if the noble metal atom goes in substitutionally and attempts to fill the tetrahedral shell in which three electrons are missing. The metal atom would tend to be quadruvalent by being an acceptor for three electrons. This evidence would indicate that the copper prefers to go into germanium substitutionally.

[3] L. Apker, private communication to F. Seitz.

A Comparison of Preyield Microstrain in Steel with Dislocation Theory

D. S. WOOD

California Institute of Technology
Pasadena, California

This report has to do with yield point phenomena in iron or, more precisely, in ordinary annealed polycrystalline low-carbon steel. Recent measurements, that confirm some older ones and have to do with the rate of release of dislocations from Cottrell atmospheres under the influence of an applied stress, will be presented and compared with theoretical results. The original theory of Cottrell and Bilby [1] for the release of a dislocation from an atmosphere under the combined influences of applied stress and thermal fluctuations is somewhat complex. Fisher [2] has proposed a simpler theory based upon certain approximations. His result for the activation energy, W^*, for the release of a dislocation from an atmosphere is

$$W^* = (\gamma_0^2/b\tau)f(\gamma/\gamma_0) \tag{1}$$

where

$$f(\gamma/\gamma_0) = \cos^{-1}(\gamma/\gamma_0) - (\gamma/\gamma_0)[1 - (\gamma/\gamma_0)^2]^{1/2}$$

γ_0 is the energy per unit length of a dislocation without an atmosphere, γ is the energy with an atmosphere, b is the Burgers vector of the dislocation, and τ is the resolved shear stress acting on the dislocation.

If a stress is suddenly applied to the material and maintained constant thereafter, the initial rate of plastic straining, $\dot{\epsilon}_{p0}$, should be proportional to the rate of release of dislocations from atmospheres. Thus

$$\dot{\epsilon}_{p0} \propto \exp (W^*/kT) \tag{2}$$

or

$$\ln \dot{\epsilon}_{p0} = C - 2(\gamma_0^2/bk)f(\gamma/\gamma_0)/\sigma T$$

where k is Boltzmann's constant, σ is the applied tensile stress, and T the absolute temperature. The stress and temperature dependence of the initial plastic strain rate are entirely contained in the term $1/\sigma T$ (neglecting the small variations in γ_0 and γ due to the temperature dependence of the elastic constants). Equation 2 applies only to the

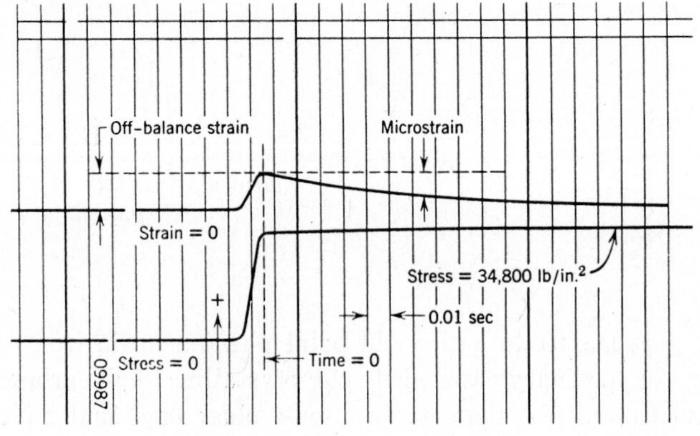

Fig. 1. Typical test record.

initial rate of plastic strain because the local stress at locked dislocations may change with time under constant applied stress due to the stress fields of dislocations previously released from atmopheres.

Figure 1 is an example of an experimental record of tensile load and preyield inelastic microstrain versus time under conditions of rapidly applied constant load. The strain trace represents the difference between the signal from a wire strain gauge on the specimen and the signal from a gauge on a heat-treated alloy steel bar loaded in series with the specimen. The cross section of the latter bar was chosen such that the signals due to elastic strains in this bar and the specimen would be nearly the same. The deflection of the strain trace which occurs during the period of rising load represents the residual unbalance between the elastic strains. Subsequent deflections of the strain trace while the load remains constant represent the preyield inelastic microstrain in the specimen. This microstrain is presumed to be associated with the release of dislocations from Cottrell atmospheres. The record shows that the rate of these microstrains decreases with time at constant load. Hence it is concluded that dislocations released from atmospheres exert back stresses which reduce the local stress at dislocations which have not yet been released.

Figure 2 shows experimental curves of microstrain versus time for several values of applied tensile stress at room temperature. For stresses less than the upper yield stress (about 40,000 lb/in.^{2}) the

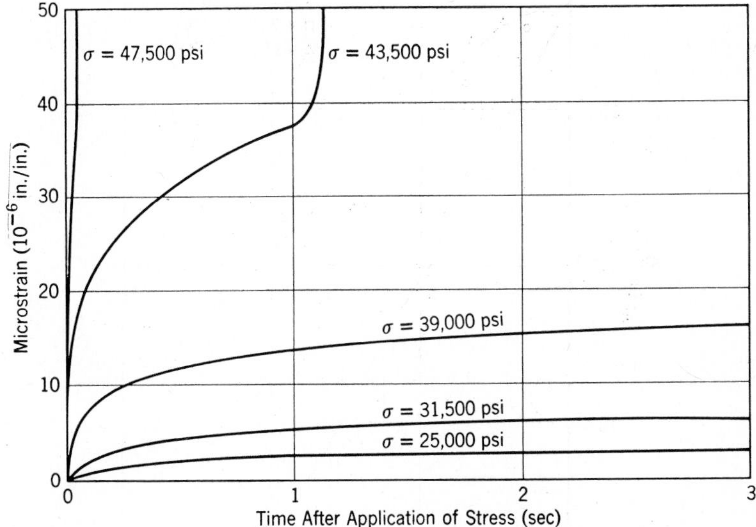

Fig. 2. Experimental curves of microstrain versus time at different rapidly applied constant stresses at room temperature.

microstrain asymptotically approaches some equilibrium value. For stresses greater than the upper yield stress macroscopic yielding occurs, as shown by a sudden large increase in strain rate, after a certain amount of preyield microstrain.

Results similar to those shown in Figs. 1 and 2 have also been obtained at temperatures of $-23°F$ (243°K) and $+150°F$ (339°K). From these experimental results, values of the initial preyield microstrain rate have been determined. Figure 3 is a plot of the logarithm of the initial microstrain rate versus $1/\sigma T$. This shows that the experimental results at room temperature and $-23°F$ are in agreement with the form of relationship predicted by eq. 2. The experimental results at $+150°F$ exhibit a stress dependence in agreement with eq. 2 but the temperature dependence is evidently not in agreement with theory. These data were obtained by J. A. Hendrickson, and some older data due to T. Vreeland, Jr., are also included.

The slopes of the lines drawn to represent the experimental points in Fig. 3 may be compared with the theoretical slope according to eq. 2, namely $-2(\gamma_0{}^2/bk)f(\gamma/\gamma_0)/\sigma T$. In particular, if the line energy of a dislocation is taken to be $\gamma_0 = Gb^2/2$, this comparison between theory

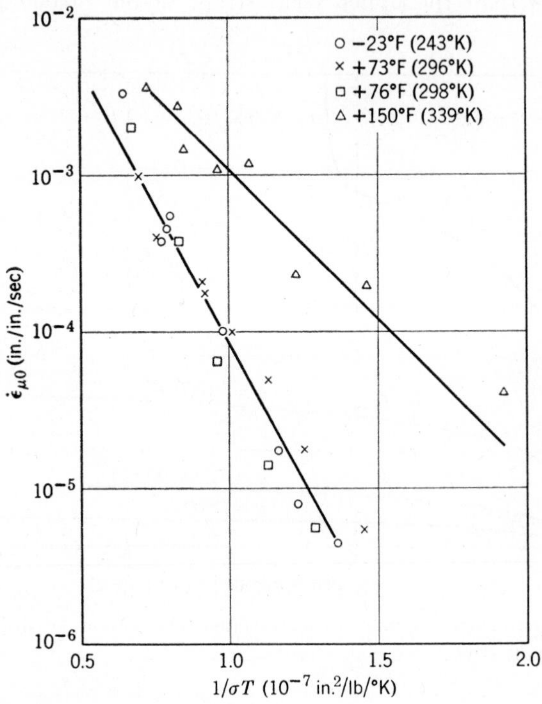

Fig. 3. Initial preyield microstrain rate versus reciprocal of the product of stress and temperature.

and experiment may be employed to obtain a value for the ratio of the binding energy of a dislocation with an atmosphere to the energy of a dislocation without an atmosphere, namely $(1 - \gamma/\gamma_0)$. When this is done the following results are obtained.

T (°K)	$(1 - \gamma/\gamma_0)$
243 and 296	0.0018
339	0.0012

These results are in considerable disagreement with theoretical [1] estimates of the binding energy between a dislocation and an atmosphere, which give values for the above energy ratio of about 0.1.

One suggestion which might lead to a resolution of this discrepancy is that the theory for the process of tearing a dislocation away from an atmosphere requires more detailed consideration than has been previously given. For example, a dislocation may happen to lie along a direction in the lattice which is at some small angle with lines connecting the sites at which the interstitial atoms can be located. In this case the closest interstitial atoms are located at various distances (up to about one-half the lattice parameter) in the slip direction on either side of the center of the dislocation, and only a fraction of them are located at the positions of maximum binding energy. The binding energy of an interstitial atom with the dislocations is quite sensitive to the distance from the center of the dislocation. Hence one might expect the activation energy for the release of a relatively long segment of the dislocation from its atmosphere to be considerably lower when the dislocation lies at an angle with respect to lines of interstitial sites than when it lies directly along such lines.

REFERENCES

1. A. H. Cottrell and B. A. Bilby, *Proc. Phys. Soc.* (*London*), *A*, **62,** Part 1, 49 (1949).
2. J. C. Fisher, *Trans. A.S.M.*, **47,** 451 (1955).

DISCUSSION

FISHER and COTTRELL asked if the disagreement with theoretical estimates of the binding energy might be due to an oversimplification of Cottrell's locking mechanism. WOOD answered that the calculations had not been made using the original formula due to Cottrell and Bilby for the breakaway, but the difference would probably not account for the indicated discrepancy, which amounts to about a factor of 50.

COTTRELL pointed out that the interaction energy which the theory predicts has been measured experimentally; for example, the vapor pressure of nitrogen atoms on a dislocation has been measured by Thomas and Leak * and confirms the theoretical value of the binding

* W. R. Thomas and G. M. Leak, *Proc. Phys. Soc.* (*London*), *B*, **68,** 1001 (1955).

energy. The line energy could not have been misjudged by a factor of 50, so the difficulty must be somewhere in eq. 1.

FISHER said that his theory gives very much the same temperature dependence of the yield stress as the Cottrell-Bilby theory. He added that he was very much bothered by the large discrepancy in binding energy. If the binding energy found by applying Fisher's formula was correct, dislocations would not be bound at all at room temperature. COTTRELL agreed that this was absurd because it is now known from other experiments that the binding energy agrees with the theoretical value.

WOOD commented that a difference in the mechanism by which an individual carbon atom is attracted to a dislocation and the mechanism by which a short segment of dislocation may tear away from an atmosphere might account for the discrepancy. COTTRELL said that this might be interpreted as an apparent reduction of γ_0. The initial configuration might be one in which the dislocation moved from one lattice row to another occasionally, so that in forming a smooth loop there would not be an appreciable increase in length of the dislocation line. COTTRELL said that if the binding energy is lower at places where the dislocation steps from one lattice row to the next, and if these steps are infrequent, the average binding energy would not be appreciably changed.

Yield Points in Al and Ni Single Crystals

C. S. BARRETT

Institute for the Study of Metals
University of Chicago
Chicago, Illinois

P. Haasen and A. Kelly have investigated the yield points that appear in Al and Ni upon reloading after prior plastic deformation and unloading.[1] The following is a brief report of their work.

The effect that is studied is shown in Fig. 1. The crystal is strained to point A on the stress-strain curve and the load is reduced. Upon reloading, the stress-strain curve temporarily rises above the extension of the previous flow curve by an amount $\Delta\sigma$. The stress increment, $\Delta\sigma$, was measured as a function of reduction in load during unloading, the temperature and duration of the aging, the testing temperature, and the stress at point A.

The behavior of Ni and Al single crystals, deformed in tension, is shown in Figs. 2 and 3. Figure 2 shows that the magnitude of the yield point in Ni is not very temperature-sensitive, but increases with stress. In Fig. 3 it is seen that the effect is slightly more temperature-sensitive in Al. The data in Figs. 2 and 3 were taken after aging at the same temperature at which the stress-strain curves were measured.

The findings of Haasen and Kelly can be listed as follows:

1. The yield point appears only if there has been previous plastic flow.

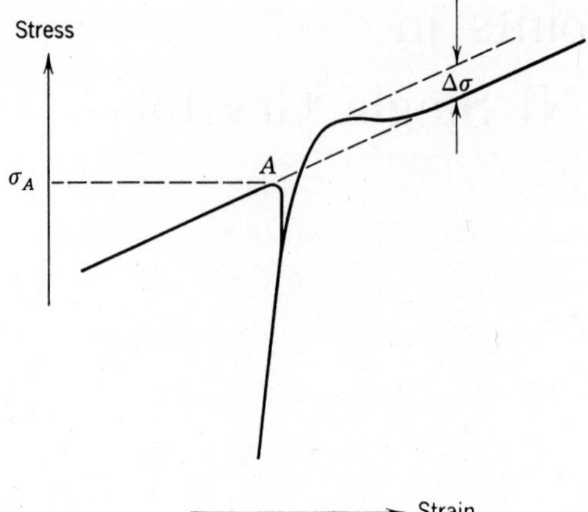

Fig. 1. Yield point effect during reloading following plastic flow and unloading.

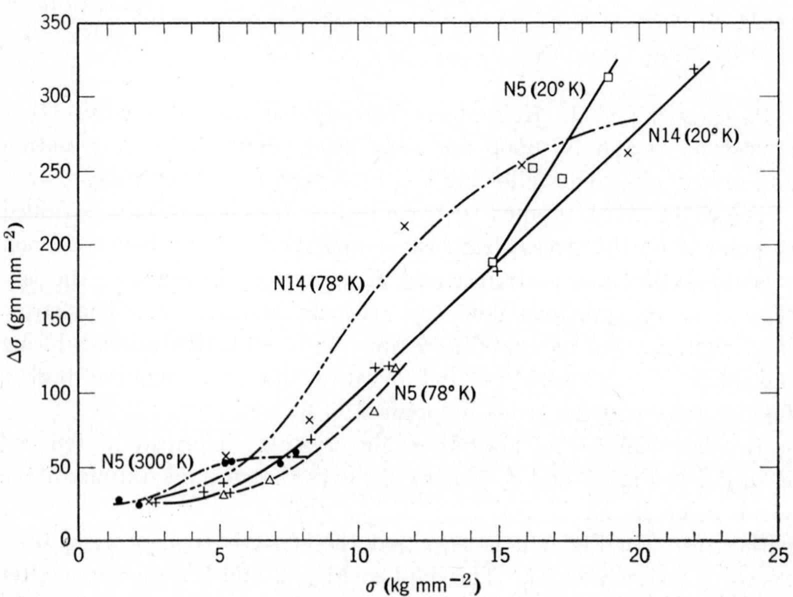

Fig. 2. Yield point effect, $\Delta\sigma$, versus stress prior to unloading, σ, for Ni single crystals.

2. The magnitude of the effect, $\Delta\sigma$, increases with the flow stress at the time of unloading.

3. The specimen must be subjected to a reduced load in order to show the effect.

4. $\Delta\sigma$ is increased by aging at temperature higher than the testing temperature.

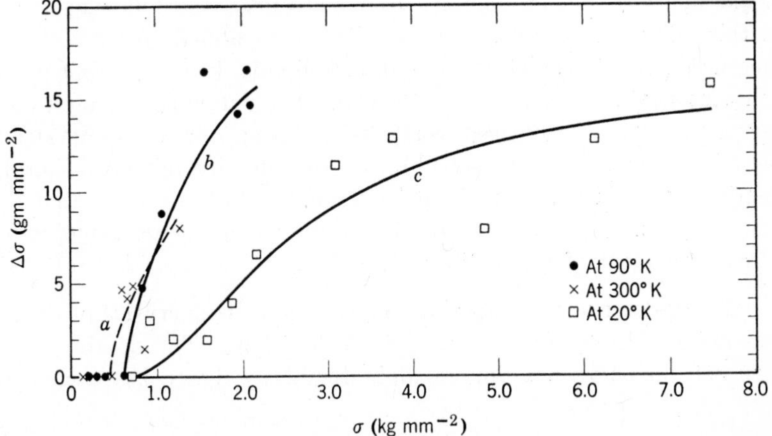

Fig. 3. Yield point effect, $\Delta\sigma$, versus stress prior to unloading, σ, for Al single crystals.

5. The effect is less marked at higher temperatures of testing, e.g., 300°K, but is relatively insensitive to temperature at low temperatures.

6. $\Delta\sigma$ appears to be independent of aging time for times greater than a few minutes at temperatures from 20°K to room temperature.

Haasen and Kelly concluded that the effect is not due to strain aging, particularly since it is independent of aging time at all temperatures down to 20°K. They suggested that the effect is due to a rearrangement of dislocations during unloading, which involves anchoring of the dislocations so that there is no extensive reverse plastic strain during unloading. The same process of anchoring is then responsible for the yield point effect on reloading.

REFERENCE

1. P. Haasen and A. Kelly, *Acta Met.*, **5,** 192 (1957).

DISCUSSION

LÜCKE referred to an experiment that is described in the paper by Lücke and Granato on damping by dislocations (the following paper in this volume), in which the damping of an aluminum crystal was measured while the crystal was deformed slightly, kept for a time under constant strain, unloaded, and reloaded. The damping increased during deformation, decreased completely during the constant strain period, and, when the load was released, the damping increased sharply nearly to the old value and then fell again. LÜCKE suggested that the very pronounced damping effects during the unloading are evidence for a rearrangement of dislocations.

BLEWITT described an experiment in which a single crystal of copper was deformed, unloaded, and reloaded at 4.2°K. The details of the stress-strain curve are illustrated in Fig. D1. There is a region of

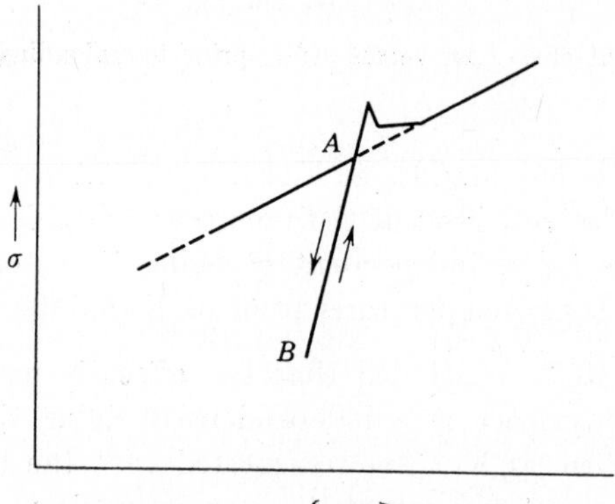

Fig. D1. Stress-strain curve of a copper single crystal which was deformed, unloaded at A, and reloaded at B at 4.2°K.

strain without work hardening after the yield point is passed and then the curve runs along an extrapolation of the stress-strain curve before unloading.

V DISLOCATION DAMPING AND FATIGUE

Internal Friction Phenomena Due to Dislocations*

KURT LÜCKE

ANDREW GRANATO

Department of Physics and Metals Research Laboratory
Brown University
Providence, Rhode Island

1. INTRODUCTION

T. A. Read[1] in 1940 first proposed that certain damping phenomena observed in metals could be attributed to the motion of dislocations. Since that time, a large body of experimental information concerning damping and modulus changes, presumably due to dislocations, has been accumulated.† The data show a rich variety in their dependence upon a great many parameters. This extraordinary sensitivity of damping measurements to dislocation behavior leads one to hope that an understanding of damping phenomena should substantially assist in the study of other dislocation effects. On the other hand, this rich variety of phenomena makes it difficult to recognize the underlying basic laws. Undoubtedly the development of this field has suffered on this account, especially since for a long time no guiding quantitative theories were available.

Recently, several theoretical models, which seem to be capable of describing at least certain aspects of the damping observed, have been proposed. Some of these theories supplement one another; some seem to contradict each other. In order to make progress in this situation

* Part of this paper was also presented at a conference on Ultrasonic Energy Losses in Crystalline Materials held at Brown University, Sept. 4, 5, 6, 1956.

† These data are partially reviewed by Nowick[2] and Granato and Lücke.[3]

it would be very much worthwhile to systematically compare all of the consequences of every proposed model with the available data. One should determine whether or not, or for what range of parameters, a given theory is in agreement with the data, and to what extent the experimental results are explained by the existing theories. However, this can only be partially done at present, since most of the theories have not yet been worked out far enough so that all of their consequences are evident.

A theory recently proposed by the writers [3,4] seems to be sufficiently developed to allow one to make such a detailed comparison. Other theories known to the authors are not developed to such an extent. In some of these, for example, the magnitude of the damping, in others, the dependence upon strain amplitude or temperature, is not worked out. Since, moreover, most of the measurements are in the range covered by the theory of the authors, the proposed detailed comparison between theory and experiment will be limited in this paper to those phenomena for which the theory of the authors should be applicable. Where other theories make predictions in the same range of data, the theories will be compared to the extent to which it is possible at the present time. To begin with, a general survey of the damping phenomena presumably due to dislocations will be given and the main theoretical ideas presented. A discussion of the state of affairs, both theoretical and experimental, in the field at the present time concludes the paper.

2. DAMPING PHENOMENA DUE TO DISLOCATIONS IN DIFFERENT FREQUENCY RANGES

Damping phenomena can be observed over a frequency range of 16 powers of ten.

A. 10^{-4} Cycles/Sec Range

Here the damping can be found by direct measurements of the stress-strain curves and the hysteresis loop. However, no systematic investigations of dislocation damping in this frequency range are known to the writers.

B. 1 Cycle/Sec Range

Most measurements in this range are made using the torsion pendulum technique described, e.g., in reference 2. Here investigations have been conducted in two different directions.

1. According to the work of Snoek [5] and Köster and collaborators,[6] a damping maximum in iron is observed at 200°C if carbon or nitrogen

is present and the metal has previously been plastically deformed. This effect is only very little understood at present.

2. Weinig and Machlin[7] measured the damping of different polycrystalline dilute copper alloys at different temperatures as a function

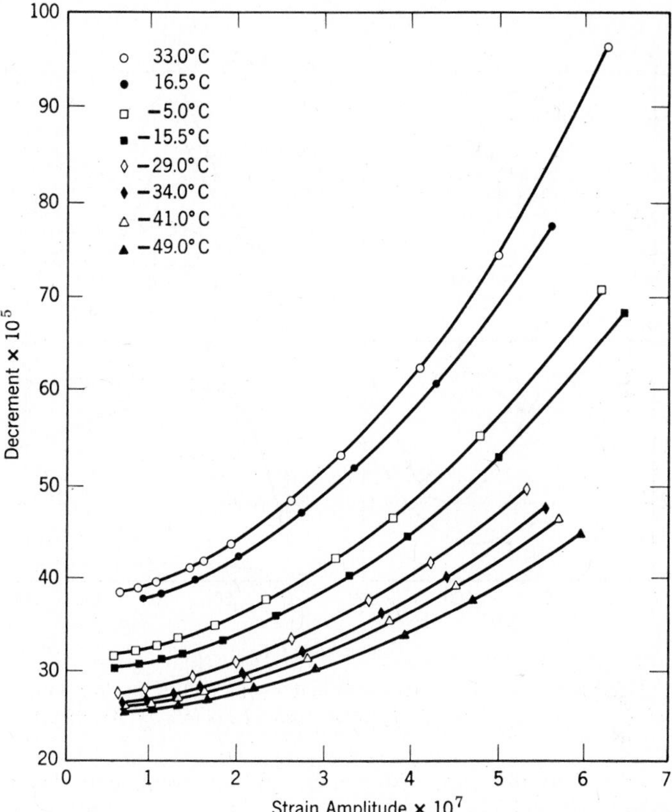

Fig. 1. Variation of the decrement with strain amplitude and temperature of a copper single crystal in the kilocycle range (Nowick[8]). (Courtesy *Physical Review.*)

of strain amplitude. They obtained curves of shape similar to those which are found in the kilocycle range (for instance, similar to those in Fig. 1).

C. 10^4 Cycles/Sec Range

Most of the presently available data for single and polycrystalline material has been obtained in this frequency range. Usually the composite oscillator technique, described, e.g., in reference 2, resulting in longitudinal vibrations near the resonant frequency of the specimen is used. Curves of the type shown in Figs. 1 and 6 with the strain amplitude as abscissa have been found. The logarithmic decrement can be thought of as being composed of two parts: one which increases with increasing strain amplitude and the residual part which remains

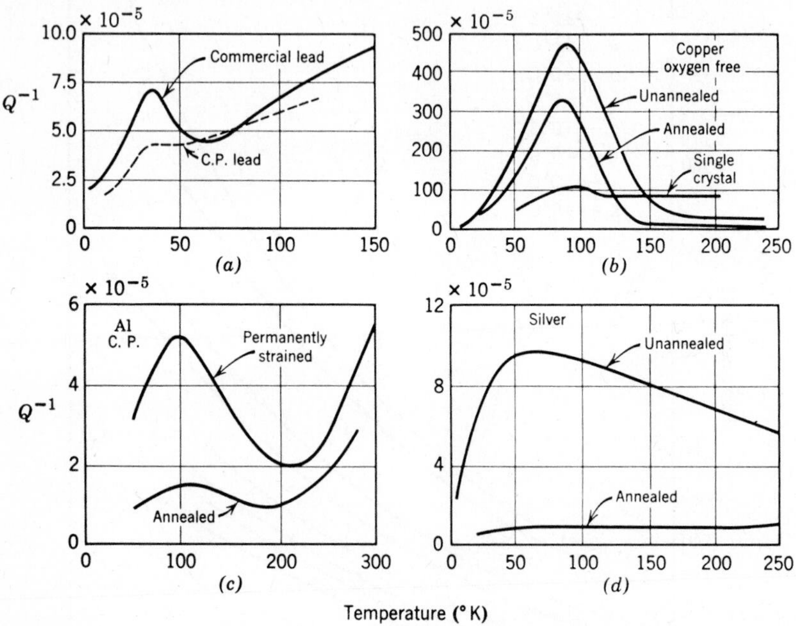

Fig. 2. Decrement of several face-centered cubic metals at low temperatures (Bordoni [9]). (Courtesy *Journal of the Acoustical Society of America.*)

at low strain amplitudes. Measurements of frequency dependence which are made by going to higher harmonics seem to be unreliable; for the same materials, there are examples of both increasing and decreasing decrements with increasing frequency. This point will be discussed later. The residual part normally increases with temperature. At low temperatures additional damping peaks, first found by Bordoni,[9] have been observed (Fig. 2). At higher temperatures also, peaks and irregularities are observed. These are, in contrast to the Bordoni peaks, often reported to be irreproducible.[10-12] Peaks for the residual decrement are found above room temperature in the range of 1 cycle/sec.[7]

D. 10^8 Cycles/Sec Range

In this frequency range the decay of the amplitude of pulses of traveling waves is usually measured. This technique is described in references 13 and 14. From the attenuation α of these waves one can obtain the decrement by means of the relation $\Delta = \alpha\lambda$, where λ is the wavelength of the wave. Normally the strain amplitudes which can be achieved are very low so that it is difficult to measure any amplitude

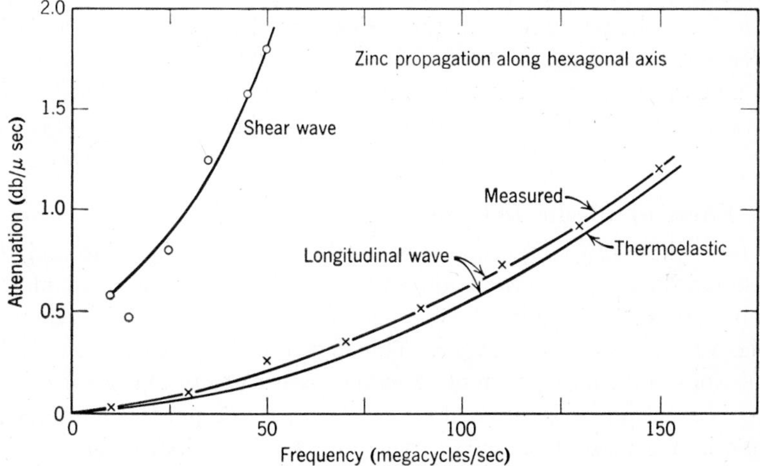

Fig. 3. Attenuation in a single crystal of zinc as a function of frequency in the megacycle range. The longitudinal wave measurements are more easily reproduced than are the shear wave measurements, which show much more scatter. (Measurements by Waterman,[15] theoretical thermoelastic curve by Lücke.[16])

dependence. However, it is relatively easy to measure frequency dependences with this method; Fig. 3 shows an example. The low-temperature Bordoni peaks have also been observed in this frequency range.[17,18]

E. 10^{12} Cycles/Sec Range

Here information about damping may be obtained by studying the thermal conductivity,* which will be reduced because of the interaction between thermal sound waves and dislocations. Such effects have not yet been well studied.

For reasons given in the introduction, only little or no attention will be given in the following to the damping peaks observed by Snoek,

* Information about the corresponding modulus changes may eventually be obtained from thermally diffused X-ray scattering measurements.

Köster and collaborators, and Bordoni. In addition to the damping (logarithmic decrement Δ), the corresponding change in elastic modulus ($\Delta E/E$) generally accompanying damping effects will be discussed.

3. THE EFFECT OF PLASTIC DEFORMATION, ORIENTATION, AND IMPURITIES

Internal friction phenomena described in the preceding section are claimed to be caused by dislocations. An exact proof of this is only possible by thorough quantitative comparison of the experimental results with the predictions of the dislocation theory. There are, however, some experimental results which supply extremely strong evidence of a qualitative type that the described phenomena are caused by dislocations. This evidence is connected with the effects of plastic deformation, orientation, and impurity content upon the damping.

A. Effect of Plastic Deformation

Both the strain-amplitude dependent part of the damping and the residual damping at low strain amplitude increase with small plastic deformation.[1,19] Figure 4 shows an example for the kilocycle and Fig. 5 for the megacycle range. This indicates the participation of dislocations in the mechanism of damping. According to Fig. 5, the damping is much more sensitive to small amounts of plastic deformation than is the stress-strain curve. One obtains large changes in damping even though the stress-strain curve does not yet show any deviations from the elastic straight line. This is understandable, since, in the stress-strain curve, the deformation due to motion of dislocations, "the dislocation strain," can only be detected if it is comparable to the elastic deformation, whereas with damping experiments the effects of the dislocations are observed directly.

With increasing deformation the damping often reaches a maximum[20] and decreases again. Also, one can decrease the damping, after plastic deformation by annealing. Such experiments will be discussed in more detail later. Finally, it should be mentioned that in the kilocycle range one can produce plastic deformation by the damping experiment itself if one uses very large strain amplitudes.[21] In these cases, the damping increases during the experiment and the decrement versus strain-amplitude curves become irreversible.

B. Effect of Orientation

The dependence of the damping phenomena upon the direction of the external stress has been studied most in zinc single crystals, presumably because zinc has only one slip plane, so that this effect should be especially pronounced. Alers [22] deformed zinc single crystals by pure shear parallel to the basal plane and propagated during the deformation an ultrasonic wave (7.8 megacycles/sec) of shear or longi-

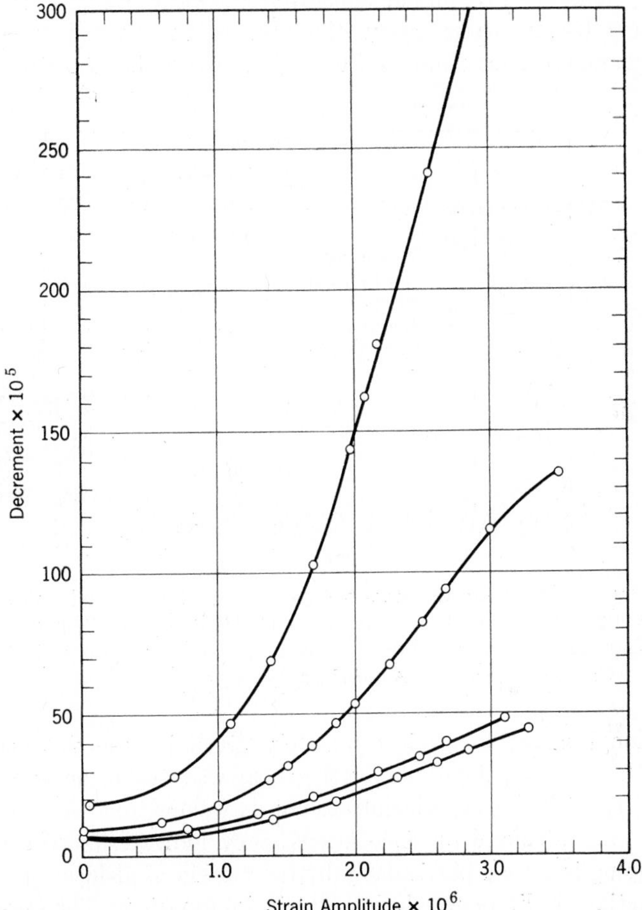

Fig. 4. Decrement as a function of strain amplitude and applied compressive stress (Read [1]). (Courtesy American Institute of Mining and Metallurgical Engineers.)

tudinal character perpendicular to the basal plane. He found that the attenuation of the shear wave increases with increasing deformation but the attenuation of the longitudinal wave remains practically unchanged. Since only the shear wave and not the longitudinal wave has a strong shear stress component in the slip plane, one can conclude that the dislocations created during the deformation are responsible for the increase of the attenuation of the shear wave.

The measurements by Waterman[15] plotted in Fig. 3 showing the attenuation of a longitudinal and shear wave in an undeformed single crystal of zinc lead to similar conclusions. One curve represents the theoretical thermoelastic attenuation due to the heat flow between wave hill and crest, according to Lücke.[16] One sees that the attenuation

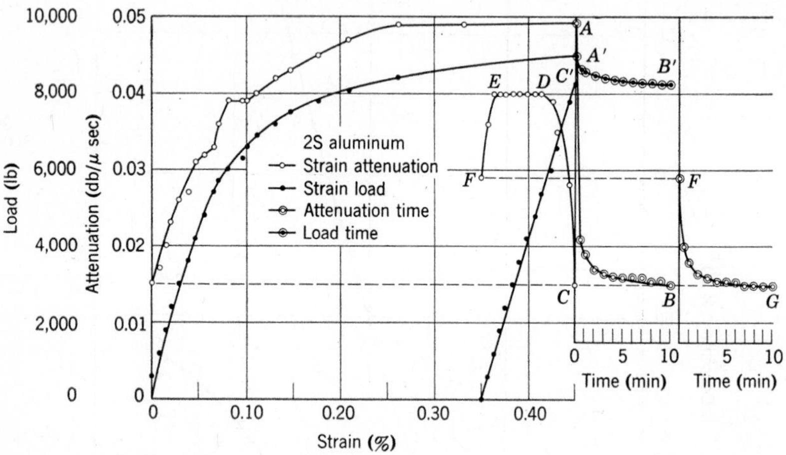

Fig. 5. Attenuation-strain and load-strain curves for loading and unloading of specimen of 2S aluminum. Time scales apply to AB, $A'B'$, and FG parts of curve representing load and attenuation relaxation or recovery with time (Hikata *et al.*[19]). (Courtesy *Journal of Applied Physics.*)

of the longitudinal waves is completely given by the thermoelastic effect, whereas the attenuation of the shear wave takes on very much higher values. These experiments do not only show that these damping phenomena are caused by dislocations; they indicate, moreover, that the damping is caused particularly by the motion of dislocations in the planes acting as slip planes during plastic deformation. The same conclusions are valid for the strain-amplitude dependent part of the damping in the kilocycle region, as will be shown later.

C. Effect of Impurities

Impurities generally decrease the damping. This is usually interpreted as an inhibition of dislocation motion by impurities. In Fig. 6 an example for measurements on polycrystalline copper[23] in the kilocycle range is given. The residual damping decreases with increasing amounts of the foreign element. However, it seems to reach a limit value which cannot be lowered by further addition of impurities. This is found also in other measurements in the kilocycle range [11] and also in the range of 1 cycle/sec.[7] Also, the strain-amplitude dependent part

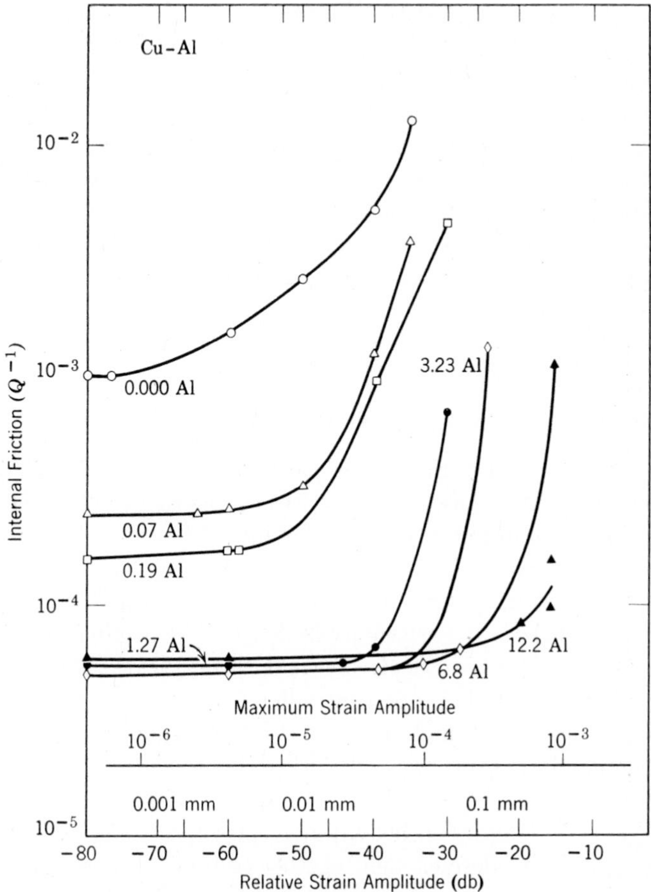

Fig. 6. Decrement of polycrystalline copper as a function of strain amplitude and added concentrations of aluminum (Takahashi [23]).

of the damping is decreased by impurities. They flatten out the damping versus strain-amplitude curves for small strain amplitudes. There seem to be some indications that the effect of impurities is largest when they are in solid solution and that by precipitation or internal oxidation the damping can be increased.[24,25] But no systematic measurements are available. Similarly, other point imperfections, i.e., vacancies, seem to produce a decrease in damping.[26,27]

4. THEORIES OF DISLOCATION DAMPING

All models discussed so far attribute the dislocation damping to the vibration of dislocations,* caused by the periodic external shear stresses. If the dislocations could move freely, these vibrations would lead, because of the fact that dislocation motion is damped, to energy losses very much larger than those observed.[4] The dislocation motion must therefore be restricted and the various theories of damping are only differentiated by different assumptions about the nature of the restrictions, and eventually about the mechanism of overcoming them. The situation in the theory of damping is similar to that in the theory of the yield point. There one has to explain why dislocations cannot move before a certain stress is reached. In both fields, essentially the same restrictions have been proposed. These are:

1. Peierls hills.
2. Other dislocations.
3. Foreign atoms.
4. Nodes of the dislocation network.

The restriction by Peierls hills is used to explain the Bordoni peaks by assuming that dislocations lying nearly parallel to the Peierls valleys throw loops over the Peierls hills into the next valley under the influence of the external shear stresses with the help of thermal fluctuations. The first treatment of this process by Mason[29] was criticized by different authors,[30-32] especially by Seeger,[31] who gave what is probably a more correct treatment. Seeger's theory, which is not yet completely worked out, does not contradict any of the other theories of damping, since it only makes use of the small fraction of dislocations which lie nearly parallel to the Peierls valleys.

The interaction of dislocations with each other seems to play an important role in damping in heavily deformed materials. Here dislocations may even be close enough together so that they are immobilized. In this way the decrease of damping with increasing deformation after the maximum[20] may be explained. There is, however, at present no satisfying quantitative theory of damping in heavily deformed materials, since the theory of Weertman and Koehler,[20] the only one published so far, is based on a questionable arrangement of dislocations.

One possibility of interaction between dislocations and foreign atoms is that the foreign atoms follow the vibrating dislocations by diffusion, causing a phase lag between the stress and dislocation motion and

* Only in the case of thermal frequencies has the scattering of the sound waves by the static stress field of dislocations been studied.[28]

therefore also a damping. This can happen, however, only at low frequencies or at high temperatures. No thorough investigation of this possibility has been made. Perhaps the effect of Snoek and Köster described earlier is caused by such a microcreep phenomenon.

A theory proposed by Koehler [33] assumes that dislocations are pinned by foreign atoms. The loops between pinning points vibrate under the influence of the external shear stress and the energy loss results from damping of the dislocation motion. Furthermore, it is assumed that at larger strain amplitudes the dislocations can break away from the impurity atoms. This model forms the basis of a more extended theory developed by the authors [4] which will be discussed later.

A theory by Weertman and Salkovitz [10] makes use of impurities in quite a different way. This theory is based upon the Mott-Nabarro theory [34] of dislocation motion in solid solution. Foreign atoms cause a stress field with wavelength $\lambda = a/c^{1/3}$, where a is the atomic spacing and c is the concentration of foreign atoms. The average height of these barriers is the Mott-Nabarro yield strength σ_M. For stresses much smaller than σ_M, dislocation loops are able to overcome the smallest of these barriers moving over a distance $\approx\lambda$ to a new equilibrium position. Under oscillating stresses a hysteresis will be obtained, leading to the formula *

$$\Delta = \Delta E/E \approx 10^{-2}\Lambda a^2/(c\eta)^{4/3} \tag{1}$$

This is considered by Weertman and Salkovitz [10] to be the residual damping.

A comparison with the experimental data seems to lead, however, to some difficulties. For example, the authors found that by assuming a dislocation density of 10^8 cm^{-2}, they could account for the measured range of the decrement (8×10^{-3} to 1.5×10^{-5}). In order to overcome certain other difficulties, the authors more recently [10] found it necessary to use dislocation densities of about 10^6 cm^{-2}, so that eq. 1 now appears to give too small values for the magnitude of the damping. Also, as will be discussed in § 7.A and B, experimental values indicate that $\Delta \ll E/E$ and $\Delta \propto 1/c^4$, in contrast with eq. 1. These difficulties show clearly that the theory cannot have general validity. On the other hand, the theory shows features which make it probable that a theory of this kind may be valid in a certain not yet exactly known range of parameters. The

* This is an approximation to the expression

$$\frac{2 \times 10^{-2}\Lambda a^2(2\pi)^{1/3}}{\eta^{4/3}c^{14/9}(\ln 1/c)^{4/3}}$$

given by Weertman and Salkovitz.

theory describes the interaction of impurities with dislocations in a non-pinned state and results in a frequency-independent loss (see § 7).

5. PINNED DISLOCATION MODEL

Based upon Koehler's idea [33] that the motion of a dislocation under an oscillating stress can be considered to be analogous to the motion of a damped vibrating string, the writers [4] developed the following model. It is assumed that the dislocations are pinned by the nodes of

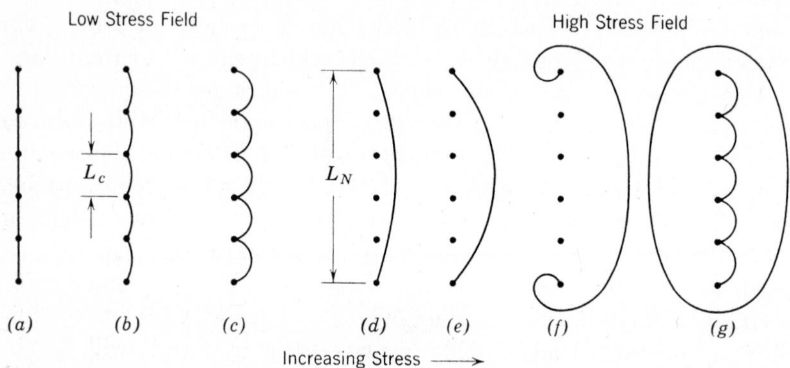

Fig. 7. The successive drawings indicate schematically the bowing out of a pinned dislocation line by an increasing applied stress. The length of loop determined by impurity pinning is denoted by L_c, and that determined by the network by L_N. As the stress increases, the loops L_c bow out until breakaway occurs. For very large stresses, the dislocations multiply according to the Frank-Read mechanism (Ref. 4). (Courtesy *Journal of Applied Physics.*)

the dislocation network and by impurities. The average length of a dislocation loop between two network points is called L_N and that between two impurity atoms L_c (Fig. 7). In general, the concentration c of impurity atoms on the dislocation line is larger than the over-all concentration c_0 of impurities in the lattice. At temperatures high enough for diffusion to take place, the concentration can attain an equilibrium value according to

$$a/L_c = c = c_0 \exp (Q/kT) \tag{2}$$

where Q is Cottrell's [35] interaction energy between a dislocation and impurity atom. The average length of loop (L) which vibrates under an applied alternating stress is given by

$$1/L = 1/L_N + 1/L_c \tag{3}$$

There are now two types of loss which result.

A. The Dynamic Loss

The first loss is due to the fact that the motion of the dislocation is opposed by some damping mechanism, so that there is a phase lag between its displacement and the applied stress. This loss is frequency-dependent, since it has a resonance-type character. For low frequencies, the motion can follow the applied stress, and the decrement is small. Near the resonant frequency determined by the loop length the motion is out of phase with the applied stress by 90° and the decrement is a maximum. The logarithmic decrement and the modulus change are given according to Granato and Lücke [3] by

$$\Delta_I = \pi\Omega\Lambda \frac{C}{A} \frac{\omega d}{[(\omega_0{}^2 - \omega^2)^2 + (\omega d)^2]} \tag{4}$$

and

$$\left(\frac{\Delta E}{E}\right)_I = \Omega\Lambda \frac{C}{A} \frac{(\omega_0{}^2 - \omega^2)}{[(\omega_0{}^2 - \omega^2)^2 + (\omega d)^2]} \tag{5}$$

where the subscript I is used to distinguish these quantities from those which depend on the amplitude of the applied stress. Ω is an orientation factor taking into account the fact that the resolved shear stress on the slip planes is less than the applied longitudinal stress. Λ is the dislocation density, $C \approx Gb^2$ is the tension of the dislocation line, and $A = \pi\rho b^2$ is the effective mass per unit length, where ρ is the density. The frequency is ω, $d = B/A$, where B is the damping constant of a moving dislocation, and ω_0 is the resonant frequency of the dislocation loop given by $\omega_0 = \pi C^{1/2}/A^{1/2}Lt_1{}^{1/4}$, where t_1 is a numerical factor defined later. Equation 4 has a maximum at $\omega_0{}^2/d$ for large damping. Using estimated values of the constants, a maximum damping of this type would be expected in the megacycle range.

For frequencies much less than that for which the decrement is a maximum, eqs. 4 and 5 become

$$\Delta_I = \frac{\Omega\Lambda L^4 B\omega t_1}{\pi^3 C} \tag{6}$$

and

$$\left(\frac{\Delta E}{E}\right)_I = \frac{\Omega\Lambda L^2 t_2}{\pi^2} \tag{7}$$

where t_1 and t_2 are factors which depend on the distribution of loop lengths assumed. For a delta function distribution t_1 and t_2 are both unity. For an exponential distribution of loop lengths, which is obtained if the pinning points are distributed randomly over the dislocation line, t_1 and t_2 take on the values 120 and 6 respectively. Expressions 6 and 7 are in agreement with the first term of a development found by Koehler.[33] However, the higher order terms in Koehler's development indicate that the decrement eventually increases more rapidly than with the first power of the frequency, whereas from eq. 4 it can be seen that the decrement may increase less rapidly than linearly with frequency at high frequencies.

B. The Static Hysteresis Loss

A loss of a different nature occurs in this model if stresses are applied which are large enough to break the dislocation away from its pinning points. If $\mathcal{L}$ is the length of two adjacent loops, then break-

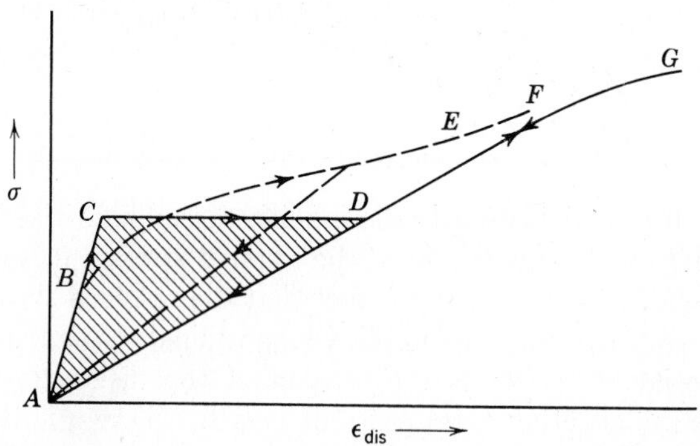

Fig. 8. The solid line shows the stress-strain law that results for the model shown in Fig. 7. The elastic strain has been subtracted out so that only the dislocation strain is shown. The path *ABCDEF* is followed for increasing stress; the path *FA* is followed for decreasing stress. The dashed line is that which would result if not all of the loops had the same length, but there was a distribution of lengths L_c (ref. 4). (Courtesy *Journal of Applied Physics.*)

away will occur when $\sigma \approx Q/b^2 \mathcal{L}$, where σ is the applied stress and Q is the Cottrell interaction energy. This process is schematically illustrated in Fig. 7. For small applied stresses, the loops L_c bow out until the breakaway stress is reached. There is then a large increase in the dislocation strain (Fig. 8) for no increase in the applied stress. When the stress is reversed, the loops L_N contract so that a different path is followed in the stress-strain diagram for increasing and decreasing applied stress. This gives a hysteresis loss which is measured by the area in the stress-strain diagram (Fig. 8). This loss is frequency-independent for frequencies much less than that for which Δ_I is a maximum. If there is a distribution of loop lengths L_c, then the longest loops break away first, giving a smoothly increasing decrement with increasing strain amplitude. (A corresponding hysteresis loop is shown by the dashed line in Fig. 8.) The breakaway event is catastropic in that whenever a loop breaks away within a network length L_N, the entire network breaks away.

Thus the model provides two types of loss, one strain-amplitude dependent and the other not; both of these should be observable. The way in which these losses would appear depends sensitively upon the concentration of pinning points on the dislocation line. There are several cases to consider.

1. $L_c \gg L_N$. This should be the case for super purity materials. Here, according to eq. 3, $L = L_N$ and the strain-amplitude independent decrement should be relatively large. No amplitude dependence should occur until plastic deformation begins; i.e., until new dislocation loops are created.

2. $L_c \approx a$, where a is the lattice spacing. This is the case of complete pinning. There should be no Δ_I in this case and breakaway should occur at the yield stress. There may, however, be other sources of damping which give rise to a background; this will be discussed in more detail later.

3. $L_N \gg L_c \gg a$. This is the range for which most of the measurements have been made so far. Within this range there should be a small region where for Δ_I the fourth power law should be valid. This region will be small because of the sensitivity of Δ_I to the loop length L. For example, if the loop length decreases by a factor of 3, the decrement should decrease by a factor of 81 so that the final value will be down in the background. The strain-amplitude dependence of the decrement has been derived for this range assuming a random distribution of pinning points and may be written as

$$\Delta_H = \frac{\Omega \Lambda L_N^3}{\pi^2 L_c} \frac{K\eta a}{L_c \epsilon_0} \exp\left(\frac{-K\eta a}{L_c \epsilon_0}\right)^* \tag{8}$$

In this expression ϵ_0 is the strain amplitude, η is Cottrell's misfit parameter, and K is an orientation-dependent factor connected with the stress needed for breakaway.† A modulus change $\Delta E/E$ of the same magnitude as Δ_H is also found from this model. The types of curves, then,

* At higher frequencies, the expression for Δ_H must be multiplied by the factor $1 + \pi\omega d/\omega_{0N}^2$, and that for $(\Delta E/E)_H$ by $1 + \pi\omega d L_c^5/\omega_{0N}^2 L_N^5$, where ω_{0N} is the resonant frequency of the network lengths.

† If the breakaway occurs according to Cottrell's formula, K would be expected to be $G/4RE$ for an isotropic material, where E is Young's modulus and R the resolved shear stress factor.

that would be expected from the model as a function of concentration of pinning points are shown schematically in Figs. 9 and 10.

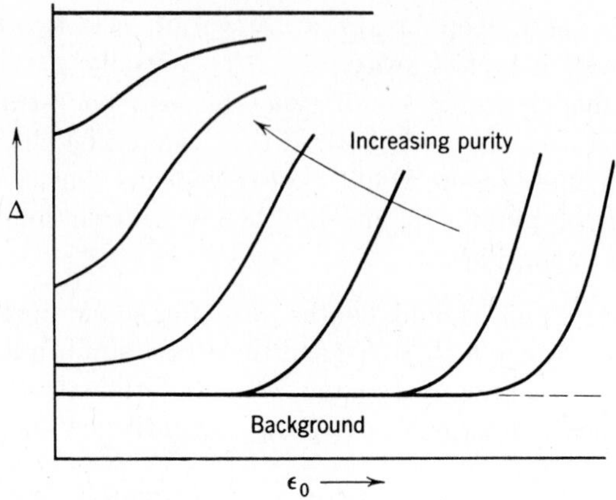

Fig. 9. Schematic drawing of expected decrement as a function of strain amplitude and impurity concentration.

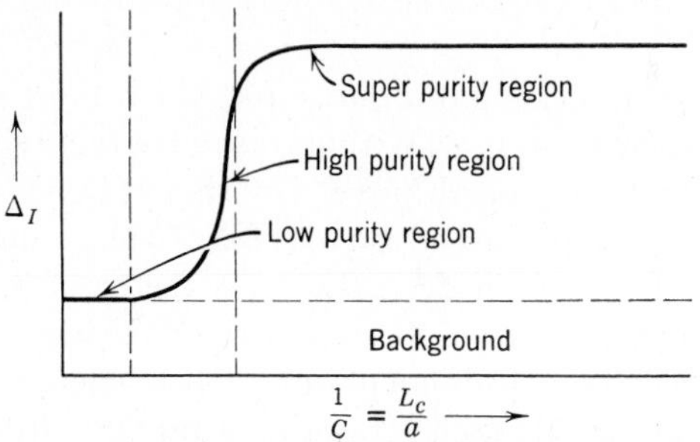

Fig. 10. Schematic drawing of the expected residual decrement as a function of the reciprocal of the concentration of impurities in the specimen.

6. STRAIN-AMPLITUDE DEPENDENT DAMPING

According to relation 8, log $\Delta_H \epsilon_0$ should be a linear function of $1/\epsilon_0$. Much of the available data was replotted in this way by the authors. The relation was found to be surprisingly successful, although deviations from straight lines often appeared for very pure materials. The reasons for the deviations are not at present understood completely. This method of plotting separates the influence of the dislocation density and the loop lengths, as the slope of such a line should be proportional to the concentration of pinning points, and the intercept to the dislocation density. The fact that this relation seemed to be satisfied for a very wide range of conditions and specimens is considered to be strong evidence for the validity of the assumed mechanism in this range.

There are, unfortunately, no experiments for which all the parameters required by the theory are reported or varied systematically. However, there are many experiments for which only one or two parameters are varied, and the results of these may be examined.

A. Concentration (c)

Weertman and Salkovitz [10] measured the strain-amplitude dependence of the damping of lead single crystals with varying concentrations of bismuth. The results for concentrations of 0.035, 0.053, and 0.65 at.

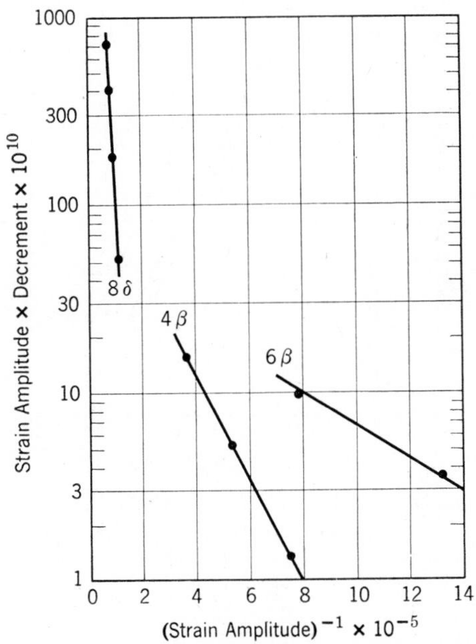

Fig. 11. The data of Weertman and Salkovitz are here plotted for lead with three different concentrations of added bismuth impurity. According to the theory, the points should lie on straight lines whose slopes are proportional to the concentration of impurity on the dislocation line. The deliberately added concentrations of bismuth in the specimens as given by Weertman and Salkovitz are 0.035, 0.053, and 0.65 at. % for samples 6β, 4β, and 8δ respectively (ref. 3). (Courtesy *Journal of Applied Physics*.)

% of bismuth are shown in Fig. 11. According to the theory, the slopes of the curves should be proportional to the concentrations of impurities on the dislocation line. Good agreement was also found by Beshers [11] for results of gold in copper.

B. Dislocation Density (Λ)

With a similar analysis of the measurements of Read [1] for a copper single crystal which has been lightly compressed, the results shown in Fig. 12 are found. Here the lines are parallel but the intercepts increase with cold work as would be expected since the intercepts should

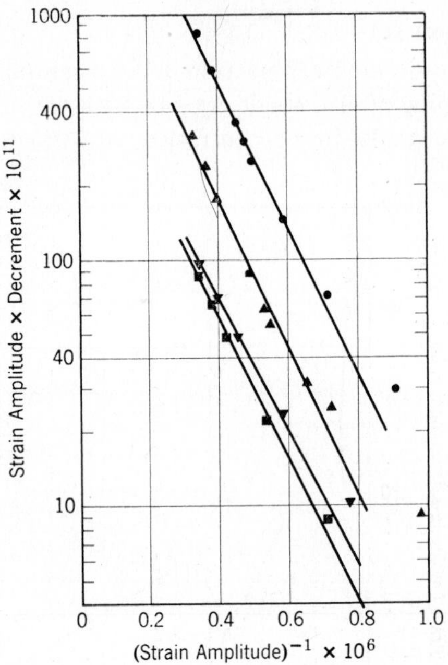

Fig. 12. Measurements made by T. A. Read of the decrement of 99.998% pure copper single crystal after applied compressive loads of 0, 60, 120, and 150 psi are here plotted by the method of the present theory. The lowest curve is that for no applied stress, and the higher curves correspond to the successively larger loads. According to the theory, it would be expected in this case that the slopes of the successive curves would not change much, but that the intercepts which are proportional to the dislocation density would increase (ref. 3). (Courtesy *Journal of Applied Physics.*)

be proportional to the dislocation density. In Fig. 13 the dislocation densities derived from Fig. 12 are plotted as a function of the applied load. It should be noticed that the derived dislocation density increases very quickly even for loads below the yield stress, which for copper of this purity should be about 210 psi.[36] This is an example of the higher degree of sensitivity to deformation that damping has over stress-strain measurements mentioned earlier.

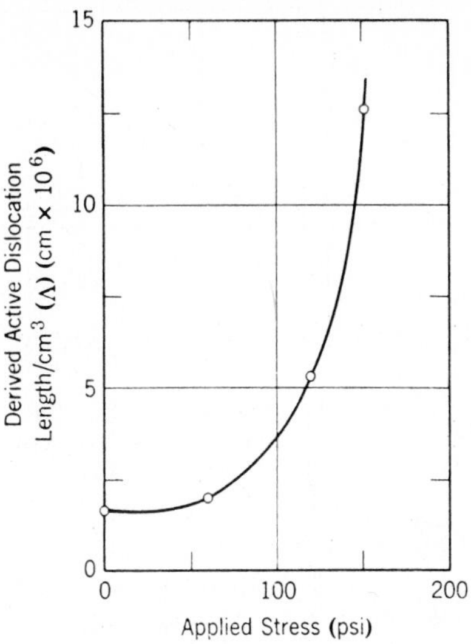

Fig. 13. Here the dislocation densities derived from Fig. 12 are plotted as a function of the applied load. The derived dislocation density increases very rapidly before any measurable strain occurs (ref. 3). (Courtesy *Journal of Applied Physics.*)

C. Temperature (T)

The only factor which should be temperature-sensitive in expression 8 is the loop length L_c, since $L_c = a/c$ and c may be determined by the Cottrell relation 2. Accordingly, one should expect that the slopes found in this analysis when plotted against $1/T$ should give a straight line at temperatures high enough so that equilibrium is established. The results of Weertman and Salkovitz for dilute PbSn alloys are shown in Fig. 14. A thermally activated process does seem to be indicated. The measured activation energy from the curve is 0.11 ev. The Cottrell interaction energy as calculated by Weertman and Salkovitz is 0.044 ev.

D. Orientation Dependence (θ)

Orientation dependences of the strain-amplitude data can be checked in both the slopes and intercepts of the log $\Delta_H\epsilon_0$ versus $1/\epsilon_0$ *plots*. The slopes should be inversely proportional to the resolved shear stress factor times the Young's modulus for a given orientation. This check is shown in Fig. 15 for measurements on zinc by Read.[1] The agreement is considered to be quite satisfactory, especially since some varia-

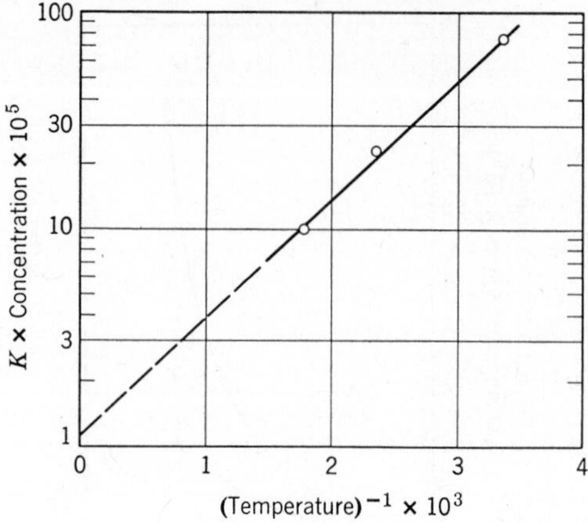

Fig. 14. The slopes of the lines found by plotting the strain-amplitude dependent decrement in this manner should be proportional to the concentration of pinning points on the dislocation line. If the pinning is of the Cottrell type, then a plot of the logarithm of the derived slopes against the inverse temperature should give a straight line. The points used here are derived from the data of Weertman and Salkovitz taken on a single crystal of lead with 0.058% tin (ref. 3). (Courtesy *Journal of Applied Physics.*)

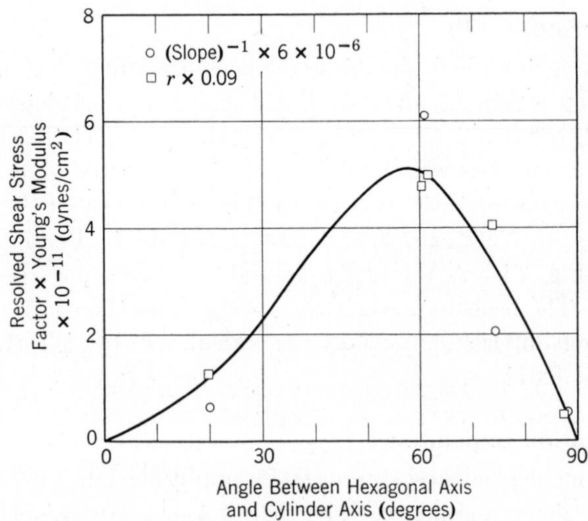

Fig. 15. The solid curve shows the dependence of the product of the resolved shear stress factor and the Young's modulus of zinc as a function of angle. The slopes found by the method of the present theory when applied to the data of T. A. Read are shown by circled points, and the ratios of the decrement to the modulus change are shown by the squares (ref. 3). (Courtesy *Journal of Applied Physics.*)

tion in the concentration of impurity from specimen to specimen could be expected. The derived intercept values are less accurate, but agreement is also obtained for this check.[3]

E. Time Dependence (t)

If the concentration of point imperfections along the dislocation line is not in equilibrium, the decrement could be expected to be time-dependent. In a certain temperature range which is just below that for which equilibrium is obtained very quickly and just above that for which diffusion is too slow to obtain equilibrium, this should be observable. The concentration should vary with time according to the law of Cottrell and Bilby,[37] i.e., $c \propto t^{2/3}$. This means that we should expect a straight-line relationship between $\log \Delta_H$ and $t^{2/3}$. An example of this type of effect seems to be provided by the data of Beshers on copper (Fig. 16). Another example is provided by recovery measurements, which are discussed in § 7.C. Also here one finds $\log \Delta_H \propto t^{2/3}$ (see Fig. 17).

It should be mentioned, that in all of the above, the derived values of the dislocation density and loop length appear to be reasonable. In addition, it is often reported that the ratio

$$r = \Delta_H/(\Delta E/E)_H$$

is a constant of order unity. This fact is also in accord with the theory.

7. RESIDUAL DAMPING AT LOW STRAIN AMPLITUDES

There are at present many difficulties both experimentally and theoretically in the interpretation of the residual loss which remains at low strain amplitudes. For reasons to be discussed, it has been difficult to obtain laws relating the loss to measurable parameters. It has therefore not been possible to say with any definiteness whether or not, or in what range, proposed theories describe available data. Because the pinned dislocation model has met with some success in the description of the amplitude dependent loss, the available data will be examined to determine to what extent the loss predicted by this theory contributes to the measured residual loss.

There is immediate evidence that at least part of the observed residual damping cannot be described as a dynamic loss according to eq. 4 or 6. This loss would be completely suppressed by adding enough impurities. Beshers,[11] however, found that by addition of gold to copper, the damping in the kilocycle region does not decrease below a value of about 10^{-4}. Similar results are also found in the range of 1 cycle/sec.[7] This "background," which is still much higher than

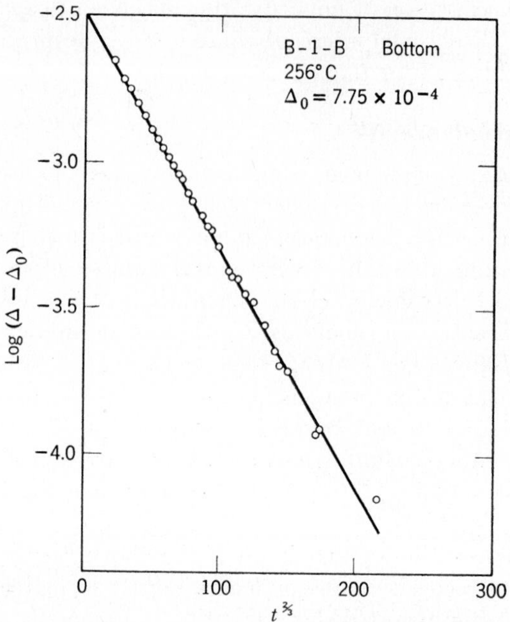

Fig. 16. Measurements of the decrement of a copper single crystal in the strain-amplitude dependent region as a function of $t^{2/3}$, where t is the time of measurement (Beshers[11]).

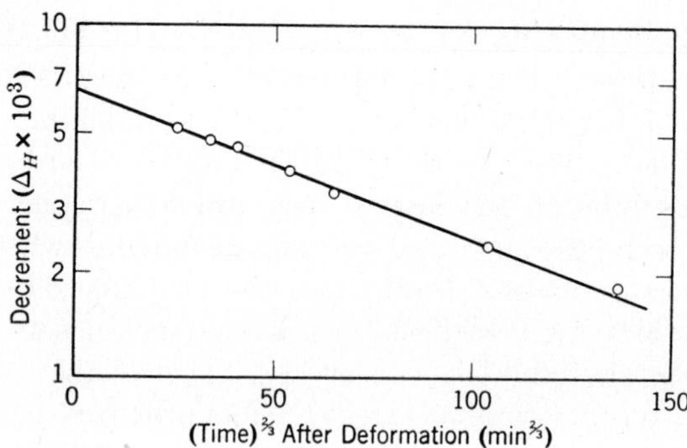

Fig. 17. The logarithm of the amplitude dependent decrement (which should be linearly related to the concentration of pinning points) is shown as a function of $t^{2/3}$, where t is the time after deformation. The points shown on the curve are not data points, but are computed from the curve of Gordon and Nowick for measurements on NaCl (ref. 25).

the minimum damping measurable in the apparatus, will not be considered in this section.

According to eq. 4 the amplitude independent decrement should be frequency-dependent, having a maximum at ω_0 for small damping or at the lower frequency $\omega_0^2 A/B$ for large damping. For a loop length L of 10^{-4} cm, the resonant frequency $f_0 = \omega_0/2\pi$ would be about 500 megacycles/sec for many materials of interest and would be higher in inverse proportion to the loop length for smaller loop lengths. The frequency for which the decrement is a maximum may be smaller if the damping constant B is large enough. The damping experienced by a dislocation moving through a lattice has been estimated by several authors for several different mechanisms.[38-42] The largest value for ultrasonic measurements seems to be that given by a formula of Leibfried,[38] which has been reinterpreted by Nabarro,[39] concerning the loss associated with the interaction of a moving dislocation with thermally excited sound waves.* This value of B, which is proportional to temperature, is about 10^{-4} in cgs units for most metals at room temperature.[3] For the values $B = 10^{-4}$ and $L = 10^{-4}$ cm, a maximum of the decrement would be expected at about 150 megacycles/sec.

A. Frequency Dependence (ω)

Frequency dependences can be determined by the methods used in the megacycle region when the various losses which contribute to the attenuation can be separated and when the measurements are accurate enough over a sufficiently wide frequency range. To date this has been possible for the dislocation damping in single crystals of germanium †[44] and for the thermoelastic damping in zinc (Fig. 3). For germanium, one finds a decrement which is for many samples close to linear in frequency in agreement with eq. 6 to as high as 300 megacycles/sec. In some cases Δ_I is slightly less than linear, which may indicate that the maximum mentioned earlier is being approached.

* Of special interest perhaps is also the radiation loss for an oscillating dislocation. Eshelby's results[40] imply that about one-eighth of the maximum kinetic energy attained by a screw dislocation is radiated away in one cycle of oscillation. This does not lead necessarily to a large damping in ultrasonic experiments, however, since for a forced vibration at low frequencies the maximum kinetic energy is much smaller than the maximum potential energy so that only a small fraction of the total maximum energy of the dislocation is lost. For an edge dislocation, this loss is an order of magnitude larger than for a screw dislocation.[43] Thus, an edge dislocation may be overdamped near its resonance frequency.

† Evidence that the loss is due to dislocations is supplied by the fact that diffusion of copper into germanium reduces the damping.[45]

The results can be accounted for by assuming values of $5 \times 10^4 < \Lambda < 5 \times 10^6$ cm^{-2} * and $L = 0.9 \times 10^{-4}$ cm, for the dislocation density and loop lengths respectively. Etch-pit counts on two of the specimens measured were 3×10^5 and 3×10^4 cm^{-2}. The value of the damping constant B found in this way is in surprisingly good agreement with the Leibfried-Nabarro value.[38,39] A further indication for the validity of eq. 6 is found for polycrystalline aluminum. The additional damping and modulus change due to plastic deformation have been measured at 5 and at 10 megacycles/sec.[46] It was found that the modulus change was the same for both frequencies but the increase in decrement was higher by a factor of two for the specimen measured of 10 megacycles/sec, as would be predicted by eqs. 6 and 7.

Although the loss in the megacycle region seems to have the expected frequency dependence, there is some evidence that the loss at lower frequency is frequency-independent. To measure the frequency dependence in the kilocycle region, higher harmonic standing waves have to be used. Results for the same materials show both increasing and decreasing values of the decrement with frequency.† Nonetheless, it is felt by many [26,47] that this unreliability is not large enough to hide a linear dependence on frequency. A further contribution to this unreliability which seems not to have been noticed so far is that the orientation factor can decrease with frequency.‡ The measured frequency dependence should therefore be less than linear.

A related question is that of the value found experimentally for the ratio r of the decrement to the modulus change. In contrast to the value of r of about unity found for the amplitude dependent quantities, values at least an order of magnitude smaller have been found for

* The value needed depends on the type of distribution of loop lengths assumed. The lower figure would be appropriate for an exponential and the higher for a delta function distribution.

† As has been pointed out by Nowick,[8] this may be due to the structure sensitivity of the measurements, since at different harmonics different parts of the specimen are excited.

‡ This arises as follows. The orientation factor takes into account the fact that the resolved shear stress on the slip planes is less than the applied stress. At low frequencies, an applied longitudinal stress leads to a longitudinal strain and lateral contraction with no lateral stresses. For high frequency, the lateral strains do not occur so there are lateral stresses. The lateral stresses have the effect of reducing the resolved shear stresses on the slip planes, so that the orientation factor is smaller at the higher frequencies. It is difficult to describe the transition region, but it should start to occur when the ratio of the specimen diameter to the wavelength is no longer negligible. For the case of a lead single crystal oriented in the [100] direction, the orientation factor can decrease in this way by more than a factor of ten.[48]

the residual quantities.[26,27,33] This is an order of magnitude that would be in agreement with eqs. 6 and 7 in the kilocycle range for pure materials.

The measurements of Weinig and Machlin[7] in the frequency range of 1 cycle/sec show residual losses of the same order of magnitude as those found in the kilocycle range. This is again evidence that the loss may be frequency-independent. On the other hand, it is not certain that the mechanism of loss at 1 cycle/sec is the same as that at 10 kc/sec. For example, the temperature dependence of the 1 cycle/sec polycrystalline loss seems to be rather different from that of single crystals in the kilocycle range.

Finally, if one extrapolates kilocycle results into the megacycle range, one obtains values for pure metals rather large compared to those usually found. But there have as yet been no measurements in the megacycle range on very pure metals (except Ge).* The results in the kilocycle region indicate, moreover, that for very pure metals a damping maximum should be found in the low megacycle region. Measurements made at both kilocycle and megacycle frequencies on the same specimen would be most desirable.

B. Loop Length Dependence (L)

Equations 6 and 7 predict that the decrement and modulus change should depend on the fourth and second power of the loop length L (or concentration of pinning points c). It is difficult to determine these laws if measurements on different specimens are compared. This is because the dislocation density is unlikely to be exactly the same for two different specimens, especially if the impurity content differs. One needs here an experiment for which the loop length is changed, but not the dislocation density.

Recently, measurements on high purity copper have been made by Thompson and Holmes[26] during neutron irradiation. It is reasonable to assume that the dislocation density remained constant during the experiments so that the changes observed are all due to the changing loop length, which decreases as a result of pinning by the point defects created by the irradiation. Under these conditions, Thompson and Holmes show that the decrement and modulus change are proportional to L^4 and L^2 respectively.

* If the values obtained for germanium in the megacycle range are extrapolated to 30 kc/sec, then values of the decrement of about 10^{-7} are obtained. Measurements in the kilocycle range have not yet been reported, but preliminary results found by Kessler[49] indicate that the decrement for a high purity germanium specimen in the kilocycle range is less than 5×10^{-6}.

Recovery measurements can be used under the assumption that the recovery of damping and modulus changes is not due to annihilation or rearrangement of dislocations, but rather to the migration of point defects to the dislocations. On this basis the writers [50] have analyzed measurements by Gordon and Nowick [27] of the recovery of NaCl after deformation. They found that the concentration of pinning points followed the law of Cottrell and Bilby, i.e., $C \propto t^{2/3}$. For the strain-amplitude dependent part of the damping, a time-dependent exponent in eq. 8 was obtained (see § 6.E and Fig. 17). For the residual damping, again the fourth power law was found.

On the basis of this theory, recovery measurements in aluminum and copper also have been analyzed by Hikata and Granato,[50] who find evidence for the L^4 and L^2 dependence. All these quantitative agreements seem to justify the original assumption that for mild deformation the recovery of damping and modulus change is, in reality, a strain-aging effect.

C. Temperature Dependence (T)

The only quantities in eq. 6 which are temperature-sensitive are B and L_c. For temperatures high enough for diffusion to occur quickly, L_c should be given by eq. 2. For low temperatures, diffusion takes too long so that L_c should be constant. Then B essentially determines the temperature dependence and the decrement should decrease with temperature much more slowly. For intermediate temperature ranges, where diffusion can take place in reasonable times, the decrement should be time-dependent. Figure 16 of data taken by Beshers on copper gives some evidence for this type of behavior. At high temperatures, the temperature dependence seem to be exponential. The deviation from this behavior (around the minimum in Fig. 18) occurs in the same region where the time-dependent effects mentioned in § 6.E are found.*

For this interpretation the measured activation energy at high temperatures should be four times the Cottrell interaction energy. Beshers [11] found values between 0.8 and 1.0 ev for copper and Weertman and Salkovitz [10] found values between 0.25 and 0.35 ev for lead. When

* The high decrement for temperatures below the minimum can be assumed to be due to handling damage in the preparation of the specimens. As the temperature is increased, point defects diffuse to the dislocation and at first pin down the dislocations. If this interpretation is correct, then it would be expected that the decrement versus temperature curve would in this case be irreversible. That is, if one returns to room temperature after having held the specimen at a temperature just elevated enough to be in the time-dependent region, then the decrement should remain low. This behavior was reported by Beshers.[11]

these are divided by 4, they appear to be not unreasonable. There are very few measurements below room temperature, and these are complicated by the Bordoni peak mentioned earlier.

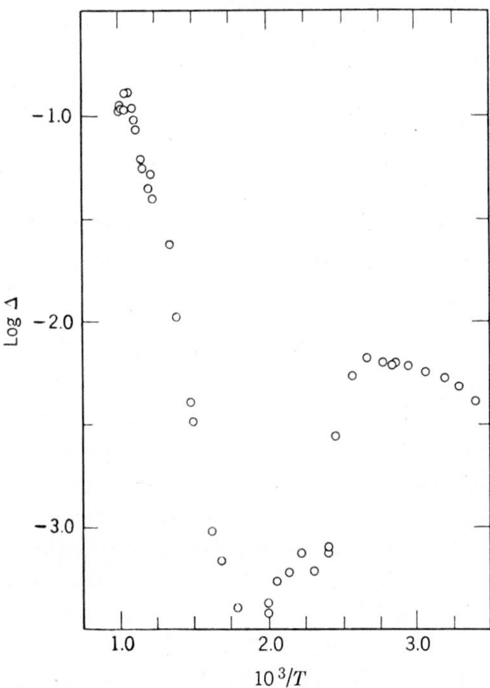

Fig. 18. The residual decrement in the kilocycle region of a copper specimen as a function of temperature (Beshers [11]).

D. Orientation Dependence

Since dislocation motion depends only on the resolved shear stress in the slip system, the residual damping in zinc should be markedly orientation-dependent regardless of the special mechanism assumed. The orientation dependence in the megacycle range for zinc has already been mentioned in § 3. Measurements by T. A. Read [1] of the residual damping in zinc in the kilocycle range show no variation with orientation, perhaps indicating that this is a "background" damping not due to dislocations. (Δ_I is found to be 1.2×10^{-5}.)

E. Magnitude of the Damping

One can obtain with reasonable assumptions * from eqs. 6 and 7 values for Δ_I up to 10^{-2}, which are close to the largest usually found

* With $\Lambda = 10^7$ cm^{-2}, $L = 3 \times 10^{-4}$ cm (so that $\Lambda L^2 \approx 1$), $B = C \approx 10^{-} f^4 =$, 30 kc/sec, and $\Omega = 0.1$, one obtains $\Delta_I = 8 \times 10^{-3}$ and $(\Delta E/E)_I = 0.06$.

at this frequency for pure materials at room temperature. Because of the L_c^4 term the decrement goes down very quickly for less pure materials, so that this mechanism can only contribute to the residual damping for relatively pure material. An examination of data so far available for this range indicates, in fact, that with the exception of lead and polycrystalline material, one only obtains a decrement significantly above the background value for materials of purity greater than 99.99%. For lead, abnormally high values are found which do not even always decrease with increasing impurity content. For example, Weertman and Salkovitz [10] find a Δ_I of 7×10^{-4}, 6×10^{-4}, and 20×10^{-4} for lead with 0.035, 0.053, and 0.65% respectively of bismuth. These values and also those for polycrystalline materials cannot be accounted for by eq. 6.

In summary, one can conclude the following from all of the above considerations. In the megacycle region, the losses can be accounted for by the pinned dislocation model. This model, however, cannot contribute to losses measured below about 10 kc/sec. It also cannot explain some of the losses observed in the high kilocycle range. For example, the background loss which cannot be reduced by the addition of impurities, and which is appreciably above the lower limit of sensitivity of the apparatus, and some losses above the background as found in lead single crystals and polycrystalline specimens cannot be accounted for by this model. The question in doubt is whether or not this model contributes to the loss in the high kilocycle region for very pure materials. There is some rather strong evidence for this, as shown in the preceding sections. On the other hand, certain evidence in opposition to this view can be found in the frequency dependence of this loss.

8. DISCUSSION

Relations 4–8 have been rather severely tested with the data presently available. It is still difficult to come to strong conclusions with regard to the residual damping to which there are undoubtedly contributions from other loss mechanisms. The detailed agreement, however, of the theory with measurements of the amplitude dependent damping for not too pure materials is striking. This agreement is all the more surprising in that it is strictly a low-temperature theory, not taking into account the effects of thermal fluctuation. The extension to high temperatures has not yet been completed and it is not known at present to what extent the present views may have to be modified or changed.

Another difficulty is related to the small displacement of the dislocation line. The maximum displacement is given by $\chi_m = \epsilon_0 L^2/8b$.

For a network length of 10^{-4} cm and a strain amplitude of 10^{-7} cm, χ_m would be one-fifth of a Burgers vector, so that the breakaway picture would become questionable. Evidence has recently been found[51] that the network length may be more nearly 10^{-3} cm, in which case this difficulty would be removed. Such large network lengths are also needed in order to account, as is done in the preceding section, for the residual damping of high purity metals with the vibrating string model. Finally, a certain difficulty arises in connection with the constant K of eq. 8, which should have a theoretical value of about $\frac{1}{3}$. With this value of K, the reasonable magnitude of 10^{-3} cm for L_N can be derived from most measurements. From Fig. 14, however, one obtains a value for K an order of magnitude smaller.* Since the measurements plotted in Fig. 14 are so far the only ones of this kind, it is not yet clear if this result has general significance; if it, for example, indicates easier breakaway as a consequence of thermal fluctuations.

Experimentally, a great deal of information is needed. Measurements of K could be found either by measuring the temperature dependence of Δ_H or by another method recently suggested by the writers.[25] Studies of the residual loss, especially as a function of temperature and frequency in the lower frequency ranges (1 to 10^5 cycles/sec), would be helpful. Measurements in the megacycle region on very pure materials should also be made to check the existence of the maximum predicted by eq. 4. Also, comparative measurements between polycrystals and single crystals would be interesting.

Although there are many questions still to be answered, it appears that the dependence of the damping on the various parameters is in some cases sufficiently well established so that damping measurements can be applied to studies of the effects of various treatments on the dislocation structure of metals.

REFERENCES

1. T. A. Read, *Trans. AIME,* **143,** 30 (1941). See also *Phys. Rev.,* **58,** 371 (1940).
2. A. S. Nowick, *Progr. Metal Phys.,* **4,** 1 (1953).
3. A. Granato and K. Lücke, *J. Appl. Phys.,* **27,** 789 (1956).
4. A. Granato and K. Lücke, *J. Appl. Phys.,* **27,** 583 (1956).

* In their original paper the writers came to the conclusion that K is about $\frac{1}{50}$, and that it is generally impossible to associate the residual damping with the dynamic damping of the same dislocations that contribute to the amplitude dependent damping, even for high purity materials. But this conclusion was based upon an assumption which now appears to be incorrect; namely, that a typical figure for L_N should be 10^{-4} cm.

5. J. L. Snoek, *Physica,* **8,** 711 (1941).
6. W. Köster, L. Bangert, and R. Hahn, *Arch. Eisenhüttenw.,* **25,** 569 (1954). See also W. Köster and L. Bangert, *Acta Met.,* **3,** 274 (1955).
7. S. Weinig and E. S. Machlin, *J. Appl. Phys.,* **27,** 734 (1956). See also *Acta Met.,* **4,** 262 (1956).
8. A. S. Nowick, *Phys. Rev.,* **80,** 249 (1950).
9. P. G. Bordoni, *J. Acoust. Soc. Amer.,* **26,** 495 (1954). See also *Ricerca Sci.,* **23,** 1193 (1953).
10. J. Weertman and E. J. Salkovitz, *Acta Met.,* **3,** 1 (1955).
11. D. N. Beshers, Thesis, University of Illinois (1955).
12. H. Sack, private communication.
13. W. P. Mason and H. J. McSkimin, *J. Acoust. Soc. Amer.,* **19,** 466 (1947).
14. R. L. Roderick and R. Truell, *J. Appl. Phys.,* **23,** 267 (1952).
15. P. Waterman, measurements made at Brown University.
16. K. Lücke, *J. Appl. Phys.,* **27,** 1433 (1956).
17. W. P. Mason, *J. Acoust. Soc. Amer.,* **27,** 643 (1955).
18. T. S. Hutchison and A. J. Filmer, *Can. J. Phys.,* **34,** 159 (1956).
19. A. Hikata, R. Truell, A. Granato, B. Chick, and K. Lücke, *J. Appl. Phys.,* **27,** 396 (1956).
20. J. Weertman and J. S. Koehler, *J. Appl. Phys.,* **24,** 624 (1953).
21. J. H. Swift and J. E. Richardson, *J. Appl. Phys.,* **18,** 417 (1947).
22. G. Alers, *Phys. Rev.,* **97,** 863 (1955).
23. S. Takahashi, private communication.
24. R. F. Hanstock, *J. Inst. Metals,* **83,** 11 (1954).
25. A. Granato and K. Lücke, to be published.
26. D. O. Thompson and D. K. Holmes, *J. Appl. Phys.,* **27,** 713 (1956).
27. R. B. Gordon and A. S. Nowick, *Acta Met.,* **4,** 514 (1956).
28. P. G. Klemens, *Proc. Phys. Soc. (London), A,* **68,** 1113 (1955).
29. W. P. Mason, *Phys. Rev.,* **98,** 1136 (1955). See also ref. 17 and *Bell System Tech. J.,* **34,** 1 (1955).
30. J. Weertman, *Phys. Rev.,* **101,** 1429 (1956).
31. A. Seeger, Theory of Lattice Defects in *Handbuch der Physik,* Vol. VII/1, sect. 72.
32. D. H. Niblett and J. Wilks, *Phil. Mag.,* **1,** 415 (1956).
33. J. S. Koehler, Chap. 7 in *Imperfections in Nearly Perfect Crystals,* W. Shockley, J. H. Hollomon, R. Maurer, F. Seitz, John Wiley & Sons, New York (1952).
34. F. R. N. Nabarro, *Proc. Phys. Soc. (London), A,* **58,** 669 (1946).
N. F. Mott and F. R. N. Nabarro, *Report of a Conference on Strength of Solids,* Physical Society, London, p. 1 (1948).
N. F. Mott, Chap. 6 in *Imperfections in Nearly Perfect Crystals,* W. Shockley, J. H. Hollomon, R. Maurer, F. Seitz, John Wiley & Sons, New York (1952).
35. A. H. Cottrell, *Report of a Conference on Strength of Solids,* Physical Society, London, p. 30 (1948).
36. F. D. Rosi, *Trans. AIME,* **200,** 1009 (1954).
37. A. H. Cottrell and B. A. Bilby, *Proc. Phys. Soc. (London), A,* **62,** 49 (1949).
38. G. Leibfried, *Z. Physik,* **127,** 344 (1950).
39. F. R. N. Nabarro, *Proc. Roy. Soc. (London), A,* **209,** 278 (1951).
40. J. D. Eshelby, *Proc. Roy. Soc. (London), A,* **197,** 396 (1949).
41. F. Seitz, *Pittsburgh Symposium on the Plastic Deformation of Crystalline Solids,* Office of Naval Research, Washington, p. 1 (1950).

42. E. Hart, *Phys. Rev.*, **98,** 1775 (1955).
43. A. Seeger, private communication.
44. A. Granato and R. Truell, *J. Appl. Phys.*, **27,** 1219 (1956).
45. L. J. Teutonico, A. Granato, and R. Truell, *Phys. Rev.*, **103,** 832 (1956).
46. A. Hikata and R. Truell, *J. Appl. Phys.*, **28,** 522 (1957).
47. See discussion in ref. 33, pp. 212–216.
48. A. Granato and K. Lücke, *J. Appl. Phys.*, **28,** 635 (1957).
49. J. Kessler, private communication.
50. A. Granato, A. Hikata, and K. Lücke, communicated to *Acta Met.* See also Technical Reports by A. Granato and K. Lücke for Office of Ordnance Research, U. S. Army under Contract DA-19-020-ORD-3650, Dec. 1956, and by A. Hikata and A. Granato for Air Force Office of Scientific Research under Contract No. AF18(603)-136, Jan. 1957.
51. J. Weertman and E. I. Salkovitz, *J. Appl. Phys.*, **27,** 1251 (1956).

ACKNOWLEDGMENT

We would like to express our appreciation for the support that has been given to studies in this field by the U. S. Army Ordnance, the U. S. Army Signal Corps, and the U. S. Air Force Office of Scientific Research.

DISCUSSION

LOMER asked what the impurity atom was that was doing the locking. LÜCKE answered that gold in copper and bismuth and antimony in lead had been used. The 0.11-ev binding energy was found with bismuth in lead. Using Cottrell's formula exactly for elastic interaction gives a value of about 0.05 ev, but a new formula by Bilby including electronic interaction seems to give a value at least 1.5 times higher, which is the right order of magnitude. LÜCKE added that the low value of the binding energy calculated by Weertman and also by himself was based on the elastic interaction of substitutional atoms and dislocations with small differences in solute and solvent atomic radii. Other considerations, such as the suggestion by Seeger that the dislocations are electrically charged, would give an additional interaction with foreign atoms and would bring the theoretical and experimental values into closer agreement.

MOTT asked if the damping occurs only when there has been some diffusion of the impurities to the dislocations, or if it occurs also after a dislocation has been moved and settles down on such impurities as happen to be in the neighborhood. LÜCKE believed that there would also be a damping if dislocations have been moved from Cottrell atmospheres, for instance, after deformation at low temperatures; but in all metals formed from the melt, except the super purity ones, there would be sufficient Cottrell locking to be of overriding importance in the damping.

LEIBFRIED asked how much the dislocations bow out. LÜCKE answered that it is a function of the loop length. For a network length of 2×10^{-3} cm, which is proposed for metals, they would bow out about 80 lattice diameters at a strain of 10^{-7}. The displacement is proportional to the strain and goes down with the square of the loop length. With very prominent impurity locking, such that the loop length is 10^{-5} cm, the displacements are much smaller than one lattice parameter. There is some question whether the formulas hold in this case.

COTTRELL asked if damping experiments had been performed on materials with a large Peierls force, as it seemed to be an ideal method to study dislocations in such materials. LÜCKE replied that in the work of J. Kessler on germanium single crystals of high purity, damping in the kilocycle range was too small to measure at room temperature (below 10^{-6}), and in the megacycle range in germanium Granato and Truell found the decrement to vary with the first power of the frequency. LÜCKE said that the measurements in germanium had been extended to dry ice temperature. The decrement was found to be rather insensitive to temperature.

SEEGER expressed his thoughts on the influence of the Peierls force. At temperatures where the dislocation overcomes the Peierls force thermally, the only way the Peierls force enters into the theory is in the friction constant for the oscillating dislocation. The region which separates the field of validity of this theory and the region where the Peierls force is important is the Bordoni peak. This peak is caused by the dislocation lines going over the Peierls field by forming kinks. By analyzing the Bordoni peak in metals like copper, lead, and aluminum, one gets Peierls forces of the order of magnitude of the theoretical value, which are definitely larger than the critical shear stress measured so far at the lowest temperatures. This indicates that we do not find the Peierls force because the dislocations are always lying across the hills. This is substantiated by an estimate of how many dislocations take part in the Peierls force relaxation process. The estimate, which is an upper limit, probably large by a factor of ten, gives one line out of 400 which lies sufficiently parallel to the close-packed direction to give a Peierls relaxation peak. The other dislocation lines lie across the hills and are able to move without thermal activation.

COTTRELL asked if each expanding dislocation loop did not have to go through this parallel stage where the Peierls force is large. SEEGER answered that he believed that they did not because the line along which the dislocation lies is determined by the balance of the line energy and the stress field of all of the other dislocations lines which is a factor 1000 times larger than the Peierls force itself. Thus the Peierls force only gives rise to small wiggles along the dislocation line. COTTRELL said that if this interpretation were correct it would mean that one should find a Bordoni peak well above room temperature in such elements as germanium and lithium fluoride, and that this should be investigated.

The Behavior of Metals Under Reversed Stresses

N. F. MOTT

Cavendish Laboratory
University of Cambridge
Cambridge, England

ABSTRACT

An attempt is made to improve the current theory of work hardening of metals, especially with reference to their behavior under cyclic stress. A model is proposed which ensures that the Frank-Read sources responsible for slip lines should not generate dislocations of the opposite sign with consequent work softening when the stress is reversed. It is shown that this model gives also an explanation of the existence of fine and coarse slip. Friedel's model of work hardening is extended so as to explain the formation of multiple slip bands. Finally, a theory for the formation of a fatigue crack is proposed.

---

1. INTRODUCTION

The purpose of this paper is to discuss the current theory of work hardening, especially with the aim of understanding, in terms of the movement of dislocations, hardening under reversed stresses and failure in fatigue.

Theories of work hardening suppose that the work-hardened material contains dislocations. Suppose first of all that these are arranged at random at a mean distance l from each other. Then within the crystal there will be a random internal stress σ_i of order given by

$$\sigma_i \sim Gb/2\pi l \sim GbN^{1/2}/\pi \tag{1}$$

where N $(= 1/l^2)$ is the number of dislocation lines per unit area. A free dislocation line can then only move through a distance greater than l if the applied stress σ exceeds σ_i. One then constructs a model of work hardening as follows. The material contains Frank-Read sources. Let us say that when a new dislocation is generated by a source it moves a distance L. Then if δN new dislocations are formed, the strain will increase by

$$\delta\epsilon = bL\,\delta N$$

where b is the Burgers vector. The stress increases by

$$\delta\sigma_i = GbN^{-1/2}\,\delta N/\pi$$

Eliminating δN and N, we have

$$d(\sigma_i^2)/d\epsilon = G^2b/2\pi^2L$$

The stress-strain curve obtained depends on the assumption made about the variation of L with ϵ. If L is constant we obtain parabolic hardening (Taylor [1]) and, if L is inversely proportional to ϵ, we obtain linear hardening.

This model has been considerably refined. For instance, the temperature dependence of σ_i depends on whether we have to do with the elastic interaction between dislocations, in which case σ_i/G is independent of temperature, or with a process in which dislocations cut through screw dislocations which intersect the slip plane (Cottrell [2]). Also, various suggestions (Mott,[3] Stroh,[4,5] Friedel [6]) have been made about the effect of piled-up groups of dislocations. These will be discussed later.

Here we wish first of all to introduce a few new concepts:

1. We ought to distinguish between the stress σ_i required to move a dislocation through distances great compared with l and the larger stress σ_i' necessary to generate new dislocations. We might write

$$\sigma_i' = \sigma_i + Gb/l$$

where l is the length of the longest Frank-Read sources. That we must make a distinction between σ_i and σ_i' under certain circumstances is shown by the existence of a hysteresis loop in the stress-strain curve under alternating stresses. Figure 1 shows such curves obtained by Thompson, Coogan, and Rider [7] for single crystals of aluminum in push-pull after up to about 1000 cycles. The parts BC, DA are elastic.

A phenomenological model which will explain the loop is that of a dislocation moving backward and forward between two barriers which repel it under a frictional force which requires a stress σ_i to overcome it. If, as we believe, σ_i is to be explained as the resistance due to the stress fields of all the other dislocations, and as the material behaves in an elastic way as soon as the stress is decreased at B, it follows that the dislocations move a distance large compared with l. Thomp-

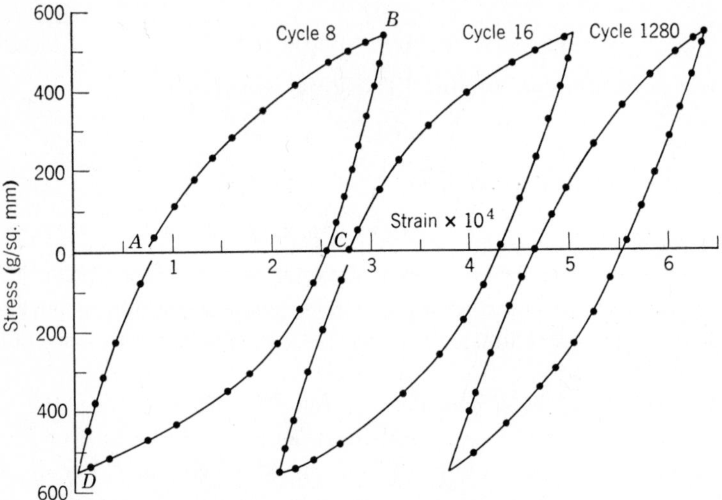

Fig. 1. Typical hysteresis loops obtained by continuous cyclic stressing of aluminum single crystals. (After Thompson, Coogan, and Rider.[7] Reprinted by courtesy of The Institute of Metals.)

son *et al.* have given strong support to the hypothesis that no further generation of dislocations occurs on going round the hysteresis loop, and if this is so it follows that a stress somewhat larger than σ_i is moving dislocations backward and forward without generating new ones.

2. We now shall consider in detail what happens to the work-hardening curve when the stress is reversed. We confine ourselves first to the case when slip is on one set of planes, taking as examples the work quoted above on aluminum for very small strains and that of Edwards and Washburn [8] on zinc single crystals. The results of the latter authors are shown in Fig. 2 and are characteristic. When the stress is reversed plastic flow begins at a very low stress, much below the original yield stress, but thereafter hardening is rapid and after quite a small additional strain the original hardening curve is continued, shifted to the right along the strain axis.

Now it has never been satisfactorily explained why a material does not *soften* when the stress is reversed. A number of mechanisms have been proposed for holding newly formed dislocations in position, such as dipole formation or Cottrell-Lomer locking. These would prevent a dislocation from moving backward when the stress is reversed. But one has to ask why the *source* where the dislocations were originally formed should not produce dislocations of the opposite sense when the stress is reversed, which would wipe out those already formed.

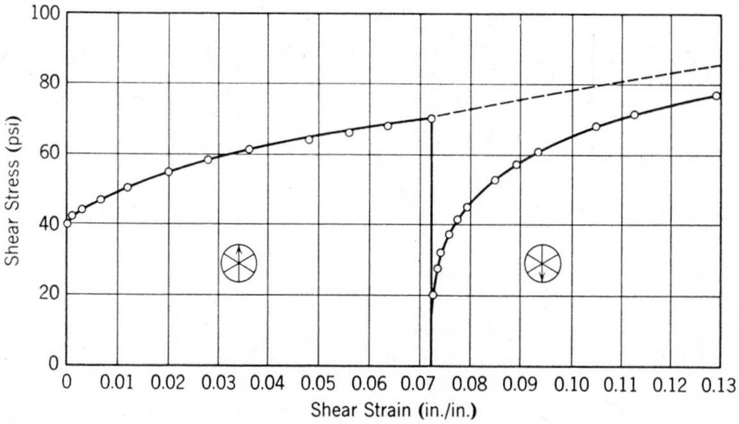

Fig. 2. Behavior of zinc single crystals on reversing direction of strain (ϵ). (After Edwards and Washburn.[8] Reprinted by courtesy of The American Institute of Mining, Metallurgical, and Petroleum Engineers, Inc.)

A possible explanation of the absence of softening when the stress is reversed is that sources, when they produce dislocations, do so in bursts, and that only a small number of the sources available are actually used. When the stress is reversed new sources, which have not already operated, come into play, and so hardening continues. To account for bursts there are various hypotheses:

1. The dynamic hypothesis of Fisher, Hart, and Pry [9] and of the present author.[10] Owing to the work of Eshelby (unpublished) and Leibfried [11] and for other reasons, this explanation now seems unlikely to be right.

2. Locking of the dislocations by Cottrell atmospheres. If the dislocation which forms the source were locked, it would produce a burst of dislocations after it broke away. The work of Friedel, Boulanger, and Crussard [12] provides strong evidence that aluminum contains a network of locked dislocations which can move with their atmospheres, probably due to traces of iron, only at high temperatures. Friedel's [13]

explanation, on the other hand, of measurements by Bradfield and Pursey [14] of the elastic constants of copper-based alloys shows that in copper containing less than about 1% of impurity, the dislocation network is not locked and can contribute to the elastic modulus. In any case one would not expect *new* sources formed during cold work to be locked. Thus we cannot in general look to locking to explain bursts, though the absence of fine slip in alloys of copper (Wilsdorf and Kuhlmann-Wilsdorf [15] and of nickel (Nagashima and Yamamoto [16]),

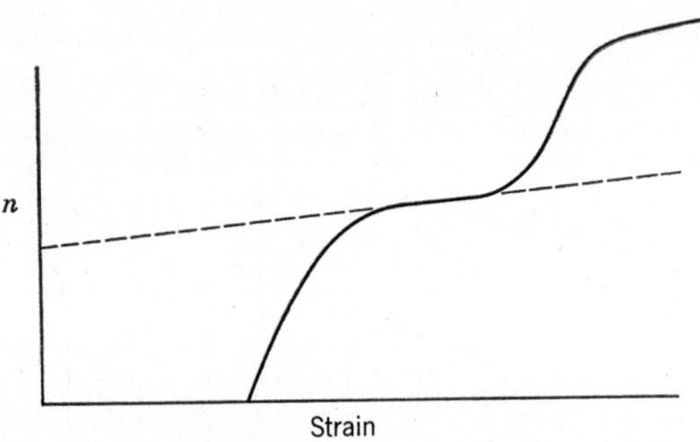

Fig. 3. Number n of dislocations from a given source plotted against strain according to the hypothesis of this paper.

while present in the pure metal, shows that locking can concentrate the slip on a small number of lines, presumably by producing bursts.

3. A third explanation, which we favor, is the following. The bursts are not dynamic events; all that occurs, in our view, is that sources produce a considerable number of dislocations during a small increase in the strain. Figure 3 shows schematically the number n of dislocations produced according to this hypothesis by a given source as a function of strain. Bursts of this type might occur for the following reason. We envisage as before a varying internal stress such that a stress σ_i must be applied to move a dislocation through it. The stress σ applied to the material undergoing hardening is greater than σ_i, because it has to operate sources. Whether a source will start to generate dislocations depends on the sum of Gb/l and the *local* value of σ_i, not the mean value; it is plausible that, to operate a source and to produce a complete dislocation ring, the ring must pass several maxima and minima of σ_i, so that we may think of a local situation for σ_i which will determine whether the source will operate. Now this local value, which we call $(\sigma_i)_0$, will be constantly changing, depending as it does on the arrangement of dislocations near to the source under consideration, which changes as work hardening proceeds. Those sources will gen-

erate dislocations, at a given point on the stress-strain curve, for which the component of σ_i in the direction of the applied stress is least. It seems reasonable to suppose that strong local fluctuations in the internal stress, as the strain increases, will give rise to strong bursts resulting in marked slip lines, whereas smaller fluctuations will give rise to a larger number of weak lines. Strong local fluctuations are to be expected rarely, when a dislocation or piled-up group from a previous burst comes to rest near a source; smaller fluctuations will occur more frequently. Also, when the stress is reversed, it will normally be new sources that generate dislocations, because a local value of σ_i favorable to the generation of dislocations of one sign will not be favorable to dislocations of the other sign under reversed stress.

We now have to ask why, when the stress is reversed, yield at a very low stress is followed by rapid hardening (Bauschinger effect). A possible explanation, which we shall put forward and later abandon, might be the following: Just before the stress is reversed *a few sources* only are generating dislocations which are being pushed, against the frictional force σ_i, up to some barrier at a distance L $(L \gg l)$, where a piled-up group will be formed. This particular source will be acted on by the field of this piled-up group and will be particularly well situated to create dislocations of the opposite sign. Thus during the initial rapid rise we envisage the sources which were in action just before the reversal of stress as creating dislocations of the opposite sign which wipe out those just formed. When this process is finished, the material should have as great a resistance to flow as before the reversal and thereafter the generation of dislocations normally occurs from dislocations that have not been in action before.

Another point of view was emphasized to the author by Dr. Wadsworth at the Lake Placid meeting. In the curves of Fig. 1, when the stress is taken off, recovery is elastic until the stress is reversed. If, as is likely, Gb/l is a good deal smaller than σ_i in a cold-worked material, this must mean that a source does not stop operating because of the back stress from its own dislocations; these must go too far for their effect to be important, and a source stops operating for the same reason as it starts, namely a sudden change in the local value of σ_i due to dislocations on other slip planes. The above explanation of the Bauschinger effect cannot then be right; a source which has just been acting is not in a more favorable situation for generating dislocations when the stress is reversed than any other. We suppose, then, that the Bauschinger effect must be due to the movement backward to the sources of some few dislocations which have not been trapped by the Cottrell-Lomer or some other mechanism.

2. THE WORK HARDENING OF SINGLE CRYSTALS

We shall now apply these ideas to a discussion of the work hardening of single crystals. A recent paper by Friedel [6] has emphasized that the stress-strain curve of a single crystal can be divided into three parts, as shown in Fig. 4. There are the region of easy glide from A to

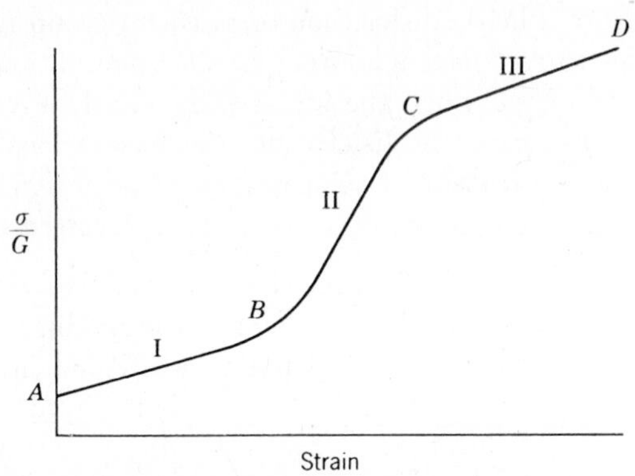

Fig. 4. Schematic stress-strain curve of a single crystal.

B, which we shall call stage I; the region of rapid hardening from B to C, which we shall call stage II; and the region from C onward where the rate of hardening becomes less rapid (stage III). The characteristics of the three stages are as follows:

Stage I

This is absent in polycrystalline metals and occurs when slip is confined to one set of planes. The duration of easy glide, and the position of point B, are therefore markedly dependent on orientation. In single crystals of hexagonal metals stage I covers the whole hardening range. In this range slip lines are weak and of length comparable with the diameter of the crystal (Diehl, Mader, and Seeger [17]). The slow hardening is thus due to a large value of the slip distance L. No detailed theory of work hardening in this range has, however, been given. Hardening is probably due to the elastic interaction of dislocations with the formation of piled-up groups.

Stage II

This occurs when slip is on more than one set of planes. It can be said with some assurance that hardening is rapid in this region because Cottrell-Lomer barriers, or barriers of similar type, are formed and these limit the slip distance L of dislocations from any one source.

As we have seen, a small value of L leads to a rapid rate of hardening. As Friedel has pointed out, in any (111) slip plane (the plane of the paper in Fig. 5), there are two directions in which Cottrell-Lomer barriers can form, so that a given source is surrounded by a square $A\ B\ C\ D$ which forms a barrier to further slip. Against this barrier a piled-up group of dislocation rings will form.

Friedel gives a detailed model of hardening in stage II, based on the assumption that all the available Frank-Read sources are brought into action together, and the piled-up groups increase in size steadily

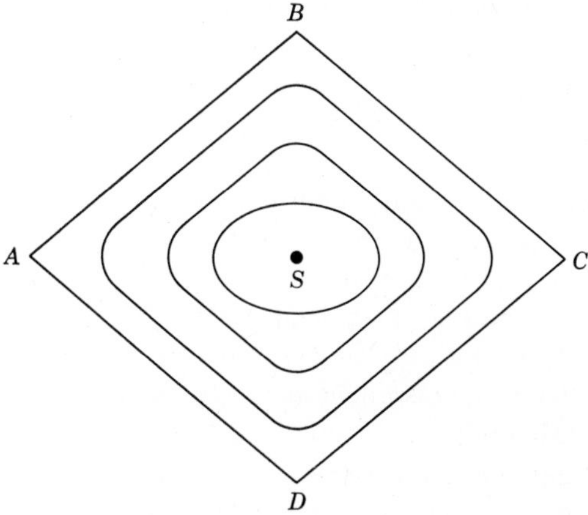

Fig. 5. A source and dislocation rings surrounded by locked dislocations.

as the strain increases. We find this model difficult to accept as it stands, because it leads to the conclusion that if the stress is reversed the sources will produce dislocation rings of the opposite sign and the dislocations will disappear. On the other hand, Friedel's prediction of short slip lines in stage II is strikingly confirmed by the observations of Blewitt, Coltman, and Redman,[18] of Kelly,[19] and by the results shown by Dr. Seeger at this conference (pages 304–305), who electropolished at the end of stage I and observed short slip lines in stage II. We think it likely that more sources are available than are actually used, that each line is formed during quite a small stress increment (for the reason given above), and that the number of lines rather than the number of dislocations in each increases throughout stage II (this could be tested experimentally). One would then envisage an internal stress σ_i due to the dislocations and particularly to the piled-up groups. As shown by Mott,[10] a given number of dislocations produce a larger internal stress σ_i if they are grouped in piled-up arrays. Apart then from the details proposed in Friedel's paper, it seems likely, as he suggests, that the hardening in stage II is due to an internal stress resulting from piled-up groups, the forward movement of the group being blocked by a sessile dislocation of Cottrell-Lomer type. Seeger has given reasons in pages 287–297 for believing that groups of, say, 30 dislocations form at intervals along each slip line in stage II.

Another criticism that can be made of Friedel's model is that it suggests that most of the work done in deforming a metal is stored, which is not the case after heavy cold work, though there is no direct evidence about stage II. It seems necessary to assume that dislocations move through a distance large compared with l, so that the random stresses from dislocations act like a frictional force.

Stage III

The important observations about stage III may be listed as follows: Although the slope of the hardening curve in stage II depends little on temperature, the stress at which the transition to stage III begins, and thus point C in Fig. 4, depend markedly on temperature. For crystals hardened well into stage III the work of Cottrell and Stokes [20] shows that the flow stress is much more dependent on temperature than in stage II, and these authors deduce that the "forest" or density of dislocations crossing each slip line increases during stage III (see also Seeger [21]). Moreover, Diehl, Mader, and Seeger [17] have shown that the beginning of stage III coincides with the onset of the formation of (long) coarse slip bands, which in polycrystalline materials can cross the greater part of a grain.

It seems clear that, under the combined influence of applied stress and temperature, at point C the piled-up groups push past the barriers which are holding them up (Friedel [6]); dislocations then move a much greater distance than in stage II, so that long slip lines are formed and the rate of hardening is decreased. So much can be agreed. But as regards the mechanism by which stress and temperature lead to a breakdown of the piled-up groups, two hypotheses have been put forward:

1. Friedel [6] and Stroh [22] suppose that the Cottrell-Lomer barrier breaks down under the combined influence of stress and temperature, so that dislocations in the "boxes" of Fig. 5 continue to move out of the box in their original slip planes. These authors show that this assumption can be made to give a quantitative explanation of the dependence on temperature of the stress at which stage III begins.

They have not extended their theory to a discussion of what happens in stage III; we shall give one below.

2. Seeger,[21] on the other hand, believes that dislocations escape from the boxes of Fig. 5, also under the influence of stress and temperature, by "cross slip." A detailed theory of the stress and temperatures required has not been given, but such a theory accounts very simply for the occurrence, observed by Diehl *et al.*,[17] of long slip lines at the beginning of stage III which broaden into bands only later. It also seems confirmed by some recent observations of Kelly[19] of slip lines in stage II and III on single crystals of aluminum. The model is as follows: Fig. 6*a* shows diagrammatically the "top" surface of a crystal

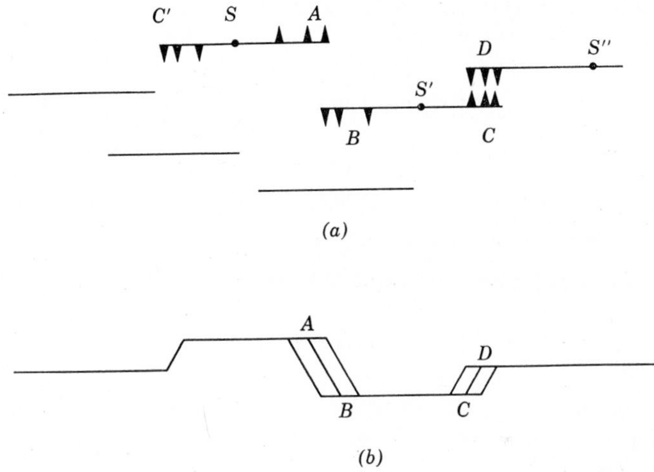

Fig. 6. Schematic representation of the top surface of a crystal before and after cross slip.

strained in stage II, i.e., a surface perpendicular to the glide vector; the piled-up dislocations shown are therefore screws or have a screw component. On electropolishing the surface, the steps which constitute the visible slip lines will of course disappear, but the dislocations remain. Suppose that the stress is increased until cross slip occurs between the screws at A and B, so that they annihilate each other. This immediately enables the sources at S and S' to generate more dislocations, and so to increase the stress on the leading members of the piled-up groups at C and C'. This in its turn will increase the stress on the dislocations at C, say, so that dislocations at C and D will annihilate each other. This will allow S'' to generate more dislocations, so that a jagged slip line as in Fig. 6*b* will spread across the crystal.

The intensity of the line cannot increase indefinitely because cross slip can get rid of screws only, not edges; we should not expect the intensity of the long line to be much greater than that of a typical short line.

There is much evidence that, as well as the short but strong slip lines of stage II and the coarse slip lines or bands of stage III, there is also present in stage III at any rate much fine slip, in which each source produces only a few dislocations. The evidence is:

1. The observations of fine slip lines by Wilsdorf and Kuhlmann-Wilsdorf [15,23] and by Nagashima and Yamamoto.[16]
2. The block formation observed in heavily cold-worked polycrystalline metals such as aluminum by Gay, Hirsch, and Kelly.[24] The temperature of these experiments seems to preclude climb, so to get this form of polygonization in a bent grain there must be a much more uniform distribution of dislocations than the coarse slip lines make apparent.
3. The apparent existence of a "forest" in stage III (Cottrell and Stokes [20]) leading to a temperature-dependent term in the flow stress for aluminum.

Fine slip can perhaps be explained as follows. We have suggested above that a source generates dislocations when the *local* stress is favorable, and that this may occur suddenly through the movement near to it of other dislocations which change the stress. Thus it will be a rare event in the history of any source that the situation becomes very favorable through the movement into its *near* proximity of another dislocation or group; but it may frequently happen that a more distant rearrangement of dislocations may enable a given source to generate a few dislocations. Thus, in stage II or III, we expect a few strong lines and a lot of weak ones.

Now a long slip line at the beginning of stage III will be formed, by one or the other of the processes mentioned above, from one of the short strong lines of stage II. But there will always be close to it other sources which have produced only fine lines but which can be allowed to generate further dislocations if neighboring screws are removed by cross slip. In this way the broadening of the initial long lines of stage III into bands can perhaps be understood.

3. FRACTURE

Two mechanisms have been proposed to explain fracture in metals:

1. The formation of piled-up groups sufficiently large to initiate fracture (Stroh,[4,5] Mott [3]).

2. The formation of vacancies and interstitial atoms in sufficient numbers to break down the cohesion of the material (Mason [25]). It seems possible that both play a role in appropriate circumstances.

The analysis given by Stroh [4] of the brittle fracture of polycrystalline ferrous and hexagonal metals makes it likely that here we have to do with piled-up groups against grain boundaries. In the case of single crystals, no fully convincing mechanism has been proposed, it being unlikely that a Cottrell-Lomer lock will give a firm enough barrier. Ductile (cup-and-cone) fracture is also probably initiatied by piled-up groups at grain boundaries at the ends of coarse (stage III) slip lines. The evidence for this is:

(*a*) The fact that ductile fracture only occurs in polycrystalline metals; Stroh has shown that the piled-up group formed at Cottrell-Lomer barriers should *not* give a large enough stress concentration to initiate fracture and so a grain boundary is necessary.

(*b*) Petch's relationship [26] between the stress σ at fracture and the grain diameter d for ductile fracture in iron ($\sigma = a + bd^{-1/2}$) suggests that a slip line extending across the whole grain and exerting a stress at the grain boundary is responsible.

In fatigue, on the other hand, the present author [27] has suggested that the formation of vacancies and interstitials along a slip line under alternating stress so weakens the material there that a crack forms. The remainder of this paper will be devoted to elaborating this hypothesis and suggesting others. First, however, we must examine in detail the proposed mechanisms for the formation of vacancies and interstitials by moving dislocations.

4. MECHANISM FOR THE FORMATION OF VACANCIES

The mechanism first proposed (by Seitz) and widely discussed in the literature is the following. If a moving dislocation cuts a screw dislocation a jog is formed; if the moving dislocation has a screw component the jog cannot move forward without forming a row of vacancies or interstitial atoms. More recently, however, various authors (Friedel,[6] Seeger [21]) have emphasized that, since a jog in a screw is a small dislocation, it will normally move sideways along the Burgers vector till it comes onto an edge region of the dislocation line, before the stress becomes large enough to form a row of vacancies.

The situation is illustrated in Fig. 7*a*, where we show a dislocation moving in the plane of the paper, containing two jogs J_1 and J_2 which can move along the dotted lines. Clearly the stress will make them move toward each other, until the situation shown in Fig. 7*b* arises, when J_2 is no longer a jog on a screw and can now move forward without forming vacancies. Similarly, a jog on the screw part of a dislocation loop will move to the edge part.

To get over the difficulty, Friedel has suggested that, if the speed with which a dislocation moves increased toward that of sound, the speed of a jog would reach the critical velocity before that of the dislocation. As it approached it the force on the jog would increase and vacancies would be produced. Seeger [21] suggests that vacancies would be formed from time to time by a sliding jog, part of the energy coming from heat motion. Van Beuren [28] considers that conservative motion

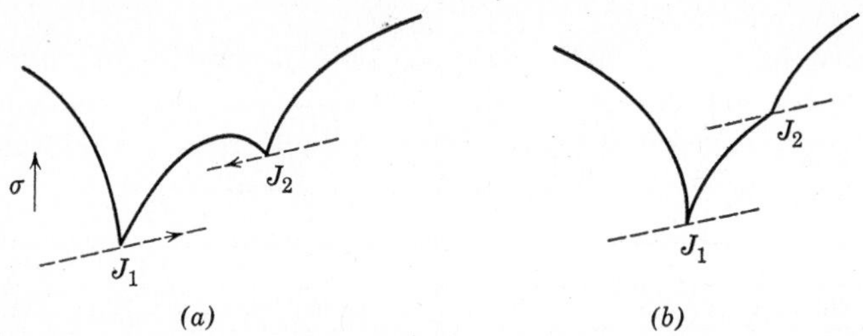

Fig. 7. Illustrating the mechanism for the formation of vacancies.

of this kind does not decrease the formation of defects appreciably, and bases his quantitative theory of defect formation on this hypothesis. We find this hard to accept.

A much simpler mechanism exists, however, which does not seem to have been pointed out in the literature.* This is shown in Fig. 8; when a dislocation line with a screw component forms a loop so that two parts of the line such as A and B meet, then, if the loop is cut by a screw, a row of vacancies or interstitials will be formed. This can happen in a Frank-Read source, and also if a dislocation is held back locally by a static dislocation ring. It seems to us likely that this second process is the most important one in forming vacancies during work hardening in stage III. The number of vacancies or interstitials formed will be of order $\epsilon lb/\lambda^2$, where ϵ is the strain, l the linear dimension of one of the loops, and λ the distance between the loops formed by a single dislocation.†

If the excess of screw dislocations of one sign threading the ring in Fig. 8 exceeds unity, *plates* of vacancies or interstitial atoms will be

* It is proposed by Friedel in his forthcoming book on dislocations that a Frank-Read source can produce vacancies by this method.

† Unless l is not much smaller than λ and both are of order 1 μ, the number formed will be insufficient to account for the experimental observations.

formed. These will not disappear at the temperature at which vacancies or interstitial atoms disappear, but *only* at the temperatures at which full thermal recovery (climb of dislocations) is expected. These plates may possibly be important in fatigue.

We now have to ask whether, when the stress is reversed and the dislocation moves back, the vacancies or interstitials produced will be annihilated, or whether new ones of opposite sign will be formed in the

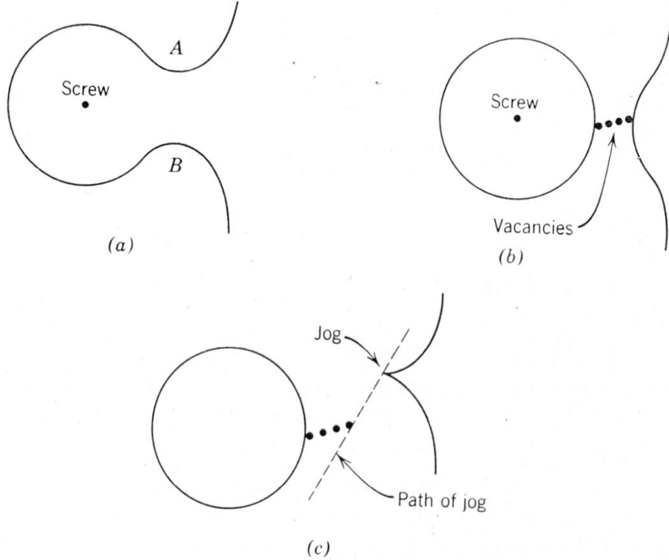

Fig. 8. Alternative mechanism for formation of vacancies.

vicinity. Certainly we should expect the latter if there is any truth in Friedel's hypothesis that jogs move fast. Figure 8*c* shows the way that the jog will slide away from the row of vacancies after it is formed; when the stress is reversed, there is no reason why it should not overshoot point *A* and form a row of interstitials lower down on the diagram. For our theory of fatigue in the next section, this is what we must assume.

5. FATIGUE

The recent work of Thompson, Wadsworth, and Louat [29] on fatigue in polycrystalline copper and of Smith [30] on aluminum suggests that in pure metals the fatigue process can be described as follows: During the first few thousand cycles the material hardens and the work done in each cycle drops. During this process slip lines are formed. The next thing that happens is that some of these lines become "persistent" in the sense that they are not removed by electropolishing. Persistent slip lines that cross a grain are cracks, in the sense that they can be opened up by an applied tensile stress. The formation of a crack across a single grain probably takes a good deal less than half the total fatigue life. The spread of the crack at a gradually increasing rate through the remainder of the specimen takes most of the life.

A theory of the spread of a fatigue crack has been given by Head; [31] in this paper we shall discuss only the initiation of the crack; we shall have to show why a slip line becomes persistent and turns into a crack.

We have first to ask whether hardening and slip-band formation under cyclic stressing is a process similar to that in unidirectional straining. There are several apparent differences. For instance, Wood [32] finds that the X-ray back-reflection photograph of a polycrystalline copper specimen fatigued in a compression-tension machine shows no broadening of the spots or asterisms. Clarebrough, Hargreaves, Head, and West [33] show that a fatigued specimen gives up its stored energy at a higher temperature than a specimen with equivalent stored energy in unidirectional stressing; the release of energy is apparently by recovery (climb of dislocations) in the former case, by recrystallization in the latter. Both these facts should be due to the same difference, the absence in cyclic stressing of any gross bending and localized heavy working of the grains, with consequent formation of deformation bands or cell structure. These bands or cells are responsible for broadening of Laue spots and are probably the nuclei at which recrystallization starts.

Paterson [34] has submitted single crystals of high purity copper to cyclic stressing in push-pull such that about 30 cycles produced a total absolute strain of about 0.5. Under these conditions no X-ray asterisms were observed and no deformation bands on the surface. The rate of hardening was about the same as in unidirectional straining and showed a similar strong dependence on the orientation of the crystal, being much more rapid when two or more glide planes were active. The easy glide region (stage I of Fig. 4) extended much further than in unidirectional stressing. When the crystals were oriented to give slip on one system only, there was a very uniform distribution of long fine slip lines, and for the specimens which hardened rapidly Paterson observed clustered primary slip and faint cross slip (see particularly his Fig. 5).

Whether stage III occurs under cyclic stressing has not yet been shown, but it is clear that stages I and II do.

Another important observation is that of McCammon and Rosenberg,[35] who show that for copper hardened in fatigue at room temperature or below there is some recovery (softening) at 100°C—although the bulk of the stored energy is released at a higher temperature than after normal cold work. This suggests that after cyclic stressing even in polycrystalline metals there are fewer barriers formed than in unidirectional stressing, so that the dislocations can rearrange themselves by glide without climb.

The evidence, then, does not show clearly as yet the nature of the slip bands that produce fatigue. They might be bands of the stage III type, or alternatively clusters of lines, the whole cluster but no individual line crossing the grain, such as observed (in stage II) in Paterson's work. The second alternative seems the more likely, but experiments are required on the stress and orientation dependence of the formation in single crystals of persistent slip lines which develop into cracks.

Whatever the mechanism, cyclic stressing produces regions, probably fairly broad and crossing a grain, in which slip has occurred. These develop into cracks. We have to ask why they do so.

One may suppose that *some* dislocations move backward and forward along these lines or bands on each cycle; our explanation of the Bauschinger effect demands that this be so. Most dislocations will be held in pairs or in groups, but there should be a few left over. We have introduced the idea that the stress required to move dislocations in a hardened material is less than the stress required to form and move new ones, so there is no contradiction in the idea that dislocations can move backward and forward without further hardening. The number moving backward and forward in polycrystalline copper can be estimated from the width of the hysteresis loop observed by Thompson *et al.*,[29] who found, when the initial hardening was over, a value of $1/Q$ equal to 0.04. If we suppose that the reversible strain on each half cycle due to movement of dislocations is ϵ_0, then the energy dissipated in each cycle is $4\epsilon_0\sigma$. The elastic energy in the specimen is $\sigma^2/2G$, so the value of the damping constant Q is given by

$$1/Q = 2G\epsilon_0/\sigma$$

G/σ is about 500, so

$$\epsilon_0 \sim \tfrac{1}{2} \times 10^{-4}$$

But the unidirectional strain required to raise the flow stress to the value of σ of the test would have to be about 0.1, so if the mechanisms of hardening in cyclic and unidirectional stressing are similar it means that the dislocation movement at each cycle is about 1/1000 of that which has taken place in hardening the material. Thus if 1000 dislocations have moved to form a given slip line, about one moves backward and forward on each cycle.

In considering how the movement of so small a proportion of the dislocations backward and forward can produce a crack, we must remember that (*a*) in the experiments of Thompson *et al.* the crack was always formed on the surface; (*b*) the presence of oxygen accelerates fatigue. Nonetheless, according to recent experiments of McCammon and Rosenberg,[36] fatigue in copper takes place at the temperatures of liquid helium at stresses only about 2½ times higher than at room temperature.

We suggest that moving dislocations, whether near the surface or not, will produce vacancies and interstitials and also the "plates" of both types of defect described above, which cannot diffuse away much below the recrystallization temperature. After 10^4 to 10^5 cycles, the atomic planes around the active slip planes in a band will be completely disordered. The crystal will consequently expand. We suggest that a crack occurs when any of the material recrystallizes, taking up the orientation of the crystal on either side, which is bound to happen at any temperature however low if the degree of disorder is great enough. It will then contract, tensile stresses being set up. Cracks formed at the surface will normally survive and spread because gases can get in and keep them open; those in the interior will close up. It would be interesting to know whether an adsorbed layer of helium would be sufficient to hold a crack open. This seems to us unlikely, but we have at present no evidence that at the temperature of liquid helium cracks do form first on the surface.

If this is a correct description of the start of the fatigue process, we have to ask why the fatigue life is so sensitive to stress. We suggest that the formation of a crack in a single grain may not be so sensitive; according to the theory outlined here it should occur as soon as a slip line of some form crosses the grain. The rate of formation of defects by a moving dislocation may be somewhat greater in a heavily cold-worked material, but this should not be a very large effect. We anticipate, following the theory of Head,[31] that the stress dependence of the fatigue life, at any rate for stresses large enough to form the initial crack quickly, depends on the rate of spread of the crack. This prediction could be tested by experiment. Experiments on the stress and orientation dependence of persistent slip lines (cracks) in single crystals would be of considerable interest.

With the experimental evidence available at present, it is not possible to say whether the vacancy theory of fatigue is the correct one. It is certainly possible to envisage alternative mechanisms; thus a screw dislocation might move backward and forward along a slip line, local stresses at each end producing cross slip there, so that a crack or protuberance would result. Further experiments and particularly the observation of dislocations in materials work-hardened under alternating stress are needed.

REFERENCES

1. G. I. Taylor, *Proc. Roy. Soc.* (*London*), *A,* **145,** 362 (1934).
2. A. H. Cottrell, *Dislocations and Plastic Flow in Crystals,* Oxford University Press, Oxford (1953).
3. N. F. Mott, *Proc. Roy. Soc.* (*London*), *A,* **220,** 1 (1953).
4. A. N. Stroh, *Proc. Roy. Soc.* (*London*), *A,* **223,** 404 (1954).
5. A. N. Stroh, *Proc. Roy. Soc.* (*London*), *A,* **232,** 548 (1955).
6. J. Friedel, *Phil. Mag.,* **46,** 1169 (1955).
7. N. Thompson, C. K. Coogan, and J. G. Rider, *J. Inst. Metals,* **84,** 73 (1955).
8. E. H. Edwards and J. Washburn, *J. Metals,* **200,** 1239 (1954).
9. J. C. Fisher, E. W. Hart, and R. H. Pry, *Phys. Rev.,* **37,** 958 (1952).
10. N. F. Mott, *Phil. Mag.,* (7), **43,** 1151 (1952).
11. G. Leibfried, *Z. angew. Phys.,* **6,** 251 (1954).
12. J. Friedel, C. Boulanger, and C. Crussard, *Acta Met.,* **3,** 380 (1955).
13. J. Friedel, *Phil. Mag.,* **44,** 449 (1953).
14. G. Bradfield and F. Pursey, *Phil. Mag.,* **44,** 437 (1953).
15. H. Wilsdorf and D. Kuhlmann-Wilsdorf, *Z. angew. Phys.,* **4,** 361 (1952).
16. T. Nagashima and T. Yamamoto, *Acta Met.,* **4,** 97 (1956).
17. J. Diehl, S. Mader, and A. Seeger, *Z. Metallkunde,* **46,** 650 (1955).
18. T. H. Blewitt, R. R. Coltman, and J. K. Redman, *Report of the Conference on Defects in Crystalline Solids,* Physical Society, London, p. 369 (1955).
19. A. Kelly, *Phil. Mag.,* **1,** 835 (1956).
20. A. H. Cottrell and R. J. Stokes, *Proc. Roy. Soc.* (*London*), *A,* **233,** 17 (1955).
21. A. Seeger, *Phil. Mag.,* **46,** 1194 (1955).
22. A. N. Stroh, *Phil. Mag.,* (8), **1,** 489 (1956).
23. H. Wilsdorf and D. Kuhlmann-Wilsdorf, *Acta Met.,* **1,** 394 (1953).
24. P. Gay, P. B. Hirsch, and A. Kelly, *Acta Met.,* **1,** 305 (1953).
25. W. P. Mason, *Madrid Colloquium on the Deformation and Flow of Solids,* Springer-Verlag, Berlin (1956).
26. N. J. Petch, *Phil. Mag.,* (8), **1,** 186 (1956).
27. N. F. Mott, *Madrid Colloquium on the Deformation and Flow of Solids,* Springer-Verlag, Berlin (1956).
28. H. G. van Beuren, *Acta Met.,* **3,** 519 (1955).
29. N. Thompson, N. J. Wadsworth, and N. Louat, *Phil. Mag.,* (8), **1,** 113 (1956).
30. G. C. Smith and D. R. Harries, *J. Inst. Metals* (in press).
31. A. K. Head, *Phil. Mag.,* **44,** 925 (1953).
32. W. A. Wood, *Phil. Mag.,* **40,** 1028 (1955).
33. L. H. Clarebrough, M. E. Hargreaves, A. K. Head, and G. W. West, *Trans. AIME,* **203,** 99 (1955); *J. Metals,* **7,** 99 (1955).
34. M. S. Paterson, *Acta Met.,* **3,** 491 (1955).
35. R. D. McCammon and H. M. Rosenberg, *Phil. Mag.,* (8), **1,** 964 (1956).

36. R. D. McCammon and H. M. Rosenberg, *Paris Conference on Low Temperatures,* Institut du Froid, Paris, p. 482 (1955).

DISCUSSION

Referring to the first part of the presentation, HART asked what sort of situation could prevent a source from operating backward upon removal of the applied stress when a large back stress is acting on the source, a stress of the order of the strain hardening. MOTT answered that pile-ups on other slip planes which are near to the source, rather than pile-ups near the end of the slip line that was generated by the source, might prevent operation in the reverse direction.

COTTRELL expressed the thought that one gets a reasonable picture of work hardening only if the back stresses on a source are considered to be due to pile-ups in other planes rather than due to back stress from the dislocations that the source itself has generated. If the latter were true, the plastic stress-strain curve would be nearly reversible because the energy put in would be stored elastically. The stored energy as measured in polycrystals is only a small fraction of the energy put in, so practically all of the energy is dispersed irreversibly. Measurements of the stress-strain curve of single crystals of copper and nickel at low temperatures, by Adams * and by Haasen,* have shown a linear unloading obeying Hooke's law after straining well into the linear work-hardening range. The generated dislocations must go through a strain field of hills and valleys from other pile-ups and dissipate the energy they gain from the applied stress.

LEIBFRIED asked what the magnitude and wavelength of the stress field due to pile-ups might be. MOTT answered that he assumed the internal stress helped to supply the Gb/l stress needed to operate a source. LEIBFRIED said that the wavelength of the internal stress should be of the order of the source length if that length is much smaller than the length of the slipped region.

NABARRO pointed out that the process of forming a semicircular dislocation loop from a straight dislocation is an essential source of energy dissipation since the loop collapses irreversibly. COTTRELL said that this is only a small portion of the total irreversible energy in the high

* Private communication to A. H. Cottrell, 1956.

work-hardening range, if the sources remain constant in length during the deformation.

CHALMERS pointed out that reversal of slip, where the slip surface intersects the surface of the material, may be inhibited by some action of the atmosphere on the slipped surface. This effect would be most prominent if all the sources were at the surface. If the majority of sources were not surface sources, the slipped regions could be much larger than the length of the slip line observed on the surface. MOTT answered that fatigue takes place in liquid helium, where one would not expect much absorbed gas on the slip surface at that temperature.

CHALMERS asked if fracture starts where slip is parallel to the surface. WADSWORTH answered that the occurrence of cracks seemed to be fairly random around copper crystals. It was not determined whether cracks occurred where there was no slip step on the surface. WADSWORTH said that the extrusions he had observed during fatigue tests on copper came out approximately 1 μ in the slip direction and that there were no extrusions where the slip was parallel to the surface.

FISHER asked if the possibility of irreversible reciprocal slip on two adjacent slip planes had been considered. This would extrude out or draw in the material between the planes. MOTT said that he thought such reciprocal slip happened in extrusion, but he did not know how.

HONEYCOMBE pointed out some experiments which support the theory that cross slip is essential for rapid fatigue failure. Crystals of zinc with the basal plane at 45° to the push-pull axis do not fail in 200,000 cycles at loads equal to 90% of the fracture stress at liquid-nitrogen temperature. The fracture stress measured after the fatigue test is nearly the same as the initial fracture stress. This fatigue resistance may be due to the fact that there is no cross slip in zinc at low temperatures. WADSWORTH said that cadmium crystals tested in push-pull with about 10° angle between the stress axis and the slip plane showed no sign of failure until the specimen suddenly twinned, perhaps after a million cycles. The specimen then cracked rapidly at the twin boundary.

HART, referring to his initial question about the lack of reversibility in the back-stress model, said that he did not see why a source held up by large back stresses from a dislocation pile-up on the same or another slip plane would not operate in the reverse direction when the applied stress was removed. MOTT answered that there may be many more sources available that have never acted, and that these may act when the stress is reversed. HART said that those sources which have been hardened should operate in the reverse direction since they have already operated and are therefore known to work. COTTRELL expressed the opinion that the stresses on a source due to pile-ups on other slip planes are not a unique back stress equal in magnitude to the applied stress, but a rather complicated stress which varies across the slipped region. The source is then trapped in the hills and valleys of this stress field.

SHOCKLEY pointed out that the results of Gilman and Johnston, presented in Part I of this volume, indicate that slip on one plane initiates slip on adjacent planes as was assumed by Mott. SHOCKLEY added that the expanding dislocations gather momentum which can carry them over hills and valleys of stress, and allow them to cut through other dislocations. This momentum is not reversible so the dislocations cannot go back so easily.

Energy Dissipation During Fatigue Tests

N. J. WADSWORTH
Royal Aircraft Establishment
Farnborough, England

1. INTRODUCTION

In this paper I propose to describe some measurements made on the changes in the rate of dissipation of energy during the fatigue testing of various pure metals. The measurements were made on a fatigue machine at the University of Bristol.

A diagram of the machine is shown in Fig. 1. The upper end of the specimen, S, was attached to a piezoelectric force meter, SM, and thence to the massive frame of the machine. A coil and coil holder were attached to the lower end of the specimen and the coil was placed in the gap of a large permanent magnet. An alternating current was made to flow in the coil at the resonant frequency of the coil former oscillating on the specimen as a spring (about 1000 cycles/sec). The force on the specimen was measured by the force meter, SM, and at resonance is Q times that produced by the coil. Q is defined, by analogy with electrical theory, as 2π (energy of oscillation)/(energy dissipated/cycle). A fuller description of the machine and method of testing is given in reference 1.

2. MEASUREMENTS OF ENERGY LOSS

The energy dissipated in the specimen could be measured in two ways. The most direct way was to measure the heat produced. (The energy stored is only a very small fraction of the total.[2]) To do this involved attaching a thermocouple to the specimen and usually necessitated stopping the machine before each reading. The second, less di-

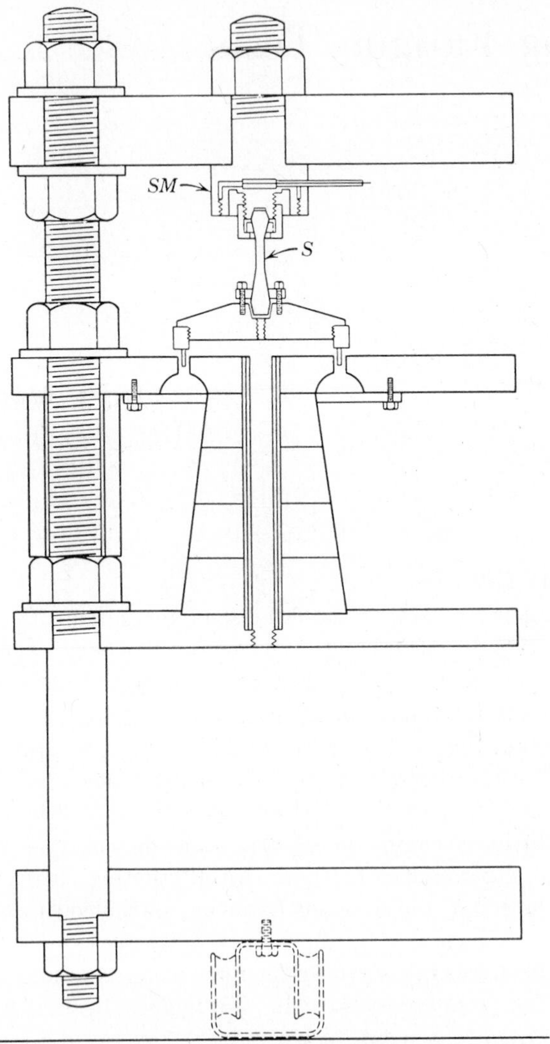

Fig. 1. The fatigue machine.

rect, method was to measure the Q of the resonant system as a whole (Q_{total}). This depended on the energy lost in the specimen grips, etc., as well as in the specimen itself but had the advantage that, since Q_{total} is given by the ratio of the reading of the force meter to that of the coil current meter, it could be measured continuously during the test. A comparison of the two methods showed that the contribution of the specimen grips, etc., to $1/Q$ was independent of stress or time for any one setting of the clamping screws, etc. Thus if $1/Q_{\text{total}}$ was measured, $1/Q_{\text{specimen}}$ could be obtained by subtracting a constant which varied from specimen to specimen. At low stress $1/Q_{\text{specimen}}$ was small, which allowed the constant to be estimated. In this report all the graphs are of $1/Q_{\text{total}}$.

3. VARIATION IN ENERGY DISSIPATION DURING THE TEST

The variations in energy dissipation observed will be discussed in two parts: first the hardening which occurred at the start of the test and then the fatigue softening which occurred during the remainder of the test.

Initial Hardening

When an annealed specimen was first tested it was very soft. The energy loss was large and it took about 1000 cycles to reach operating stress. The amplitude of the cyclic stress was then held constant and the specimen hardened rapidly. Figure 2 shows the results of measurements made at successively higher stresses on a copper single crystal. In each case cycles were measured from the time the operating stress was reached. At all stresses the crystal hardened in a similar manner and was fully hard after a few thousand cycles. The energy dissipated in the specimen was then small, almost all the measured energy loss occurred in the grips, etc. The lower initial values of $1/Q$ in the tests at higher stresses reflect the increased time needed to obtain these stresses rather than a fundamental change. Similar hardening curves were obtained from copper polycrystals (Fig. 3), aluminum polycrystals (Fig. 4), and silver polycrystals. In all these cases hardening was virtually completed in about 6000 cycles. If the material were not completely soft at the start of the test, $1/Q$ was low and the initial drop did not occur.

The hardening shown here is similar to the decrease in hysteresis loop width found by Thompson, Coogan, and Rider [3] on aluminum single crystals stressed in push-pull at a rate of 1 cycle in 4 min. Their measurements only covered the first thousand cycles, whereas those reported here are not reliable until after this. Also, the speeds of the two tests differ by a factor of about 2×10^5. Either of these facts may explain the less rapid hardening found in the earlier, slower tests.

Cadmium single crystals also hardened under reversed stress but the hardening occurred very much more slowly and was still continuing after 10^6 cycles. Figure 5 shows a typical set of results. This much slower rate is probably connected with the fact that cadmium has only one slip plane, whereas all the other metals tested have four.

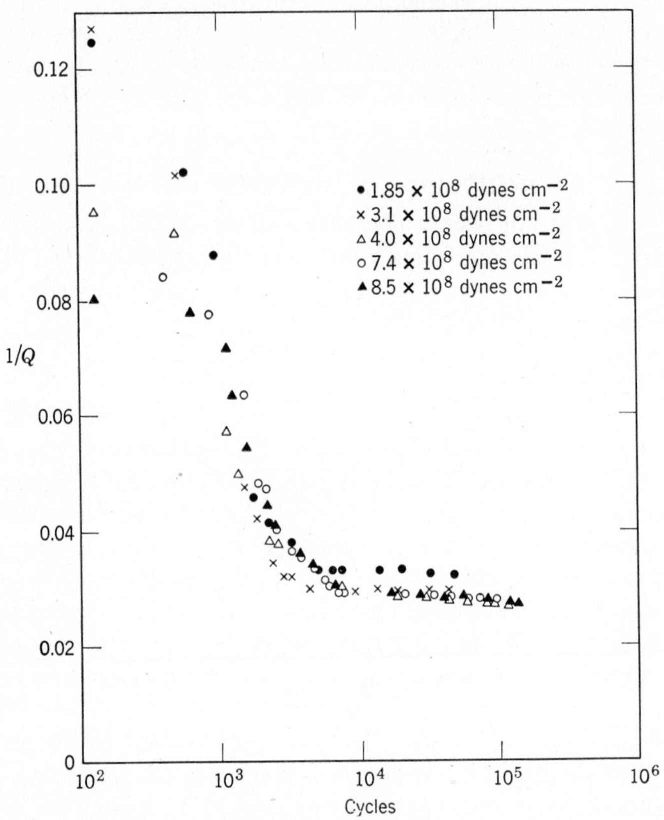

Fig. 2. The hardening of a copper single crystal.

The hardening of each material occurred in a similar manner at all stresses investigated and did not appear to be directly connected with fatigue which is very stress-sensitive.

Fatigue Softening

If the stress applied to the specimen was below the endurance limit, then, once the initial hardening was over, the energy loss remained small as shown in Fig. 3. However, if the stress was above the endurance limit, it was found that the energy loss started to increase again. This was most fully investigated on polycrystalline copper specimens which had been previously heated to 400°C for 1 hr. These were not soft

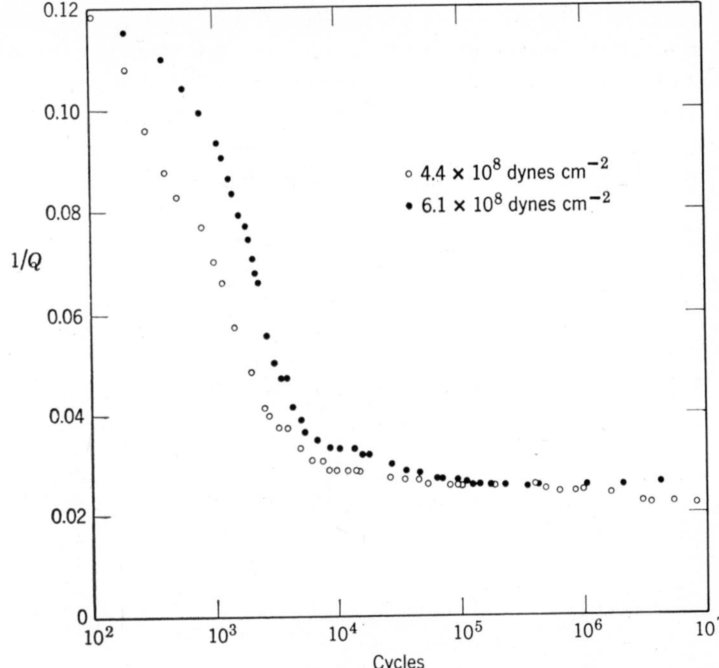

Fig. 3. The hardening of a copper polycrystal.

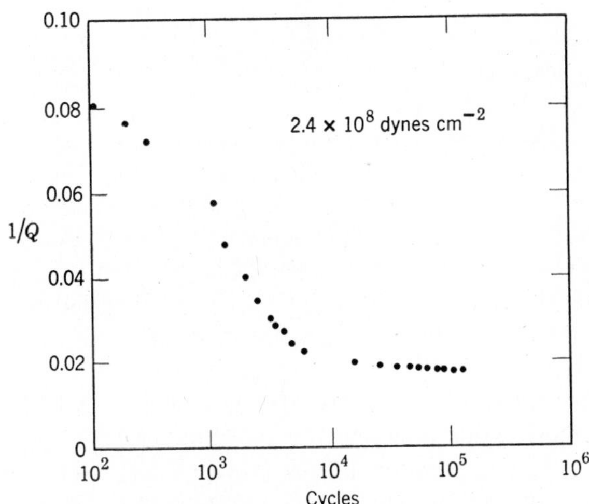

Fig. 4. The hardening of an aluminum polycrystal.

enough to show the initial hardening described in the previous section. Figure 6 shows that at the start of a typical test $1/Q_{\text{total}}$ was independent of stress. The energy dissipated in the specimen itself was only a small fraction of the total. The specimen was then fatigued at 10.8×10^8 dynes cm^{-2} and the variation of $1/Q$ with stress is shown after various numbers of cycles. As the test progressed the energy loss

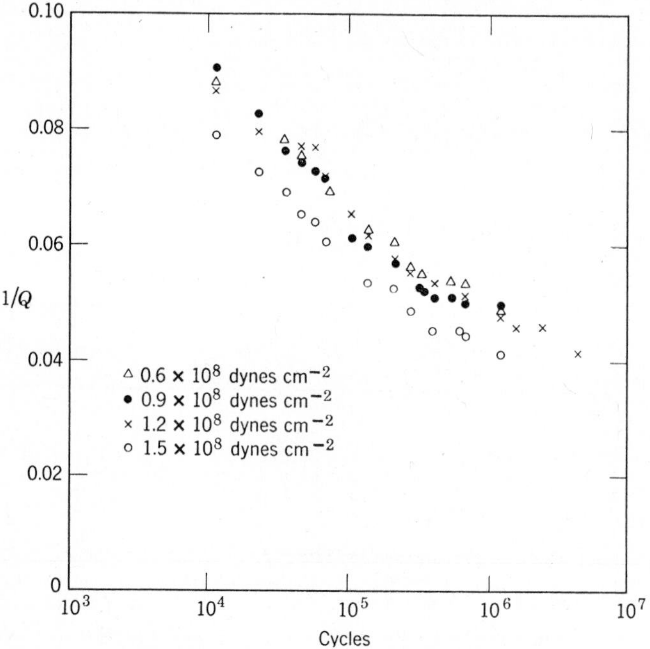

Fig. 5. The hardening of a cadmium single crystal.

at high stress increased steadily, but at low stress it remained low. This specimen broke after about 1.5×10^7 cycles. For other specimens the variation of $1/Q$ was measured only at the fatigue stress and Fig. 7 shows the results obtained. In each case $1/Q$ increased steadily during the test. A quite small increase in stress resulted in a large reduction in life and a large increase in the slope of the $1/Q$ versus cycles curve. (The range of stress represented in Fig. 7 is 1.16:1.) There was a close correlation between the rate of increase of $1/Q$ at the start of the test and the eventual life of the specimen. This is shown in Fig. 8, where the initial rate of rise of $1/Q$ is plotted against the life of the specimen. The scatter here is similar to that on the plot of life against stress, i.e., the prediction of life from the rise of $1/Q$ is about as accurate as the prediction from stress.

A second batch of copper was tested after annealing for 1 hr at 500°C or 600°C. These specimens were soft and gave the variation of $1/Q$ with cycles shown in Fig. 9. Again there was a correlation between rate of increase of $1/Q$—measured after the initial hardening was over—and the eventual fatigue life. The results obtained with this material are also shown in Fig. 8. The correlation is good but it is different from

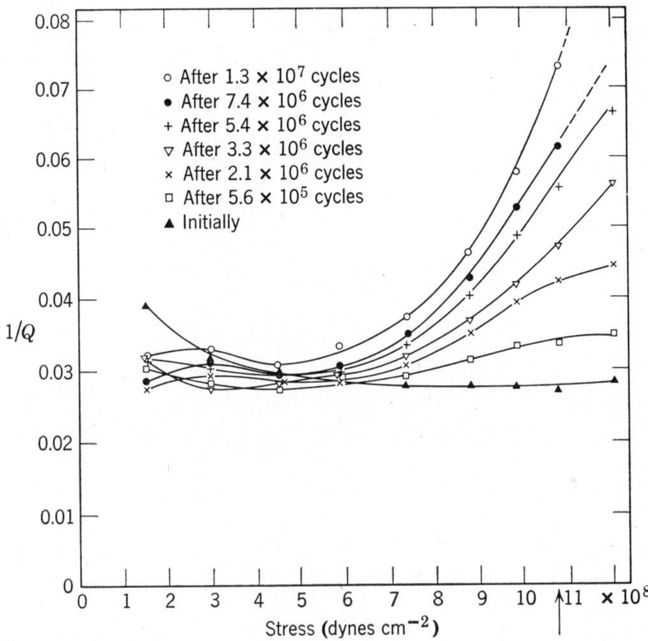

Fig. 6. The variation with stress of $1/Q$ of a copper polycrystal after various numbers of cycles at 10.8×10^8 dynes cm^{-2}

that for the unsoftened specimens. However, the difference between the two lives in Fig. 8 is much less than the difference between the stress-life curves for the two materials.* For example, the ratio of the lives of the two materials at the same stress was 100:1 (10^8:10^6 cycles), whereas the ratio of lives for the same rate of increase of $1/Q$ was about 1:2. It thus seems there is a fairly direct connection between energy loss and fatigue, and it looks as if energy loss might be used as a sensitive indicator of fatigue damage. Unfortunately this is not so.

It was found [1] that the fatigue cracks always formed on the surface of the specimen and that they could be removed by electropolishing the surface deeply at intervals during the test. Alternatively, both the

* These are shown as lines *A* and *B* of Fig. 2 of reference 1.

deepening and spreading of cracks could be slowed down considerably by surrounding the specimen by nitrogen instead of air. Neither of these actions affected the energy dissipation in the specimen or its rate

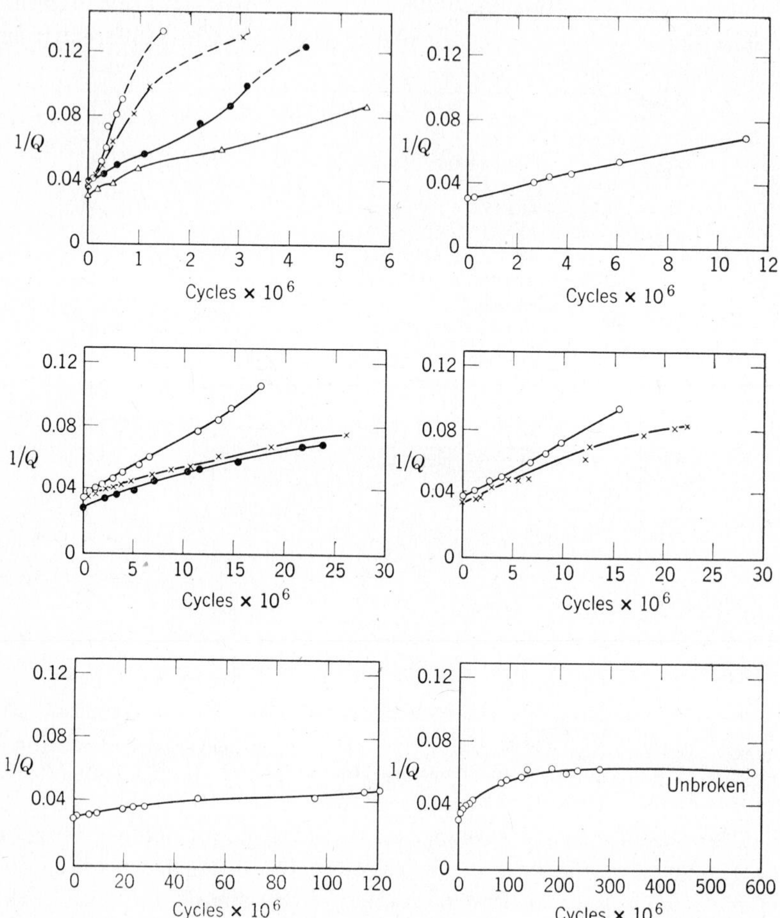

Fig. 7. The variations of $1/Q$ during the fatigue life of a number of polycrystalline copper specimens.

of increase. On the other hand, it was possible to reduce the fatigue softening without affecting the fatigue damage by annealing the specimen. If the specimen was annealed for 1 hr at 600°C after being partially fatigued, it became soft and hardened rapidly on being stressed again. After hardening, its energy loss was almost as low as that for a new specimen and on continuing the fatigue test it softened

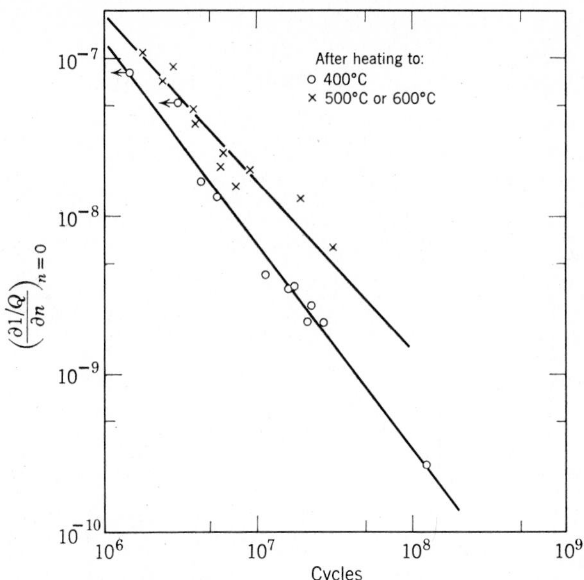

Fig. 8. The relation between initial rate of increase of $1/Q$ and the eventual fatigue life of polycrystalline copper specimens.

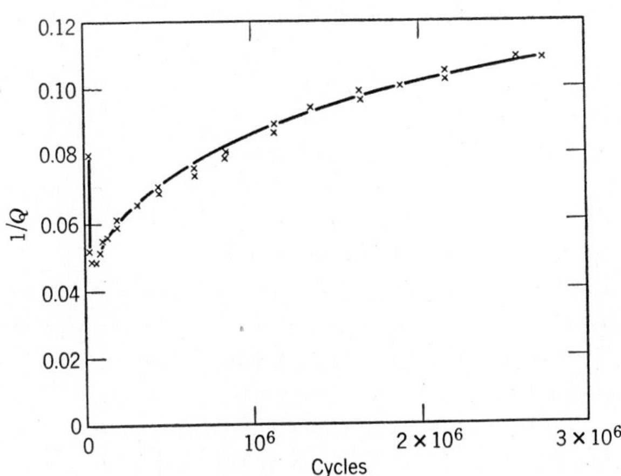

Fig. 9. The variation of $1/Q$ during the fatigue life of fully softened polycrystalline copper specimens.

again. Most of this new softening could be removed by a second anneal. Figure 10 shows the variation of $1/Q$ during a test in which the specimen was annealed after every 20% of its normal life. The specimen broke at the start of the sixth run, indicating that the anneals had not affected the life.

The fatigue softening of other material has not been investigated in such detail but the variation of $1/Q$ during tests on copper single

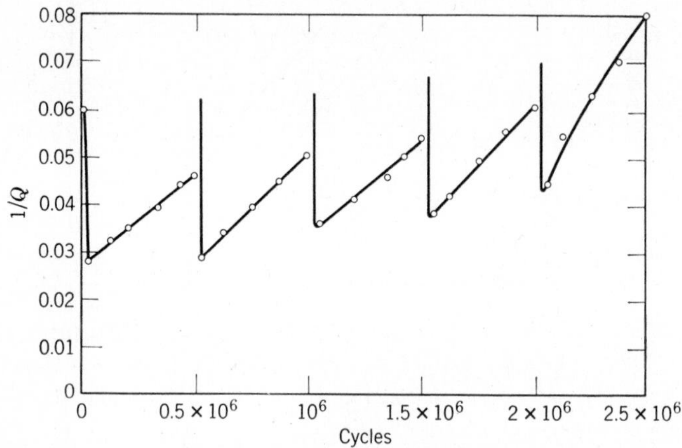

Fig. 10. The variation of $1/Q$ during the fatigue life of a polycrystalline copper specimen which was annealed at 600°C at intervals.

crystals, aluminum polycrystals, and silver polycrystals appeared to be very similar. In cadmium the fracture was associated with deformation twins and the variation of $1/Q$ was quite different.

4. DISCUSSION

The previous results may be summarized as follows. If the specimen was soft initially, the hysteresis loop was large at the start of the test and narrowed rapidly. The manner in which this happened was independent of stress over the range investigated and the hardening took place during the first few thousand cycles for the face-centered cubic metals tested and over some millions of cycles for cadmium. If the metal was hard at the start of the test, this hardening did not occur.

If the stress was below the endurance limit, little further change took place. Above this limit the rate of energy dissipation increased steadily during the test. Under similar conditions there was a close correlation between the initial rate of increase of energy loss and fatigue life. However, the energy loss was unaffected by surface conditions but could be altered by annealing, whereas the growth of cracks could be altered by surface effects but was not affected by an annealing treatment which caused considerable change in the energy dissipation.

The simplest explanation appears to be that the energy was dissipated in the broad fatigue slip bands which appeared on the specimens. Their number increased throughout the test in the same way as the rate of energy loss did. (These bands appear to occur throughout the bulk of the specimen.[4]) The fatigue cracks formed in the bands at the surface of the specimen so a correlation between energy loss and crack formation would be expected. Changes in surface conditions could affect crack formation without altering the bulk energy dissipation, whereas annealing could alter the energy loss without affecting the growth of already existing cracks.

REFERENCES

1. N. Thompson, N. Wadsworth, and N. Louat, *Phil. Mag.*, **1,** 113 (1956).
2. L. M. Clarebrough, M. E. Hargreaves, A. K. Head, and G. W. West, *J. Metals,* **7,** 99 (1955).
3. N. Thompson, C. K. Coogan, and J. R. Rider, *J. Inst. Metals,* **84,** 75 (1955).
4. D. S. Kemsley, *Nature,* **178,** 652 (1956).

DISCUSSION

SEEGER asked if fatigue tests had been performed on a metal under conditions of stress and temperature which did not produce slip bands, and if the endurance limit coincided with the stress level required to produce slip bands. The answer to that question would be of interest because of recent views that at least one type of fatigue crack starts in the slip bands. WADSWORTH answered that neither point had been investigated. At stresses giving long lives the fatigue slip bands formed slowly, so long tests would be needed to find if they occurred at all at lower stresses. Copper probably does not have a fatigue limit below which failure would never occur.

WADSWORTH said that the cracks started in slip bands, and in polycrystals they tended to come from slip bands near twin boundaries. Incipient cracks could be found by lightly electropolishing the surface. Dark markings were seen which turned into macroscopic cracks on further loading. In a single crystal with a slip band intersecting the surface all the way around, incipient cracks were found all the way around. The markings were a little longer when the slip direction was parallel to the surface, but there were no large gaps between markings.

HONEYCOMBE asked if glide-band formation is altered by polishing a thick layer off the crystal. WADSWORTH answered that after 25% of the life, polishing off approximately 30 μ would remove all the markings, but after 50% of the life there were real cracks a few tenths of a millimeter deep, so much more material would have to be polished off to remove them. A specimen was fatigued for 25% of its normal life and polished to remove about 30 μ. This was repeated nine times and each time slip bands and incipient cracks reappeared on restressing. After these nine tests, the specimen was unbroken and looked as good as new, so it appears that the fatigue damage was confined to the surface layers even under uniform stress.

BOAS said that the stored energy measured in copper in push-pull fatigue was rather small. The energy stored in the bulk of the specimen after removal of the fracture surfaces corresponds to the energy stored in such a specimen after 30% elongation. BOAS added that this energy came out of the fractured specimen at a time when the specimen had not recrystallized. COTTRELL asked if the contribution of point defects had been found in the annealing. BOAS answered that no contribution from point defects was found in copper, but that additional work was being done.

LOMER asked how accurately the energy dissipated in the specimen and the temperature rise could be measured in order to determine the stored energy. WADSWORTH answered that the stored energy is a very small fraction of the total energy dissipated and the experimental inaccuracy did not allow it to be detected. BOAS pointed out that in Wadsworth's experiment the stored energy was found by taking the difference between two relatively large quantities; therefore the accuracy is limited.

SHOCKLEY asked if experiments were done with an alternating stress superimposed on a nonzero stress. SHOCKLEY speculated that a bias stress might make a difference in whether an extrusion or a crack is formed. WADSWORTH said that this was not done deliberately but it was found that with soft single crystals a very small asymmetry in the stress made the specimen deform quite appreciably in the slip bands which developed in fatigue. In the tests on polycrystalline specimens the weight of the coil holder did not cause any extension. No large mean stresses were used.

BARRETT reported that Dr. George Sines at the Institute for the Study of Metals of the University of Chicago has been conducting fatigue tests in an attempt to determine the fatigue characteristics of highly brittle metallic specimens. He chose an extremely brittle intermetallic compound, gamma brass, prepared rotating beam fatigue specimens of the material by grinding the cast bars, and tested them with a testing program designed to see whether they broke immediately on increase of stress or only after a number of cycles at a given stress; in other words, to determine whether failure was solely dependent on stress magnitude or was cycle-dependent as it is in ductile metals. The current situation regarding the results is that eight out of the ten specimens tested underwent failure while the stress on the rotating specimen was being increased. The two exceptions, which failed after some cycling at constant stress, were found to have larger grains than the rest, and thus far it is not known whether this characteristic accounts for their different behavior. To carry out this test in an effective way that avoided trouble from accidental vibrations, Sines raised the stress by a given increment and then immediately lowered it to the constant stress level used for the cycling. At the conclusion of the run at that stress level the same procedure was repeated at a higher stress, and so on until a break occurred. By this sequence it was found that the fatigue strength at 3×10^6 cycles was within 10% of the brittle rupture strength.

VI THEORY OF DISLOCATIONS

Thermal Motion of Dislocation Lines

G. LEIBFRIED

Institute for Theoretical Physics
University of Göttingen
Göttingen, Germany

In this paper some aspects of the thermal behavior of dislocations will be treated. Two points will be regarded in detail:

1. The thermal forces on anchoring points.
2. The thermal amplitudes in a region where the dislocation is held by an internal shear stress.

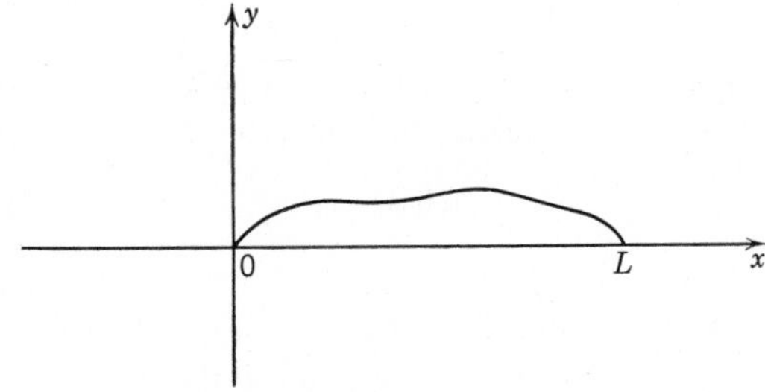

Fig. 1. Dislocation fixed at the points $x = 0, L$.

The dislocation line is given by $y(x, t)$; it is anchored at the points $x = 0, L$ of the x-axis (Fig. 1); the x-y plane is the glide plane. If one only regards states in which the derivative $y' = \partial y/\partial x$, and the ratio

$\dot{y}/c$ of the dislocation velocity, $\dot{y} = \partial y/\partial t$, and the velocity, c, of sound * are small as compared with 1, one gets for the kinetic energy (cf. Seeger [1])

$$\epsilon_{\text{kin}} = \int_0^L dx\, E\dot{y}^2/2c^2 \tag{1}$$

and for the "potential energy" †

$$\epsilon_{\text{pot}} = \int_0^L dx\, Ey'^2/2 \tag{2}$$

E, the line energy of the dislocation, is approximately $Gb^2/2$, b is the Burgers vector, and G the shear modulus (isotropic media).

Let there exist an internal shear stress

$$\tau(x, y) = -\tau_0 y/b$$

which tends to keep the line along the x-axis and which in some sense corresponds to a "potential trough" for the dislocation. Then eq. 2 has to be replaced by

$$\epsilon_{\text{pot}} = \int_0^L dx\, \{Ey'^2/2 + \tau_0 y^2/2\} \tag{2a}$$

(τ_0 may depend on x; for instance, it may be different from zero only along a certain interval of the x-axis.) Then the equation of motion is

$$Ey'' - \tau_0 y = E\ddot{y}/c^2 \tag{3}$$

The boundary conditions $y(0, t) = y(L, t) = 0$ are satisfied by an adequate expansion

$$y(x, t) = \sum_{n=1,2,3\cdots} a_n(t) \sin k_n x, \qquad \text{where } k_n = n\pi/L \tag{4}$$

If τ_0 is independent of x, one gets for the coefficients a_n the equations of a set of harmonic oscillators according to eq. 3

$$\ddot{a}_n + \omega_n{}^2 a_n = 0, \qquad \text{where } \omega_n{}^2 = k_n{}^2 c^2 + \tau_0 c^2/E$$

Therefore, one can easily apply the laws of statistical mechanics. The amplitudes a_n are independently distributed according to a Gauss law. The mean value $\langle a_n \rangle_{\text{av}}$ is zero, and the square fluctuation is

* In isotropic media c equals c_t, the velocity of transverse sound waves, for screw dislocations. For edge dislocations one has: $c^2 = c_t{}^2 \cdot 2(1 - c_t{}^2/c_l{}^2)(1 + c_t{}^4/c_l{}^4)$, where c_l is the velocity of logitudinal waves. In the second case c is nearly equal to c_t too.

† According to eq. 2, ϵ_{pot} is the change of line energy due to the deviation of the line from the normal position along the x-axis.

$$(EL/4c^2)\langle \dot{a}_n{}^2 \rangle_{\text{av}} = (EL/4c^2)\omega^2 \langle a_n{}^2 \rangle_{\text{av}} = \epsilon(\omega, T)/2 \tag{5}$$

$\epsilon(\omega, T)$ is Planck's function: $\epsilon(\omega, T) = \begin{cases} kT \text{ for } kT \geq \hbar\omega. \\ \hbar\omega/2 \text{ for } T = 0. \end{cases}$

The finite number of degrees of freedom resulting from lattice structure may be taken into account by cutting off at a maximum k-value: $k_m = \pi/a$ (or $n_m = L/a$), i.e., only wavelengths larger than twice the lattice constant a are allowed.*

One can easily see that the above assumptions y', $\dot{y}/c \ll 1$ are valid. For y' at $x = 0$, where the largest derivatives occur, one gets from

$$y'_0 = \sum_n k_n a_n$$

the square fluctuation †

$$\langle y'_0{}^2 \rangle_{\text{av}} = \sum_n \langle a_n{}^2 \rangle_{\text{av}} k_n{}^2 \tag{6}$$

Introducing the mean values $\langle a_n{}^2 \rangle_{\text{av}}$ according to eq. 5 and choosing L so large that one can replace the summation over n by an integration, one gets ‡

$$\langle y'_0{}^2 \rangle_{\text{av}} = 2kT/Ea \qquad \text{for high temperatures} \tag{7a}$$

$$\langle y'_0{}^2 \rangle_{\text{av}} = hc/4Ea^2 = k\theta/2Ea \qquad \text{for } T = 0 \tag{7b}$$

where θ is the Debye temperature.§

Let $a = b$ for a rough approximation; one has, using an empirical relation ‖ $kT_s/Gb^3 \cong 3 \times 10^{-2}$ between melting temperature T_s and shear modulus G,

$$\langle y'_0{}^2 \rangle_{\text{av}} = 12 \times 10^{-2}\, T/T_s \qquad \text{for high temperatures}$$

$$\langle y'_0{}^2 \rangle_{\text{av}} = 3 \times 10^{-2}\, \theta/T_s \qquad \text{for } T = 0$$

There are, therefore, essentially y'-values up to 0.35; the values of $\dot{y}/c$ are of the same order of magnitude if T is near T_s. The initially made assumptions are evidently valid for not too high temperatures.

The calculated value of $\langle y'_0{}^2 \rangle_{\text{av}}$ which is independent of L has still another physical meaning. Imagine that the dislocation is fixed along

* For wavelengths of the order a the above simple treatment does not apply. But this would not change the results essentially.

† y'_0 is a linear function of the a_n and is, therefore, gaussian distributed too, with the mean value zero.

‡ The results are independent of τ_0 as long as $\tau_0 a^2/E\pi^2 \ll 1$.

§ $hc/2a$ is about equal to $k\theta$.

‖ This relation is valid for f.c.c. metals; b is the shortest Burgers vector in the f.c.c. lattice.[2]

an interval l (Fig. 2). Then the force, K, on one anchoring point is $K = Ey'_0$. The same force is acting on the other anchoring point and therefore the mean square force acting on the whole interval l is $\langle K^2 \rangle_{av} = 2E^2 \langle {y'_0}^2 \rangle_{av}$, independent of l, i.e.,

$$\langle K^2 \rangle_{av} \cong 2E^2 \times 10^{-1}\ T/T_s \qquad \text{for high temperatures}$$

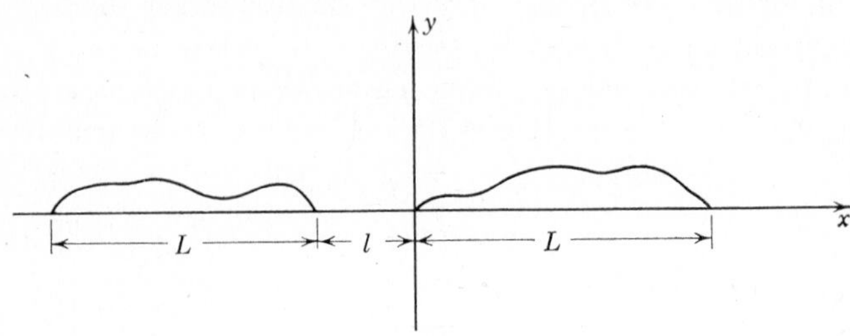

Fig. 2. Fixed length, l, of a dislocation line with neighboring free lines.

One should compare this force with a shear stress τ_l acting on the length $l(K = \tau_l bl)$; then

$$\langle \tau_l^2 \rangle_{av} = (Gb/l)^2 \times 10^{-1}\ T/2T_s$$

or

$$\{\langle \tau_l^2 \rangle_{av}\}^{1/2} = (Gb/l)\{10^{-1}\ T/2T_s\}^{1/2}$$

If l is of atomistic order of magnitude one gets, therefore, equivalent shear stresses $\tau_l \approx 10^{-1}\ G$ [even at low temperatures, where one has to use eq. 7(b) instead of 7(a)]. τ_l seems to be very large, but when comparing it with the effect of an external shear stress τ_a in the same situation, one has $\tau_l l = \tau_a L$; i.e., the external stress is magnified by a factor L/l and depends strongly on L. If L is about $10^4\ b$, the corresponding τ_a is about $10^{-5}\ G$, the elastic limit. Anyway, the result shows that thermal forces on localized obstacles (anchoring points) may be very high, and that therefore a possibility exists to overcome the obstacles by thermal motion.* At first sight one would expect that this effect is important at low temperatures too, but the next example will show that this is not the case.

When the line is embedded in a "potential trough" τ_0,† one gets for the lowest possible oscillation

* The same treatment is possible when taking into account external stresses. In this case one has to start from the static equilibrium position of the dislocation, expanding $y(x, t)$ in an analogous way.

† If the x-axis lies along a certain crystallographic direction, and one would like to take the potential trough as a model for the Peierls force τ_P, one has with $\tau_0 \sim 4\tau_P$, the condition $\langle a_1^2 \rangle_{av} > b^2/4$ for overcoming the Peierls force thermally.

$$\langle a_1{}^2\rangle_{\text{av}} = 2kT/(\pi^2 E/L + \tau_0 L) \tag{8a}$$

and for the free line ($\tau_0 = 0$)

$$\langle a_1{}^2\rangle_{\text{av}} = b^2 4LkT/\pi^2 bGb^3 \tag{8b}$$

This is practically the same as the fluctuation of $y(L/2)$ in the center of the interval. According to eq. 8(b) and with $L/b \sim 10^4$, one has $(\langle a_1{}^2\rangle_{\text{av}})^{1/2} \sim 10b$. The value, eq. 8($a$), for the fluctuation has a maximum when $L \cong 2b\{G/\tau_0\}^{1/2}$. For larger L too much energy has to be spent for the potential trough; for smaller L, too much for the lengthening of the line.

A more realistic model for a localized obstacle is to take

$$\tau_0(x) = \begin{cases} \tau_0 & \text{in the interval } (x, x + l) \\ 0 & \text{otherwise} \end{cases}$$

If one choses especially for x the center of the line $L/2$, one gets for the deviation $y_{1/2} = y(L/2)$ a result very similar to eq. 8(a), namely

$$\langle y_{1/2}{}^2\rangle_{\text{av}} = 2kT/(\pi^2 E/L + 2\tau_0 l) \tag{9}$$

This is calculated in the following way: In the potential energy,

$$\epsilon_{\text{pot}} = \int_0^L dx\ \{Ey'^2/2 + \tau_0(x)y^2/2\} = \sum_n ELk_n{}^2 a_n{}^2/2 + \tfrac{1}{2}\sum_{n,m} a_n a_m \int_0^L \tau_0(x) \sin k_n x \sin k_m x\, dx$$

one can replace the integral in the double sum, if l is not too large, by

$$\tau_0 l \sin k_n L/2 \sin k_m L/2 = \tau_0 l \sin n\pi/2 \sin m\pi/2$$

The "Zustands integral" $Z = \int \exp\ (-\epsilon_{\text{pot}}/kT)\, da_1\, da_2 \cdots$ can be evaluated exactly in this case: *

$$Z = (2\pi kT)^{n_m/2} \left\{ \prod_{n=1}^{n_m} \alpha_n{}^2 [1 + \tau_0 l \sum_{m(\text{odd})} \alpha_m{}^{-2}] \right\}^{-1/2}$$

where $\alpha_n{}^2 = ELk_n{}^2/2$ and $n_m = L/a$. Then one gets

$$\langle a_n{}^2\rangle_{\text{av}} = -2kT\partial \ln Z/\partial \alpha_n{}^2$$

and especially for

* If one has $\epsilon_{\text{pot}} = \sum_{m,n} \tfrac{1}{2} C_{mn} a_m a_n$, one gets Z easily by an orthogonal transformation to principal axes. Then Z depends mainly on the determinant of the matrix C_{mn}, which may be straightforwardly calculated.

$$y_{\frac{1}{2}} = \sum_n a_n \sin n\pi/2$$

$$\langle y_{\frac{1}{2}}{}^2 \rangle_{\text{av}} = -2kT\partial \ln Z/\partial(\tau_0 l)$$

Since $\sum_{m\,(\text{odd})} \alpha_m{}^{-2}$ is very nearly equal to $\alpha_1{}^{-2}$, the result for $\langle y_{\frac{1}{2}}{}^2\rangle_{\text{av}}$ and $\langle a_1{}^2\rangle_{\text{av}}$ is the same according to eq. 9. If one calculates the frequency of the ground wave approximately by taking the corresponding diagonal element of the oscillation matrix, then

$$\omega_1{}^2 \cong c^2\{\pi^2/L^2 + 2\tau_0 l/EL\}$$

If τ_0 is relatively large, i.e., $\tau_0 \gg Gb^2/lL$, one has $\langle y_{\frac{1}{2}}{}^2\rangle_{\text{av}} = kT/\tau_0 l$ and $\omega_1 \cong (2c/b)\{\tau_0 l/GL\}^{\frac{1}{2}}$; and this classical formula holds down to temperatures $kT \cong \hbar\omega_1$, i.e., temperatures small as compared to Debye temperatures. If l is nearly equal to b and taking $\langle y_{\frac{1}{2}}{}^2\rangle_{\text{av}} > b^2$ as a condition for overcoming the stress τ_0, stresses

$$\tau_0 < G(kT/Gb^3) = G(3 \times 10^{-2}\ T/T_s)$$

are easily overcome by thermal motion. Because the classical calculation holds down to very small temperatures, the zero point motion cannot have a marked influence on this effect, contrary to the results when calculating the thermal forces. In our case correlational effects are fully taken into account. There is no use in having big thermal forces with high corresponding frequencies. The correlation time of the thermal force is on the order of the reciprocal Debye frequency and this time is too short to make a big displacement. The biggest effect is due to the lowest frequency, which is small compared with the Debye frequency.

REFERENCES

1. A. Seeger, Theory of Lattice Defects in *Handbuch der Physik,* Springer, Berlin, Vol. VII/1 (1955).
2. G. Leibfried, *Z. Physik,* **127,** 344 (1950).

DISCUSSION

LÜCKE suggested that one ought, in addition to the calculations made by Leibfried, to include the damping force as computed by Eshelby.*

* J. D. Eshelby, *Proc. Roy. Soc. (London), A,* **197,** 396 (1949).

LEIBFRIED replied that the damping was, in a sense, already included in the thermal motion. That is, if one writes down the equation of motion in the dislocation, a damping force is included which is partly of a thermal nature.

SHOCKLEY said that to him the problem of radiation of the dislocation line seemed similar to the family of problems such as the Johnson noise or thermal noise in a resistor, or the viscosity of a sphere in brownian motion, and he wondered if Leibfried had tried to work the problem backwards. A dislocation line of this sort should have a certain amount of viscous damping and if this were calculated, one should come out with the same result as had been obtained by carrying out the calculation in the forward direction. He asked if Leibfried had carried out this self-consistent procedure. LEIBFRIED replied he had thought of doing something like this, but if one tries to carry the problem backwards, then one needs to know the whole spectrum of the correlation. It turns out that the spectrum does not have the same characteristics as the spectrum of the Johnson noise or of the viscous motion; i.e., the spectrum is not a white spectrum. LEIBFRIED admitted, however, that in this sense the theory was really not quite complete.

SEITZ asked if the method Leibfried has applied could be used to obtain the relationship between the entropy of the dislocation and the temperature. In particular, would the entropy of a dislocation be anything more than the entropy of a system of oscillators? LEIBFRIED replied that the entropy should be precisely that of the entropy of a system of oscillators and that it could be obtained by an application of the usual treatments of statistical mechanics. He mentioned that the dislocation degrees of freedom would subtract from the lattice degrees of freedom, and that since the lattice is really a collection of particles, the contribution of the lattice is also changed.

SEEGER suggested that in treating problems of thermal activation of dislocation lines it is sometimes useful to introduce the entropy of activation of a dislocation. For instance, if we have the potential energy of the dislocation drawn as in Fig. D1 (say due to the Peierls stress), then the dislocation has to move out of one of the valleys of the lattice potential over an energy barrier into the following valley. The simplest

Fig. D1. Potential energy of the dislocation.

approach to the calculation of the rate of such a process is to assume that the frequency with which the dislocation moves over the barrier is given as a product of a frequency factor times an exponential containing the activation energy; $\nu e^{-F/kT}$. $F = U - TS$ is the free energy of activation. The activation energy U is that energy which is necessary to push a critical length of the dislocation over the barrier. The frequency factor, ν, is simply the frequency of the dislocation as it oscillates in its potential well due to thermal motion. The activation process just described is believed to give rise to the Bordoni peaks of internal friction.* However, one does not get good agreement with experiments if in the preceding formula the entropy of activation S is neglected. In the present problem one does indeed have a negative entropy of activation due to the flexibility of the dislocation line. In the ground state (i.e., when the dislocation lies in the bottom of the valley) adjacent parts of the dislocation line may oscillate in different phases, the dislocation line undergoing a sort of wavelike motion. In the activated state the critical length of the dislocation must move in the forward direction and not undergo any wavelike motion. If d_{cr} denotes the critical length of activation and d_f is a flexibility length, giving the minimum distance along the dislocation of points which move independently of each other, the entropy of activation is, by Boltzmann's principle,

$$S = k \log [(\tfrac{1}{2})^{d_{cr}/d_f}]$$

The frequency of successful activations is therefore given by

$$\nu[(\tfrac{1}{2})^{d_{cr}/d_f} e^{-U/kT}]$$

This formula is in good agreement with the experiments.

LEIBFRIED remarked that one would obtain the same result by calculating the thermal behavior of the dislocation displacement averaged over the critical length; i.e., only wavelengths larger than the critical length are effective.

LOMER and NABARRO felt one could not calculate the entropy of a dislocation line in the simple way suggsted by Seeger. For instance, new degrees of freedom are not added to the whole lattice simply by putting a dislocation into a crystal. One always has only a certain number of particles, N, and there are actually no new degrees of freedom. The whole problem is really a very complicated one of setting

* A. Seeger, Theory of Lattice Defects in *Handbuch der Physik,* Vol. VII/1, Springer, Berlin, sect. 72 (1955); *Deformation and Flow of Solids,* Springer, Berlin, p. 322 (1956); *Phil. Mag.,* **1,** 651 (1956).

up a new system of normal modes for the crystal. As a result of the dislocation, one lowers some of the frequencies of the modes, and thus changes the entropy of the entire crystal.

SEEGER agreed entirely with the remarks of Lomer and Nabarro as far as the change in entropy of the entire crystal on the introduction of a dislocation is concerned. The entropy of activation discussed above is of a different nature; just as does any entropy difference, it measures the difference in randomness of two states, the ground state and the activated state. It appears, therefore, to be a perfectly well-defined concept.

Some Effects of the Nonlinearity of the Elastic Laws in the Environment of a Dislocation Line

ALFRED SEEGER
Max Planck Institute for Metals
Stuttgart, Germany

I would like to discuss the breakdown of the linear elastic laws in the core of a dislocation. Consider a close-packed plane of atoms which has been sheared heavily as in Fig. 1. In the figure we see that the large shear automatically leads to a volume increase. The volume increase is due partly to a nonlinear part of the force law between atoms (causing deviations from Hooke's law) and partly to the finiteness of the strain. At large distances, r, from the dislocation, the dilatation due to these effects, Δ, is proportional to the square of the strain and, therefore, inversely proportional to the square of the distance.

$$\Delta = \frac{\alpha}{r^2} \tag{1}$$

By integration of eq. 1, it is found that in this approximation the total volume change per unit length of the dislocation is infinite if the integration is over all space. Of course, we are used to such divergent integrations in the line energy of a dislocation and, in fact, one has to cut the integration off at both the high end and the low end. The similarity to the integrations one finds in calculating the line energy of a dislocation is not accidental, as shown by Zener.[1] One can make reasonable estimates of the upper and lower limits of the integration which are similar to the limits taken in the integration for the energy of a dislocation line. In addition, one can deduce the constant of proportionality in the expression for the dilatation from the compressibility of the atoms and its pressure dependence or from the pressure dependence of the elastic constants. The result is [2] that the volume change per unit length of dislocation line is approximately 1 to 1.5 atoms. (The unit length here is the Burgers vector length.) This value agrees very well with what one obtains [3] from the ratio of stored energy to change in density as measured by Boas and his co-workers.

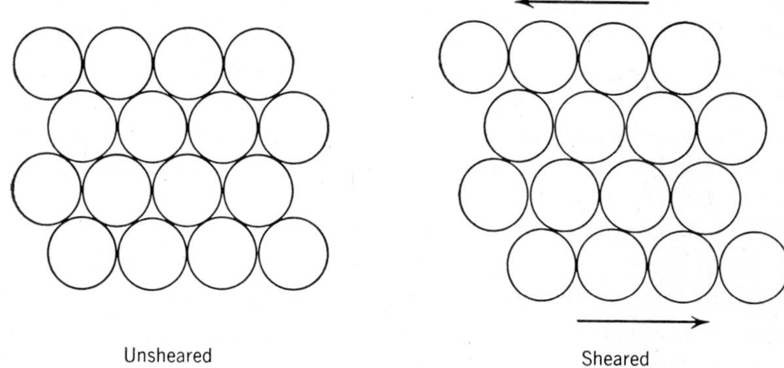

Fig. 1. Close-packed plane of atoms which is sheared heavily.

The induced change in volume around a dislocation line has a direct bearing on the electrical resistivity of a dislocation. Let us confine our attention for the moment to a discussion of screw dislocations. Everything said about the screws can be carried over directly to edges in a somewhat more complicated way. Since the center of the screw has a slightly smaller density than the main part of the crystal, electrons whose energy is proportional to $v^{-2/3}$ (v = specific volume of electrons) will want to flow into the center. They are, of course, screened out and the problem must be treated in a self-consistent way. The result is that the center of the dislocation line is electrically charged and is thus an effective scatterer of electrons. We have applied a phase-shift analysis to the scattering of the electrons due to the dislocation [2] and have found that the difference in scattering power between a screw and an edge dislocation is very much reduced from the value given by Hunter and Nabarro.[4] The result shows that Hunter and Nabarro's estimate of the electrical resistance due to the screw dislocation in copper must be increased by a factor of three. It turns out that the edge-dislocation scattering is less anisotropic perpendicular to the dislocation line than calculated in the earlier papers. The electrical resistance of dislocations calculated here is still not nearly enough to explain the experimental data on copper. One needs an additional factor of 30 to 40. One is still reduced to the conclusion that the electrical resistivity of dislocation is due mainly to a stacking-fault region between the split dislocation.[3] Calculations of the scattering power of stacking faults confirm this supposition.[5] We found that in a monovalent metal the reflection coefficient of a stacking fault, averaged over all angles of incidence and at high temperature, is of the order of ¼, which agrees with the experiments. We also considered electron scattering at very low temperatures where dislocations are the main scatterers, and at high temperatures where dislocations contribute only a small additional resistivity compared to the thermal scattering, and the result is that Matthiessen's rule does not hold. Matthiessen's rule holds best when all scattering mechanisms are nearly isotropic and breaks down both for edge and screw dislocations. It is even worse for the extended dislocations.

The volume change due to a dislocation in a crystal also has bearing on the low-angle scattering of cold-worked crystals that was first observed by Guinier [6] in 1939. In addition, this effect was studied experimentally in some detail by Blin [7] in his thesis. The low-angle scattering is sensitive to the local density of atoms in the crystal, and in the case of a dislocation, one has an extended region which has a lowered density. If one works out the details, one finds that the total amount of scattering comes out to be approximately that observed. We would like to propose, then, that the low-angle scattering in crystals is not due to scattering by cavities as proposed by Dexter,[8] Blin, and others, but is to be explained rather by the change in density of the crystal caused by the existence of dislocation lines.

In closing, I might just say that if our interpretation of low-angle X-ray scattering proves to be correct, it should lead to a promising method for the study of, say, the total number of dislocations in a crystal and perhaps even their detailed arrangement in the crystal. One may, for instance, vary the direction of incidence of the X ray on a crystal and in this way obtain information on a number of parameters which will depend upon the detailed arrangement of the dislocations in the crystal. This method of studying dislocation arrays would have the further advantage that one would not be observing the dislocations in the immediate neighborhood of the surface only, but would presumably be obtaining information about the interior of the crystal.

REFERENCES

1. C. Zener, *Trans. AIME,* **147,** 361 (1942).
2. H. Stehle and A. Seeger, *Z. Physik,* **146,** 217 (1956).
3. A. Seeger and H. Stehle, *Z. Physik,* **146,** 242 (1956).
4. S. C. Hunter and F. R. N. Nabarro, *Proc. Roy. Soc.* (*London*), *A,* **220,** 542 (1953).
5. A. Seeger, On the electrical resistivity of stacking faults in monovalent metals. *Proceedings of the Ottawa Conference* (1956).
6. A. Guinier, *Compt. Rend.* (*Paris*), **208,** 894 (1939).
7. J. Blin, Thesis, Diffusion centrale des rayons X par les métaux. Paris, Imp. des Ministère de l'Air (1956). See also J. Blin and A. Guinier, *Compt. Rend.* (Paris), **233,** 1288 (1951); **236,** 2150 (1953).
8. D. L. Dexter, *Phys. Rev.,* **90,** 1007 (1953).

DISCUSSION

BOAS expressed considerable interest in Seeger's remarks, particularly since in his laboratory various experiments had been performed measuring stored energy, density changes, and resistivity, which are discussed in his paper in Part III of this volume. He there presents two alternatives to the suggestions put forward by Seeger, one of which is rather similar to Seeger's ideas.

LEIBFRIED expressed some doubt that the size of the hole in the center of the dislocation or the change in volume could be calculated on a purely elastic basis. He suggested that the dilatation in the center of the dislocation should depend strongly on the exact nature of the forces and would depend upon whether or not the material was a metal or an ionic solid, etc. He suggested that it should be possible to settle the question of the volume change in a material only by doing an atomistic calculation. Perhaps one could obtain the result by setting up a program in which the dislocation dilatation content was determined by a variational procedure in the energy.

SEEGER replied that the calculation is based upon the idea that the missing atom is spread or smeared throughout the volume of the crystal and that very little of it actually resides in the core of the dislocation. This, incidentally, is the reason why it gives rise to a detectable small-angle scattering of X rays or neutrons. SEEGER agreed that a more exact procedure would be to do the calculation of the volume change from the point of view of the atomistic forces. However, the change in the result should be quite small, say of the order of 5%, as is the case if similar refinements are applied to the calculation of the line energy of the dislocation.

The Intersection of Gliding Screw Dislocations

A. H. COTTRELL
Atomic Energy Research Establishment
Harwell, England

1. SIMPLE ORTHOGONAL SLIP

Although it is now widely accepted that gliding dislocations produce point defects, the mechanism is still not clear. The usual view is that the defects are produced by the nonconservative motion of jogs, formed on screw dislocations by screw-screw intersections; but Friedel [1] has argued that there is no obvious reason, unless the dislocation is traveling at great speed, why a jog formed on a screw dislocation should not glide along it conservatively and so remove itself from the screw segment of the dislocation line without producing point defects.

The purpose of this paper is to point out another effect that makes the screw-screw mechanism appear doubtful. We shall see that when two systems of moving dislocations meet and intersect each other the screw-screw intersections are mostly of the type to produce interstitials, not vacancies; whereas experiments on low-temperature annealing in cold-worked metals suggest that vacancies, not interstitials, are formed in practice by plastic deformation.[2] It appears, therefore, that other processes, e.g., the wrapping of a dislocation loop round a close pair of opposite screw dislocations in a forest, may be responsible for the formation of point defects by slip.

The physical basis of the argument can be seen very simply by considering, in Fig. 1a, a crystal about to slip on diagonal planes under the given applied forces. If these planes slip simultaneously, as is necessary if screw dislocations gliding in them are to intersect, overlapping of the crystal occurs along the line of intersection and interstitials are produced (Fig. 1*b*). To produce vacancies the planes have

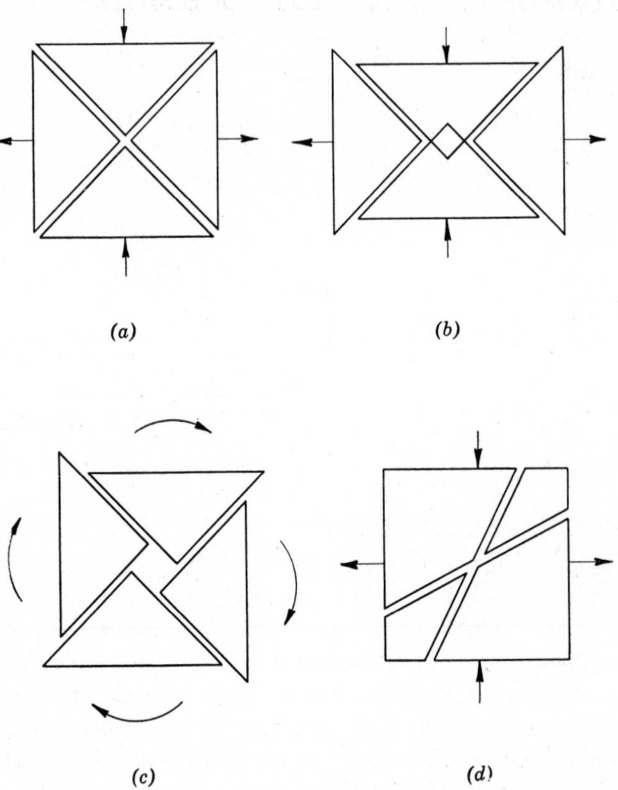

Fig. 1. (*a*) and (*b*) A crystal which slips simultaneously on diagonal planes and produces interstitials. (*c*) Planes sheared in opposite senses produce vacancies. (*d*) A crystal in which the glide systems are not orthogonal.

to shear in opposite senses (Fig. 1*c*) but this is an ineffective mode of deformation of the crystal since no work is done by the applied forces. In terms of dislocations the essential condition is that the direction of glide of a dislocation is always such that the applied stress does work through this glide. The direction of glide thus cannot be chosen independently of the Burgers vector and it so happens that the permissible choices are such that the intersections of gliding screws are mostly of the interstitial type.

There are exceptions, of course. An obvious one is that where a bundle of parallel screws, which includes some of opposite signs, glides as a unit through the crystal. When intersected by a screw gliding in some other system, jogs of both signs are produced; however, provided the applied stress does work on the bundle as a whole, more interstitial jogs than vacancy jogs are created. Another case is that where two nonparallel screws move in the same direction, the leader moving less quickly than its follower. When they intersect, vacancies are produced. However, since the frequency of such intersections is measured by the difference in the velocities of the dislocations, such intersections will be rarer than those where the dislocations move towards one another. A third exceptional case is that where the glide systems are not orthogonal (Fig. 1*d*). Here it is possible to orientate the applied stresses so that they do work on both slip planes by shears in opposite senses on them. As we shall see below, the resolved shear stress on such glide systems is usually rather low for these special orientations by comparison with that on other glide systems in the crystal.

The formal geometrical proof of these results for arbitrary states of stress and nonorthogonal glide systems is straightforward but tedious. We shall not reproduce it here, apart from verifying that in the face-centered cubic case the situation envisaged in Fig. 1*d* is unlikely.

2. FACE-CENTERED CUBIC SLIP

Since the slip systems in the face-centered cubic lattice are not orthogonal, it is not essential that the resolved shear stresses, σ_a and σ_b, on the two intersecting systems be equal. There are three possibilities: $\sigma_a = \sigma_b$, $|\sigma_a| \neq |\sigma_b|$, and $\sigma_a = -\sigma_b$. The second is connected with unequal hardening on the glide systems, and we shall not discuss it further. One or the other of the two possibilities, $\sigma_a = \pm\sigma_b$, favors the formation of vacancy jogs rather than interstitial jogs, but it is necessary to ensure that the critical shear stress is not exceeded on any other glide system. Adopting the notation of Bishop and Hill,[3] we denote the four slip planes of the face-centered cubic lattice by p, q, r, and s, and attach suffixes 1, 2, 3 to denote positive shears on them, thus:

Plane:		(111)			$(\bar{1}\bar{1}1)$			$(\bar{1}11)$			$(1\bar{1}1)$	
Shear:	p_1	p_2	p_3	q_1	q_2	q_3	r_1	r_2	r_3	s_1	s_2	s_3
Direction:	$01\bar{1}$	$\bar{1}01$	$1\bar{1}0$	$0\bar{1}\bar{1}$	101	$\bar{1}10$	$01\bar{1}$	101	$\bar{1}\bar{1}0$	$0\bar{1}\bar{1}$	$\bar{1}01$	110

Then if the components of applied stress are σ_{ij}, referred to cube axes, the components of shear stress multiplied by $\sqrt{6}$ on the glide systems are as follows:

$$\begin{array}{lll} A - G + H(p_1) & B + F - H(p_2) & C - F + G(p_3) \\ A + G + H(q_1) & B - F - H(q_2) & C + F - G(q_3) \\ A + G - H(r_1) & B + F + H(r_2) & C - F - G(r_3) \\ A - G - H(s_1) & B - F + H(s_2) & C + F + G(s_3) \end{array}$$

where

$$\begin{array}{lll} A = \sigma_{22} - \sigma_{33} & B = \sigma_{33} - \sigma_{11} & C = \sigma_{11} - \sigma_{22} \\ F = \sigma_{23} & G = \sigma_{31} & H = \sigma_{12} \end{array}$$

All pairs of systems capable of intersections suitable for producing jogs can be grouped into three classes, typified by p_1q_1, p_1q_2, and p_1q_3. In the third of these the Burgers vector of one dislocation (q_3) is parallel to the slip plane of the other (p_1), and interstitial jogs and vacancy jogs are equally favored.

We shall consider p_1q_1 intersections. Assuming equal hardening on all systems, we have $|A - G + H| = |A + G + H|$, with the solutions

$$\begin{array}{ll} A + H \neq 0, & G = 0 \\ A + H = 0, & G \neq 0 \end{array}$$

The first of these leads to $\sigma_a = \sigma_b$, and to the same conclusions as for the elementary model of Fig. 1a. The second solution, $G \neq 0$, leads to the interesting case $\sigma_a = -\sigma_b$. Since G occurs in the above array of shear stresses in all combinations of signs with the terms A, C, F, and H, the flow stress must be exceeded on some other system unless $A = B = C = F = H = 0$. The solution $G \neq 0$ is, therefore, valid only for the unique orientation of applied stress in which σ_{13} is the only nonvanishing component. Even if this orientation happens to be reached, the lattice rotations accompanying slip on the active systems are such as to rotate the crystal into another orientation, so that this state, if formed at all, could only be transient.

A similar analysis of p_1q_2 intersections can be made, but this leads back essentially to the situation of Fig. 1a again. We thus conclude that the mutual intersections of gliding screw dislocations are in the majority of cases of the interstitial type, rather than the vacancy type, for slip in both a simple orthogonal system and in the face-centered cubic system.

REFERENCES

1. J. Friedel, private communication (1955).
2. T. H. Blewitt, R. R. Coltman, and J. K. Redman, *Report of 1954 Conference on Defects in Crystalline Solids,* Physical Society, London, p. 369 (1955).
3. J. F. W. Bishop and R. Hill, *Phil. Mag.,* **42,** 1298 (1955).

Prismatic Loops as Frank-Read Sources

J. C. FISHER

General Electric Research Laboratory
Schenectady, New York

D. Turnbull in considering precipitation from solid solution, and F. C. Frank, J. H. Hollomon, and I in trying to get around Gilman and Johnston's experiments (described in Part I of this volume), where dislocations seemingly start from nowhere, have been considering the precipitation of vacancies into little plates that collapse into prismatic dislocation loops. The numerical possibilities here are quite interesting.

Suppose we start out with 10^{-5} atom fraction of vacancies in excess of the solubility limit, and allow them to precipitate. If they make little plates, ten atoms on a side, that will use up about 100 vacancies per plate. Let us assume that this is about the smallest size that can collapse and form a reasonable dislocation loop. How many such loops are there per cm^3? There are about 10^{23} atoms per cc and about 10^{-5} of those are vacancies, giving 10^{18} vacancies. When these precipitate they produce 10^{16} of the little loops per cc, which is a considerable number. The distance around such a loop is about 10^{-6} cm and there are 10^{16} of them per cc, giving about 10^{10} dislocations per cm^2, which is an appreciable density of dislocations.

Now, if you get such a number of little loops by precipitating out lattice vacancies, the loops will coarsen, the same as any other precipitate will. The smaller loops have a higher vapor pressure for vacancies than do the bigger ones, and the little ones will shrink and disappear and the big ones will grow at their expense. You will get a collection of loops that will coarsen at a steadily decreasing rate. Suppose they grow a while and get to be 1 μ on a side; this takes 10^7 vacancies per loop which is 10^5 as many as before, giving 10^{11} loops per cc of micron size. Their circumference is about 3×10^{-4} cm, giving 3×10^7 such dislocations per cm^2. That is about the size loop you would need to act as a Gilman-Johnston source if this is indeed where their dislocations come from.

As a matter of fact, putting it backwards, the fact that Gilman and Johnston get the results that they do indicates to me that vacancies do precipitate in plates that collapse and act as sources, because I cannot believe that dislocations can be generated out of nothing at such low stresses. A prismatic loop can act as a Frank-Read source, and get us out of this difficulty.

DISCUSSION

COTTRELL raised the question of whether the vacancies would precipitate as spheres, or as platelets that could then collapse to form dislocation loops. He pointed out that the spheres would have a lower surface energy, but that it is not clear which form the precipitate will take.

FRANK stated that this question cannot be answered from theoretical considerations alone. The energy of the sphere, E_s, goes as $\gamma b^2 n^{2/3}$ where γ is the surface energy and n the number of vacancies in the aggregate, and the energy of the dislocation loop, E_1, goes as $Gb^3 n^{1/2} \log n^{1/2}$, where G is the shear modulus. Hence, if we write approximately

$$E_s/E_1 \propto (\gamma/Gb)n^f$$

$$f < \tfrac{1}{6}$$

Thus the value of n for which the two energies are equal is

$$n_c \propto (Gb/\gamma)^{>6}$$

For small n the sphere is more stable, and for large n the loop has the lower energy. However, if n_c is large ($n_c > 10$), then the aggregate will have to pass through higher energy states in order to change from a sphere to a loop. If n is small enough ($n_c \lesssim 4$), then the loop will form from the sphere. One cannot calculate n_c accurately enough to tell whether $n_c \lesssim 4$, or $n_c > 10$. A great deal of this uncertainty arises because γ is a surface energy that must be corrected for the small sizes involved, and is not known to an accuracy of even 25%. This uncertainty is raised to a power greater than 6, in the expression for n_c. FRANK emphasized that without doing further experiments one cannot answer the question of whether spheres or dislocation loops will form by such calculations.

Written comment by FRANK:

When making an estimate of this kind before, I have used data for metals. Dr. Johnston points out to me that with a reasonable estimate for surface energy (Gb/γ) is more than 10 times as large for LiF as for Cu (about 90 and 7 respectively). On the face of it, the conclusion of this simple argument is, therefore, that whereas aggregation to a dislocation loop is probably (but not certainly) preferred in metals, the open aggregate is preferred in LiF. But part of my point is that the fate of the aggregate is decided when the value of n is too small for simple general arguments of this kind to be relied on. For the specific case of LiF, we may make another argument, considering the build-up of an aggregate of vacancies by successively adding vacancies of opposite sign always in the position of lowest energy, determining this by simple electrostatic considerations, neglecting the energies of interaction between ion cores, and leaving all ions on exact lattice sites. This procedure, starting with a square of two cation and two anion vacancies adjacent on (100), which is the lowest energy state for these four, gives firstly a lengthening rectangle, along [010] in (100), two ions wide, growing to an infinitely long ribbon. The position of lowest energy for addition of another vacancy otherwise than at the ends is alongside the edge of this ribbon, and the successive positions of lowest energy after this extend it into a third row, making a ribbon three ions wide. Continuation according to the same prescription gives further rows, all in the same plane. Though the compact aggregate undoubtedly represents a state of lower energy, at every stage in this sequence the energy is raised by a displacement of one or two ions from the planar configuration of the aggregate. At some stage, probably when it is about four ion-rows wide, this planar aggregate would become unstable and collapse into a dislocation loop.

MITCHELL suggested that one might try to anneal LiF at a temperature within 200°C of the melting point in order to cause the loops which have been postulated to transform into large three dimensional aggregates, which could be detected. He pointed out that, during annealing, CaF_2 crystals become opaque, which could be due to a separation of vacancies into large aggregates which can scatter light. FISHER replied that the loops would tend to dissolve again at the high temperature to give the equilibrium vacancy concentration.

HOLLOMON suggested that if the mobilities of the defects produced during radiation damage differ sufficiently, the vacancies might disappear or collapse by the mechanism which was discussed by Fisher. Annealing experiments should then depend very much on past history of the specimen; the experiments should not be very reproducible,

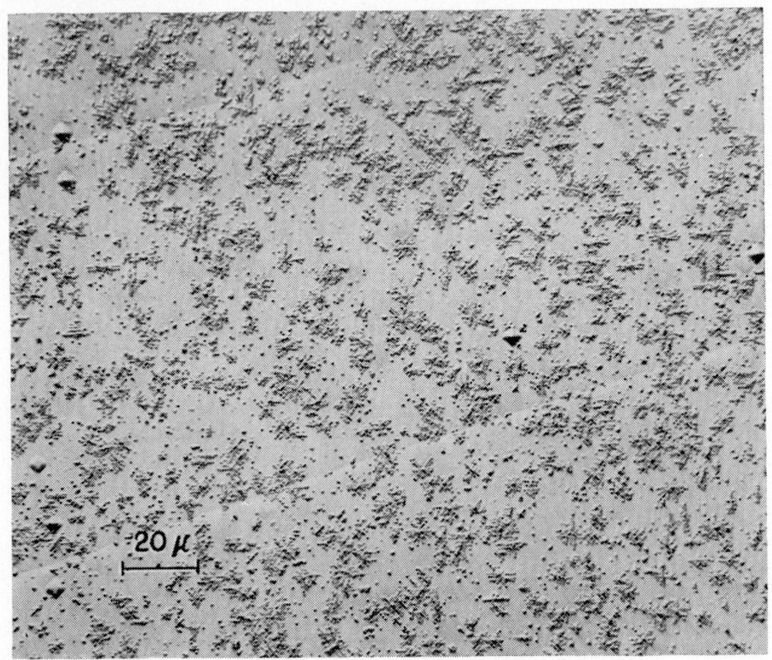

Fig. D1. LiF crystal was etched heavily, 75 to 100 μ, Al_2O_3 spheres were dropped onto it from 1-cm height, and the crystal was etched very lightly. The small pits correspond to dislocations that were produced by the impacts of the spheres.

and should show very complicated kinetics. SHOCKLEY objected to this because if the vacancies and interstitials are made in the same region of the crystal by the radiation damage, they will tend to annihilate each other. It is unlikely that they will precipitate separately to collapse and give loops of opposite Burgers vector. SHOCKLEY pointed out that in an experiment such as he has suggested for surface radiation damage (Shockley's paper, in Part VIII of this volume), one might have interstitials driven into the interior of a crystal to remove to some extent the sort of loops that Fisher has described.

BLEWITT recalled that there is some evidence that in radiation damage the interstitials and vacancies are separated. This idea is due to Kinchin and Pease,* who suggested that the interstitials can rapidly move far into the lattice, away from the creation site.

Written comment by GILMAN and JOHNSTON:

The X-ray evidence in our paper (in Part I of this volume) indicates that the dislocation density in as-grown LiF crystals is much lower than the 10^7 cm^{-2} postulated by Fisher. Therefore, it is very doubtful that such loops exist.

An experimental lower limit can be placed on the number of dislocation nucleation sites in LiF crystals. These are places where dislocations can be created at stresses smaller than 1% of the elastic shear modulus. Aluminum oxide spheres † of 75 to 100 μ diameter were dropped onto the surface of a LiF crystal from a height of 1 cm. The crystal was etched heavily before the spheres were dropped, and lightly afterward. Figure D1 shows the dislocations created by the spheres when they struck the crystal, and a very few large pits locating the dislocations that were previously present. From the illustration, one can deduce that there were at least 2×10^6 cm^{-2} nucleation sites. The new dislocations extended less than 3 μ into the crystal, so a lower limit for the density of nucleation sites is about 7×10^9 cm^{-3}.

The maximum shear stress that was developed under the spheres, as calculated from the Hertz impact theory, is about 3×10^9 dynes cm^{-2}. The sphere-crystal contact areas were about 3 μ in radius.

* G. H. Kinchin and R. S. Pease, *J. Nuclear Energy,* **1,** 200 (1955).

† We are indebted to Dr. R. L. Coble of the General Electric Research Laboratory for preparing the Al_2O_3 spheres.

VII WHISKERS AND THIN CRYSTALS

The Theory of Whisker Dekinking

F. R. N. NABARRO

Department of Physics
University of the Witwatersrand
Johannesburg, South Africa

ABSTRACT

Several different mechanisms are discussed for the straightening on annealing of a single crystal whisker which has been plastically kinked. The analysis shows that the only mechanism of straightening which will explain the high and roughly uniform rate of the process is that of dislocation climb by the migration of vacancies or interstitial ions. The rate of evolution of vacant lattice sites from jogs in dislocations is only sufficient to maintain this rate of climb if the edges of the dislocations are densely packed with jogs. Dislocation glide may account for the rapid initial recovery.

---

1. INTRODUCTION: ARRANGEMENT OF DISLOCATIONS IN THE KINK

It has been known for some time that "whiskers" of metal, presumably almost perfect single crystals or even single crystals containing a single screw dislocation, can withstand very large elastic strains. Yielding is accompanied by the formation of a single rather sharp kink. The preparation and properties of these whiskers have been described by Brenner.[1] More recently, Gyulai [2] has observed that kinked whiskers of sodium chloride spontaneously straighten on annealing, and Brenner and Morelock [3] have observed the same effect in whiskers of copper, and have studied the kinetics of dekinking. Since whisker dekinking represents the simplest annealing process so far known, it seems desirable to have at least a rough quantitative theory of its mechanism. Possible mechanisms fall into two main classes: those in which the dislocations move principally by glide, and those in which the dislocations move principally by climb. We discuss these two classes in turn.

We have to derive a satisfactory model for the dislocation array in the kinked state, and assume at first that the kink is ideally sharp, consisting of a sheet of edge dislocations, more or less evenly spaced. The wire straightens because these dislocations find their way to the surface.

Consider a whisker with cross section a square of side w, kinked through a finite angle θ. For simplicity we neglect the actual crystal structure, and visualize the lattice as simple cubic with lattice spacing b. The kink then consists of a wall of $w\theta/b$ dislocations, spaced b/θ apart. It is well known [4] that the stresses in the lattice are effectively confined to a sheet of thickness b/θ surrounding the wall of dislocations, and that the energy E of the wall is given [5] approximately by

$$E = \frac{w^2 b\mu}{4\pi(1-\sigma)}\,\theta \ln \frac{e\theta_0}{\theta} \tag{1}$$

where μ is the rigidity, σ is the Poisson ratio of the metal, regarded as isotropic, and θ_0 is a constant angle which for copper is about 26.5°. In order to simplify the calculations, we have taken the area of the wall to be w^2 instead of the correct value $w^2 \sec \frac{1}{2}\theta$.

This energy is released when the kink straightens. According to eq. 1, E reaches a maximum when $\theta = \theta_0$, whereas experiment shows that E has a roughly constant value when $\theta > \theta_0$. The initial stages of dekinking, when $\theta > \theta_0$, only lead to a decrease of free energy if the kink is composed of several smaller kinks each of angle less than θ_0. This agrees with the rounded appearance of the kinks in the published photographs. A total kinking of the order of 1 radian corresponds to an average of one dislocation on each glide plane. For the whiskers observed by Brenner and Morelock, w was of order 8×10^{-4} cm, and for copper $b = 2.56 \times 10^{-8}$ cm, so the kink contains about 30,000 dislocations, which lie within an area of linear dimensions w.

Suppose that each of n glide planes contains m dislocations, with $mn = 30{,}000$. The behavior of the kink will be very different according as $m > n$ or $m < n$. If $m > n$, there is a strong repulsion between the m like dislocations on each glide plane, and the separate glide planes interact relatively weakly. If the crystal were otherwise perfect, the kink would straighten spontaneously even at low temperatures. If the process of kinking introduces dislocations on intersecting glide planes, the escape of dislocations is hindered, but we can easily show that it is not possible for the number of dislocations actually present to be retained in the crystal if they form an array with $m > n$. The number of dislocations crossing each glide plane is almost certain to be less than the total number mn which form the kink. We assume that γmn dislocations cross the glide plane in an area w^2, so that their mean separation is $l = w/(\gamma mn)^{1/2}$. The distribution of the m primary dislocations over a strip of glide plane of width w will be influenced by the presence of these crossing dislocations, but the stress driving the outermost pair out of the crystal will not differ greatly from the stress on the outermost pair of a set of m dislocations moving freely over a stretch w of the glide plane. This is given by Eshelby, Frank, and Nabarro [6] as

$$P = \frac{b\mu}{4\pi(1 - \sigma)} \frac{m^2}{w} \tag{2}$$

The critical stress P_0 required to drive this pair of dislocations through the forest of intersecting dislocations is given [7] by

$$P_0 = \alpha\mu b/l \tag{3}$$

where for copper the value of α is approximately 1.[8] Substituting the value of l, we see that the dislocations will escape if

$$\frac{m}{n} > \frac{4\pi(1 - \sigma)\gamma^{1/2}}{(mn)^{1/2}} \tag{4}$$

which is approximately equal to $\gamma^{1/2}/20 < 0.05$. Since the analysis was based on the assumption $m > n$, we deduce that the assumption is false, $m < n$, and thus $m < (mn)^{1/2} = 170$. Thus the correct model is one in which the dislocations are arranged in a number of walls, with weak interaction between the walls. The high initial rate of dekinking may be produced by the escape of dislocations by glide during the process of polygonization which forms this array of relatively low energy.*

* W. Shockley pointed out in discussion that the structure of the kink is more probably one of polygonized walls, each wall containing dislocations of two glide sytems. The properties of this model, which is discussed in Appendix I, will not differ greatly from those of the model used in the text.

2. DISLOCATION MOVEMENT BY GLIDE

We suppose that the glide planes of the dislocations make a finite angle ϕ with the wire axis (Fig. 1), so that dislocations can leave the crystal by gliding a finite distance. If the whole pattern of dislocations in Fig. 1 glides to the right without changing its configuration, the last dislocation will leave the lattice when it has traveled a distance w cosec ϕ, and the energy E is released. Consider the situation when the dislocations have moved half this distance. Roughly half of the energy E has been released, but the crystal now contains long-range

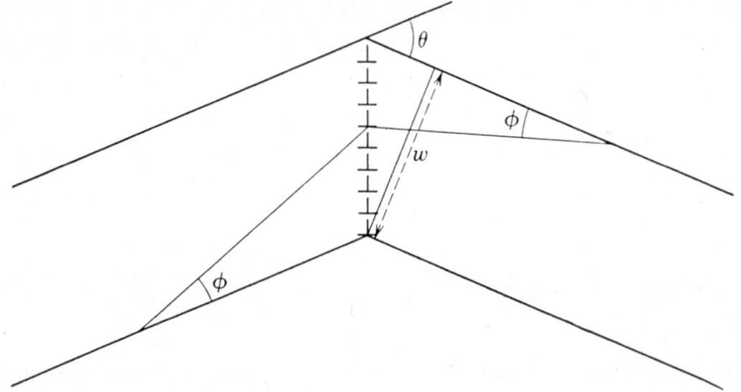

Fig. 1. Whisker with a kink formed by a single sheet of edge dislocations.

strains. These are of the same order as the strains produced by driving a wedge of angle θ halfway into the crystal. A volume of order $\frac{1}{2}w^3\theta$ is subjected to strains of order $\frac{1}{2}\theta$, and the elastic energy of the long-range strains is of order $\frac{1}{16}w^3\mu\theta^3$. This exceeds the energy which has been released at this stage by a large factor of order $\theta^2 w/b$, so that dekinking by this process requires an activation energy $\frac{1}{16}w^3\mu\theta^3$, or say $2^{-7}w^3\mu$. Since w is of order 8×10^{-4} cm, and μ for copper is 4.4×10^{11} ergs cm^{-3}, the activation energy for this process is of order 2 ergs, quite outside the range of possible thermal activation. If a single wall containing only $\frac{1}{100}$ of the total number of dislocations moves, the energy is reduced to 2×10^{-4} ergs, which is still unattainably large.

We now consider the possibility that dislocations may glide one by one out of the kink, so that the density of dislocations in the boundary remains roughly uniform, but gradually decreases. If the spacing of dislocations is completely regular, a dislocation which glides out of a wall is attracted back during all stages of its journey.[9] If, after moving a distance of order b/θ, it climbs into the glide plane of a neighboring dislocation of the wall, it is repelled by the wall and attracted by its image in the free surface. The dislocation cannot climb into this glide plane until it has traveled at least this distance, because of the repulsion of its nearest neighbor. The force pulling the dislocation back into the wall if it chooses the most favorable route of escape has a maximum value of order $wb\mu\theta/4\pi$, and a range of order b/θ. The activation energy is thus of order $wb^2\mu/4\pi$, or about 2×10^{-8} erg

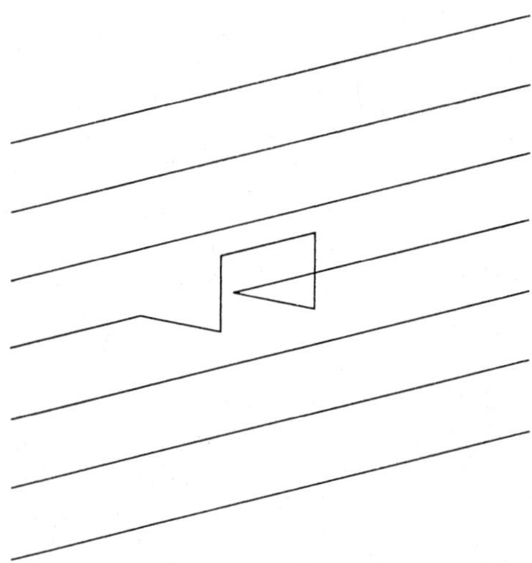

Fig. 2. Loop thrown off by one dislocation in a wall of dislocations.

in the most favorable case in which the number of walls is small. The annealing temperatures T used were below 1300°K, giving a mean thermal energy kT of order 1.8×10^{-13} erg. This process also is seen to have a negligible rate.

Since the dislocation cannot escape from the walls by moving rigidly according to the sequence glide-climb-glide, we now inquire if it is possible for it to escape by throwing off a loop which moves in this sequence, the loop then broadening itself at the expense of the stationary part of the dislocation without further activation energy. The troublesome factor w in the activation energy is then replaced by b, but the activation energy is increased by the line energy of the segments of dislocation joining the loop to the stationary portion. To estimate the activation energy, we assume (Fig. 2) that the mestastable loop of lowest energy has a length b/θ equal to the spacing between dislocations in the wall, and that it glides a distance b/θ before climbing b/θ into the next glide plane. The energy required to move the original segment is, by the argument of the previous paragraphs, about $b^3\mu/4\pi\theta$, and the added segments have a line energy which is of order $b^3\mu/\pi\theta$, giving a total activation energy $5b^3\mu/4\pi\theta$. This is about $3 \times 10^{-12}/\theta$ ergs, or $17kT/\theta$ at the temperature of annealing.

It follows that this process could occur at an observable rate when θ is of order 1 radian, but would become unmeasurably slow when θ has decreased below about $\frac{1}{10}$ radian. The experimental curves show a rapid recovery of the order of 10° within the first minute, which may be due in part to this process of glide, followed by dekinking at a very uniform rate until the angle of kink has fallen to about 5°. The whisker then straightens more slowly, but appears to be perfectly straight after a few more minutes. These last two stages do not fit even approximately a relation of the form

$$\frac{d\theta}{dt} = -A \exp\left(-\frac{B}{\theta}\right) \tag{5}$$

This process comes to an end even sooner if the total angle of kink θ is distributed among a number of walls.

It is geometrically possible for the kink to disappear by the migration into it of dislocations of opposite signs generated at the surface. These dislocations cannot be stored in the body of the crystal, for, if they were, the ends of the whisker would be parallel. If they have run out of the crystal, producing steps on the surface, they cannot move back to the kink wall by thermal activation, because the necessary activation energy is of the order of $wb^2\mu$. This follows from the fact that the energy per unit length of a dislocation exceeds the energy per unit length of a surface step by a quantity of order $b^2\mu$. A dislocation entering the surface is pulled back by its image, and is attracted into the kink wall only when it has approached within b/θ of the wall. It must thus travel a distance of order w before it is attracted, and the critical metastable loop will thus also be of length w and of energy $wb^2\mu$. There remains the possibility that in the process of kinking the dislocations may approach the surface but not break through because of the presence of an oxide film. When the stress is released, they are unable to return to the kink band because of the resistance of crossing dislocations. The activation energy to penetrate these is small enough to be provided thermally. This process seems unlikely, because the recovery takes place in an atmosphere of hydrogen. It would be useful to look for slip bands on the surfaces of kinked crystals.

3. DISLOCATION MOVEMENT BY CLIMB

We now consider mechanisms in which the dislocations climb up or down in the kink plane by the migration of vacancies or interstitial ions. We concentrate attention on lattice vacancies. Figure 3 shows

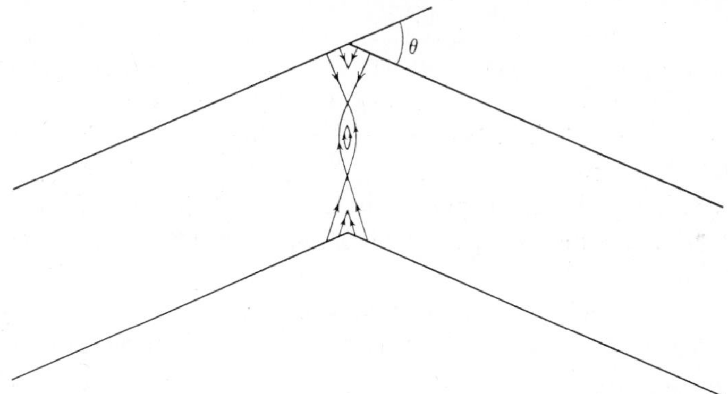

Fig. 3. Stream lines of vacancy diffusion at a kink.

the stream lines of vacancy diffusion. Initially we neglect the influence of the repulsion between the dislocations on the concentration of vacancies, and take this to have its equilibrium value of n_0 vacancies cm^{-3}. The energy given by eq. 1 is associated with the transfer of a wedge of material of volume

$$V = \tfrac{1}{8}w^3\theta \tag{6}$$

from the bottom to the top of the whisker. The energy released by the transfer of a single vacancy of volume b^3 is thus

$$\begin{aligned}\delta E &= b^3 \frac{dE}{d\theta}\frac{d\theta}{dV} \\ &= \frac{2b^4\mu}{\pi(1-\sigma)w}\ln\frac{\theta_0}{\theta}\end{aligned} \tag{7}$$

This work is done when the vacancy travels a distance of order $\frac{1}{4}w$, so that the mean force on a vacancy is $4\delta E/w$. If the diffusion coefficient of vacancies is D_0, their mobility is D_0/kT, and their mean drift velocity is $4D_0\ \delta E/wkT$. The average width of the stream of drifting vacancies is about $\frac{1}{4}w$ in the plane of Fig. 3 and w at right angles to this plane, and their concentration is n_0 cm^{-3}. The number of vacancies transferred per second is thus $n_0D_0w\ \delta E/kT$, and the volume flux per second $n_0 D_0 b^3 w \, \delta E/kT$. Since $n_0 D_0 b^3 = D$, the self-diffusion coefficient of the metal, this may be written

$$\frac{dV}{dt} = -\frac{Dw\,\delta E}{kT}$$

Then

$$\frac{d\theta}{dt} = \frac{dV}{dt}\frac{d\theta}{dV}$$

$$= \frac{16Db^4\mu}{\pi(1-\sigma)w^3kT} \ln \frac{\theta_0}{\theta} \tag{8}$$

The value of D for copper is given[10] by the formula $D = 11 \exp(-57{,}000/RT)$ cm² sec⁻¹. At 1290°K, the mean temperature of the experiments reported, this gives $D = 2.42 \times 10^{-9}$ cm² sec⁻¹. Taking $\ln(\theta_0/\theta)$ to be unity, we find $d\theta/dt = 4 \times 10^{-5}$ radian sec⁻¹, which is about a tenth of the observed rate. We see that this mechanism accounts both for the order of magnitude of the rate of dekinking and for the fact that the rate of recovery is almost constant. Before discussing effects which could modify this result, we remark that the flow illustrated in Fig. 3 occurs in a band of width $\frac{1}{4}w$, whereas appreciable internal stresses are confined to a band of width b/θ. The "force" causing vacancies to drift through the wider band is thus the osmotic pressure of vacancies, and not the gradient of internal stress. It is shown in Appendix II that the use of a hypothetical "average force along the path" is permissible. If the angle of kink θ is divided among m walls, the rate of dekinking is increased by a factor $m \ln m$.

The rate of dekinking given by eq. 8 cannot be increased appreciably by the fact that the interaction between dislocations in a wall increases the equilibrium concentration of vacancies in the neighborhood of those dislocations which climb upward on dekinking. The energy δE given by eq. 7 is released when a vacancy travels a distance $\frac{1}{4}w$. In the step in which it is freed from a jog in the dislocation, the vacancy has work $4b\,\delta E/w$ done on it by the internal stresses. This is of order 10^{-20} ergs, and much less than $kT = 1.8 \times 10^{-13}$ erg, so that the concentration in equilibrium is not appreciably different from n_0.

We finally examine the suggestion of Mott[11] that the flow of vacancies is not a quasi-equilibrium process. The calculation leading to eq. 8 is based on the idea that the increased rate of generation of vacancies produced by the internal stress causes the concentration of vacancies to build up until the increased rate of generation is balanced by an increased rate of reabsorption at jogs. This increase in equilibrium concentration is independent of the concentration of jogs. We now consider the possibility that the additional vacancies produced in the kink plane by the internal stresses do not build up to an equilibrium concentration. They diffuse into the bulk of the material, and find their way to the surface, to dislocations on which their absorption is favored by the internal stresses, or to interstitial ions emitted by these latter dislocations. The frequency with which a jog emits and absorbs vacancies in an unstrained lattice is of order Db^{-2}, if the activation energy for emission is taken to be the same as the activation energy for vacancy migration. This frequency is increased, as a result of the stress, by a factor $1 + 4b\,\delta E/wkT$, and we assume that the additional $4D\,\delta E/bwkT$ vacancies created at each jog each second contribute directly to the dekinking process. At high temperatures, about half the sites on the edges of dislocations may adjoin jogs. If this is so, the number of jogs on dislocations for which vacancy emission is favored is $w^2\theta/4b^2$, and the rate of emission of vacancies from these is $w\theta D\,\delta E/b^3kT$. The volume flowing from one side of the whisker to the other in unit time is

$$\frac{dV}{dt} = -\frac{w\theta D\,\delta E}{kT}$$

and

$$\frac{d\theta}{dt} = \frac{dV}{dt}\frac{d\theta}{dV}$$

$$= -\frac{16Db^4\theta}{\pi(1-\sigma)w^3kT}\ln\frac{\theta_0}{\theta} \tag{9}$$

Equation 9 differs from eq. 8 only in the presence of the factor θ, which is of order unity. In the dekinking process, Mott's mechanism is not an alternative to the directed flow of vacancies. Equation 8 represents the rate of flow when the equilibrium concentration of vacancies is maintained; eq. 9 represents the maximum possible rate of generation of vacancies. Their approximate equality indicates that the equilibrium concentration can only be maintained in the very favorable circumstances assumed in the derivation of eq. 9, namely, that half the sites on the edges of dislocations are occupied by jogs. When θ is small, the rate given by eq. 9 falls to zero, and the final curved portion of the experimental graphs is thus caused by the inability of the jogs in the few remaining dislocations to maintain the equilibrium concentration of vacancies.

In general the rate will be determined by the slower of the two processes represented by eqs. 8 and 9. If eq. 8 is the faster, the equilibrium concentration will not be maintained; if eq. 9 is the faster, the excess vacancies produced at jogs will not all diffuse away, and some will be reabsorbed. Here the assumption that the rate at which vacancies enter and leave jogs is equal to the rate at which they enter and leave normal lattice sites is relevant. Probably, because of the looseness of the lattice structure near a dislocation, the activation energy U^1 of the former process is less than the activation energy U of the latter, and the rate, eq. 9, should be multiplied by $\exp [(U - U^1)/kT]$.

4. CONCLUSION

The array of dislocations in a kink can best be represented by a series of polygonized walls. Several mechanisms of whisker dekinking are examined, and only three of these are found to be capable of producing the observed high rates of straightening. In the first of these, dislocations escape by glide during the process of polygonization. In the second, the dislocations forming the kink walls send out loops which, by a process of glide, followed by climb, followed by further glide, escape to the surface. This second mechanism leads to dekinking according to the law $d\theta/dt = -A \exp(-B/\theta)$. These two processes are probably responsible for the rapid straightening observed during the first minute of annealing, but cannot account for the removal of the last few degrees of kink. The approximately uniform rate of straightening during most of the annealing process is attributed to the climb of dislocations produced by the diffusion of vacancies (and possibly of interstitial ions). The observed rate is possible only if a large part of the edge of each dislocation is occupied by jogs, and the decrease in speed at the end of the process is attributed to a decrease in the concentration of vacancies below the equilibrium value.

APPENDIX I

W. Shockley pointed out in discussion that the dislocation array sketched in Fig. 1 would not be in equilibrium, because the wall of dislocations is not perpendicular to the glide plane. A stable wall necessarily contains dislocations of two glide systems. Moreover, the most plausible mechanism for the formation of a kink involves slip on two systems. We consider for simplicity a whisker in which two glide planes are each inclined at 45° to the axis (Fig. 4*a*). If slip starts at A under the influence of the bending moment indicated by the arrows, edge dislocations of the sign indicated move down the glide plane AD and accumulate near O. This leads to a stress concentration at C, and dislocations of the sign indicated travel up the glide plane CB. These dislocations also accumulate near O. The region near O is then a plastic hinge, and the bending moment can be transmitted across the plane EOF only if the tensile stress in the neighborhood of E is greater than its original value. New disloca-

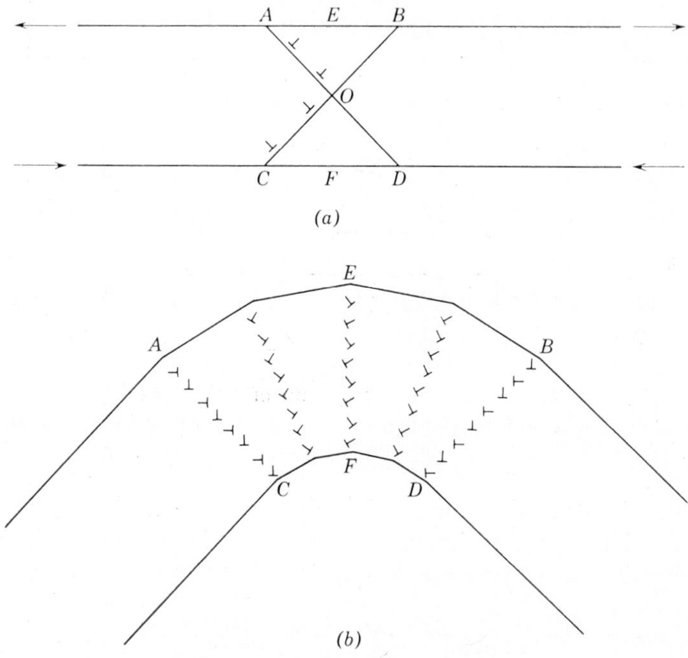

Fig. 4. (*a*) Whisker with two glide planes, each inclined at 45° to the axis. (*b*) Kinks formed by stable walls of dislocations on two slip planes.

tions are created along the line AEB, and move into the wedge AOB, while other sources are created along CFD and move into COD. Since dislocations of either family can leave any part of AEB and any part of CFD, the array of stable walls in Fig. 4*b* can be formed by glide alone.

For the array of Fig. 4*b* the movement of a single wall by glide alone is impossible, and the escape of single dislocations by glide is governed by the considerations already given. A wall such as BD disappears during dekinking by each dislocation climbing perpendicular to its own glide plane and then slipping along its new glide plane back into the line BD.

APPENDIX II

THE EQUIVALENCE OF THE MOBILITY AND THE FREE DIFFUSION FORMULATIONS OF VACANCY MIGRATION

We consider an idealized system consisting of a lump of metal under pressure p connected by a rod of length l and cross section A, also under pressure p, to another lump of the same metal under pressure $p - dp$ (Fig. 5).

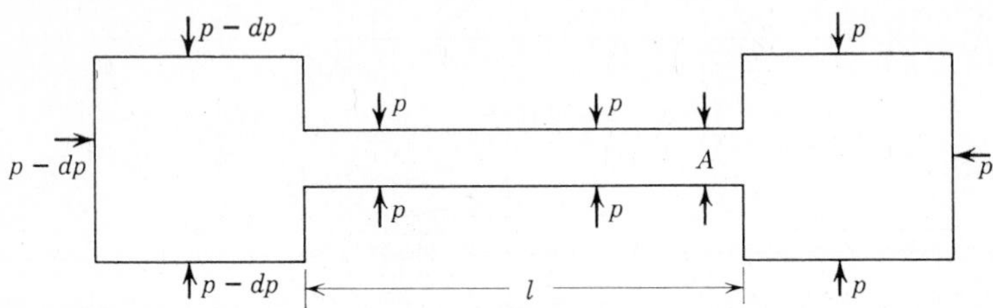

Fig. 5. Idealized system consisting of a lump of metal under pressure p connected by a rod of length l and cross section A, also under pressure p, to another lump of the same metal under pressure $p - dp$.

In the free-diffusion formulation we say that if the equilibrium concentration of vacancies under pressure p is n_0, the equilibrium concentration under pressure $p - dp$ is

$$n_0 \exp\left(\frac{b^3 dp}{kT}\right) = n_0\left(1 + \frac{b^3 dp}{kT}\right)$$

The excess concentration $n_0 b^3\, dp/kT$ leads to a flow of vacancies by diffusion down the rod of $n_0 D_0 b^3\, dp\, A/kTl$ vacancies per second.

In the mobility formulation we say that the work done when a vacancy moves from one block to the other is $b^3\, dp$. The average force over the trajectory of length l is $b^3\, dp/l$, the mobility of vacancies is D_0/kT, and so their average velocity is $D_0 b^3\, dp/kTl$. The density of vacancies is n_0, and they move in a stream of cross-sectional area A. The flow of vacancies per second is thus $n_0 D_0 b^3\, dp\, A/kTl$, agreeing with the previous result.

REFERENCES

1. S. S. Brenner, *Acta Met.*, **4**, 62 (1956).
2. Z. Gyulai, *Z. Physik*, **138**, 317 (1954).
3. S. S. Brenner and C. R. Morelock, *Acta Met.*, **4**, 89 (1956).

4. J. M. Burgers, *Proc. Acad. Sci. Amsterdam,* **42,** 293 (1939).
5. W. T. Read, *Dislocations in Crystals,* McGraw-Hill, New York (1953).
6. J. D. Eshelby, F. C. Frank, and F. R. N. Nabarro, *Phil. Mag.,* **42,** 351 (1954).
7. A. H. Cottrell, *Dislocations and Plastic Flow in Crystals,* Oxford University Press, Oxford, p. 174 (1953).
8. *Ibid.,* p. 206.
9. F. R. N. Nabarro, *Advances in Phys.,* **1,** 269 (1952).
10. J. Steigman, W. Shockley, and F. C. Nix, *Phys. Rev.,* **56,** 13 (1939).
11. N. F. Mott, *Report of the 9th Solvay Conference on Physics,* Stoops, Brussels, 515 (1952).

ACKNOWLEDGMENT

I am indebted to various colleagues, and especially Drs. H. J. Logie and Doris Wilsdorf, for valuable discussions.

DISCUSSION

SHOCKLEY asked if the particular configuration of the dislocations that produce the kink was important in the dekinking process. An alternating array of dislocations on two slip systems (such as in Fig. 4*b*) appears very different from the array that Nabarro analyzed, and SHOCKLEY asked if the analysis would come out the same for such an array. He also asked what was known about the angle of the kink. NABARRO replied that the calculations involving dekinking by glide alone would not apply to the more complex configuration of dislocations on two slip systems, but the formula for dekinking by climb would hold for Shockley's more complex boundary, since the wall can get away only by climb.*

HOLLOMON said that in kinking experiments in copper the angle at the kink was observed to be sharp, within the degree of resolution currently used. The axis of the copper whisker was a [100] direction. NABARRO stated that published pictures of kinked whiskers show a gentle bend rather than a sharp kink, but that better resolution might show a sharp kink.

* Z. S. Basinski has since remarked that an array such as that of Fig. 4*b* may be further stabilized against glide by Cottrell-Lomer locking (private communication to Nabarro).

READ asked what difference it would make if the dislocation walls were at an angle to the specimen axis as shown in Fig. D1 rather than normal to the axis. Such an array could be formed in a material with

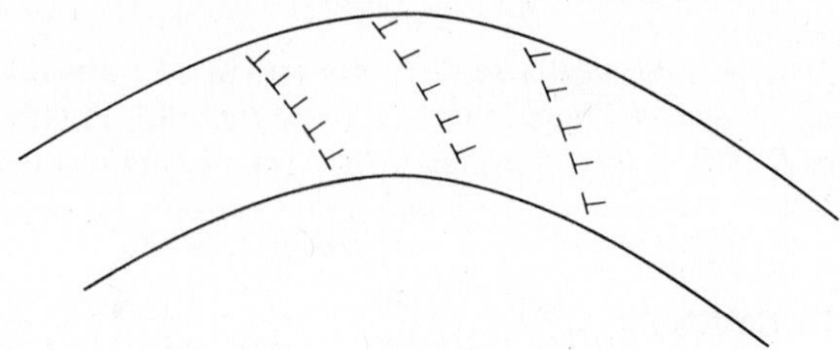

Fig. D1. Dislocation walls at an angle to the specimen axis.

only one slip system. READ discussed experiments on the unbending (rather than dekinking) of silicon crystals. The plane of the bend was (111). The change in angle was found to vary with time as shown in Fig. D2. These experiments indicated that the change in angle was proportional to the rate of climb.

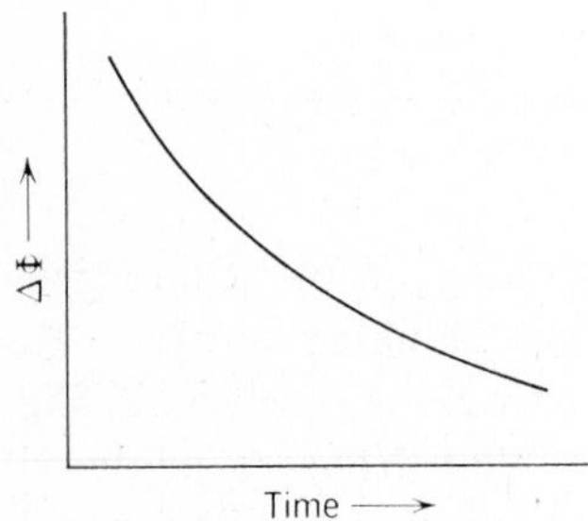

Fig. D2. Change in angle of a bent silicon crystal versus time.

SEEGER asked Nabarro if he neglected the problem of jogs. NABARRO answered that it was assumed that every other lattice site on the dislocation was a jog, and that the rate of emission of vacancies from jogs was equal to the rate at which an ordinary lattice site was visited by vacancies. Then the rate of emission of vacancies would be just sufficient to make up for those swept away during climb.

SEEGER said that in copper, jogs should be hard to get, since the jog energy in edge dislocations is usually estimated at about 4 ev in copper. A tentative explanation of dekinking in copper whiskers based on the rather high jog energies of copper (compared with materials that dekink at lower temperatures) is given in § 10 of Seeger's paper (pages 319–325 in this volume).

CHALMERS asked if the dislocations were usually considered to be not dissociated in arrays of the sort considered by Nabarro. SEEGER said that this would mean the dislocations were *not* on (111) planes, which appears somewhat unlikely.

FRIEDEL asked if it was not true that in copper, dislocations climbed appreciably, if somewhat more slowly than in aluminum, indicating that the jog energy was not much larger in copper than in aluminum. He said that this was possibly because the jog has a different form from that which is usually assumed. The form generally assumed is shown in Fig. D3*a*. It considers only the repulsions between L_1 and L_2

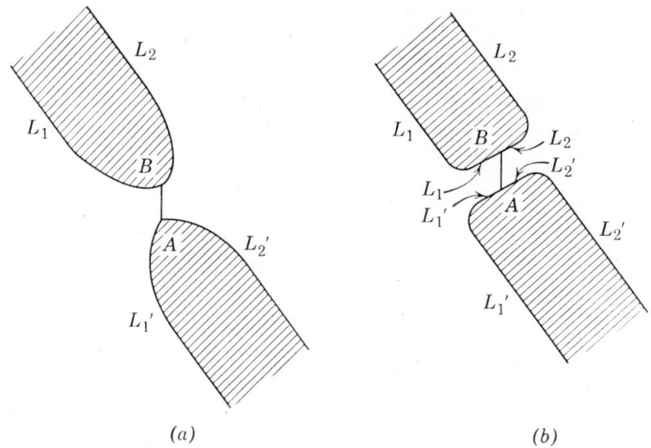

Fig. D3. Two possible forms of a jog in a dissociated dislocation.

and also between L_1' and L_2'. The form shown in Fig. D3*b*, when the attraction between parallel pairs L_1L_1' or L_2L_2' is considered, has a lower energy: one-fifth of the energy of a jog of the form shown in Fig. D3*a* for strongly dissociated dislocations such as in copper, where the contribution of the bit AB is negligible.

FRANK said that Young and Cabrera * found polygonization in impure copper, but not in pure copper. The copper had not been cold-worked. It appears that pure copper will not polygonize.

SEEGER asked Friedel if the line energy of the dislocations in the extended jog had been considered, adding that he had made estimates also, and found the change in energy due to the extension of the jog as shown in Fig. D3*b* to be much smaller than a factor of five, in agreement with the conclusions drawn by N. Thompson.† SEEGER thinks that the present experimental situation (including the polygonization

* F. W. Young, Jr., and N. Cabrera, *J. Appl. Phys.*, **28**, 787 (1957).

† N. Thompson, *Report of a Conference on Defects in Solids*, Physical Society, London, p. 153 (1955).

experiments on pure copper of Young and Cabrera) could not be accounted for with a jog energy in edge dislocations of copper smaller than about 3 ev.

Written reply by FRIEDEL:

The factor five is obtained by noting that, owing to their attraction, pairs such as L_1L_1' exert no distortion in the lattice at distances large compared with the interatomic distance AB. Their line tension is thus small. It has been taken into account in the computation, with the usual estimate for the core energy. A similar result is obtained by treating a pair L_1L_1' as a high-energy grain boundary of width AB.

SHOCKLEY pointed out that the dislocation lines in the whisker had been assumed to be straight and normal to the surface, and asked if the curvature of a whisker of small diameter would not influence the shape of a dislocation line. If the dislocation lines have a curvature comparable to the circumference of the whisker, of the order of a few microns, the line tension in the dislocation might play an important role.

Deformation and Fracture of Silicon

W. T. READ, JR.
G. L. PEARSON
Bell Telephone Laboratories, Inc.
Murray Hill, New Jersey

1. INTRODUCTION

Small silicon crystals have been shown to have unusually high fracture strength at room temperature.[1,2] We have observed elastic behavior up to 2.7% strain in a whisker 16 μ in diameter. This suggested that such crystals might be free of dislocations like the small metal crystals studied by Herring and Galt[3] and Brenner.[4] The original purpose of this investigation was to study the stress-strain behavior of perfect crystals in the plastic range. However, tests in the temperature range where silicon deforms plastically showed that even the smallest crystals were not free of defects. Apparently fracture and deformation are caused by different types of defects and only those defects responsible for fracture have been eliminated in the small crystals.

The experiments have thrown a good deal of light on the mechanism of plastic deformation in silicon and the dominant effect of impurities even in the purest silicon now available. The behavior is strikingly similar to that of iron containing carbon. There is a pronounced yield point at the beginning of plastic flow, the lower yield stress being less than half the upper yield stress. The locking impurity is oxygen. Aging experiments provide a simple means of studying the diffusion of oxygen in silicon. The binding energy of an oxygen atom to a dislocation appears to be over 2 ev.

2. EXPERIMENTAL PROCEDURE

The experimental techniques have been described by Pearson, Read, and Feldmann.[2] The crystals, which are about 1 mm long, are supported at the ends and deformed in bending by a force applied in the center through a quartz hook. Both the force and deflection are measured with the crystal in a furnace at a controlled temperature that can be varied from room temperature up to 900°C. Tests were made on:

1. whiskers, which are crystals grown from the vapor, and
2. rods, which are machined and etched from bulk silicon. Figure

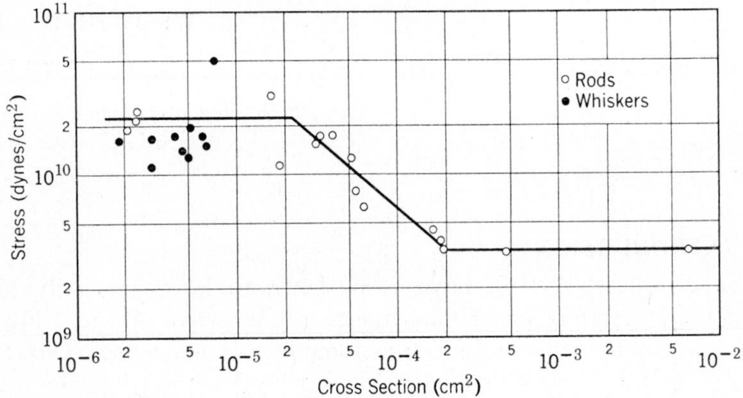

Fig. 1. Effect of size on the room temperature fracture stress of silicon whiskers and rods.

1 shows the room temperature fracture stress plotted versus cross-sectional area. It is seen that:

(*a*) the fracture strength of rods is about equal to that of whiskers at the same size,

(*b*) there is a pronounced size effect, and

(*c*) the scatter is large for small sizes as would be expected if fracture is due to random defects.

At 800°C the yield stress of rods did not vary with size; rods less than 20 μ in diameter had the same yield stress as etched and annealed bulk silicon.

3. FRACTURE AND YIELD

The low yield stress and absence of size effect at 800°C indicate that dislocations are present in even the smallest crystals tested but these have no effect on fracture at room temperature. In other words, the stress required to move dislocations at room temperature is greater than the fracture stress of the strongest crystals tested; i.e., the critical strain for plastic deformation is greater than 2.7%. To test this hypothesis, whiskers were deformed at 800°C so as to introduce 10^8 dislocations/cm^2 and then compared with undeformed samples at room temperature. The fracture stress at room temperature was not changed by the prior deformation. Thus fracture appears to be completely brittle and unrelated to the dislocation density. The size effect in fracture indicates that fracture is due to some defect or distribution of defects other than dislocations and that the density of these is low enough that they are unlikely to be present in the small rods and whiskers, which have a volume of 10^{-7} to 10^{-6} cm^3 and a surface area of about 2×10^{-4} cm^2.

4. YIELDING AND AGING

Above about 600°C silicon deforms plastically. The deformation is elastic up to the upper yield point where the stress drops by about 60% at constant strain. The drop is not instantaneous, however; at 800°C several minutes are required. After the initial yield, deformation continues almost indefinitely at the lower yield stress with no apparent work hardening. If the crystal is aged at zero stress, the yield point is gradually recovered. The time to complete recovery varies with temperature and impurity content. In general, the number of impurities is more than sufficient to saturate the dislocations. Thus for a given impurity concentration the aging time is inversely proportional to the diffusion constant of the locking impurity. By measuring aging time as a function of temperature, we found that the activation energy of diffusion was 3.3 ev. This is typical of substitutional impurities in silicon. Aging times were measured for five different samples, each with a different oxygen content. The oxygen content as measured by gas analysis and by infrared absorption [5] was about 2×10^{-7} atom fractions in the purest sample and about 2×10^{-5} in the least pure. In all cases the lower oxygen content was associated with a longer aging time. This strongly suggests that oxygen is the locking impurity.

Oxygen in silicon is not electrically active and is therefore extremely difficult to detect. The measurements of aging time provide a simple method for studying its behavior.

5. BINDING OF OXYGEN TO DISLOCATIONS

The yield stress at 800°C was independent of aging temperature for temperatures up to 1200°C and for oxygen contents down to 2×10^{-7} atom fractions. This indicates that the dislocations were saturated in all the crystals tested. If the temperature had been above the condensation temperature, changes in temperature would have caused

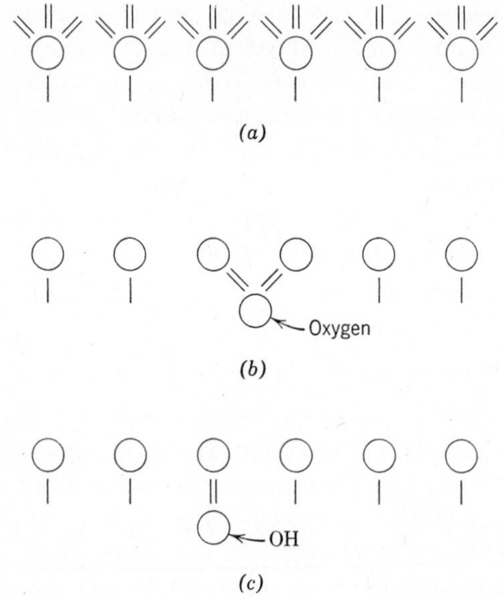

(a)

Oxygen

(b)

OH

(c)

Fig. 2. Possible ways of binding impurities at an edge dislocation. (*a*) Silicon atoms at the end of the half plane have dangling bonds. (*b*) Binding of an oxygen atom. (*c*) Binding of an OH ion.

changes in the density of oxygen atoms on the dislocations. The temperature at which impurity atoms begin to boil off from the dislocations is related to the impurity concentration C and the binding energy ϵ per atom by $\epsilon = -kT \ln C$.[6] Taking our minimum C and maximum T we find that ϵ is over 2 ev. Binding so strong must be electronic rather than elastic. This is not surprising in view of the unsaturated bonds along a dislocation having some edge component. The atoms on the edge of an extra plane have only three nearest neighbors. Hence one bond is broken and one electron dangles. This is illustrated in Fig. 2*a*, which shows the row of atoms on the edge of the extra plane of an edge or a near edge dislocation. Figure 2*b* shows how an oxygen atom can form a bond between two such atoms. There is some bending of the silicon bond angles but two free radicals are eliminated per oxygen atom. Another possibility is shown in Fig. 2*c*. Here an OH ion has been absorbed and shares a pair of electrons with a silicon atom on the edge of the extra plane.

6. YIELD STRESS AND TEMPERATURE

Both the upper and lower yield points vary roughly as the inverse fifth power of the absolute temperature in the range from 600°C to 800°C. This may be due to the temperature dependence of the Peierls-Nabarro [7] force which should play a dominant role in a covalently bonded structure. Dietze [8] has shown that above the Debye temperature the Peierls-Nabarro force drops with temperature because the dislocation becomes wider. This could give the strong temperature dependence observed.

7. FRACTURE AND DEFORMATION

Figure 3 summarizes schematically our view of how the yield and fracture stresses of silicon vary with temperature. Quantities that can be measured are shown by the solid lines. The true fracture stress shown dashed is probably almost independent of temperature. Its actual value is not known but it must lie at or above the highest

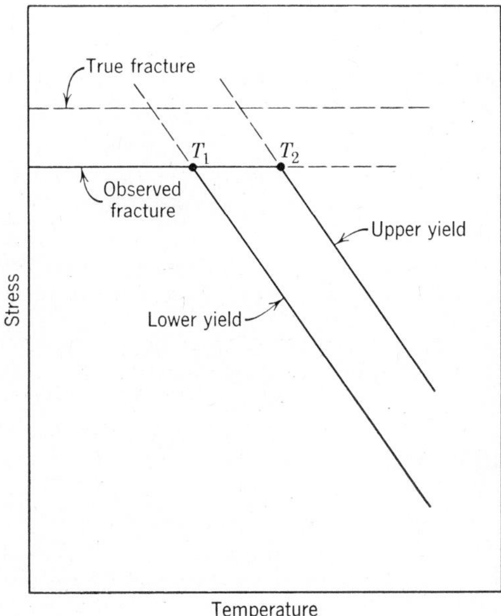

Fig. 3. Temperature dependence of fracture stress, yield stress, and flow stress in silicon.

fracture stress measured. Below the true fracture stress is the observed fracture stress which within the experimental scatter is likewise found to be independent of temperature. Presumably the observed fracture stress is the applied stress for which the highest local stress, perhaps at a surface irregularity, is equal to the true fracture stress. The observed fracture stress varies with specimen size as shown in Fig. 1. The upper and lower yield stresses are independent of size but vary rapidly with temperature.

The upper yield stress in whiskers intersects the observed fracture stress at the temperature T_2 which in silicon whiskers is about 600°C. Above T_2 yield occurs; below T_2 brittle fracture. Plastic flow can, however, be observed below T_2 by first deforming at a temperature above T_2 so as to get on the lower yield stress curve and then retesting before the impurities have diffused back to the dislocations. The lower yield stress can be measured in this way for the temperature range from T_2 down to T_1 at which the curve of lower yield stress intersects the observed fracture stress. In silicon whiskers T_1 was about 450°C. Thus the overstrained, or yielded, crystals will deform at temperatures as much at 150°C lower than unyielded crystals.

From the results illustrated in Fig. 3 it seems likely that the stress required to move dislocations in silicon may, at the lower temperatures, be as great as the true fracture stress.

REFERENCES

1. R. L. Eisner, *Acta Met.*, **3**, 414 (1955).
2. G. L. Pearson, W. T. Read, Jr., and W. L. Feldmann, *Acta Met.*, **5**, 181 (1957).
3. C. Herring and J. K. Galt, *Phys. Rev.*, **85**, 1060 (1952).
4. S. S. Brenner, to be published.
5. W. Kaiser, P. H. Keck, and C. F. Lange, *Phys. Rev.*, **101**, 1264 (1956).
6. A. H. Cottrell, *Dislocations and Plastic Flow in Crystals*, Oxford University Press, Oxford (1954).
7. F. R. N. Nabarro, *Proc. Phys. Soc.* (*London*), **59**, 256 (1947).
8. H. D. Dietze, *Z. Physik*, **132**, 107 (1952).

ACKNOWLEDGMENTS

The oxygen analyses in our silicon samples were made by H. Hrowstowski, to whom we are greatly indebted. Special thanks are due to W. L. Feldmann for his patience and skill in making many of the experimental measurements discussed here.

DISCUSSION

LOW pointed out that a survey of the available information on whisker strength versus size shows that there is strong dependence on size. The data show considerable scatter, but there is a strong trend in the broad scatter bands that indicates a strong size dependence even to sizes below 10 μ. This includes the data of S. S. Brenner * on copper and silver, the data of P. D. Gorsuch * on iron, those on silicon in the present paper by W. T. Read and co-workers, and the data of Z. Gyulai † on sodium chloride whiskers. GILMAN added that the data of Andrade and Makin ‡ on small cadmium crystals extrapolates to whiskerlike strengths at sizes characteristic of whiskers. The yield stress in cadmium changes by 14 times as the diameter goes from 0.5 mm to 0.025 mm.

MOTT inquired if the upper yield point should not be something quite different from the Peierls force, and READ replied that it may be that the stress to pull dislocations off impurities is added to the stress to overcome the Peierls force to give the upper yield stress.

WOOD asked about the rates of loading, adding that the behavior of the whiskers was reminiscent of delayed yielding. READ said that the variation in yield stress from whisker to whisker and the high sensitivity to the kind of stress that is applied were such that it was difficult to make a systematic study of loading rates. However, the phenomenon of delayed yielding is observed in that if a whisker is loaded to below the yield stress it will start deforming after a long interval of time.

GILMAN called attention to the work on LiF (presented by Gilman and Johnston in Part I of this volume) in which polished crystals were compared with crystals that had fresh dislocations at their surfaces. At room temperature, the polished crystals had yield points whereas the crystals with surface dislocations had none. The flow stresses of both kinds of crystals were roughly 1 kg/mm^2. At liquid-nitrogen

* Private communication.

† Z. Gyulai, *Z. Physik,* **138,** 317 (1954).

‡ E. N. da C. Andrade, "The Effect of Surface Conditions on the Mechanical Properties of Metals, Mainly Single Crystals," *Monograph No. 13,* Institute of Metals, London (1952).

temperature, neither kind of crystal had a yield point, and both kinds of crystal deformed at about 5 kg/mm^2. The fresh dislocations were introduced just before testing, so there was little time for impurity locking. GILMAN pointed out that the strong temperature dependence that was observed in both kinds of crystal must be that of the Peierls force. The yield point of the polished crystal at room temperature seems to result from the fact that new dislocations must be created before glide can occur. If the temperature dependence of the stress to create new dislocations is smaller than the temperature dependence of the Peierls force, the former stress would be obscured at low temperature.

VREELAND suggested that the apparent strong temperature dependence of the flow stress of LiF at low temperature may merely reflect a rate dependence, and inquired whether the stresses below the observed flow stress had been applied for a long time. GILMAN replied that the rate dependence had not been studied at liquid-nitrogen temperature, but there is very little rate dependence of the macroscopic yield stress at room temperature. VREELAND pointed out that Gilman has shown * that fast-moving cracks make no observable dislocation loops, and slow-moving cracks make dislocation loops in LiF. Although this can be explained by a limited rate of growth of loops, it can also indicate a nucleation time for loop formation.

* J. J. Gilman, "Nucleation of Dislocation Loops by Cracks in Crystals," *Trans. AIME,* **209,** 449 (1957).

X-ray Experiments on Tin Whiskers

PETER B. HIRSCH
Cavendish Laboratory
University of Cambridge
Cambridge, England

While I was at the University of Illinois in 1955, I performed some experiments on tin whiskers loaned to me by Professor Koehler, to determine if the whiskers have screw dislocations along their axes. X-ray pictures were taken to determine the twist of the lattice of the whiskers. About a half-dozen tin whiskers were examined, several of which showed considerable asterism and were discarded. In the remaining three, there was no twist of the lattice to within the experimental accuracy of the arrangement. The photographs were X-ray Laue photographs. If any of the three good whiskers contained a lattice twist, the twist was less than one-tenth the twist which a screw dislocation would have given to the whisker. On the basis of this result, I concluded that the whisker contained no dislocations. I understand that similar experiments have been performed at Bell Telephone Laboratories. They have found lattice twists in tin whiskers which were also smaller by a factor of 10 from the expected twist. They concluded, however, that there was a measurable twist present which may have been related in some way to a screw dislocation. I do not know the answer to this dilemma. It must be said that in the bad whiskers I certainly did find spotty asterism, or in other words, the whiskers appeared to be deformed. They were discarded because I thought the imperfection was due to a deformation caused during handling of the whiskers, and not due to dislocations which were present in them.

I would now like to make a comment about a possible mechanism for the formation of a kink in a whisker. In whiskers which are grown from the base, we often find kinks which look like Fig. 1. One possible

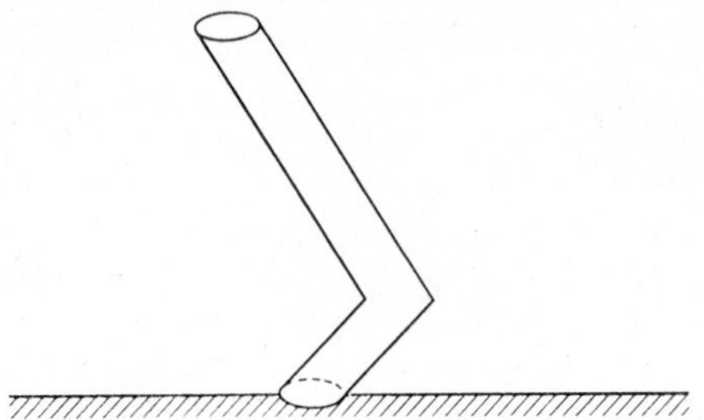

Fig. 1. A kinked whisker grown from the base.

way of making sure a whisker grows at the base is by means of the Frank mechanism, shown in Fig. 2*a*. Assume that the screw dislocation is a part of a dislocation network and that some distance below the surface there is a dislocation node. Suppose the whisker is formed by a rotation of the screw dislocation around the base of the whisker. For each rotation of the dislocation one plane of atoms is added to the whisker. The direction of the whisker is parallel to the Burgers vector

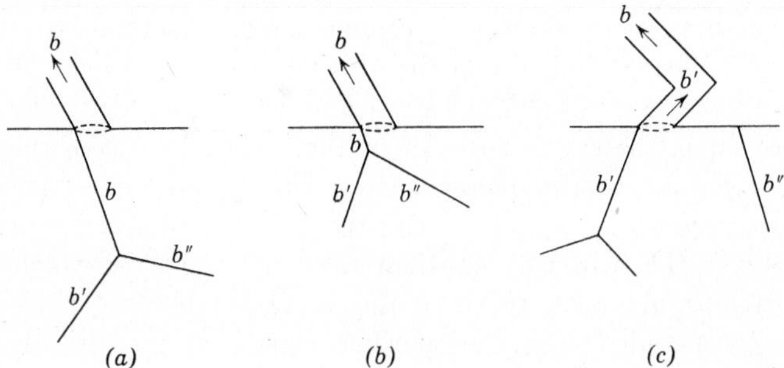

Fig. 2. A mechanism for the formation of a kink in a whisker growing from the base.

b, and experiments on the orientation of whiskers have, in fact, shown that the whiskers are in general parallel to directions which could be Burgers vectors. Now imagine that the node climbs to the surface (Fig. 2*b*, *c*). If one of the dislocations b' continues to spiral about the base of the whisker to form the whisker, and the other dislocation b'' moves along the surface, then we see that the whisker will grow in the direction of the new Burgers vector b' and will develop a kink, as shown in Fig. 2*c*. Note that the whisker should continue to be a single crystal and should have the same crystallographic orientation in the two parts. The kink simply corresponds to a change in the direction of growth of the whisker. It would be interesting to carry out experiments on the orientation relationship between the two pieces of the whisker on the two sides of the kink.

DISCUSSION

AMELINCKX asked under what influence Hirsch expected the node to move to the surface. HIRSCH answered that it would move simply by climb. BARRETT remarked that Dr. George Sines of the Institute for the Study of Metals has grown whiskers from tin plate under pressure, and some of them have a peculiar crystallographic feature. In determining the orientation of the whiskers, Dr. Sines found that the two ends of one whisker had different orientations even though the whisker was straight. Low indices directions were parallel to the axis of the whiskers at each end, namely [101] and [100] respectively, and the two crystals came together in a sharp boundary which could be seen with polarized light under a microscope. BLEWITT asked if Sines had grown a tin whisker with a spiral in it. BARRETT replied that Sines had obtained whiskers with a lot of kinks which could be interpreted in terms of a series of nodal points moving to the surface of the material. He had also seen one well-developed spiral whisker, shown in Fig. D1.

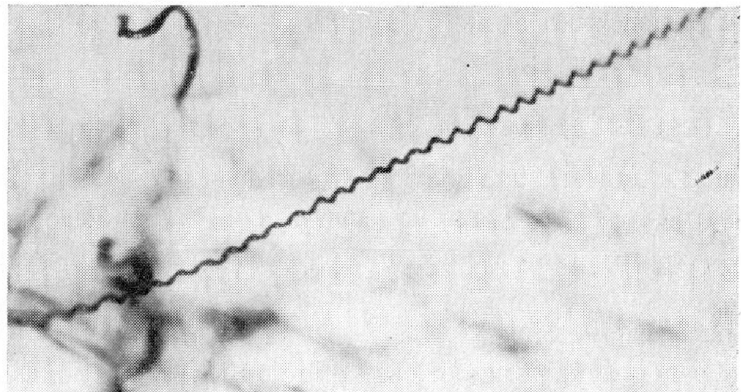

Fig. D1. Spiral whisker of tin grown by pressure in commercial tin plate. 300×. (G. Sines, Institute for the Study of Metals, University of Chicago.)

Deformation of Thin Metal Crystals

H. SUZUKI

S. IKEDA

S. TAKEUCHI

Research Institute for Iron, Steel, and Other Metals
Tohoku University
Sendai, Japan

The effect of crystal radius on the deformation of single crystals of copper [1] and alpha-brass has been studied. In particular, the effect of crystal radius on the range of easy glide has been measured. Copper and alpha-brass single crystals were grown from the melt with a diameter of 2 mm. The crystals were etched down to smaller sizes so that a range of 2 mm to 0.12 mm diameter was obtained. The shear stress-glide curves were measured as the crystals were deformed in tension.

The curves for specimens from two copper crystals with axes near the [011] orientation are shown in Fig. 1. The range of easy glide increases as the crystal radius decreases. The dependence of easy glide range on crystal radius varies with orientation as is shown in Fig. 2. Similar curves for alpha-brass single crystals are shown in Fig. 3, and there are two marked differences in the behavior of the two materials. There is far less increase in the range of easy glide in the alpha-brass than in the copper as the radius decreases; and the brass exhibits an increase of hardening in the easy glide region with decreasing crystal radius.

The dependence of range of easy glide on crystal radius is shown in Fig. 4, in which the range of easy glide is plotted on a logarithmic scale against the crystal radius. It is remarkable that the maximum

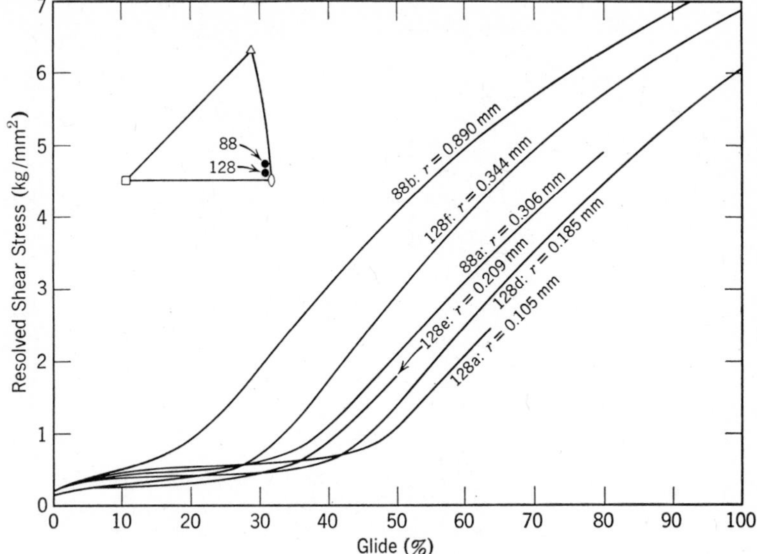

Fig. 1. Shear stress-glide curves of copper crystals having various radii; in the vicinity of [011].

range of easy glide extrapolated to an infinitesimal radius is independent of crystal orientation and of composition.

REFERENCE

1. H. Suzuki, S. Ikeda, and S. Takeuchi, *J. Phys. Soc. Japan,* **11**, 382 (1956).

DISCUSSION

LÜCKE reported that measurements of aluminum single crystals ranging from 5 mm to nearly 0.5 mm diameter did not reveal any size effects. H. SUZUKI replied that he and his co-workers have found that the size effect in aluminum becomes apparent when the crystal diameter is less than 0.5 mm.

HONEYCOMBE reported work on the size effect in copper crystals where it was found that there is a size dependence up to ¼ inch and even ⅜ inch diameter. HONEYCOMBE asked whether the deformation of the

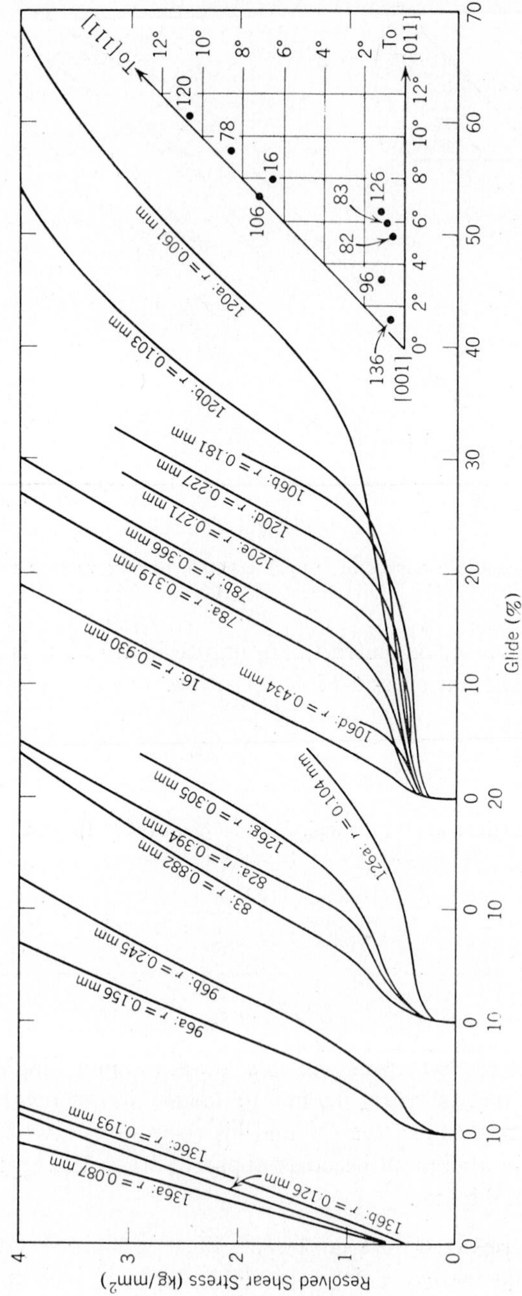

Fig. 2. Shear stress-glide curves of copper crystals having various radii; in the vicinity of [001].

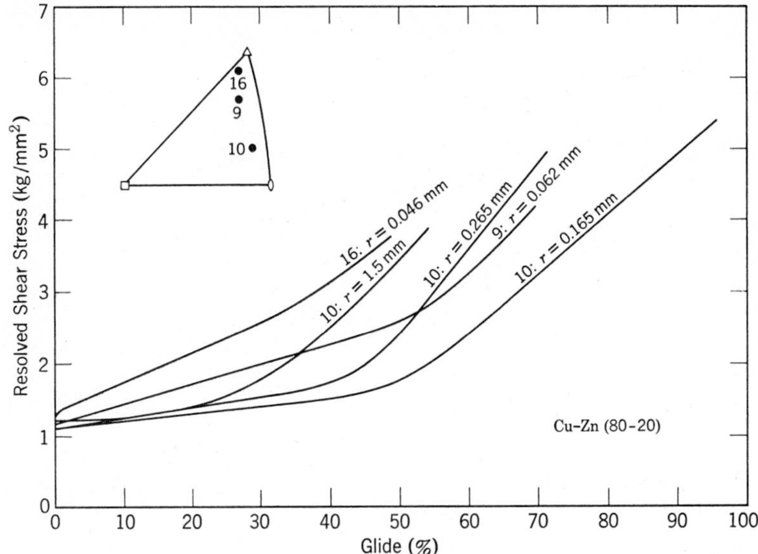

Fig. 3. Shear stress-glide curves of alpha-brass crystals having various radii.

brass single crystals had been uniform, or if it proceeded by a Lüders band mechanism, where the deformation often starts at one end and propagates along the crystal. H. SUZUKI said that the deformation was not by Lüders bands. The finer crystals had some fluctuations in diameters so that in many cases the deformation did not start at one end, but began in a region of small diameter.

COTTRELL suggested that perhaps the rising stress-strain curve of alpha-brass in the easy glide region could result from the fluctuations in diameter of the small crystal. Such a curve could result if the deformation started in the narrower part of the crystal and then proceeded into the thicker parts.

SHOCKLEY felt that the behavior of the thin crystals seemed reasonable in view of the work that had been described by Gilman and Johnston and by T. Suzuki (papers in Parts I and II of this volume), where the slip appears to be starting at the surface of a crystal. If dislocations which start at the surface and move into the crystal have a certain range before they get piled up inside, the effect of crystal size should be that observed by H. Suzuki.

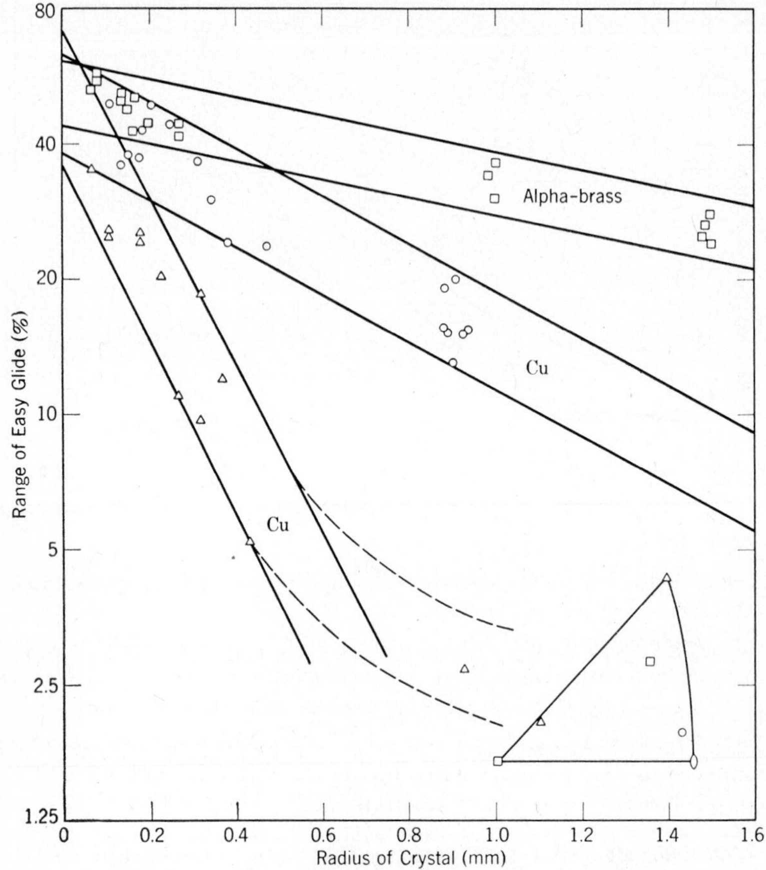

Fig. 4. The relation between the range of easy glide and radius of crystal.

VIII RADIATION DAMAGE

On the Formation of Cavities Along Dislocations

P. COULOMB

J. FRIEDEL

Centre de Recherches Métallurgiques de L'Ecole Nationale Supérieure des Mines Paris, France

ABSTRACT

Conditions under which vacancies in supersaturation may precipitate to form cavities along dislocations are studied from a theoretical point of view. Large supersaturations, mobile vacancies, small density of dislocations, and jogs with high energy help the nucleation process in a certain range of temperature; and it is shown that, for usual metals, an initial concentration of vacancies of 10^{-5} should be sufficient at room temperature. The cavities should grow rapidly up to a certain critical size where they are almost spherical, and should not grow very much after that, except if submitted to very high temperatures or if new vacancies are introduced in supersaturation. This critical size should be of the order of at least 20 interatomic distances at room temperature, and somewhat larger for large initial supersaturations. These cavities should appear on screw as well as on edge dislocations; they should pin them down very effectively, and prevent them from climbing and from gliding. The resulting high stability and high hardening effect are emphasized. It is also shown that platelets of interstitials or cylindrical tunnels along the dislocations require higher concentrations to appear and are less stable than the spherical cavities, except for tunnels along dislocations with large Burgers vectors.

The stable hardening, and the formation of cavities by quenching or irradiating metallic and ionic crystals and in the Kirkendall effect, are attributed to a nucleation of this kind.

1. CAVITIES AND HARDENING DUE TO A SUPERSATURATION OF VACANCIES

Two of the technically most important consequences of a strong neutron irradiation on uranium are a large increase in hardness and a decrease in density due to the formation of cavities (cf. Foote, 1955). These effects are certainly a consequence of the atomic displacement due to the "Wigner effect" (Seitz, 1948). They are especially strong in uranium because of its induced fission, but are observed after strong irradiations in practically any crystal (Kinchin and Pease, 1955). Two of the exhibits of the Geneva conference were, for instance, (1) a piece of irradiated copper, which "rang" like a piece of brass, i.e., where the internal friction due to the displacement of dislocations was suppressed by the pinning down of the dislocations; and (2) a piece of irradiated quartz, showing fairly large cavities (Geneva, 1955).

As these effects are independent of the purity of the crystals, they seem to be due to a direct action of the point defects introduced by irradiation, most probably the vacancies. Other cases where *vacancies are introduced in supersaturation* show actually similar effects. For instance, a large increase in the elastic limit may be obtained by quenching metals from near their melting point (Maddin and Cottrell, 1955); cavities are formed in alloys, in the Kirkendall experiment, etc.

The *small* concentrations of defects sufficient to have observable effects may seem a priori difficult to explain. Thus

1. Cavities are formed under supersaturations well below reasonable values for their nucleation in a perfect crystal (cf., e.g., Seitz, 1953, for the Kirkendall effect).
2. A strong hardening is obtained with a relatively small number of vacancies.

As in the very similar case of low-carbon steels, one may think that *dislocations* present in the crystals attract the point defects and build up some kind of Cottrell clouds. These clouds would pin down the dislocations without hardening the volume of the crystals: this should *increase the elastic limit* σ_c *without altering very much the stress-strain curve* $\sigma(\epsilon)$ *for large deformations* ϵ. Such an effect is indeed observed in both irradiated and quenched crystals (Fig. 1; cf. Wilson and Billington, 1956; Maddin and Cottrell, 1955). It is of course analogous to what is observed in steels. Again as in carbon steels, such Cottrell clouds could help the nucleation of "precipitates," i.e., here of cavities.

As pointed out by Nabarro (1948), vacancies (and interstitials) act somewhat differently from other impurities, because they can *disappear at the jogs of the dislocations.* One could therefore expect the Cottrell clouds formed to be quickly eaten away by the dislocations, thus providing only a very transitory hardening (Cottrell, 1954). The hardening due to irradiation or quench is, however, fairly stable. And the purpose of this paper is to show that *Cottrell clouds made up by vacancies can be stabilized by condensing as small cavities along the dislocations. Such cavities should be fairly stable; they should pin the dislocations down quite effectively, and thus provide a fairly strong*

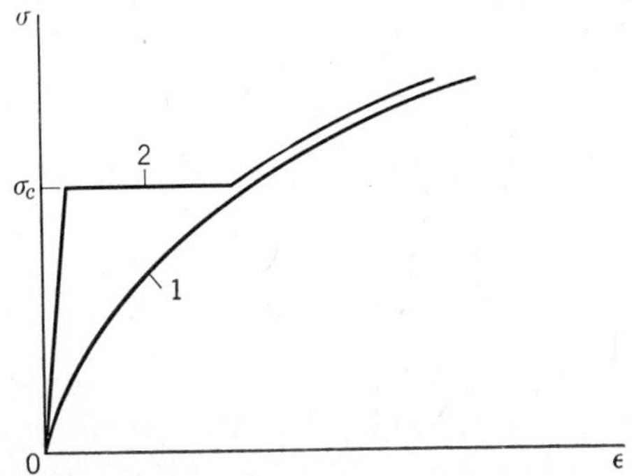

Fig. 1. Stress-strain curve $\sigma(\epsilon)$ of a polycrystal: (1) before and (2) after quench or irradiation (schematic).

and stable hardening. Finally, they could be the nuclei of the larger cavities observed in some cases.

As we shall see, these cavities are expected to have *small sizes,* down to perhaps 10^{-6} cm. They are therefore not necessarily visible under the microscope. In addition to their hardening effect, two somewhat indirect proofs of their existence may be given: (1) Small *colloidal metallic particles* precipitate along dislocations in suitably treated ionic crystals (Hedges and Mitchell, 1953; Amelinckx, 1956); such particles are only likely to appear if a cavity of at least equal size is provided before or during their formation. (2) There is some X-ray evidence that small cavities and small platelets may be formed in irradiated LiF (Lambert and Guinier, 1956).

2. FORMATION OF COTTRELL CLOUDS OF VACANCIES OR INTERSTITIALS

Vacancies (or interstitials) in supersaturation can build up Cottrell clouds around dislocations *when their rate of arrival near to the dislocations is larger than their rate of disappearance at the jogs.* An analysis of these two rates will show that Cottrell clouds build up only at the *beginning* of the diffusion process.

A. Rate of Arrival of the Defects

Let

$$W \simeq W_M \left(\frac{b}{r}\right)^n \tag{1}$$

be the energy of interaction of a point defect with a dislocation. Here r is their separation distance; b the Burgers vector; W_M the "binding energy," when the defect is in the immediate neighborhood of the dislocation ($r \simeq b$); and the angular dependence of W has been neglected.

The defects diffuse toward the dislocation under a force $F \simeq -(dW/dr)$, with a velocity $v = DF/kT$, where D is the diffusion coefficient of the defects. After a time t, all the defects in supersaturation at a distance less than

$$r = vt = \frac{DFt}{kT} = \frac{nDW_M tb^n}{kTr^{n+1}} \tag{2}$$

will have arrived at the dislocation. Let $c + c_0$ be the initial concentration of defects and c_0 their equilibrium concentration. Their rate of arrival at the dislocation, per unit length of dislocation, is, using eq. 2 and the fact that b^3 is usually near to the atomic volume,

$$R = \frac{2\pi r\, dr}{b^2\, dt} c = \frac{2}{n+2} \frac{c_1}{bt} \tag{3}$$

if their concentration near to the dislocation is

$$c_1 + c_0 = c_0 + \frac{\pi r^2}{b^2} c = c_0 + \pi c \left(\frac{nDW_M t}{b^2 kT}\right)^{\frac{2}{n+2}} \tag{4}$$

B. Rate of Disappearance of the Defects

Once at a dislocation, a defect has to diffuse to the next jog. At *thermal equilibrium,* the average distance between jogs is

$$l \simeq b e^{\frac{U_j}{kT}} \tag{5}$$

where U_j is the energy necessary to form a jog; and the concentration of defects is c_0 near to the jog. The defects are then submitted, along the dislocation, to a concentration gradient of the order of c_1/l. Their velocity is $v' \simeq D'c_1/lc$, if D' is their diffusion coefficient along the dislocation. Their rate of disappearance at jogs is then, per unit length of dislocation,

$$R' = \frac{cv'}{lb} = \frac{c_1 D'}{l^2 b} \tag{6}$$

From eqs. 3 and 6 we see that Cottrell clouds build up at the beginning of the diffusion process: $R' < R$ for

$$t < t_1 = \frac{2}{n+2} \frac{l^2}{D'} \tag{7}$$

We have assumed here that jogs were in thermal equilibrium. This is a reasonable assumption *because the excess concentration c_1 we will be interested in is near to unity.* Such a small number of defects can be absorbed by jogs without altering their distribution very much from that of thermal equilibrium; inversely, in quenched crystals, the jogs in excess retained from high temperature will be eliminated by absorbing somewhat less than one vacancy per unit length of dislocation, i.e., a concentration c_1 of the order of unity.

3. CONDENSATION OF THE COTTRELL CLOUDS

If the concentration $c_0 + c_1$ of defects near to the dislocations reaches a value near to unity, the defects must tend to precipitate: interstitials release their elastic energy by forming platelets; vacancies release their surface energy by forming cavities. We study first the concentrations c_1 necessary for such a precipitation to become likely, then the conditions under which such a concentration may be obtained.

A. Platelets from Interstitials

Interstitials interact with the dislocations mainly through their large size factor * (Cottrell, 1953). They are attracted toward the expanded side of the *edge* dislocations by a force proportional to r^{-2} ($n = 1$ in eq. 1). The binding energy is

$$W_M \simeq \mu b^3 \eta \tag{8}$$

if μ is the shear modulus and η the size factor. With $\eta \simeq 100\%$, this is several electron volts. It is of the same order of magnitude as the elastic energy E stored around an interstitial atom in the perfect crystal,

$$E \simeq \mu b^3 \eta^2 \tag{9}$$

And as interstitials are likely to repel each other (cf. Eshelby, 1955),

* In ionic crystals, *charged* defects may be attracted by the local charge of a dislocation or of a jog. But defects with like charges will repel each other so strongly that no precipitation can occur. Only *neutral* interstitials could precipitate.

there is no tendency for the interstitial reaching the core of the dislocation ($r \simeq b$) to precipitate. It is only when this core is saturated that further interstitials tend to precipitate in platelets to relax their elastic energy. High concentrations c_1, *of the order of unity,* are therefore required for platelets to appear.

B. Cavities from Vacancies

Vacancies have a small size factor: their presence does not displace very much the neighboring nuclei in a perfect lattice. But being nearly empty, they are weak spots in the crystal. Owing to this *"deformability"* factor, they are attracted toward any center of stress (Crussard, 1950; Eshelby, 1951). Their energy of interaction W with a dislocation of *any* kind (screw as well as edge) is of the order of the elastic energy stored by the dislocation, which is locally relaxed by the vacancy. This varies as r^{-2} ($n = 2$ in eq. 1), with a maximum value (Friedel, 1956)

$$W_M \simeq \tfrac{1}{10}\mu b^3 \tag{10}$$

This is probably less than the energy E to form a vacancy:

$$E \simeq \tfrac{1}{5}\mu b^3 \tag{11}$$

for usual metals. Therefore vacancies, even at the core of the dislocation, gain some energy by condensing into cavities. As two vacancies probably attract each other at short distance, at least in metals,* we can therefore expect precipitation to be easier than with interstitials, *with probably* $0.01 < c_1 < 0.1$ (cf. Seitz, 1953).

C. Maximum Available Concentration c_1 of Defects in the Clouds

We want to show that the concentrations c_1 necessary for the condensation of the clouds are easily obtained, at least for vacancies.

The maximum value of c_1 is obtained at the time t_1 when jogs begin to eat defects more quickly than they arrive at the dislocations. Thus, from eqs. 4 and 7,

$$c_1 \leq c_1(t_1) = \pi c \left(\frac{2nDl^2W_M}{(n+2)D'b^2kT} \right)^{\frac{2}{n+2}} \tag{12}$$

By writing that this value is larger than those necessary for condensation, we obtain the minimum excess concentrations c of defects necessary for condensation to occur. Owing to uncertainties in the

* The formation of pairs reduces the surface energy of the cavities they form, or reduces the number of broken bonds.

quantities D, D', and l, these values are difficult to ascertain, but certainly *small*. Thus we may write, using eq. 5,

$$\frac{Dl^2}{D'b^2} \simeq e^{\frac{2U_j+U_d'-U_d}{kT}} \tag{13}$$

where U_d and U_d' are the energies of displacement of the defects respectively in a perfect crystal and along a dislocation. As seen above, n is of the order of unity and W_M of the order of an electron volt. Concentrations $c \simeq 10^{-4}c_1$ are therefore sufficient if

$$kT < \tfrac{1}{10}(2U_j + U_d' - U_d) \tag{14}$$

In usual metals, $2U_j + U_d' - U_d$ is probably a few tenths of an electron volt for both vacancies and interstitials: condensation should occur at or below room temperature. With the values of c_1 discussed above, the corresponding values of c are 10^{-4} for interstitials and less than 10^{-5} for vacancies. It is indeed observed that cavities nucleate at small supersaturations, for which a nucleation in the perfect crystal is unlikely.

Equation 12 shows from a more general point of view that the *condensation of defects is favored by*

1. High supersaturations (c large).
2. Mobile defects (D large).
3. High jog energy (U_j, thus l, large).

It is the question of *jog energy* which predominates by far.

Three further conditions for condensation are usually fulfilled:

1. There must be enough defects to saturate the dislocations. With a density ρ_D of dislocations, this gives

$$c > b^2 c_1 \rho_D \tag{15}$$

With $c_1 \leq 1$ and $\rho_D \leq 10^7$ cm^{-2} for well-annealed crystals, a concentration $c > 10^{-8}$ is sufficient.

2. Defects must gain more internal energy than the entropy lost by coming to the dislocation. Thus (Cottrell, 1953)

$$c > c_1 e^{-\frac{W_M}{kT}} \tag{16}$$

Equation 13 shows that this condition is fulfilled when eq. 12 is, in the usual case where W_M is not much smaller than $[2/(n+2)](2U_j + U_d' - U_d)$.

3. The time for the necessary concentration c_1 to be reached must not be too long: a rapid precipitation of certain types of defect indicates that they are fairly mobile at the temperature considered. Equation 4 indicates, for instance, that a condensation in 1 hr with an excess concentration $c \simeq 10^{-4} c_1$ requires a diffusion coefficient D of defects of the order of 10^{-14} to 10^{-12} cm^2 sec^{-1} at room temperature, thus activation energies U_d less than 1 ev.

4. STABILITY OF THE PRECIPITATES

Once nucleated by the mechanism discussed above, the precipitates will quickly grow somewhat in size, so as to assimilate all the defects in supersaturation arriving at the dislocations. If this supply is stopped, as it must be after a while in a quench experiment, the precipitates may either be eaten away by the dislocations or grow at the expense of each other. We want to show that the first possibility is likely for the platelets and the second for cavities. Thus *the cavities should be much more stable than the platelets.* We show then that *the size of these cavities should remain fairly small* if no more vacancies in supersaturation are introduced.

A. Possibility for the Dislocations to Eat Away the Precipitates

One could expect the concentration gradients, along the dislocations from the precipitates to the jogs, to draw the defects to the jogs, where they would disappear. Precipitates should then quickly disappear by diffusion along the dislocation. This should probably be the case for the *platelets* due to interstitials: their diffusion along the dislocations is certainly rapid; we have pointed out in § 3.A that their concentration in the core of the dislocations should remain high even when platelets have been nucleated. Finally the platelets should *not* very effectively prevent the dislocation lines from climbing: the platelets are not usually formed in the glide planes of the dislocations; their energy of interaction with the dislocations is therefore weak and changes little when the dislocations climb over a few interatomic distances (Fig. 2*a*).

Cavities, on the contrary, exert a strong image force on the dislocations, which always induces them to arrive normal to the surface of the cavity (cf. Appendix II). They should therefore pin the dislocations down very effectively, and prevent them from climbing.

More precisely, we show in Appendix I that cavities larger than a few interatomic distances take an almost *spherical* shape. We therefore expect vacancies to condense along the dislocations lines, as a succession of little spheres, like dew on a spider's web (Fig. 2*b*). The discussion of § 4.B shows that one thus expects the cavities to remain of small size R, at small distances L. As the curvature ρ of a loop such as AB cannot become large, it cannot climb over a large distance y. One has of course

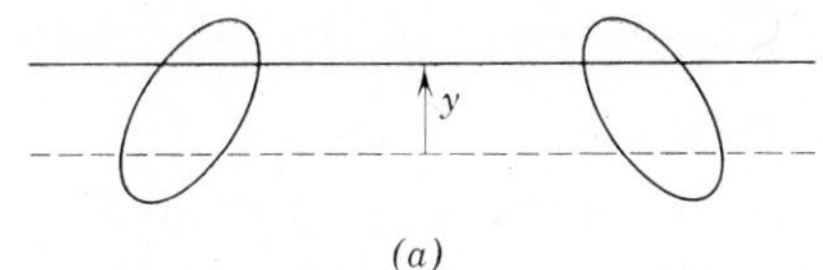

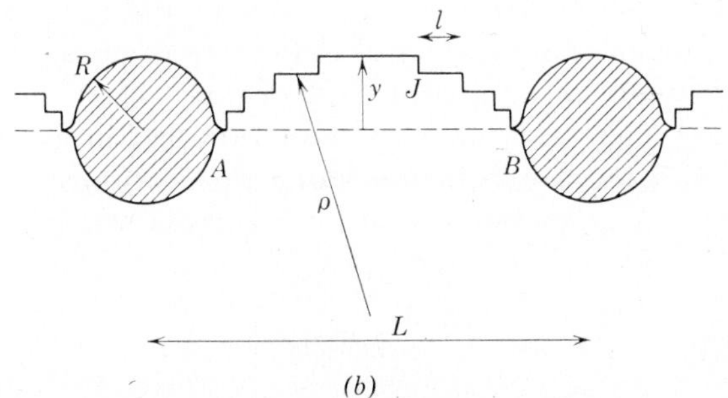

Fig. 2. Climb of a dislocation with precipitates: (*a*) platelets; (*b*) cavities.

$$y \simeq \frac{L^2}{8\rho} \tag{17}$$

and the equilibrium curvature $1/\rho$ is obtained by equating the force on a jog due to the vacancy gradient dc/dx to the force due to the jog gradient. Thus (Friedel, 1956)

$$\frac{dc}{c\,dx} = -\frac{dl}{l\,dx} = \frac{l}{b\rho} \tag{18}$$

The concentration c of vacancies increases from the equilibrium value c_0 at the mid-point of the loop AB to the value

$$c_R = c_0 e^{\frac{2\gamma b^3}{kTR}} \tag{19}$$

of the Thomson-Gibbs relation at the ends A and B.

Thus

$$y \simeq \frac{Lb}{l} \sinh \frac{2\gamma b^3}{kTR} \tag{20}$$

It will be shown below that the cavities grow rapidly to sizes R such that $[(2\gamma b^3)/(kTR)] \simeq 1$. With reasonable jog energies ($U_j \geq 0.3$ ev), and L certainly less than 10^{-4} cm, one sees that climb is negligible ($y < b$) up to fairly high temperatures. The dislocations can therefore absorb no vacancies (cf. Bardeen and Herring, 1952).

B. Growth of the Cavities

In these conditions, vacancies can only disappear at the surface or on the grain boundaries, a slow process with *large* grains. But they can *diffuse readily from the smaller cavities to the neighboring bigger ones.* We want to show that: (1) This growth of cavities occurs mainly by diffusion *along the dislocation lines.* Volume diffusion is important only at high temperature and for already large cavities. (2) Cavities grow up fairly quickly to a *small critical size.* Their further growth is much slower, unless new vacancies are introduced in supersaturation.

Volume diffusion or diffusion along dislocations. The relative importance of these two types of diffusion is given by the product

$$X = \frac{D}{D'} \cdot \frac{R^2}{b^2}$$

of the ratio of the diffusion coefficients of the vacancies and the ratio of the cross sections for diffusion. Analogy of D' with coefficients of grain boundary diffusion indicates that $D/D' \simeq e^{-U/kT}$ with activation energies U varying from perhaps 0.2 ev (Cd) to 2 ev (Ni). Thus, at least for metals, the rapid formation of small cavities at or below room temperature discussed below ($R \leq 100b$) should occur by diffusion along the dislocations. The slow growth or disappearance of large cavities ($R \geq 10^4\, b$) near to the melting point should occur by volume diffusion.

Critical size R_0 of cavities. The size at which growth slows down may be fixed by two factors, depending on the initial supersaturation considered.

1. *Small excess concentrations c* (quench or usual irradiations). The cavities nucleated at the dislocations are then small enough in size and number to be well separated: $R \ll L$, Fig. 3. In the initial stages of recovery, where diffusion along the dislocations predominates, the growth of bigger cavities at the expense of smaller ones ($R_1 > R_2$, Fig. 3) is given, according to eq. 19, by

$$-\frac{4\pi R_2{}^2\, dR_2}{b^3\, dt} = \frac{4\pi R_1{}^2\, dR_1}{b^3\, dt} = \frac{D'b^2}{b^3}\frac{c_2 - c_1}{L} = \frac{D'c_0}{bL}\left(e^{\frac{2\gamma b^3}{kTR_2}} - e^{\frac{2\gamma b^3}{kTR_1}}\right) \quad (21)$$

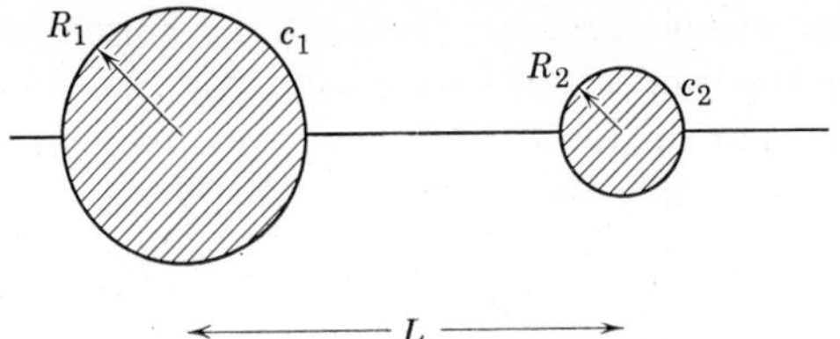

Fig. 3. Growth of a cavity at the expense of a neighboring smaller one.

In a number of crystals, $2\gamma b^2$ is of the order of 1 ev, thus much larger than kT. We must therefore distinguish between two successive stages.

In the *initial* stage, where R_1 and R_2 are equal to a few b, thus much smaller than

$$R_0 = \frac{2\gamma b^3}{kT} \simeq \frac{10^4 b}{T} \tag{22}$$

the exponentials in eq. 21 are much larger than unity, and growth is fairly rapid. As R_1 is assumed larger than R_2, the second exponential is negligible, and an integration of eq. 21 gives, for the time t necessary for a cavity of radius R_2 to disappear,

$$t \simeq 4\pi \frac{R_2{}^4 L}{b^2 R_0 D'} e^{-\frac{R_0}{R_2}} \tag{23}$$

With silver at room temperature, for instance, where $D'c_0 \simeq 10^{-16}$ cgs, smaller cavities of radius $R_2 = 4b$ disappear in $t \simeq 10^{-3}\ (L/b)$ sec, thus at most in a matter of *seconds* for $L \leq 10^{-4}$ cm. Cavities of radius $R_2 \simeq 40b$ would disappear in $t \simeq 10^6\ (L/b)$ sec, thus in a matter of years.

The *critical radius* which separates the initial stage of quick growth from the later one of very slow growth is therefore of the order of $\frac{1}{2}R_0$, eq. 22. This radius is *very small*, of the order of $20b$ at room temperature and smaller above. As each sphere contains few vacancies, *their average distance L along the dislocations must be fairly small* as soon as the initial excess concentration c of vacancies is not negligibly small. One has

$$L \simeq \frac{4\pi}{3} \frac{(R_0/2)^3 \rho_D}{c} \tag{24}$$

if ρ_D is the density of dislocations. For well-annealed crystals, where ρ_D is at most 10^7 cm^{-2}, a value $c = 10^{-6}$ gives $L \simeq 300b$ at room temperature.

2. *Larger excess concentrations* (perhaps the Kirkendall effect). For large initial excess concentrations c, the spheres studied above are contiguous. This arises for $L \leq R_0$, i.e., from eq. 24 for

$$c \geq \frac{\pi}{6} R_0^2 \rho_D \simeq \frac{300}{T^2} \tag{25}$$

We expect in this case the initial formation along the dislocations of a continuous *tunnel* of radius R_0' such that

$$c = \pi R_0'^2 \rho_D \tag{26}$$

For reasons developed in Appendix I, this tunnel should soon split up, by *surface* diffusion, into a series of contiguous spheres, of radius evidently not much larger than R_0'. As $R_0' \gg R_0$, the growth of these spheres at the expense of each other should soon stop, except at fairly high temperatures or if new vacancies are introduced. *The critical radius should therefore be of the order of R_0' in this case, and the spheres almost contiguous.* As an order of magnitude, a concentration $c = 10^{-3}$, with $\rho_D = 10^7$ cm^{-2}, corresponds to $R_0' = 200b$.

5. HARDENING DUE TO CAVITIES

We now want to show that hardening due to cavities must be high and not too dependent on temperature. This is because: (1) they are *formed* on screw as well as on edge dislocations (cf. § 3.B); (2) once

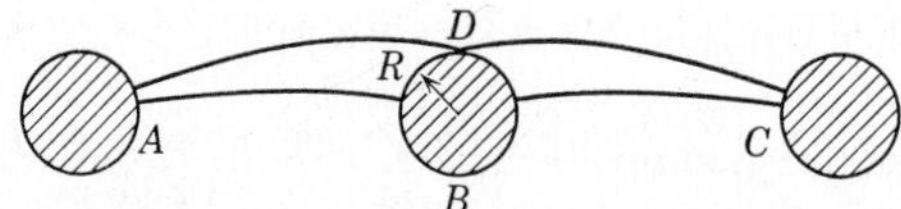

Fig. 4. Thermally activated release of a dislocation loop AC from a cavity B.

formed, they *pin down* screw as well as edge dislocations very effectively.

We treat here the case of least hardening, for small well-separated cavities. Similar results are obtained for a continuous tunnel (Appendix II). This case occurs with small initial excess concentrations. There is, of course, *no noticeable hardening* as long as the average distance L between cavities is larger than the Frank-Read sources, i.e., a few 10^{-4} cm. But the previous discussion showed that at concentrations c where precipitation occurs, L is usually much shorter than this value. Every Frank-Read source is then pinned down by a number of cavities (Fig. 4).

By analogy with the simpler case discussed in Appendix II, we can say that the image forces exerted by the cavity on a dislocation tend to make it arrive normal to the surface of the cavity. At small distances from the cavity, the forces are much larger than any likely applied stress σ_a, but they do not extend at distances much greater than R from the cavity.

When a stress σ_a is applied, each loop such as AB, BC moves somewhat forward and takes a certain curvature. For $L \gg R$, the average curvature is near to that due to the applied stress only: $1/\rho = (2\sigma_a)/(\mu b)$; and when $L \ll 10^{-3}$ cm, the displacement of the loop is slight. The activation energy required to free the loops AB, BC from the cavity B by thermal agitation is therefore the energy necessary for AB and BC to go to the excited state ADC, Fig. 4. Adding contributions from the line tension and from the work of the applied stress, we have

$$U \simeq \tfrac{1}{2}\mu b^2 \cdot 2R - \sigma_a b \cdot LR = \mu b^3 \frac{R}{b}\left(1 - \frac{\sigma_a}{\mu}\frac{L}{b}\right)$$

With $\mu b^3 \simeq 5$ ev and $R \simeq 20b$, we see that the probability of escape is negligibly small *unless* $\sigma_a \simeq \mu b/L$, i.e., *if each loop such as AB acts as a Frank-Read source.* Such hardening is not very temperature-dependent; it is as efficient for screw as for edge dislocations. It becomes extremely high when L is reduced to values comparable with R. It should disappear only by high-temperature recovery, making the cavities grow to much larger size or perhaps disappear by diffusion of the vacancies to the grain boundaries. One knows indeed that this type of hardening may be large, that it is fairly stable, and that it disappears at high temperature by volume diffusion.

APPENDIX I

EQUILIBRIUM FORM OF A CAVITY AROUND A SCREW DISLOCATION

Let us assume for simplicity that the cavity accepts the screw dislocation line as an axis of revolution Oz. Let

$$z = f(r) \tag{A.1}$$

be the equation of its surface (Fig. 5).

The part of the energy of formation of the cavity which varies with its form may be written

$$E = 2\pi\gamma \int_{\rho_0}^{R} r\sqrt{1 + f'^2}\, dr - \frac{\mu b^2}{4\pi}\int_{\rho_0}^{R} \log\frac{r}{b} \cdot f'\, dr \tag{A.2}$$

if ρ_0 and R are the extremal values of the radius r. In this expression, the first term is due to the surface energy expended, and the second to the elastic energy released with the formation of the cavity. The second term is only approximate, and valid for r not too small and varying not too rapidly with z.

In the elastic approximation, the equilibrium radius ρ_0 of an empty

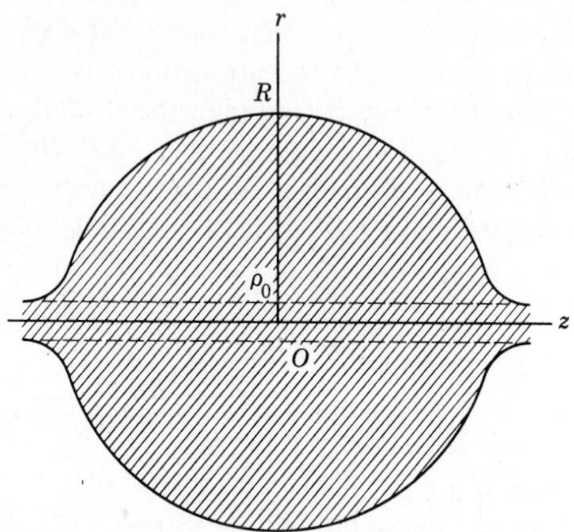

Fig. 5. Equilibrium form of a cavity around a dislocation of axis Oz (for $R = 100\rho_0 \simeq 15b$.

cylinder around the dislocation is obtained by minimizing eq. A.2 with respect to ρ_0 for $R = 0$ and f' infinite. This gives

$$\rho_0 = \frac{\mu b^2}{8\pi^2\gamma} \simeq \frac{b}{8} \tag{A.3}$$

for a reasonable value of the surface energy $\gamma \simeq (\mu/10)b$ (Frank, 1951). If the cavity considered has a volume larger than that of such a cylinder,* it will bulge out up to a radius R. And its equilibrium form will be obtained by minimizing eq. A.2 with the two conditions:

1. Constant excess volume, thus

$$V = \pi \int_{\rho_0}^{R} r^2 f' \, dr = \text{const} \tag{A.4}$$

2. Suitable boundary conditions, thus

$$\frac{dz}{dr} = f' = \infty \qquad \text{for } r = \rho_0 \text{ and } r = R \tag{A.5}$$

* As noted by Frank (1951), the radius ρ_0 is negligibly small, and the dislocation actually has a full center in its most stable state, unless it has a large Burgers vector.

Euler's equation for the minimum of E − const V gives

$$-\text{const}\ \pi r^2 + \frac{2\pi\gamma r f'}{\sqrt{1+f'^2}} - \frac{\mu b^2}{4\pi}\log\frac{r}{b} = \text{const}' \tag{A.6}$$

The use of conditions A.5 gives then

$$\frac{f'}{\sqrt{1+f'^2}} = \lambda = \frac{r^2 + R\rho_0}{(R+\rho_0)r} + \frac{\rho_0}{r}\left(\log\frac{r}{R} + \frac{R^2 - r^2}{R^2 - {\rho_0}^2}\log\frac{R}{\rho_0}\right)$$

A numerical integration of this equation shows that, as soon as R is much larger than ρ_0, the cavity is nearly *spherical;* Fig. 5 gives, for instance, the form of $z = f(r)$ for $R = 100\rho_0$ ($\simeq 15b$), for which the radius of curvature R_0 at the mid-point is not much larger than R:

$$R_0 = \left(\frac{dr}{d\lambda}\right)_{r=R} = R\left[\frac{R^2 + {\rho_0}^2}{R(R+\rho_0)} - \frac{2\rho_0 R}{R^2 - {\rho_0}^2}\log\frac{R}{\rho_0}\right]^{-1}$$

$$\simeq R - \rho_0\left(1 + 2\log\frac{R}{\rho_0}\right) \simeq 1.1R$$

APPENDIX II

INTERACTION BETWEEN A SCREW DISLOCATION AND A PARALLEL HOLLOW CYLINDER

We consider a dislocation line parallel to a hollow cylinder in a large crystal. Let R be the radius of the hole, R' the radius of the crystal, and ξ the distance from the dislocation to the axis of the hole (Fig. 6).

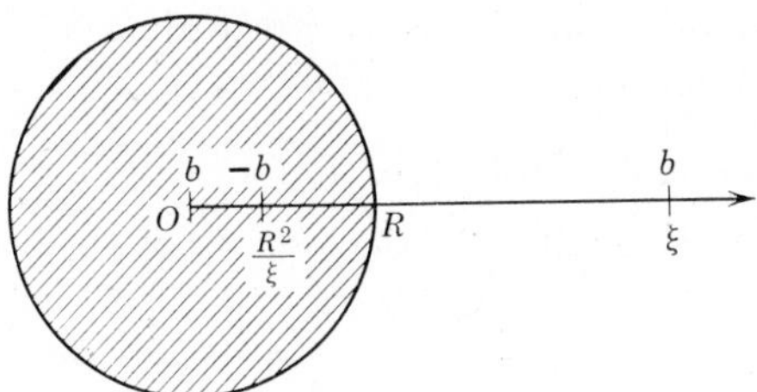

Fig. 6. Interaction between a screw dislocation and a hollow cylinder.

The dislocation, when in the crystal, will be attracted towards the cavity by an image force which must increase from very small values for $\xi \gg R$ to values of the order of the elastic limit when ξ tends to R. When it is a screw dislocation, this force has a very simple algebraic form. We show that the liberation by thermal agitation of a dislocation line from a hollow cylinder is unlikely except under very high stress.

Dislocation Line in the Crystal ($\xi > R$)

When a cavity of radius R is created near the dislocation b at ξ, the surface stresses due to the dislocation are cancelled by considering two "image" dislocations (Fig. 6):

1. A dislocation $-b$ at R^2/ξ, to relieve the stresses on the surface of the cavity (Eshelby, 1953).
2. A dislocation b at the center O, to compensate for the Burgers vector of the first.

The *image stress* acting on the dislocation considered is therefore

$$\sigma(\xi) = \frac{\mu b}{2\pi}\left(\frac{1}{\xi} - \frac{1}{\xi - R^2/\xi}\right) = -\frac{\mu b R^2}{2\pi\xi(\xi^2 - R^2)} \tag{A.7}$$

This increases from small values $\simeq -[(\mu b R^2)/(2\pi\xi^3)]$ for $\xi \gg R$ to infinity in the neighborhood of the cavity. The elastic model actually breaks down for perhaps $(\xi - R) \leq b$. The corresponding *maximum* value of $-\sigma$ is $\mu R^2/2\pi(R + b)(2R + b)$. This limit is of the order of $(1/4\pi)\mu$, thus of the *theoretical elastic limit*, for cavities with radius R larger than the Burgers vector b.

The *energy of interaction* of the dislocation with the cavity is obtained by integrating eq. A.7 from infinity:

$$\Delta E = \int_\xi^\infty \sigma b \, d\xi = -\frac{\mu b^2}{4\pi}\log\left(1 - \frac{R^2}{\xi^2}\right) \tag{A.8}$$

The *maximum* value of $-\Delta E$, for $\xi = R + b$, is thus $(\mu b^2/4\pi)\log[(R + b)^2/b(2R + b)]$, or about $(\mu b^2/4\pi)\log(R/2b)$ for $R \gg b$.

Dislocation Line in the Hole ($\xi < R$)

When the dislocation line is at the *center* O of the hole, its energy of interaction is $\Delta E = -(\mu b^2/4\pi)\log(R/b)$. This value is somewhat more negative than for $\xi = R + b$ in the usual case where $[(R + b)^2/b(2R + b)] < R/b$, i.e., $R > (1 + \sqrt{5})b/2 \simeq 1.6b$ (Fig. 7).

This shows that a dislocation line is usually more stable at the center of the hole than on its edge. No satisfactory treatment was found for $\xi \neq 0$. We did not investigate, for instance, if ΔE had a minimum value lower than $\Delta E(O)$ in that region.

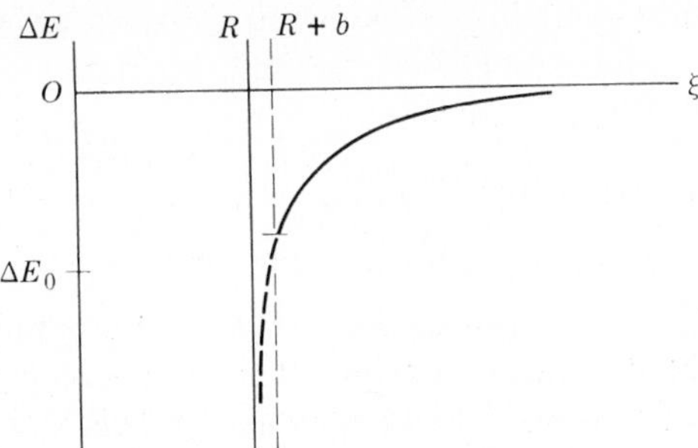

Fig. 7. Energy ΔE of interaction of a screw dislocation with a hollow cylinder.

Thermally Activated Escape of a Dislocation from a Hollow Cylinder

We want to show that a hollow cylinder pins a dislocation down very effectively. The stress necessary for the escape without thermal activation is of the order of the elastic limit, usually impossible to reach. On the other hand, the binding energy $\Delta E(O)$ is so large that thermal activation cannot help very much, except for very small radii R.

A thermally activated escape is of course easier, the smaller the radius R: according to the two preceding sections, the binding energy is smaller and the image stresses decrease more rapidly with an increasing distance ξ. We shall therefore only consider the case of small radii R, more precisely of *radii R small compared with the equilibrium radius of curvature $\rho = \mu b/2\sigma$ under the applied stress σ.* According to eq. A.7, the image force due to the hole is then negligible compared with σ at a distance $\xi \simeq (\rho R^2/\pi)^{1/3}$ from the hole, which is large compared with R but small compared with ρ. A loop AB of dislocation which has escaped from the hole has therefore a radius of curvature near to ρ along most of its length (Fig. 8). It has also a line tension close to that in a crystal without a hole.

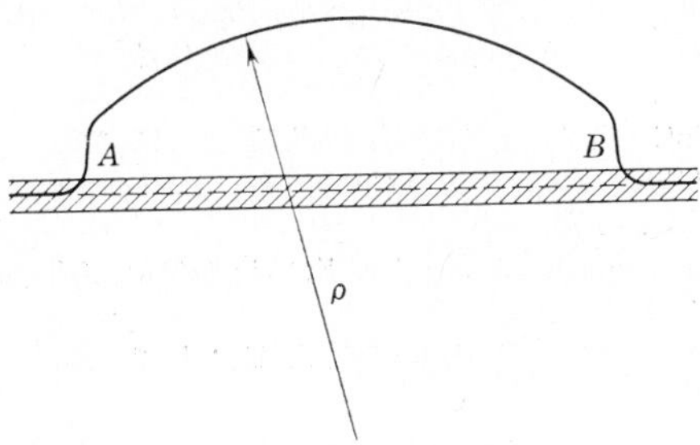

Fig. 8. Escape of a dislocation loop from a hollow cylinder.

Fisher's theory (1955) for the escape of a dislocation from a Cottrell cloud therefore applies. The activation energy for escape may be written (Friedel, 1956)

$$U = \frac{7}{6}\frac{\mu^2 b^3}{\sigma}\left[\frac{|\Delta E(O)|}{\mu b^2}\right]^{3/2} = \frac{7}{6}\frac{\mu}{\sigma}\left(\frac{\log (R/b)}{4\pi}\right)^{3/2} \mu b^3 \qquad (\text{for } R \geq 1.6b)$$

The activation energy varies as σ^{-1}; thus the yield point σ varies as T^{-1} under constant strain rate $d\epsilon/dt$. The discussion of the text shows that $R < 20b$ is unlikely. The binding energy $|\Delta E(O)|$ is therefore at least of the order of $\frac{1}{4}\,\mu b^2$, or about 1 ev per interatomic distance b. This is equal to approximately 100 times the binding energies deduced from the variation of $\sigma(T)$ in low-carbon steel. It would correspond to yield stresses about 100 times larger, thus of the order of the theoretical elastic limit $\mu/10$ at room temperature.

REFERENCES

Amelinckx, S. (1956), *Phil. Mag.*, (8), **1**, 269.

Bardeen, J., and Herring, C. (1952), Chap. 10 in *Imperfections in Nearly Perfect Crystals,* W. Shockley, J. H. Hollomon, R. Maurer, and F. Seitz, John Wiley & Sons, New York, p. 261.

Cottrell, A. H. (1953), *Dislocations and Plastic Flow,* Oxford University Press, Oxford; (1954), ASM Seminar on Microstructure, p. 131.

Crussard, C. (1950), *Métaux & corrosion,* **25,** 203.

Eshelby, J. D. (1951), *Phil. Trans., A,* **244,** 87; (1953), *J. Appl. Phys.,* **24,** 176; (1955), *Acta Met.,* **3,** 457.

Fisher, J. C. (1955), *Trans. ASM,* **47,** 451.

Foote, F. G. (1955), *International Conference on the Peaceful Uses of Atomic Energy,* pub. by United Nations.

Frank, F. C. (1951), *Acta Cryst.,* **4,** 497.

Friedel, J. (1956), *Les Dislocations,* Gauthier-Villars, Paris.

Geneva (1955), *International Conference on the Peaceful Uses of Atomic Energy,* Réacteurs à recherches des Etats-Unis, pub. by United Nations, p. 13.

Hedges, J. N., and Mitchell, J. W. (1953), *Phil. Mag.,* **44,** 223.

Kinchin, G. H., and Pease, R. S. (1955), *Rep. Progr. Phys.,* **18,** 1.

Lambert, M., and Guinier, A. (1956), *Rayonnements de grande énergie,* Gauthier-Villars, Paris, p. 117.

Maddin, R., and Cottrell, A. H. (1955), *Phil. Mag.,* **46,** 735.

Nabarro, F. R. N. (1948), *Report of a Conference on the Strength of Solids,* Physical Society, London, p. 75.

Seitz, F. (1948), *Discussions Faraday Soc.,* **5,** 271; (1952), *Advances in Phys.,* **1,** 43; (1953), *Acta Met.,* **1,** 355.

Wilson, J. C., and Billington, D. S. (1956), *J. Metals,* **8,** 665.

DISCUSSION

LEIBFRIED asked if the hardening due to the cavities should be temperature-independent; and FRIEDEL replied that it should not be very temperature-sensitive. COTTRELL pointed out that it is experimentally observed that the yield stress of an irradiation-hardened metal is fairly sensitive to temperature.

BLEWITT reported that D. K. Holmes of the Oak Ridge National Laboratory has devised a new theory to explain radiation hardening, which takes into account the observed temperature dependence of the yield stress. Holmes assumes that the defects do not migrate to dislocations, but that they are arrayed in clumps and form barriers randomly distributed through the material. Two experimental facts that suggest such a model are that the flow stress is proportional to the cube root of the flux, and that the flow stress is proportional to the inverse square root of the temperature. Holmes assumes that thermal fluctuations enable the dislocations to get over the barriers. He uses a thermal fluctuation field in accordance with that suggested by Kochendorfer.

FRIEDEL wondered whether there were enough of the randomly formed clumps formed to harden the material appreciably. BLEWITT said that there were enough, and that fluxes up to 10^{20} nvt had been used without evidence of radiation annealing or of saturation. If it were a matter of defects going to dislocations, the hardening effect should saturate for much lower fluxes; therefore, it seems that the regions of interest are very large and numerous.

LÜCKE protested that the ideas described by Blewitt were not in agreement with recent work of Thompson and Holmes,* in which it was suggested that the internal friction decreases during irradiation because the defects migrate to the dislocations and pin them. BLEWITT replied that the feeling at Oak Ridge is that the two effects are entirely different, since the complete saturation of damping and of change in elastic constants occurs for 10^{15} nvt, whereas there is no saturation in the hardening for 10^{20} nvt.

* D. O. Thompson and D. K. Holmes, *J. Appl. Phys.*, **27**, 713 (1956).

MOTT asked whether, according to Friedel's theory, most of the vacancies go to dislocations or if there are a lot of them scattered in the body of the material. FRIEDEL was of the opinion that this should depend on the temperature of recovery. At room temperature it would take a long time for all the vacancies to go to dislocations, so that one might expect some cavities in the bulk of the material. According to FRIEDEL, these random cavities should not harden the material very much.

COTTRELL pointed out that one difficulty with a theory such as Friedel's is that if one irradiates between room temperature and 100°C, there is considerable hardening; yet the defects are very mobile and should move directly to dislocations as soon as they are formed. One would not expect to build up a high supersaturation of vacancies.

BLEWITT suggested that in the case of radiation damage the pinning is not due to vacancies. If the material is bombarded at liquid-nitrogen temperature, tested for shear stress, and then warmed to room temperature where the vacancies are mobile, then upon measuring the critical shear stress in liquid nitrogen again there is little change from the previous value.

GILMAN reported some experiments that Johnston and he have done in co-operation with C. W. Tucker, Jr., of the Knolls Atomic Power Laboratory on neutron irradiation of lithium fluoride. The LiF single crystals have been exposed to thermal neutron fluxes of 10^{12} to 10^{18} nvt. The crystals show hardening, even at the lowest irradiations, but the point of interest is that it is not only the existing dislocations that are made less mobile by the irradiation. If new dislocations are introduced after the irradiation, these new dislocations are much more difficult to move in the irradiation-hardened crystals than they are in the unirradiated crystals. It is as if the Peierls force has been increased in the crystals. At the lower irradiations the only obvious defects are color centers. Density changes have not yet become apparent. If a crystal is etched before and after irradiation, it is observed that there has been no motion of existing dislocations, nor creation of new dislocation during the irradiation.

MOTT suggested that if the low irradiation produces hardening in crystals containing no fresh dislocations, then if one accepts the hardening mechanism which Friedel has put forward, it can be inferred that sources were present in the crystal and that these sources have been hardened by the irradiation.

LOMER felt that one must be cautious with regard to evidence on neutron irradiation damage in LiF, since most of the damage is done by the breakup of Li into He and H, both of which can stabilize small cavities as they diffuse, and produce centers of pressure.

SHOCKLEY said that it might be reasonable to expect vacancies to precipitate to form cavities in crystals with two species, such as ionic crystals. He did not feel that it is reasonable to expect cavities to form on dislocations in metal; rather, one would expect the vacancies that arrive at a dislocation merely to make new jogs.

Written reply by FRIEDEL:

I agree that vacancies, arriving near a dislocation, might prefer to build new jogs than to build a cavity. Shockley's argument, as I understand it, is that a vacancy on the compressed side of an edge dislocation is equivalent to two jogs of opposite signs; other vacancies, coming near the first one, might be absorbed by one of these jogs and separate them. I do not think this process would be very likely to occur on a dislocation which is *not dissociated:* it can happen only (1) on a pure edge or nearly pure edge dislocation, and (2) when vacancies are on the compressed side of the dislocation, a position not much more stable than any other around the dislocation line if the vacancies interact with it by their deformability factor more than by their size factor. On a *dissociated* dislocation such as those of copper, Shockley's process is clearly impossible: too much energy would be needed for the pinching of the dislocation necessary to transform a vacancy into two jogs (Fig. D1). An independent climb of the two partials

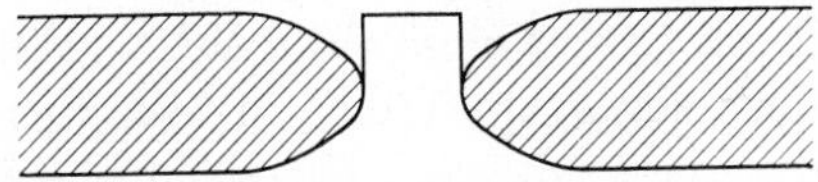

Fig. D1. Two jogs resulting from a vacancy on an extended dislocation.

PP', leaving the stacking fault SS' behind, has been suggested by Mott* for this case (Fig. D2). The partials would have to develop incoherent stacking faults SP, $S'P'$ with high energy. This makes the climb unlikely for vacancies, but perhaps possible for interstitials of high energy as in copper.

THOMSON said that when the voids form on the dislocation lines they ought to be eaten up fairly quickly. The mechanism is that shown in Fig. D3. There are two voids with a stretch of dislocation line between. Vacancies leak out of the voids and cause the dislocation line to climb, the center of the line bulging out meanwhile. The ends of the lines now exert a pull on the voids, and if the voids are not too large they can be dragged along with the climbing dislocation line, by

* Private communication.

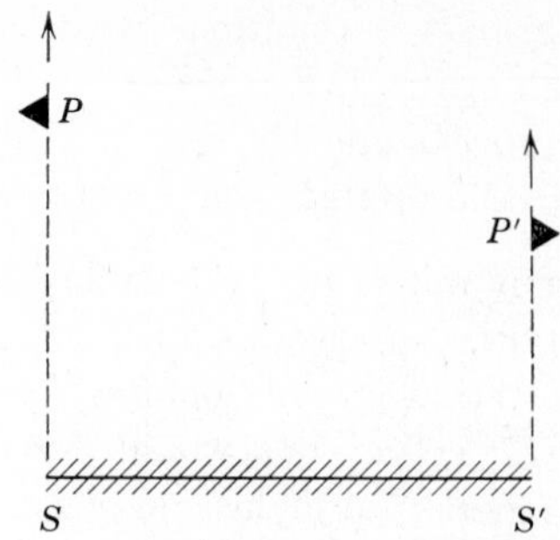

Fig. D2. Independent climb of two partials P and P' of a dissociated dislocation. The stacking fault SS' is left behind.

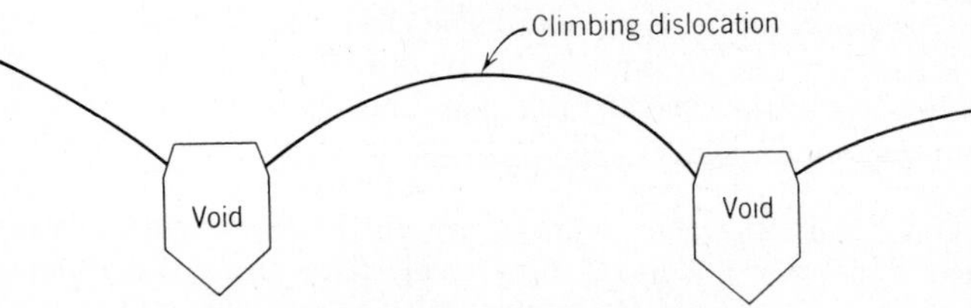

Fig. D3. A climbing dislocation with voids on it.

atoms diffusing from the top of the void to the bottom on the internal surface. The driving force for the diffusion is the surface energy of the void. FRIEDEL replied that in order to discuss the effect of the climbing voids, we must know more about surface diffusion. SHOCKLEY said that Thomson's suggestion seems to lead to a very interesting manner of looking at the way dislocations tie into cavities. Presumably the thermal etch pits are formed in just such a way, in which the shape of the pit is determined by the diffusion on the surface.

On Radiation and Quench Hardening in Metals

A. H. COTTRELL
Atomic Energy Research Establishment
Harwell, England

My view about radiation hardening and quench hardening in metals is similar in part to that suggested by Dr. Friedel in his interesting paper at this conference (preceding paper), but differs in one main respect.

I agree with Friedel in supposing that some hardening results from the migration of point defects to dislocations. In favor of this view is the strong effect of irradiation [1,2] and quenching [3,4] on dislocation damping. Furthermore, the way in which the plastic properties of metals are changed by irradiation [5-7] and quenching [8,9]—e.g., the increased yield stress, the sharp yield point, the long easy glide, overshooting, the high temperature and strain rate coefficients of yield stress, the coarse slip lines—suggests that the main effect on a slip line is to make its nucleation harder than its growth, i.e., to anchor dislocations in Frank-Read sources.

It seems to me that the point defects probably become incorporated into the dislocations, rather than form aggregates or cavities on them, for two reasons. First, if a metal such as copper is irradiated at temperatures where the point defects are mobile, above room temperature, it hardens at the full rate provided that the temperature is not so high as to allow self-diffusion to occur; this suggests that the point defects are able to harden the metal by reaching the dislocations a few at a time, as they are formed, and by being incorporated without building up a high steady-state concentration necessary to nucleate aggregates. Second, quenching experiments made recently at the University of Illinois on gold (Professor F. Seitz, private communication) and in Japan on nickel and aluminum [10] have shown that the volume of the quenched material decreases simultaneously with its resistivity, suggesting that the vacancies are actually disappearing and not merely aggregating into voids.

If the point defects are incorporated into the dislocations, we have to attribute the hardening to the jogs formed on the dislocations by these defects. Jogs on an edge dislocation offer a resistance to the motion of the dislocation, since an evenly spaced sequence of similar jogs is equivalent to the edge dislocation gliding in some plane other than the close-packed one and we know that in close-packed metals slip on such planes requires high stresses and thermal energy.

One difficulty with this view is that jogs of opposite signs on a dislocation line can be expected to cancel one another out by atomic migrations along the line at temperatures below those of self-diffusion, whereas in practice the hardening persists until the range of self-diffusion is reached. But if the nodes at the ends of the lines climb by different amounts, through statistical variations in the rate of climb in different parts of the material, some jogs must necessarily remain until the temperature range is reached where the entire dislocation network can be readjusted.

A second problem concerns whether the jogged sources are hard to operate at any but the lowest temperatures, since the activation energy to overcome the resistance of the jogs (or the Peierls force) is unlikely to be very large even when the applied stress is zero. However, if the metal is to be strained at some standard rate it is necessary either to operate more sources in order to compensate for their slower rate of operation when jogged, or to operate them at the same speed as before they were jogged in which case it is not possible to wait long for thermal fluctuations to overcome the resistance to motion. In either case the applied stress has to be increased. The effect of the thermal energy should, in fact, show itself rather as a substantial loss of yield strength at very low rates of strain in the irradiated or quenched material, by comparison with the same material in the unhardened or work-hardened states. There is some evidence for such an effect in the experiments of Wilson and Billington [11] on the sensitivity of the flow stress of irradiated stainless steel to the rate of straining. It would be most useful if a detailed test of this theoretical prediction were to be made.

REFERENCES

1. D. O. Thompson, D. K. Holmes, and T. H. Blewitt, *J. Appl. Phys.*, **26,** 1088 (1955); D. O. Thompson and D. K. Holmes, *J. Appl. Phys.*, **27,** 713 (1956).
2. R. S. Barnes and N. H. Hancock, Atomic Energy Research Establishment Report, to be published.
3. M. Levy and M. Metzger, *Phil. Mag.*, **46,** 1021 (1955).
4. A. E. Roswell and A. S. Nowick, *Acta Met.*, **5,** 228 (1957).
5. T. H. Blewitt and R. R. Coltman, *Phys. Rev.*, **82,** 769 (1951).
6. F. W. Kunz and A. N. Holden, *Acta Met.*, **2,** 816 (1954).
7. M. J. Makin, Atomic Energy Research Establishment Report, to be published.
8. C. H. Liu and E. R. Parker, *J. Metals,* **5,** 1223 (1953).
9. R. Maddin and A. H. Cottrell, *Phil. Mag.*, **46,** 735 (1955).
10. J. Takamura, *Metal Phys.*, **2** (3), 112 (1956).
11. J. C. Wilson and D. S. Billington, *Preprint 91,* Nuclear Engineering and Science Congress, Cleveland (1955).

DISCUSSION

MOTT asked if it is clear that the jogs on a dislocation that results from radiation damage will increase the shear stress in a temperature-dependent way. The jogs on the screw dislocations should slide off by conservative motion, and any dislocation that acts as a source will become a screw dislocation over part of its length during the process of making loops. COTTRELL explained that what he had in mind is that in order to accommodate a large number of jogs, the normally extended dislocation becomes narrow, so that it has a large Peierls force.

SEEGER recalled that at the 1954 Bristol Conference * he had discussed the glide resistance of jogs with particular reference to a theory of H. Blank. Blank was able to explain the dying out of the room temperature creep rate of aluminum, copper, and nickel single crystals. Although in the meantime Blank (to be published) has accumulated more experimental and theoretical material (pertaining also to the temperature dependence of creep in single crystals) supporting his views, SEEGER had difficulty in understanding from first principles the large effect of the jogs, as demanded by Cottrell's theory. He thought

* A. Seeger, *Report of a Conference on Defects in Solids,* Physical Society, London, p. 391, particularly para. 4, 1 (1955).

that at room temperature their effect should be largely overshadowed by the action of the thermal energy.

GILMAN felt that the above treatment of irradiation hardening does not account for the behavior of dislocations that are introduced *after* the irradiation. Such new dislocations are not jogged since they have not been affected by the irradiation. Why new dislocations are more difficult to move in a previously irradiated crystal than in an unirradiated one must be explained.

COTTRELL said that it has not been established that the behavior which was described by Gilman is characteristic of metals. LOMER added that even if fresh dislocations are introduced into a crystal, the main part of the plastic flow will occur by the operation of jogged sources. GILMAN replied that he was speaking of observations on individual dislocations as well as large-scale plastic flow in LiF.

Localized Radiation Damage as a Means of Studying Vacancies and Interstitials

WILLIAM SHOCKLEY

Shockley Semiconductor Laboratory
Beckman Instruments, Inc.
Mountain View, California

It is evident that the study of vacancies and interstitials will be greatly facilitated by the development of sources of vacancies and interstitials. The writer has previously suggested[1,2] the possibility of using a temperature gradient as a means of producing a flow of either vacancies or interstitials. This method has a variety of disadvantages, however, which are largely overcome by the proposal discussed below. In essence, the method proposed here is to produce a large number of vacancies and interstitials near the surface of the specimen being studied. Both of these species can be eliminated by diffusion to the surface. However, it seems most unlikely that both will be equally readily eliminated and consequently there will, in all probability, be an unbalance which will result in a net flow of vacancies or interstitials towards the interior of the material.

The opportunity to study the behavior of vacancies and interstitials is greatly enhanced by the techniques discussed in this conference for observing individual dislocations.

One means of carrying out such studies is suggested in Fig. 1. Here a beam of rare gas ions, e.g., xenon ions, is represented as striking a small area on a block of silicon which contains two tilt boundaries. The energy of bombardment is such that the radiation damage is produced very near the surface. Under these conditions a flow of vacancies or interstitials will be initiated and these will flow towards the interior. This flow will be influenced by the dislocations constituting the tilt boundaries and in turn the flow will influence the vacancies. By observing the effect upon the dislocations, it should be possible to study many of the properties of the vacancies and interstitials.

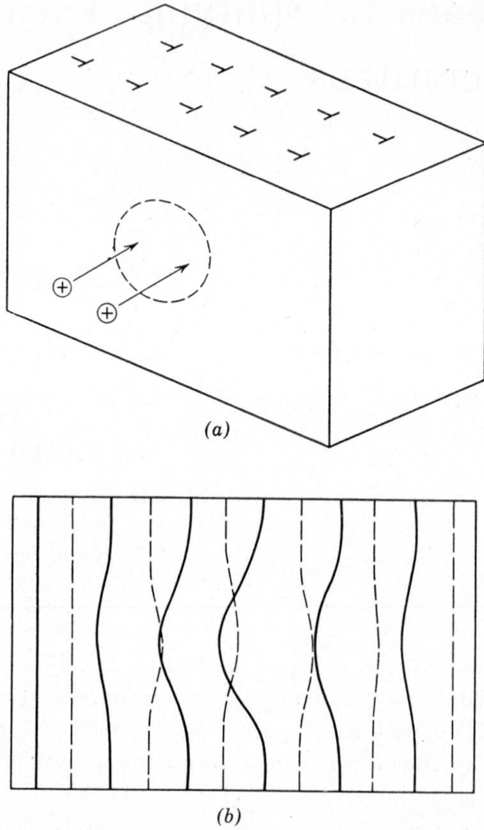

Fig. 1. (*a*) Silicon crystal with two tilt boundaries bombarded by a beam of rare gas ions. (*b*) A possible change in the shape of the dislocation lines of (*a*) as the result of the bombardment.

Before considering the expected effects it is instructive to note that it should be possible to produce very large disturbances from a thermal equilibrium situation by such experimental means. This can be shown by comparing the rate at which vacancies, for example, might be generated in such an experiment with the rate at which they would be thermally generated. This latter can be estimated if one assumes that the mechanism of self-diffusion is due to vacancies. Thus if the fraction of sites occupied by vacancies is c_v and the diffusion constant for a vacancy is D_v, then the coefficient of self-diffusion, as measured by using radioactive tracers, will be

$$D(\text{self}) = c_v D_v \tag{1}$$

If the value of the self-diffusion constant is known, then the rate at which vacancies are exchanging with the surface can be readily estimated as follows: The density of vacancies in the atomic plane lying just below the surface is c_v times the number of atoms per cm^3. We shall take the atomic volume as being a^3. The densities of atoms in the first plane below the surface can then flow to the surface as if it had this concentration in the plane with a concentration gradient equal to that which would make the concentration fall to zero in one atomic distance. This means the flow of vacancies to the surface is given by

$$\text{Flow vacancies to surface} = D_v(c_v/a^3)/a \tag{2}$$

For the case of self-diffusion in germanium, discussed by Frank in Part IV of this volume, the self-diffusion constant at a temperature of about 700°C was 10^{-15} cm^2/sec. Using this value for the self-diffusion constant, we estimate for the flow of vacancies to the surface the value

$$D_v c_v/a^4 \cong 10^{-15} \times 10^{+30} = 10^{15} \text{ vacancies/cm}^2 \text{ sec} \tag{3}$$

This value is small compared to the rate of generation that may be readily obtained by beams of ions.

For example, if singly charged xenon ions strike the surface at sufficient energy to produce vacancy interstitial pairs with approximately unit efficiency, then a current density of 1 amp/cm^2 will give

$$1 \text{ amp/cm}^2 = 6.2 \times 10^{18} \text{ electrons/cm}^2 \text{ sec} \tag{4}$$

This value corresponds to a current density nearly 10^4 times larger than the thermal equilibrium interchange. It is thus evident that if even a very small unbalance exists between the rate of recombination of vacancies with the surface as compared to the interstitials with the surface, then there will be a net flow of one species towards the interior. Such a high density in an ion beam would be hard to obtain over an area as large as 1 cm^2. However, ion beams of a few microamperes can be readily obtained and focused on areas of the order of 1 mm^2. This would mean a current density lower by several orders of magnitude. However, if the temperature is reduced slightly, the coefficient of self-diffusion will be correspondingly reduced by a large amount so that a very large disturbance in the equilibrium situation can be readily produced.

We shall next consider the effect which such bombardment might have in the experimental situation represented in Fig. 1. If a flow of both interstitials and vacancies is produced, then these will have a probability of being captured by the row of dislocations in the tilt boundary nearer the surface. It is probable that the capture cross section of the dislocations will be different for interstitials and vacancies, so that it is likely that, even if the flow initially consists of equal numbers, the flow past the grain boundary will consist predominantly of one type. Thus a grain boundary may act as a preferential filter for separating interstitials and vacancies. In order to analyze this for any particular case it is, of course, necessary to consider the effect of spacing between the dislocations in comparison with the distance of the source from the plane of dislocations.

If the grain boundary preferentially absorbs vacancies, then the half planes of atoms constituting the edges of the dislocations will be eaten away by the vacancies so that the first grain boundary will be distorted as shown by the solid lines in Fig. 1*b*.

If interstitials then diffuse farther to the second grain boundary, they will add to the extra half planes of atoms, thus causing the dislocations to be distorted as shown by the dashed lines in Fig. 1*b*. The situation represented in Fig. 1 is not intended to be a prediction of what will result from a particular experiment. Instead, it is intended simply to illustrate the types of effects which might result from carrying out an experiment of the sort discussed here.

The effects represented in Fig. 1*b* may well be obtained by reasonable amounts of bombardment. This can be seen by noting that if one vacancy per atomic area is absorbed in a plane of a tilt boundary, then each dislocation will be shifted by one dislocation spacing. If we suppose that the grain boundary lies several microns below the surface, say 10,000 atom layers deep, and vacancies are generated one atom layer below the surface, then the probability that a given vacancy will diffuse to the grain boundary is only about one part in 10^4. Thus a density of 1 amp/cm^2 if each ion produces one vacancy will cause a shift of the spacing between dislocations about once per second. It is thus evident that the effects to be expected may be large enough so as to be readily observable.

A possible disadvantage of the experiment illustrated in Fig. 1 is the presence of the rare gas ions themselves. The probability that one of these diffuses into the depths of the material may be comparable to the probability that a vacancy or interstitial may diffuse in the depths. Thus the effects of vacancies and interstitials may be obscured by the flow of rare gas atoms. There are several possible ways of overcoming this disadvantage. One would be to use atoms of the same species for the ionic bombardment. This may be difficult in some cases since the vapor pressure of such atoms might be inconveniently low. Another possibility is to produce the radiation damage by electron bombardment.

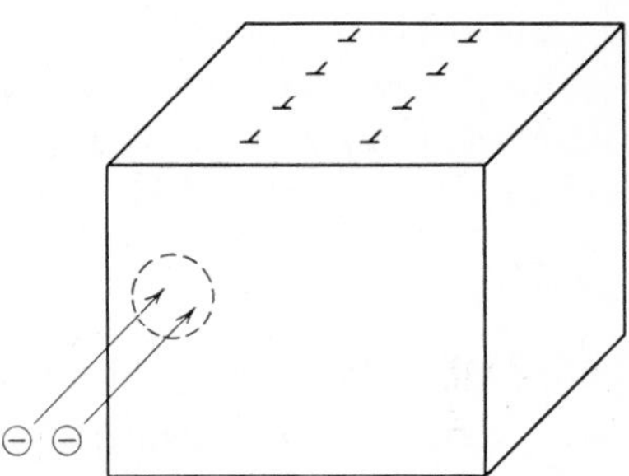

Fig. 2. A crystal with two tilt boundaries bombarded by a beam of electrons.

The chief disadvantage of electron bombardment is the fact that electron beams of adequate energy to produce damage are highly penetrating and thus it is hard to localize the radiation damage near the surface of the material. Figure 2 represents one way of carrying out an experiment which may not suffer too much from this disadvantage. A specimen with two tilt boundaries is represented. An electron beam passes through the specimen near one of the tilt boundaries. Vacancy interstitial pairs diffusing from the beam will be separated to some degree by the first boundary and a net flow to that boundary of one species will result. A net flow of the opposite species will flow to the other boundary. It is evident that other variations of this technique are possible and may actually be easier to try. For example, an electron beam may fall at nearly grazing incidence on a specimen in which the surface has a relatively high concentration of dislocations due to cold working or to mechanical polishing. Under these conditions an unbalanced flow of vacancies away from the dislocations in the surface will probably result.

REFERENCES

1. W. Shockley, *Phys. Rev.*, **91,** 1563 (1953).
2. *Ibid.*, **93,** 345 (1954).

DISCUSSION

COTTRELL wondered if the heat supplied by the depositing material on the surface might vaporize material off the surface. SHOCKLEY made the following estimate: If 1 amp of material is deposited on the surface and the voltage is of the order of 100 volts, one would get approximately 100 watts/cm^2. He suggested that the power is thus rather small, especially if the material bombarded has good thermal contact with a cooling base.

KOEHLER suggested that one might use ions to bombard the material that were the same as the atoms of the material itself. SHOCKLEY replied that there would be certain advantages to such an arrangement; certainly bombarding the sample with a rare gas might cancel out some of the effects one expected. He said it would be hard to predict with precision what would actually happen to the material, but it seemed to him that it would be an interesting experiment to try, that a number of interesting things might happen. SHOCKLEY then suggested that it might be of interest to try bombarding a germanium sample with GeH_4. In this case, the hydrogen might be stripped in the material and evaporate off. One might also be able to run a discharge in silicon between two silicon electrodes. READ pointed out that probably the interstitial component would be the one to diffuse into the material because, intuitively, the interstitials would tend to fall into vacancies, and if one shoots atoms into the surface on one side of the material, one would expect the interstitials to go out the other side.

The Thermal Annealing of Imperfections in the Noble Metals*

J. S. KOEHLER

† J. W. HENDERSON

J. H. BREDT

Department of Physics
University of Illinois
Urbana, Illinois

ABSTRACT

The annealing of irradiated, quenched, cold-worked, and evaporated noble metals is examined. Six stages of annealing are described; the associated activation energies range from 0.1 to about 2.1 ev. An attempt is made to assign each stage of annealing to a particular atomic process. The magnitude of the resistance introduced by dislocations is considered.

---

1. INTRODUCTION

In this article an attempt will be made to survey all the annealing data and to associate each annealing drop with some atomic process. In some cases the assignment cannot be made uniquely, and in others several schools of thought exist and mention will be made of the divergent views. The discussion will deal mainly with pure noble metals.

At least four types of treatment exist which will produce imperfections which can be annealed. The metals can be cold-worked, irradiated with nuclear particles, evaporated onto a very cold substrate, or

* Research supported in part by The National Science Foundation.

† Now at Hughes Research and Development Laboratories, Culver City, California.

quenched. Each treatment produces a characteristic annealing spectrum; by comparing the various spectra it is possible to determine which process is common to the various kinds of treatment.

2. QUENCHING

Consider the quenching experiments first. Kauffman and Koehler [1] and later Bauerle *et al.*[2] quenched 16-mil wires of 99.999% pure gold from temperatures in the range of 500 to 950°C. The quenched-in resistance ΔR varies as

$$\Delta R = Ae^{-E_F/kT} \tag{1}$$

where Bauerle finds $E_F = 1.02 \pm 0.05$ ev for gold. An annealing process is found which removes the quenched-in resistance and is accompanied by a decrease in the length of the wire. This process occurs with measurable velocity at temperatures in the range from 10 to 50°C. The process has complicated kinetics. The annealing rate is at first slow and then increases. The long-time portion of the annealing curve can be fit to second-order annealing kinetics. On quenching from 800°C or lower, the rate of annealing varies exponentially with temperature, giving an activation energy of motion which is $E_M = 0.65 \pm 0.05$ ev. A quench from 900°C gives a lower energy of motion. The 900°C quench is probably accompanied by a small amount of deformation. Between 80 and 90% of the resistance quenched in at 800°C can be annealed out at 25°C. Okkerse [3] has measured the activation energy for self-diffusion in gold and finds it to be 1.71 ± 0.02 ev. The sum of E_F and E_M from Bauerle's work is 1.67 ± 0.10 ev. These results show that the defect quenched in is associated with self-diffusion in gold.

3. EVAPORATED FILMS

Consider next the experiments of Buckel, Hilsch, and co-workers.[4] They evaporated various metals on crystalline quartz which was maintained at a temperature of 4°K. The resulting films were about 500 A thick and had a high resistance. In addition, the Debye-Sherrer X-ray lines were very broad. On warming, the resistance gradually dropped and the X-ray lines sharpened. Figure 1 shows the behavior of aluminum. Similar data have been obtained for copper by Rasor.[5] In the case of gallium and bismuth Buckel and Hilsch found an abnormally low resistance for the freshly evaporated film. In addition, electron diffraction data gave very broad lines whose position indicated a closer atomic packing than that found in the normal solid. Buckel and Hilsch pointed out that the freshly evaporated films seem to resemble the liquid state of gallium and bismuth. Both gallium and bismuth contract on melting and show a resistance drop on melting. The gallium and bismuth show a sudden increase in resistance at a rather well-

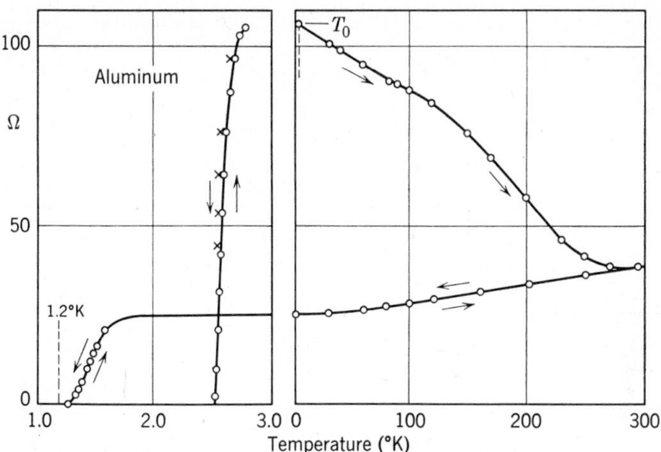

Fig. 1. Resistance changes produced by warming and cooling an evaporated aluminum film. The film was 200 A thick and was deposited onto crystalline quartz at 4°K (after Buckel and Hilsch).

defined temperature (60°K for gallium and 15°K for bismuth). The electron diffraction lines are considerably sharper and more spotty at temperatures above the transformation temperature.

4. NUCLEAR IRRADIATION

Let us next examine the annealing spectrum after nuclear irradiation. Cooper and co-workers [6] irradiated 99.95% copper with 12-Mev deuterons at about 12°K. Figure 2 shows the annealing spectrum observed during a subsequent warm-up. There is a sharp drop near 35°K followed by a region in which more annealing occurs during each increment of temperature. From 220°K to room temperature more rapid annealing occurs. Overhauser [7] made isothermal annealing studies on 99.99% copper irradiated by 12-Mev deuterons at about 100°K. He found that the activation energy associated with the annealing increases from 0.2 ev to 0.55 ev as the temperature of annealing is raised from 100°K to 220°K. His data in this range are associated with a low rate of annealing. In fact, if one fits his data to first-order kinetics using:

$$\frac{d\rho}{dt} = \rho\nu e^{-E/kT} \tag{2}$$

ρ is the residual resistivity, E the activation energy, and ν is the frequency factor, then ν is found [8] to be 10^9 cycles/sec rather than the 10^{13} expected for a simple point defect migration. In the region from 220°K to room temperature Overhauser found a single process obeying approximately second-order kinetics and possessing an activation energy of 0.68 ev in copper.

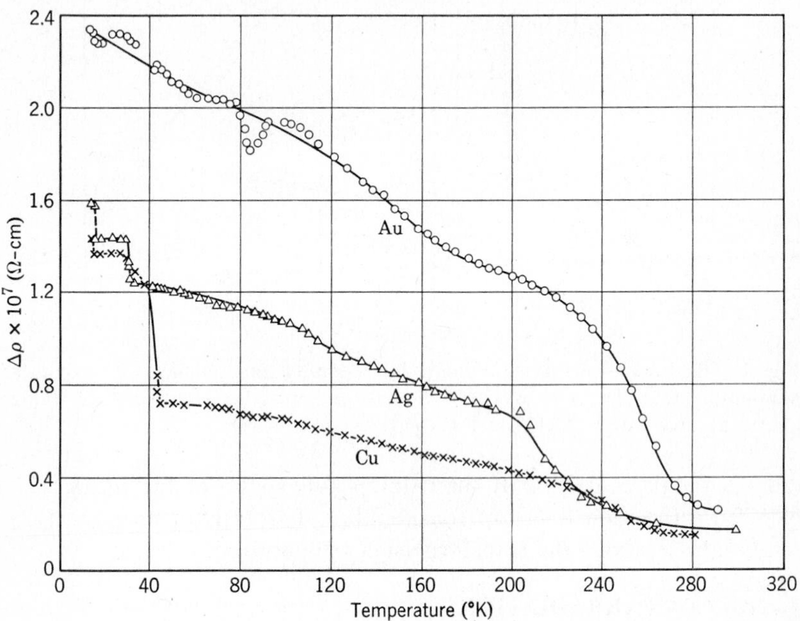

Fig. 2. The residual resistance remaining in deuteron-irradiated copper after warming to various temperatures (after Cooper, Koehler, and Marx).

Blewitt, Coltman, and Redman [9] irradiated 99.999% copper single crystals in a pile at about 50°C. They found a tenfold increase in the yield stress. This increase anneals out in the range from 280 to 400°C with an activation energy of 2.2 ± 0.2 ev. Eggleston [10] observed an activation energy of 2.12 ± 0.06 ev for 99.99% copper polycrystals irradiated with 33-Mev alpha particles. McReynolds *et al.*[11] showed that in 99.99% copper the increase in yield stress was present at 100°K after pile irradiation at that temperature and that it does not anneal out at temperatures much below 300°C. Their work and that of Overhauser [7] and Eggleston [10] indicates that only a small amount of annealing occurs in irradiated copper between 30 and 250°C (i.e., about 5% of the resistivity change produced by irradiation at 80°K).

Blewitt and co-workers [12] have measured the energy released on warming 99.999% copper which had been irradiated in the pile at about 20°K. The energy released in the range from 30 to 50°K was less than 0.1 cal/mole. The resistivity drop found on warming a companion specimen was about 2.5×10^{-9} Ω-cm.

Meechan and Brinkman [13] have irradiated 99.999% copper with 1.25-Mev electrons at 80°K. They observed the continuous annealing from 80°K to 250°K and the second-order process near room temperature. In addition, they observed annealing in the range from 100 to 400°C with an activation energy which increases as the temperature increases from 1.0 to 2.1 ev.

5. COLD WORK

Consider next the annealing of cold work. Blewitt and co-workers [14] pulled 99.999% copper single crystals in tension at 4.2°K. They found no decrease in resistance on warming to liquid-nitrogen temperature.

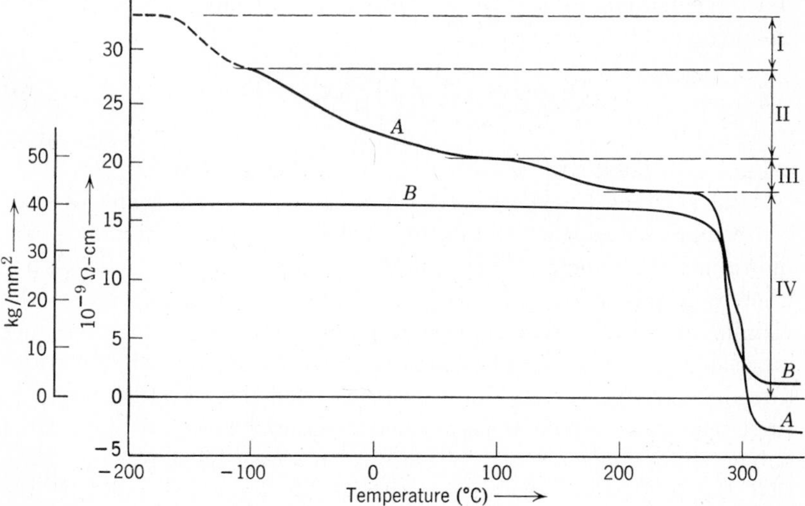

Fig. 3. The resistivity (*A*) and yield stress (*B*) of cold-worked copper after annealing to various temperatures (after Berghout).

Druyvesteyn and Manintveld [15] pulled 99.95% polycrystalline copper, silver, and gold in tension at 80°K and then measured the annealing of the resistivity. They found four annealing processes as illustrated in Fig. 3. The two processes occurring at the lowest temperatures were studied by isothermal annealing and were associated with the following activation energies:

	Step I	Step II
Cu	0.20 ± 0.03 ev	0.88 ± 0.09 ev
Ag	0.18 ± 0.02 ev	0.69 ± 0.07 ev
Au	0.29 ± 0.03 ev	0.69 ± 0.06 ev

Blewitt and co-workers [16] have measured the increase in resistivity of 99.999% pure copper single crystals extended at 4°K. They find that the resistivity increase is proportional to the square of the resolved shearing stress. The stress-strain curve is linear. About a third of the resistivity change disappears on warming to 20°C. Quantitatively Blewitt's results are as follows:

$$\Delta\rho = 1.3 \times 10^{-10} \sigma^2 = \Omega\text{-cm} \tag{3}$$

For a soft orientation which deforms to a large strain by single slip:

$$\sigma = -1.925 + 14.8\epsilon = \text{kg/mm}^2 \tag{4}$$

Here σ is the resolved shearing stress, ϵ is the resolved shearing strain, and the equation is not valid in the easy glide region. The resistivity remaining at 20°C is given by:

$$\Delta\rho_{20°\text{C}} = 0.9 \times 10^{-10} \sigma^2 = \Omega\text{-cm} \tag{5}$$

Berghout [17] has recently shown that the first three stages of annealing are not associated with recovery of the yield stress (see Fig. 3).

Henderson and Koehler [18] have compressed polycrystals and Bredt [19] has compressed single crystals of 99.999% copper. Their data are shown in Figs. 4 and 5. They find the usual annealing at −25°C, but whereas Manintveldt found only a single drop in resistivity in the vicinity of −100°C they observe a complex structure which becomes increasingly more obvious the larger the strain. In addition, the structure differs in polycrystalline specimens from the structure found in single crystals. Figure 6 shows Henderson and Koehler's data for a polycrystalline specimen of alpha-brass containing 4.5 at. % zinc. Note that the total stored energy is considerably increased and that the annealing spectrum is blurred and spread out. This specimen shows annealing in the range from 20 to 80°C whereas the pure metals gave no energy release in this range.

The data can be summarized in a plot of the fraction of the damage annealing with a given activation energy as a function of the activation energy. Such a plot for the various types of damage is shown in Fig. 7. The various stages of annealing have been labeled starting with those which anneal at the lowest temperatures.

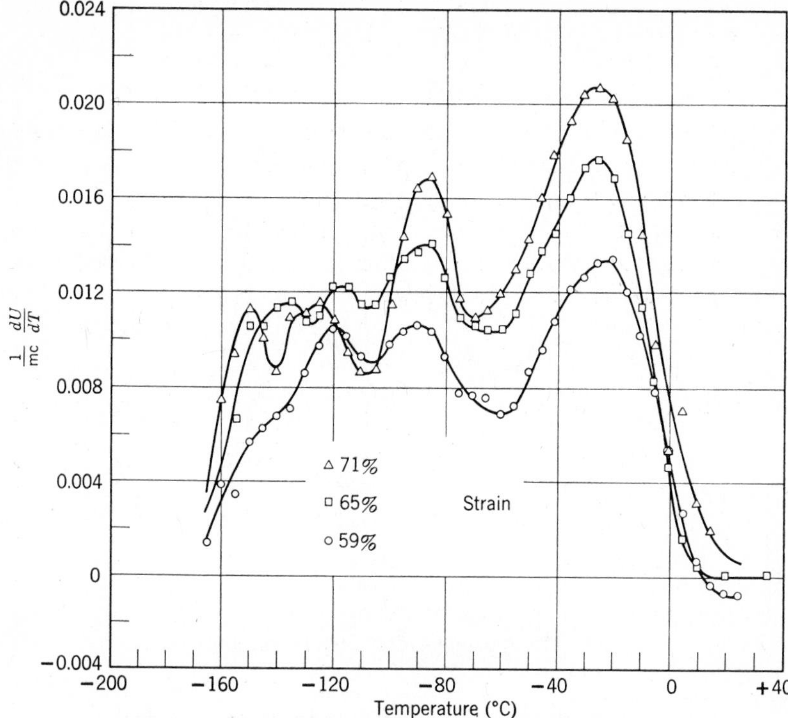

Fig. 4. The energy release spectrum for three copper polycrystals compressed at liquid-nitrogen temperature (after Henderson and Koehler).

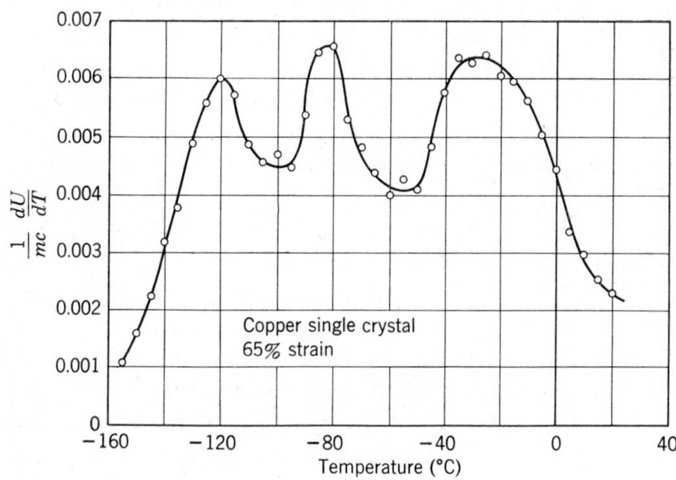

Fig. 5. The energy release spectrum for a single crystal of copper compressed at liquid-nitrogen temperature (after Bredt).

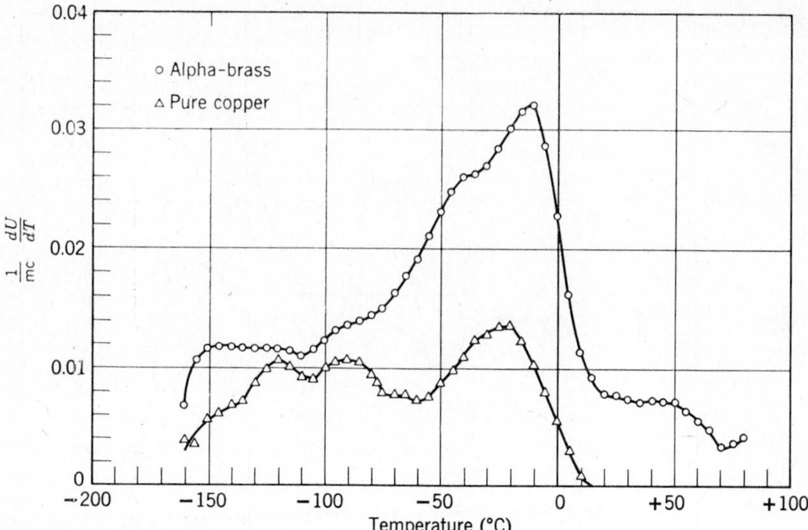

Fig. 6. The energy release spectrum for a polycrystal of copper containing 4.53 at. % zinc together with that of a 99.999% pure copper specimen. The strains were 0.58% for the brass and 0.59% for the copper. The large differences produced by impurities are apparent (after Henderson and Koehler).

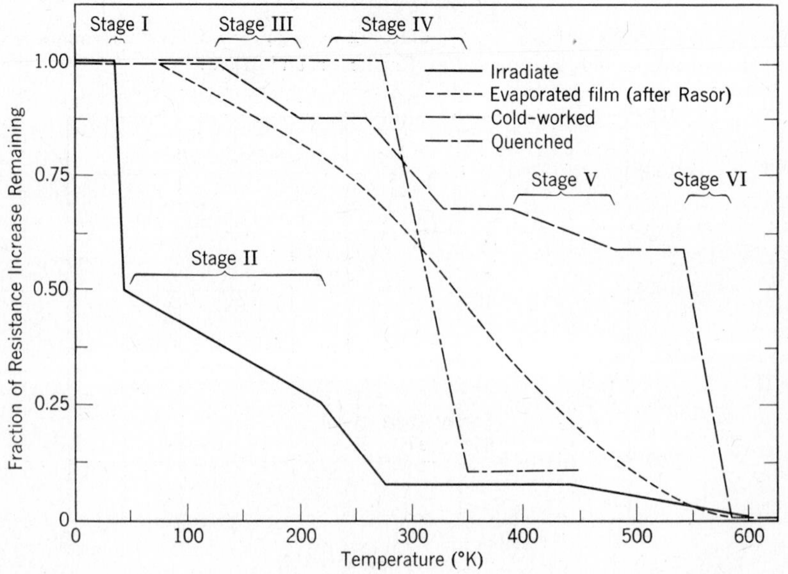

Fig. 7. Showing the various stages in the annealing out of imperfections produced in copper by various methods.

6. INTERPRETATION

A. Stages I and II

The processes which give rise to stages I and II are present only in specimens irradiated with nuclear particles. Neither process is found in quenched or cold-worked noble metals. It might be claimed that the low temperature process seen by Manintveldt, by Henderson and Koehler, and by Bredt is the same as stage II; however, in the case of cold work what seems to be observed is a discrete spectrum containing a few well-defined processes rather than a continuous spectrum of activation energies such as Overhauser found.

Let us tentatively assign stage I to the motion of interstitial atoms in a relatively ideal lattice. This assignment is in agreement with the calculations of Huntington [20] who found an energy of motion for interstitial copper atoms in the range from 0.07 to 0.27 ev. In addition, let us assume that stage II results from the annealing out of interstitial crowdions which have been trapped at lattice vacancies in the manner first proposed by Lomer and Cottrell [21] and recently applied to irradiated specimens by T. H. Blewitt. Since Blewitt *et al.* mentioned the reasons for this assignment in the preceding paper in this volume, we shall deal with the other stages of annealing.

B. Stages III and IV

Huntington and Seitz [22] estimated that the energy required to form a vacancy in copper is about 1.5 ev, whereas the energy to move it is about 1.0 ev. This leads one to assign stage IV, which occurs in the quenched gold specimens, to vacancy migration. A number of investigators * would like to assign this stage of annealing to interstitial

* (*a*) C. J. Meechan and R. R. Eggleston, *Acta Met.*, **2,** 680 (1954) found E_F(Cu) $= 0.90 \pm 0.05$ ev, E_F(Au) $= 0.67 \pm 0.07$ ev by fitting ρ at high temperature to a theoretical expression which takes into account thermal lattice expansion plus thermal production of vacancies. J. F. Nicholas, *Acta Met.*, **3,** 411 (1955) has shown that the lattice thermal expansion is so poorly known that Meechan and Eggleston's data can be fitted without taking into account any vacancies.

(*b*) B. G. Lazarev and O. N. Ovcharenko, *Doklady Akad. Nauk. S.S.S.R.*, **100,** 875 (1955) have quenched 99.99% pure gold by simply interrupting the heating current. They obtain $E_F = 0.79$ ev and $E_M = 0.52$ ev. On quenching from 800°C they quench in $\Delta\rho = 4.4 \times 10^{-9}$ Ω-cm, whereas Bauerle, Klabunde, and Koehler [2] quench in $\Delta\rho = 1.16 \times 10^{-8}$ Ω-cm on water quenching from 800°C. Thus, it may be that Lazarev and Ovcharenko do not retain all of the vacancies in equilibrium at the quenching temperature.

(*c*) Various investigators have made measurements on ordered alloys and on solid solutions and then used their data to infer E_F and E_M for vacancies in pure

migration. Such an assignment would mean that the quenching experiments are completely unreliable since one would certainly not expect to quench in an appreciable concentration of interstitials whose formation energy in copper or gold is of the order of 4 ev. Using water quenching Bauerle is able to avoid deformation of the wire so that any possibility that interstitials are introduced by deformation seems unlikely. Furthermore, the agreement between the activation energy for self-diffusion and the sum of the formation and motion energies is certainly against any interstitial interpretation since the interstitial formation energy is too large.

Consider next stage III. Bartlett and Dienes [23] estimate that the activation energy required to move a divacancy in copper is between a half and a third of the energy to move a single vacancy. If we suppose that stage IV represents single vacancies and use Overhauser's measurement for the energy of motion of a single vacancy, then the activation energy for the motion of a divacancy is between 0.23 and 0.34 ev. This is slightly larger than the values found by Druyvestyn and Manintveldt for their first annealing step. Let us therefore assume that stage III results from the motion of divacancies. It is then necessary to explain why several low temperature peaks occur in the release of the energy stored during cold work at 80°K. It will be assumed that the multiple peaks in the energy release below 200°K arise from the influence of the residual internal stress on the migration energy of the divacancies. Such internal stresses are appreciable in the massive energy specimens, but not in the thin resistivity samples.

The multiple peaks may arise as follows: According to Barrett [24] the preferred orientation produced during wire drawing in copper is that in which about 60% of the grains have a [111] direction parallel to the

noble metals. One would not expect that the values in either kind of alloy should be the same as those found for the pure metal. Experimentally R. E. Hoffman and D. Turnbull, *Impurities and Imperfections,* article by D. Lazarus, pp. 115 ff., ASM, Cleveland (1955), find 8% changes in the activation energy for the self-diffusion of silver when 5% of lead is put into solution. Similar data exist for other alloys.

(*d*) A. Seeger, Theory of Lattice Imperfections in *Handbuch der Physik,* Vol. VII, Springer, Berlin, p. 402 ff. (1955), has adopted the viewpoint that E_M is greater than E_F in the noble metals. Recently F. G. Fumi, *Phil. Mag.,* **46,** 1007 (1955) has recalculated E_F and E_M for copper. He finds $E_M = 0.6$ ev and $E_F = 0.9$ ev. He feels that E_M as calculated is too low because the repulsive terms are evaluated near the equilibrium separation distance rather than in the compressed state. He estimates that E_M might be larger by a factor of two.

wire axis while 40% of the grains have a [100] direction along the wire axis. Consider first the [111] type grains. The divacancies in such grains are divisable into two classes, one of which is perpendicular to the [111] direction, the other making an angle of about 35° with the [111] direction. If a compressive stress exists in the [111] direction these perpendicular and slant divacancies can possess three different migration energies, i.e., $\perp \rightarrow \perp$, $\perp \rightarrow /$or$/ \rightarrow \perp$, and $/ \rightarrow /$. In the case of the [100] type grains the two possibilities are $/ \rightarrow /$ and $/ \rightarrow \perp$.

An estimate of the change in the activation energy of divacancy migration resulting from the presence of internal stress has been made using the methods of Huntington.[25] The internal stresses are of the order of a third of the applied stress.[26] Since the applied stress was about 5×10^9 dynes/cm^2, the internal stresses were of order 2×10^9 dynes/cm^2. The strain was thus of order 10^{-3}. A calculation of the change in the saddle point energy resulting from such a strain predicts that the migration energy would change by about 0.008 ev. The experimentally observed change is about 0.03 ev. The uncertainties in the above calculation and in our knowledge of the internal stresses are probably large enough to account for the difference. We plan to attempt to observe changes in resistivity samples when a static load in the elastic range is applied to a specimen during the process of annealing.

C. Stages V and VI

Stage VI is associated in cold-worked specimens with recrystallization. In irradiated materials one also finds a similar process. Since the process is thermally activated and seems to require both the formation and motion of vacancies, it is probably associated with a complex dislocation rearrangement involving climb at the grain boundaries.

Stage V is not very prominent in irradiated specimens. It also does not appear in some of the experiments on cold-worked specimens.[27] In contrast to stage VI, the annealing which occurs during stage V does not appear to affect the yield stress. This indicates that no major dislocation rearrangement occurs during stage V. It is, of course, possible that dislocation jogs could move and anneal out at this temperature. Another possibility is that if vacancy clusters exist they might be altered, either by coalescence or collapse. To date we have only rather limited experimental information concerning stage V.

D. The Resistance Associated with Dislocations

Experimentally it is found that about half of the resistivity introduced during cold work is removed during recrystallization. This resistivity change amounts to 2.5×10^{-8} Ω-cm for 99.99% polycrystalline copper after 25% extension.[28] Such an increase would require a density of dislocation of 6.2×10^{12} lines/cm^2 if we use the theoretical estimate of Hunter and Nabarro.[29] Such a large dislocation density is not indicated by X-ray measurements.[30] Van Bueren [31] has found that a transverse magnetic field produces an increase in the resistance of a deformed wire which is not present for an annealed copper wire. This magnetoresistance anneals out only when recrystallization occurs. It is difficult to see how clustered vacancies can give rise to any appreciable magnetoresistance. However, in the case of dislocations a magnetic field can cause the electrons to execute a Burgers circuit around the dislocation and hence be scattered. Van Bueren therefore concluded that the large resistivity change on recrystallization results because the dislocation density decreases. He also believes that the dislocation resistance is about ten times larger than the theoretical estimate. A similar conclusion was reached earlier by Blewitt, Coltman, and Redman,[32] who deformed 99.999% copper single crystals at 4°K. It was also suggested [33] that the discrepancy may arise from the presence of stacking faults. However, improved calculations [34] indicate that the scattering by stacking faults may not be sufficiently large to explain the experimental results. Data on aluminum single crystals [35] deformed at 4°K exist but the annealing data thus far are not sufficiently detailed to enable one to separate the dislocation from the point defect contribution. In the case of aluminum no stacking fault contribution should be present because of the large energy associated with faulting. The aluminum data indicate that the resistance introduced is isotropic and that what remains after annealing to 78°K and also to 300°K is also isotropic. This finding indicates that the dislocation portion of the resistivity in deformed aluminum is equal to or smaller than 2×10^{-9} Ω-cm. The corresponding dislocation density is of the order of 5×10^{11} lines/cm^2 or less where we have used Hunter and Nabarro's theoretical estimate. The above dislocation density is not in disagreement with the X-ray findings of Gay, Hirsch, and Kelly.

Thus, at present the situation is not clear. If future measurements of the magnetoresistance associated with low temperature cold work show that the effect in aluminum is much smaller than in copper, one would be tempted to say that the dislocation resistance is inherently larger in copper than in aluminum and that perhaps stacking faults are responsible. It is also possible that the resistivity which remains after a room temperature anneal in cold-worked copper is associated with large vacancy clusters.[36] It is possible that measurements of the anisotropy of the resistance of copper single crystals deformed in tension might settle this question.

In conclusion, it appears that although serious differences of opinion still exist concerning the annealing of point defects, there does seem to be some reason to feel that a few more critical experiments will stabilize the picture. The annealing processes involving dislocations are not as well understood. This reflects the fact that as yet no one has devised a reliable way of measuring the dislocation density and arrangement in a metal.

REFERENCES

1. J. W. Kauffman and J. S. Koehler, *Phys. Rev.*, **88,** 149 (1952); *Phys. Rev.*, **97,** 555 (1955).
2. J. E. Bauerle, C. E. Klabunde, and J. S. Koehler, *Phys. Rev.*, **102,** 1182 (1956).
3. B. Okkerse, *Bull. Amer. Phys. Soc.*, series II, vol. I, no. 3, p. 149 (1956).
4. W. Buckel and R. Hilsch, *Z. Physik*, **138,** 109 (1954); W. Rühl, *Z. Physik*, **138,** 121 (1954); W. Buckel, *Z. Physik*, **138,** 136 (1954).
5. N. S. Rasor, *Phys. Rev.*, **98,** 1555 (1955).
6. H. G. Cooper, J. S. Koehler, and J. Marx, *Phys. Rev.*, **97,** 599 (1955).
7. A. W. Overhauser, *Phys. Rev.*, **90,** 393 (1953).
8. F. Seitz and J. S. Koehler, *Solid State Physics*, Vol. 2, Academic Press, New York, p. 417 (1956).
9. T. H. Blewitt, R. R. Coltman, and J. K. Redman, *Phys. Rev.*, **91,** 448 (1953).
10. R. R. Eggleston, *Acta Met.*, **1,** 679 (1953).
11. A. W. McReynolds, W. Angustyniak, M. McKeown, and D. Rosenblatt, *Phys. Rev.*, **98,** 418 (1955).
12. T. H. Blewitt, R. R. Coltman, T. S. Noggle, and D. K. Holmes, *Bull. Amer. Phys. Soc.*, series II, vol. I, no. 3, p. 130 (1956).
13. C. J. Meechan and J. A. Brinkman, *Phys. Rev.*, **103,** 1193 (1956); see also C. J. Meechan, *Phys. Rev.*, **100,** 1807 (1955).
14. T. H. Blewitt, R. R. Coltman, and J. K. Redman, *Report of a Conference on Defects in Solids*, Physical Society, London, p. 372 (1954).
15. M. J. Druyvesteyn and J. A. Manintveld, *Nature*, **168,** 868 (1951); J. A. Manintveld, *Nature*, **169,** 623 (1952); J. A. Manintveld, Thesis, Delft, Technische Hogeschol, 1954.
16. See reference 14. See also T. H. Blewitt, *Phys. Rev.*, **91,** 1115 (1953).
17. C. W. Berghout, *Acta Met.*, **4,** 211 (1956).
18. J. W. Henderson and J. S. Koehler, *Phys. Rev.*, **104,** 626 (1956).
19. J. H. Bredt, to be published.
20. H. B. Huntington, *Phys. Rev.*, **91,** p. 1092 (1953).
21. W. M. Lomer and A. H. Cottrell, *Phil. Mag.*, **46,** 711 (1955).
22. H. B. Huntington and F. Seitz, *Phys. Rev.*, **61,** 315 (1942); H. B. Huntington, *Phys. Rev.*, **61,** 325 (1942).

23. J. H. Bartlett and G. J. Dienes, *Phys. Rev.*, **89,** 848 (1953).
24. C. S. Barrett, *Structure of Metals,* 2nd Ed., McGraw-Hill, New York, p. 443 (1952).
25. H. B. Huntington, *Phys. Rev.*, **91,** 1092 (1953).
26. J. S. Koehler, article in *Impurities and Imperfections,* American Society for Metals, Cleveland, p. 167 (1955).
27. P. A. Beck, *Advances in Phys.*, **3,** 252 and 271 (1954).
28. C. W. Berghout, *Acta Met.*, **4,** 212 (1956).
29. S. C. Hunter and J. R. N. Nabarro, *Proc. Roy. Soc.* (*London*), *A,* **220,** 542 (1953).
30. P. Gay, P. B. Hirsch, and A. Kelly, *Acta Met.*, **1,** 315 (1953).
31. H. G. van Bueren, *Acta Met.*, **3,** 524 (1955).
32. T. H. Blewitt, R. Coltman, and J. K. Redman, *Report of a Conference on Defects in Crystalline Solids,* Physical Society, London, p. 379 (1955).
33. P. G. Klemens, *Australian J. Phys.*, **6,** 122 (1953).
34. F. Blatt, F. S. Ham, and J. S. Koehler, *Bull. Amer. Phys. Soc.*, series II, vol. I, no. 3, p. 114 (1956).
35. A. Sosin and J. S. Koehler, *Phys. Rev.*, **94,** p. 1422 (1954).
36. D. L. Dexter, *Phys. Rev.*, **103,** p. 107 (1956).

DISCUSSION

BOAS said that there was a very strong effect due to specific impurities on the annealing of the imperfections above room temperature. He and his co-workers have found a variety of effects, depending upon whether one worked with pure copper or with a sample containing impurities. BOAS agreed that there is no change in mechanical properties up to a high temperature, namely the temperature associated with recrystallization. In pure copper they had found virtually no release of energy in the region around 70°C to 140°C; but if the sample contained impurities, a considerable release of energy was noticeable in this range.

BLEWITT made two comments: (1) If one accepts the scattering cross section for a Frenkel pair suggested by Overhauser and Gorman, then in a deuteron bombardment one should have only one displacement for every ten collisions. (2) If one combines the results of J. M. Denney on electron bombardment, which are unpublished, with the results obtained at North American Aviation by Meechan and Brinkman, one finds the same stages in electron bombardment as in pile bombardment. Hence, there is a question whether frozen liquid drops can actually ever form even in the irradiation by heavy particles.

SEITZ said that J. E. Bauerle had done experimental work which had some bearing on the present paper and the paper by Coulomb and Friedel (in Part VIII of this volume). Bauerle had studied the annealing of the resistivity injected into the crystal by quenching as a function of time at room temperature in gold. The time scale of the experiment ran over the order of hundreds of hours. He found that the annealing has the shape given in Fig. D1. It is not out of the question that the annealing shown in this figure is due to the voids suggested by Coulomb and Friedel. Bauerle has studied in a limited series of cases the change in dimension of a specimen during the annealing, and the results are that the points showing the annealing of the dimensional changes follow precisely the same curve as the resistivity anneal. It takes some time to start the measurement of dimensional anneal, hence the points do not start as soon for dimensional anneal as they do for the resistivity anneal. The conclusion is that the vacancies or vacancy clusters which cause the dimensional changes which are annealed at dislocation lines disappear at precisely the same rate as the defects which cause the resistivity.

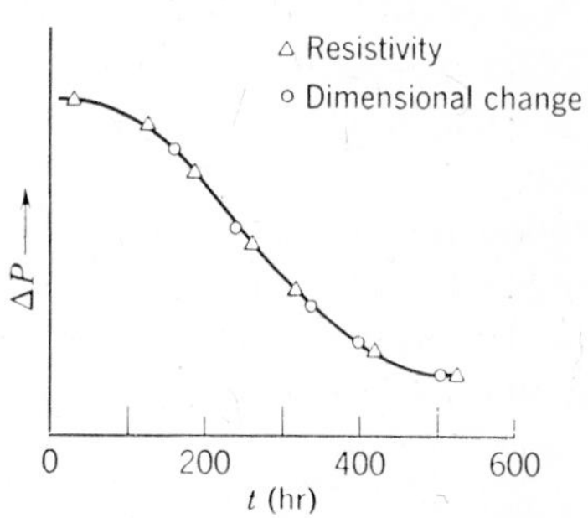

Fig. D1. Annealing curve of resistivity and dimensional change in cold-worked gold (after J. E. Bauerle).

LOMER asked how the dimensional changes were measured. KOEHLER replied that they were measured simply by taking a wire clamped as

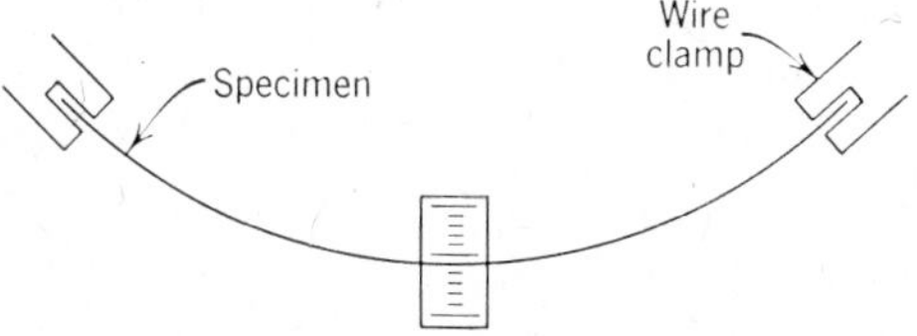

Fig. D2. Method of measuring dimensional changes in a cold-worked wire during anneal (after J. E. Bauerle).

in Fig. D2. One then measures the position of the middle of the wire and uses a creep test microscope to watch the wire as it anneals. It turns out to be possible to measure a length change of one part in 10^6 by this technique. It is not possible to measure the wire during quenching because there is a change of shape which ruins the sensitivity of the experiment. The experiment is quite sensitive to the temperature, which must be carefully controlled.

SEEGER expressed concern that in low temperature anneal of cold-worked copper one did not find interstitials and asked if that was Koehler's conclusion. KOEHLER agreed that his interpretation of the experiment was that interstitials were not produced by cold work at low temperatures. MOTT asked if there was evidence that vacancies or vacancy clusters were produced. KOEHLER replied that presumably vacancies and vacancy clusters would be produced. He suggested the following guess for the reason why interstitials were not produced. It might be possible that instead of dislocations cutting through one another during the cold work, they simply form long strings representing a line of interstitials running back to the cutting dislocation. The scattering of such a geometrically linked series of interstitials presumably would be different from that of the randomly scattered interstitials. SEITZ remarked that such a correlated pattern had also been suggested in a series of experiments done by G. Chiarotti at the University of Illinois. Chiarotti had been looking for isolated negative ion vacancies after plastic flow, using the fact that the isolated negative ion vacancy is tagged because it produces the alpha-band in the alkali halides. He has not found the alpha-band in plastically deformed sodium chloride even though it is known that vacancy clusters of some kind do form. The conclusion one is inclined to draw is that isolated negative ion vacancies are not produced during plastic deformation of rock salt at any temperature from room temperature on down. This fact implies that, in general, some kind of a cluster is formed involving negative ion vacancies as the result of plastic flow. In metals it seems to be true that if Koehler's interpretation is correct, isolated vacancies are not formed. MOTT suggested that it was difficult to understand how isolated vacancies could be obtained and not isolated interstitials. KOEHLER replied that it might be simply due to the difference in the energy of formation. The energy to form a vacancy is considerably less than that to make an interstitial. Perhaps there is a competition between the tendency to form single defects versus the correlated defects corresponding to a dislocation double line.

Mechanism of Annealing in Neutron-Irradiated Metals

T. H. BLEWITT

R. R. COLTMAN

D. K. HOLMES

T. S. NOGGLE

Solid State Division

** Oak Ridge National Laboratory*

Oak Ridge, Tennessee

1. INTRODUCTION

The effect of nuclear radiation on the properties of solids has received considerable attention since E. Wigner [1] correctly forecast that such effects would have important consequences in reactor design. The research on radiation damage was initiated after the Oak Ridge Graphite Reactor was in operation and concentrated on solving problems arising from radiation effects in the reactor materials themselves.

Since 1947, research in the field has been characterized by an increase in improved experiments on metals and alloys which have yielded a better insight into the mechanism by which reactor irradiations affect the physical properties of solids. The temperature instability of radiation-induced defects has led to the employment of low temperature irradiations to freeze in all defects, particularly in those experiments designed to increase knowledge in the fundamental mechanism of radiation damage. On the theoretical side, important new concepts in the mechanism of the production and migration of radiation-induced defects have been introduced. Brinkman [2] has introduced the displacement spike; Kinchin and Pease [3] the concept of interstitialcy migra-

* Oak Ridge National Laboratory is operated by Union Carbide Nuclear Company, a Division of Union Carbide and Carbon Corporation, for the Atomic Energy Commission under contract No. W-7405-eng-26.

tion; and Lomer and Cottrell[4] a new defect, the crowdion. Computations improving the original calculations of Seitz[5] have been made by Neufeld and Snyder,[6] as well as by Harrison and Seitz.[7]

Most recently attention has been focused on experiments which have studied the changes in resistivity associated with bombardments at very low temperature,[8] i.e., in range of 10 to 20°K. The manner in which this enhanced resistivity changed while the sample was heated to room temperature has been of particular interest. In fact, the explanation of the resulting recovery of the electrical resistivity has been a major pastime in the field of radiation damage in the past few years. The fact that the available data have been extremely meager has led to the situation where the number of explanations approaches the number of scientists actively engaged in the field of radiation damage. The purpose of this paper is to evaluate the various interpretations of the annealing spectrum which arises from low temperature irradiation.

2. DETERMINATION OF THE NUMBER OF DEFECTS PRODUCED DURING IRRADIATION

One of the central problems in the past few years has been the experimental verification of the calculations of the number of interstitial atoms and lattice vacancies produced by a neutron hit (one interstitial atom and one vacant lattice site are sometimes called a Frenkel pair or a Frenkel defect). For the most part the experimental technique has involved the measurement of the irradiation-induced change in the electrical resistivity, and this, coupled with the theoretical estimate of the electrical scattering cross section of a Frenkel pair, leads to an estimate of the number of Frenkel pairs per neutron hit. Unfortunately, it has not been possible to determine experimentally the scattering cross section. These attempts to determine the defect density are somewhat less than satisfactory. The theoretical attempts to calculate the scattering factor show a wide divergence. For example, Jongenburger,[9] refining the results of Dexter,[10] obtained a scattering factor of 1.3 $\mu\Omega$-cm for 1% of vacancies. Blatt,[11] making a similar computation for interstitial atoms, arrived at 1.4 $\mu\Omega$-cm/at. % of interstitials. Recently Overhauser and Gorman[12] have pointed out that Blatt's computation did not correctly take into account the strain field around the interstitial atom. Their results, including the increase in scattering due to the strain field, raised the estimate of the scattering cross section of an interstitial atom to about 9 $\mu\Omega$-cm/at. %. Overhauser and Gorman have thus demonstrated that the strains set up around an interstitial atom can have far-reaching effects on the magnitude of the resistivity change. It is not clear, at the present time, how the relaxation of the strains will occur about an interstitial atom. In view of the uncertainty as to the exact nature of the relaxation, it would appear that the calculation of the scattering factor cannot be taken too seriously.

Neufeld and Snyder [6] have made theoretical calculations on the

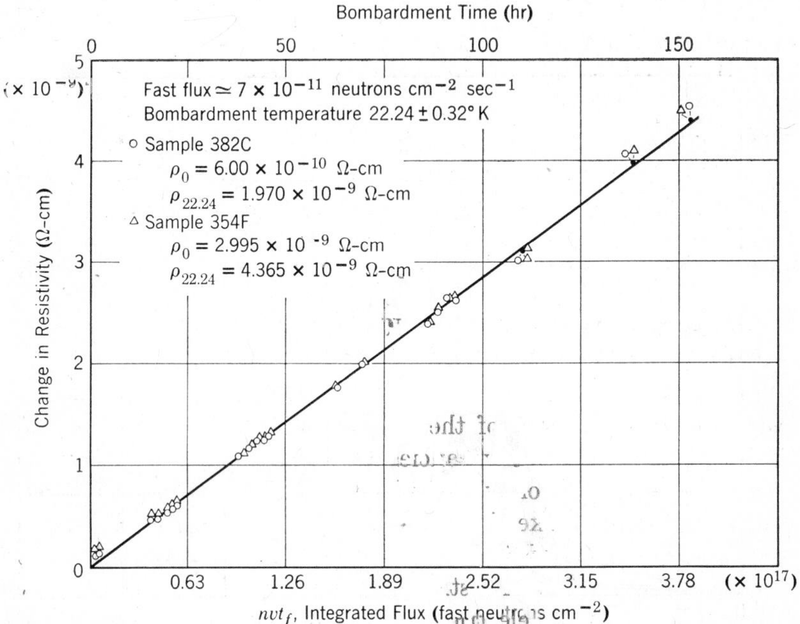

Fig. 1. The effect of neutron bombardment at 22.4°K on the resistivity of copper single crystals. The two samples of different initial resistivity were bombarded simultaneously in the ORNL Graphite Reactor hole #12 cryostat. The change in resistivity is proportional to the flux within the precision of the experiment. Many other experiments with bombardment temperatures as low as 16°K have reproduced these data.

number of displacements per neutron hit as a function of the incident neutron energy. For the flux distribution measured in hole #12 in the ORNL Graphite Reactor, Neufeld and Snyder's theory leads to an estimate of about 110 displacements per neutron hit.

The experimentally determined change in electrical resistivity of high purity copper single crystals irradiated at 22°K in the hole #12 cryostat is shown in Fig. 1. From the known neutron elastic scattering cross section and using Jongenburger's and Blatt's values to give the electrical scattering factor per Frenkel pair, the data in Fig. 1 give an estimate of about 20 displacements per neutron hit. This estimate drops to about 5 per hit if Overhauser and Gorman's values for the scattering factor of the interstitial atom are used instead of Blatt's. It is thus seen that even if the entire resistivity change is attributed to Frenkel pairs, the number estimated from resistivity measurements is smaller by a factor of five than the theoretical number even if the most favorable electron scattering cross section is used.

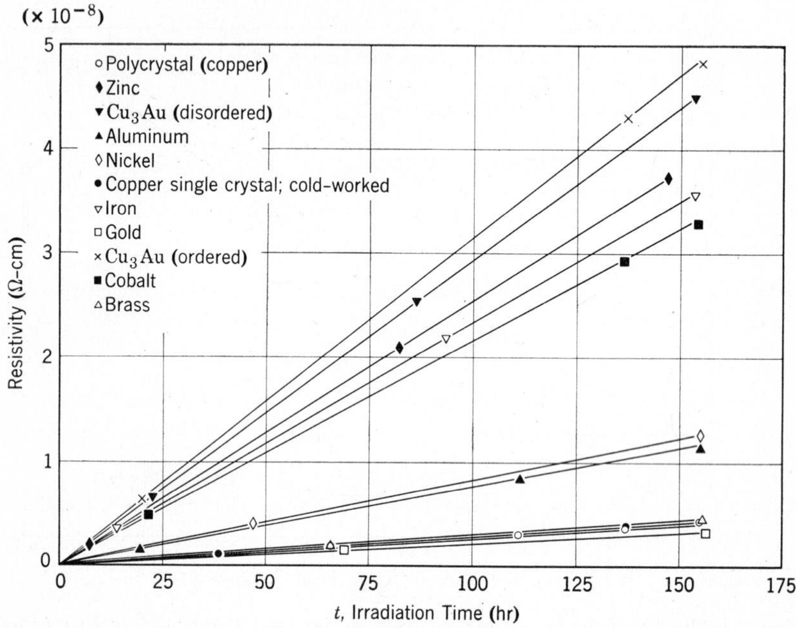

Fig. 2. The effect of neutron bombardment on the resistivity of several metals. All samples were simultaneously bombarded in the hole #12 cryostat of the ORNL Graphite Reactor at 18°K. The experimental points established the linearity of flux versus resistivity although these were deleted from the figure. No correction has been applied to these data for temperature fluctuations.

The analysis of radiation-induced resistivity as a result of cyclotron bombardment at low temperature leads to the same conclusion; i.e., the number of defects per primary displacement deduced from Blatt's and Jongenberger's theoretically determined scattering factor and the change in resistivity are too small by a factor of about five when compared with the number expected from theory. The results of electron bombardment at low temperature at present yield inconclusive results, since the probability of a displacement will strongly depend on the threshold energy needed to displace an atom and the shape of the well. Neither of these is well understood at present.

The study of the effect of low temperature reactor irradiation on electrical resistivity has been extended to include several metals and alloys. Figure 2 summarizes the results of the different metals. It may be concluded that these data are representative since at least two subsequent bombardments were made with identical results. The ex-

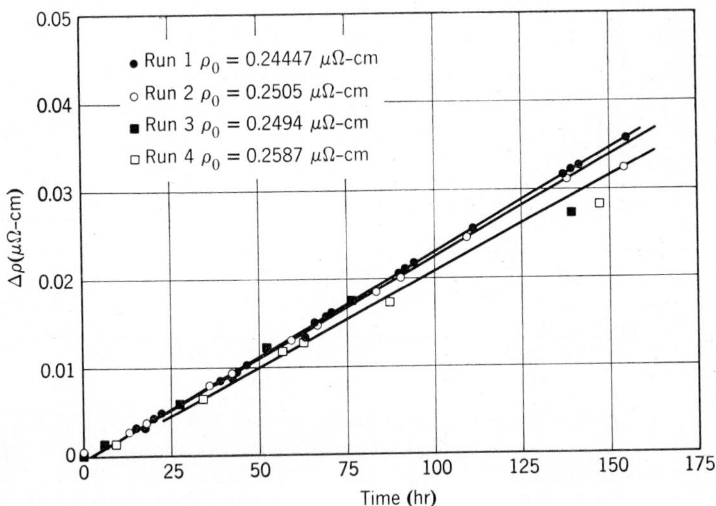

Fig. 3. The effect of neutron bombardment on the resistivity of NRC iron. The samples were bombarded in the hole #12 cryostat of the ORNL Graphite Reactor at the following bombardment temperatures: run 1, 14.5 ± 1.5°K; run 2, 14.5 ± 1.5°K; run 3, 17.6 ± 0.8°K; run 4, 19.3 ± 1.8°K. No correction has been applied for temperature fluctuations and at the last point of each run the measured resistivity will be too small, as the temperature falls about 4°K when the reactor is turned off.

tent of the reproducibility can be judged from Figs. 3, 4, and 5. It should be noted that in all of the metals the change in resistivity is directly proportional to the neutron flux, indicating the absence of radiation annealing. It can thus be inferred that there is only slight, if any, interaction between the adjacent damaged regions.

It is not clear why the various metals show such a drastic difference in the rate of change of the electrical resistivity with neutron flux. There does not seem to be any correlation between the lattice structure, Debye temperature, neutron elastic scattering cross section, atomic weight, dislocation density, purity, initial resistivity, or outer shell electrons. A further understanding of the process will be required before it can be decided whether this different behavior is a result of a

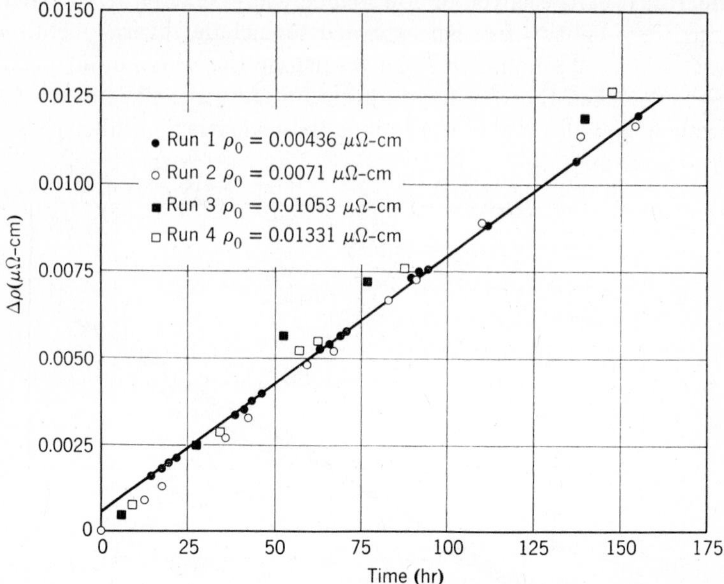

Fig. 4. The effect of neutron bombardment on the resistivity of 99.996% aluminum. The samples were bombarded in the hole #12 cryostat of the ORNL Graphite Reactor at the following temperatures: run 1, 14.5 ± 1.5°K; run 2, 13.8 ± 0.8°K; run 3, 17.6 ± 0.8°K; run 4, 19.3 ± 1.8°K. The experimental points are not corrected for temperature.

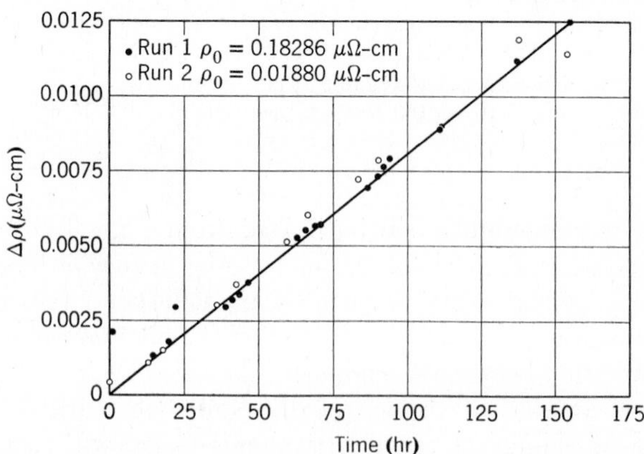

Fig. 5. The effect of neutron bombardment on the resistivity of NRC nickel and of Mond process nickel. These samples were bombarded in the hole #12 cryostat of the ORNL Graphite Reactor at the following temperatures: run 1 (NRC nickel), 14.5 ± 1.5°K; run 2 (mond nickel), 13.8 ± 0.8°K.

different resistivity scattering cross section per defect or a variation in the number of defects per neutron hit, or both.

3. RECOVERY OF THE RESISTIVITY OF REACTOR-IRRADIATED METALS

The relatively crude annealing data of cyclotron-irradiated copper clearly showed that radiation-induced resistivity recovered at temperatures as low as 40°K. An annealing spectrum of irradiated copper

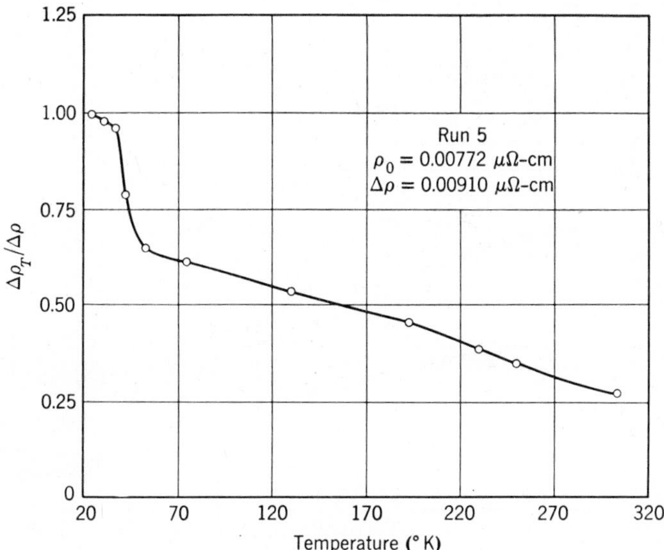

Fig. 6. The annealing spectrum of reactor irradiated copper. The zone refined copper sample (which was kindly furnished by W. G. Pfann of the Bell Telephone Laboratories) was bombarded for 8×10^{17} nvt in the hole #12 cryostat of the ORNL Graphite Reactor at 17.5°K ± 1°K. The resistivity at each point on the curve was measured at 14°K following a 3-min pulse at this indicated temperature.

bombarded at 18°K in the ORNL Graphite Reactor is shown in Fig. 6. This annealing spectrum, which is typical of many metals, has been the source of considerable speculation. The tempering curve of Fig. 6 can be interpreted as the result of three distinct processes. One process is evident in the range of temperature from 30°K to 50°K (call this process I); a second in the region from 50°K to 240°K (process II); and a third in the region from 240°K to 300°K (process III).* A

* It is not clear from Fig. 6 that there is an annealing process in region III distinct from that of region II; however, sufficient evidence has accumulated to

fourth process occurring in the region from 600°K to 900°K which strongly affects the mechanical properties has also been found (call this process IV).

The annealing spectra of copper samples irradiated by deuterons at 10–20°K [13] are very similar to those shown above, as can be seen by Fig. 7. Since these samples were warmed up without any control, the

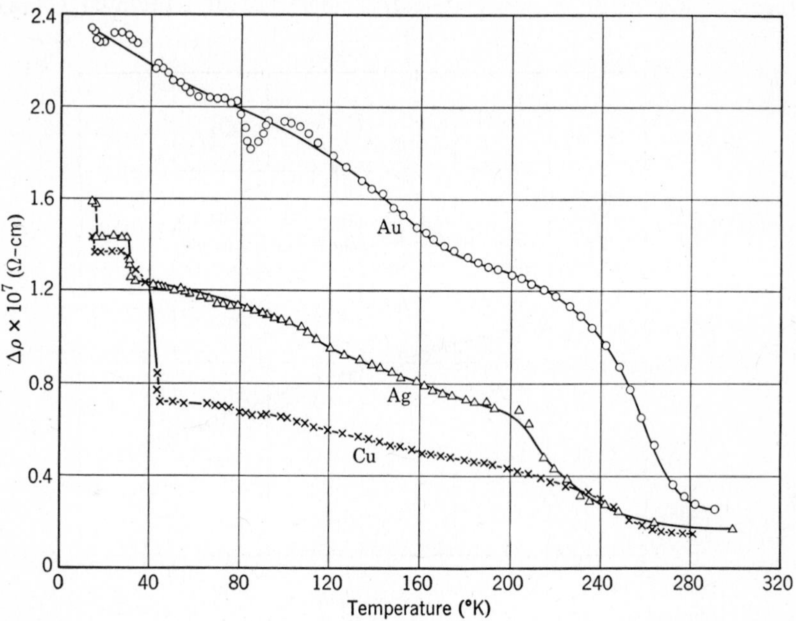

Fig. 7. The decrease of bombardment-induced resistivity of copper, silver, and gold as the samples are warmed slowly from liquid helium temperatures. (After Cooper, Koehler, and Marx.[13])

details of Fig. 7 may appear different from the details of Fig. 6. However, there can be little doubt that processes I, II, and III are present. Other data also show the presence of process IV. In order to ascertain the effect of thermal and displacement spikes, it would be very interesting to compare those spectra arising from a warm-up of low temperature deuteron and neutron bombardment with that arising from low temperature electron bombardment. Denney and co-workers [14] have recently examined the annealing in the range of temperature from

make it clear that such a unique process exists in region III. The short-term pulse utilized in Fig. 6 does not permit equilibrium to exist. Longer pulse times would show process III annealing and would modify the shape of the entire tempering curve from 50°K to 300°K.

10°K to 80°K of the resistivity induced in copper by irradiation at 5°K to 10°K with 1.3-Mev electrons. They find a process similar to what has been termed process I; however, a greater portion of the resistivity appears to anneal at this temperature than in the case of low temperature neutron and deuteron bombardment. Meechan and Brinkman,[15] on the other hand, have examined the annealing spectrum of copper bombarded at 80°K with 1-Mev electrons. The results show a spectrum indicating that annealing process II and process III are occurring. It is thus apparent that since processes I, II, and III are present in low temperature neutron, deuteron, and electron bombardment that the displacement or the thermal spike in themselves cannot play a predominate role in damaging the sample insofar as the low temperature annealing peaks in electrical resistivity are concerned.

In the following pages of this article, each of these annealing processes will be examined in detail and various interpretations critically examined.

4. MIGRATION BY AN INTERSTITIALCY PROCESS

Siegel[16] discovered that the neutron bombardment of an initially ordered specimen of Cu_3Au caused a disordering reaction to occur. The number of atoms necessary to interchange in order to explain the observed rate of disorder greatly exceeded the calculated number of displacements. This disordering was initially attributed to thermal spikes, but subsequent considerations indicate that the time duration of the spike and its energy are not sufficient to account for the observed disordering.

In order to explain this phenomenon, a mechanism called an interstitialcy migration was suggested by Kinchin and Pease.[3] They suggested that in the final stage of the motion of a displaced atom, i.e., when its energy is too low to produce additional displacements, it will induce the resulting interstitial atom to travel large distances by a replacement process. Instead of coming to rest and becoming an interstitial atom, the displaced atom will fall into a lattice site, pushing the atom which occupied that site into the adjacent interstitial location. This atom in turn pushes its neighbor into an interstitial location while it occupies the lattice site. This process requires little energy, and the motion of the interstitial atom finally ceases due to frictional losses. There has been some objection to this process on the basis that considerable energy will be lost unless the atoms strike each other almost head-on. The utilization of the concept that the interstitial atom exists as a crowdion would remove this objection since this defect can only move in specific lattice directions.

Lomer and Cottrell [4] have postulated that strains set up by an interstitial atom will result in a relaxation so that the interstitial defect will exist as a crowdion. In this defect it is assumed that the lattice strains, instead of being spherically distributed, are linearly distributed about a row of atoms. This defect is postulated to be in the [110] direction about 8 atomic distances in length and its structure is constrained to move in the [110] direction. Unfortunately, there has been little ex-

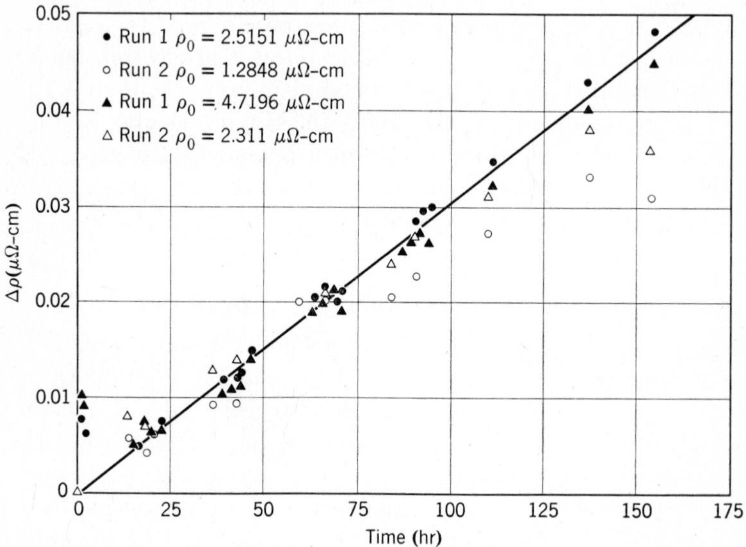

Fig. 8. The effect of neutron bombardment on the resistivity of Cu_3Au of different degrees of order. It can be seen that the change in resistivity is unaffected by the initial resistivity. The last point of run 2 in both samples is uncorrected for a large temperature change.

perimental evidence to support this postulate that the interstitialcy migrates, although Barnes and Makin [17] have pointed out that this process appears to be the only one which can explain the radiation annealing observed by Cooper and co-workers.[13] The results of recent experiments at Oak Ridge suggest that defects migrate a long distance from the site of an initial neutron hit. Two separate experiments should be discussed.

Consider first the data obtained on Cu_3Au. In the initial survey experiments made in hole #12, two samples of Cu_3Au were included which had different thermal histories. One of these samples had a residual resistivity (i.e., the resistivity at 15°K) of 4.7212 μΩ-cm and the other had a resistivity of 2.5151 μΩ-cm. Thus, there was a factor of two in the resistivity. The results of this run can be seen in Fig. 8.

It was quite surprising to note that the electrical resistivity change was the same in both samples. There can be little doubt that the change in electrical resistivity is predominantly the result of disordering, for the rate is some ten times greater than that of copper and is in agreement with the disordering rate as found by other experiments where the disordering reaction was uniquely shown. To check this surprising result, which was at first attributed to some unknown experimental blunder, two additional samples of different order were again bombarded in the hole #12 cryostat with similar results. (These results are also shown in Fig. 8.) It thus seems safe to conclude that the same number of gold-copper pairs are broken in each sample. Another way of expressing it would be to say that the volume of the alloy affected by each neutron hit is determined by the order present.

Let us consider the details of the process for the sample with a resistivity of 1.3 $\mu\Omega$-cm (sample A) and for the sample with a resistivity of 4.7 $\mu\Omega$-cm (sample B). Since the latter sample has a higher percentage disorder, it would be expected that the neutron damage would be less effective in producing further disorder. However, the change in resistivity in both samples is about 0.04 $\mu\Omega$-cm from Fig. 8. Since the residual resistivity of disordered Cu_3Au is about 9 $\mu\Omega$-cm, it may be deduced that in sample A 3×10^{21} atoms are affected per mole. For the bombardment of 5×10^{17} nvt the number of primary knock-ons will be about 2×10^{18} so that it may be concluded that for sample A the disordered region is 1.5×10^3 atoms per neutron hit and that for sample B the region is 2.7×10^3 atoms. The number of disordered atoms per displacement will depend on the number of Frenkel pairs per displacement. If one considers the theoretical number, then about 20 atoms are affected per neutron hit for sample A and roughly twice this or about 40 atoms for sample B. An upward revision in these numbers would, of course, be required if the number of displacements per hit were changed. The important consequence appears that the disordering process seems to determine the number of atoms affected per neutron hit. Since the disordering energy is relatively small, being of the order of 0.05 ev, one should look for a low energy mechanism to explain this phenomenon. The mechanism of Kinchin and Pease would seem to be able to explain these data, as the range of the interstitialcy would be determined by the degree of order either as a result of the increased frictional forces or the ordering energy.

Consider now the elastic constant and damping data that have recently been obtained by Thompson and co-workers [18] in the hole #12 cryostat. It will be recalled that Thompson and Holmes [19] have studied the effect of irradiation on the elastic constants and logarithmic decrement in copper single crystals at room temperature in the graphite reactor. They found that their results were explainable on the basis that dislocations are pinned by radiation-induced defects. A sample, which received numerous prior bombardments at room temperature so that an estimate of the number of dislocations could be made, after an appropriate heat treatment removed all the effects of prior bombardment, was rebombarded at an ambient temperature of 22°K in the hole #12 cryostat. It may safely be assumed that there is no defect mobility at this temperature, yet a change in both the damping and the elastic constants, well beyond experimental error, was observed. This change proceeded at a rate several orders of magnitude smaller than at room temperature; however, in order to explain the results, it was necessary to assume that each neutron hit must have an effective radius of 150 atomic diameters. It is difficult to imagine a neutron hit affecting a region bounded by a sphere of such a large radius as a result of a displacement spike. Not only do the theoretical considerations reject such a picture, but with such a volume affected radiation annealing would be apparent at fluxes much lower than the 5×10^{17} neutrons/sq cm. Figure 1 clearly shows that no radiation annealing occurs for this flux. The interstitialcy-crowdion mechanism proposed here would, however, satisfactorily explain the data as the interstitial could move 150 atomic diameters by the interstitialcy process to pin the dislocation. There are thus three pieces of experimental data which would tend to support the interstitialcy-crowdion mechanism. There is the radiation annealing data of Cooper *et al.*[13] as analyzed by Barnes and Makin,[17] the rate of disordering of Cu_3Au in the hole #12 cryostat, and finally the data of Thompson and coworkers [18] on the elastic constant and damping of copper single crystals. Although these data should not be construed as overwhelming evidence in support of the interstitialcy-crowdion mechanism, it certainly is reasonable to assume that this mechanism may play a role in radiation effects. It would then seem that following bombardment of a pure metal at low temperature, the interstitial atoms would exist as crowdions and lie as far as 150 atomic diameters from the source of the primary displacement. The vacant lattice sites will remain clustered in the vicinity of the initial neutron hit, probably within a volume given by a sphere of radius of 10 atomic distances. There may be some damage remaining also as frozen-in debris from the displacement spike. With this picture in mind let us examine the annealing kinetics of low temperature irradiated metals.

5. ANNEALING PROCESS I

Process I is the annealing associated with the motion of defects commencing in the vicinity of 30°K. Relatively crude estimates of the activation energy of the process based on a temperature of 40°K yield a value of about 0.1 ev if it is assumed that a unique process occurs

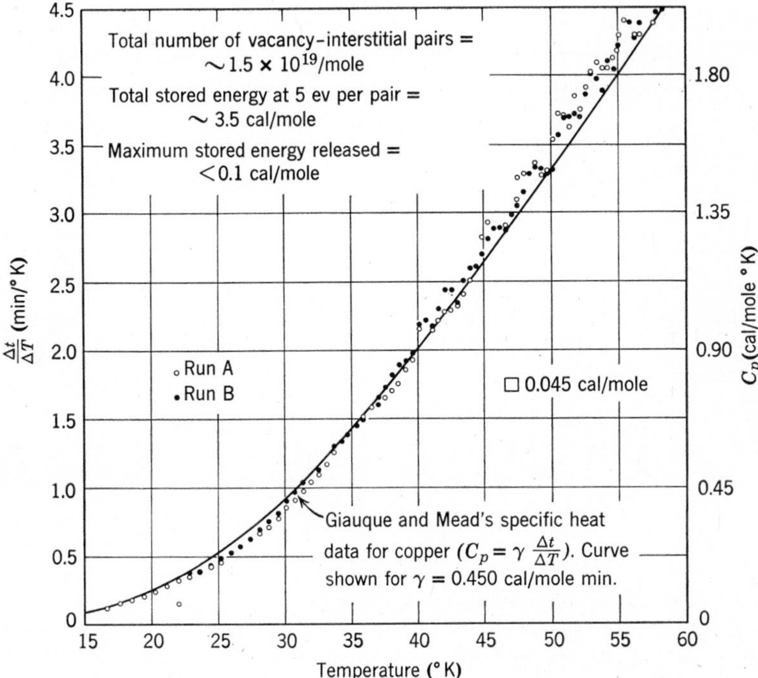

Fig. 9. The energy release associated with process I annealing in a copper single crystal sample which was bombarded at 21.7°K for an integrated neutron flux of 4×10^{17} nvt. The solid line is the specific heat of copper as given by Giauque and Mead.[12] The energy release in the temperature range of 30 to 50°K does not exceed 0.1 cal/mole.

and that the atomic frequency factor is 10^{13} sec^{-1}. This hypothetical activation energy is well within the range of activation energies calculated by Huntington [20] for the motion of an interstitial atom. It is then natural to postulate that process I was the direct result of the motion and annihilation of interstitial atoms and one school of thought led by Seitz and Koehler [8] supported such a scheme. In the past 6 months sufficient data have been obtained to raise some question as to the feasibility of this scheme. Consider the stored-energy measurements made at Oak Ridge associated with this process. Samples of high purity copper crystals were bombarded at 22°K in the hole #12 cryostat for 160 hr or 4×10^{17} nvt. The sample was then thermally isolated from the cryostat and the gamma rays in the reactor heated the sample. Since the heating is homogeneous, the slope of the time-temperature curve will be proportional to the specific heat. Two such warm-ups were determined successively in the range from 15 to

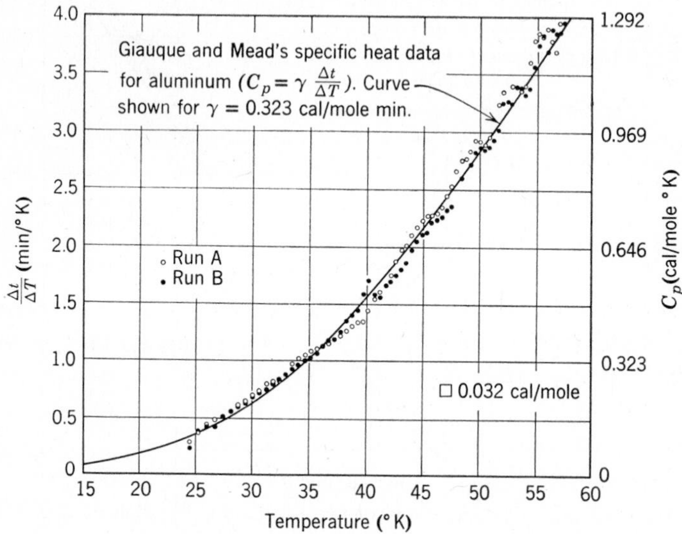

Fig. 10. The energy release associated with process I annealing in an aluminum single crystal. The sample was bombarded at 19.2°K for 4×10^{17} nvt. The solid line is the specific heat of aluminum as given by Giauque and Mead.[21] The energy release in the temperature range of 30 to 50°K does not exceed 0.1 cal/mole.

60°K. The integrated difference between the slopes of the two warm-up curves is then a measure of the stored energy. The results are indicated in Fig. 9. The number of interstitials can be estimated as 1×10^{19} from the resistivity change of about 2×10^{-9} $\mu\Omega$-cm and Blatt's scattering cross section of 1.4 $\mu\Omega$-cm/at. %. If all the interstitials were annihilated at vacancies or dislocations, about 5 ev would be liberated per annihilation so that a total energy of about 2.5 cal/mole would be liberated. The experimental results show that less than 0.1 cal/mole is liberated. These results mean either that there are considerably fewer defects than suggested by the resistivity data or that this process is not the result of the migration and annihilation of interstitial atoms. Measurements of the stored energy associated with this process have been made in like fashion at Oak Ridge for high purity aluminum single crystals. A very low energy-to-resistivity ratio was also found for this metal as can be seen from Fig. 10.

Consider now the details of the annealing kinetics which were recently studied at Oak Ridge. In the experiments originally planned,

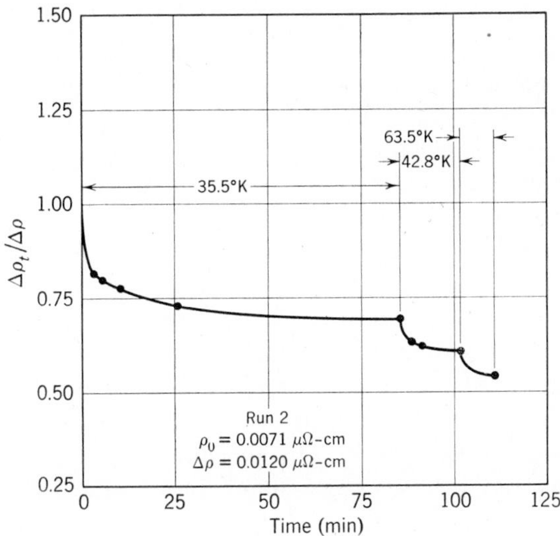

Fig. 11. Isothermal annealing of 99.996% aluminum single crystals at 35.5°K following a bombardment in the ORNL Graphite Reactor of 4×10^{17} nvt at 18°K. The annealing was done by a pulse technique with all measurements made at a reference temperature of 14°K. Approximately 15 sec were required to bring the sample from 14°K to equilibrium at 35.5°K. Following the isothermal anneal at 35.5°K, the sample was isothermally annealed at 42.8°K and at 63.5°K.

isothermal annealing was to be studied at a minimum of three temperatures so that an activation energy could be measured. The results of the first isothermal anneal for aluminum at 35.5°K are shown in Fig. 11. It was apparent that this was not a singly activated process with a low order of reaction. It did seem possible, however, that two processes were occurring, one accounting for the decrease in resistivity in the first pulse and the second for the tailing-off of the resistivity over longer times. Consequently, the temperature was raised and a second isothermal anneal was made at 42.8°K; and it can be seen that a similar curve results at this higher temperature. It thus became apparent that a single activated process did not occur in aluminum, but rather that a spectrum of activation energies was involved. The same conclusion is apparent in the case of copper, cobalt, and nickel. The results are seen in Figs. 12, 13, and 14. In the case of copper, additional isothermal data have been obtained, further resolving the change in resistivity which anneals during the first 3 min. The results are given in Fig. 15. It can be seen that significant annealing occurs during the first few seconds of the pulse. Recent work [22] on the annealing kinetics of copper bombarded at 18°K in hole #12 of the ORNL Graphite Reactor indicates that the previous history of the copper does not affect the process I annealing. Single crystals of high and relatively low purity copper, polycrystal samples, worked and annealed samples, and whisker samples * [22] were all bombarded and annealed together. An additional sample was also bombarded at 70°C for 10^{20} nvt prior to insertion. The annealing curves of all of these samples were the same in the range from 30 to 50°K. These data are suggestive of small distances of defect migration.

These three new pieces of information appear to make it difficult to account for the annealing by the motion and annihilation of interstitial atoms. The stored-energy data would necessitate the adoption of a scattering cross section for an interstitial in excess of that calculated by Overhauser and Gorman.[12] The annealing data also raise considerable objection to the concept that simple interstitial atoms are migrating with a unique activation energy; and a reaction rate of order no higher than two would be expected for such a process.

It may be possible, however, to concoct a scheme utilizing close Frenkel pairs of various separation distances with a range of activation energies for recombination. If the Kinchin and Pease [3] mechanism is operative as the previous discussion indicates, then it would appear that close pairs would be rather rare in a pure metal. Even without a full application of the Kinchin and Pease scheme, it would seem difficult to account for close pairs when the activation energy for the motion of an interstitial is so small.

There does not appear to be a satisfactory explanation for process I. One would like to assign the recovery of a frozen-in, liquid-like region to process I. The continuous spectrum of activation energies, the small number of jumps involved, and the low ratio of energy to resistivity would all be compatible with such a scheme. It hardly seems possible that process I can be completely explained from frozen-in debris arising from displacement or thermal spikes, since bombardment with 1.3-Mev electrons introduces defects which apparently anneal in ac-

* The copper whiskers were provided by the courtesy of D. Turnbull and his group at the General Electric Research Laboratory.

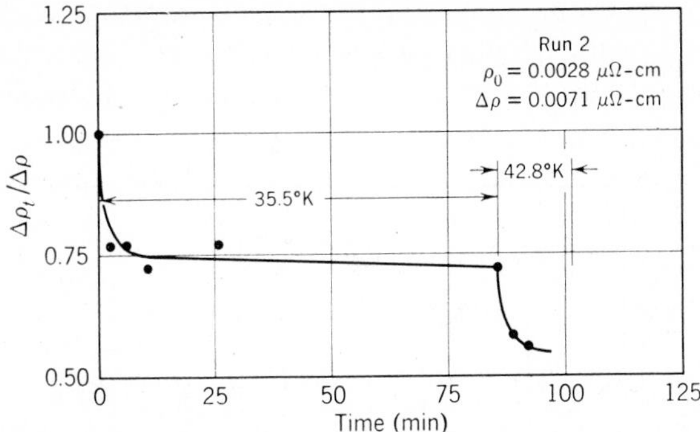

Fig. 12. Isothermal annealing of 99.999% copper single crystals following a bombardment in the ORNL Graphite Reactor of 4×10^{17} nvt at 18°K. The sample was bombarded and annealed simultaneously with the aluminum crystal whose results are shown in Fig. 11.

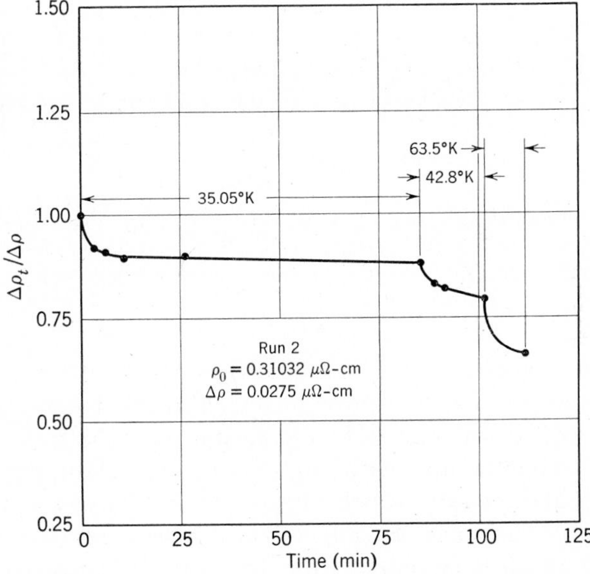

Fig. 13. Isothermal annealing of cobalt polycrystalline samples following a bombardment in the ORNL Graphite Reactor of 4×10^{17} nvt at 18°K. This sample was bombarded and annealed simultaneously with the aluminum crystal whose results are shown in Fig. 11.

cord with process I.[14] It may be that the crowdion concept can account for the spectrum of activation energies in process I. In a scheme utilizing the crowdion,[4] it is possible that the interstitial moves after it has been formed, in accordance with a modified Kinchin and Pease

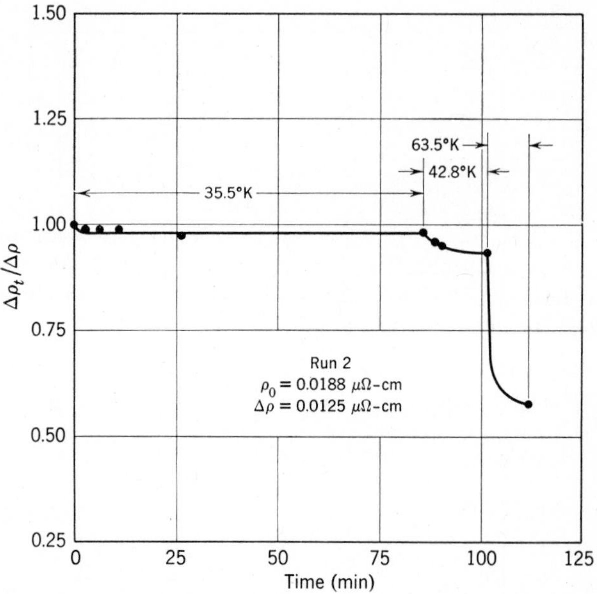

Fig. 14. Isothermal annealing of Mond process polycrystalline nickel following a bombardment of 4×10^{17} nvt at 18°K. This sample was bombarded and annealed simultaneously with the aluminum crystal whose results are shown in Fig. 11.

mechanism. For relatively high velocities, the interstitial will move in a random direction, dissipating energy due to frictional forces. After it has slowed to the point where its kinetic energy is an electron volt or so, relaxation occurs and a crowdion forms. The energy to move this defect and the rate at which it dissipates its energy will be small; consequently, the range of the crowdion will be large. It may be that the crowdions on being formed will migrate until they are within a few atom distances of a dislocation, vacancy, or impurity atom where the interacting strain fields will hold them while a few may be held in deeper traps by coming head-on with an impurity atom or other defect. It would appear that the freeing of the crowdion from these shallow traps by thermal activation could explain the low temperature anneal-

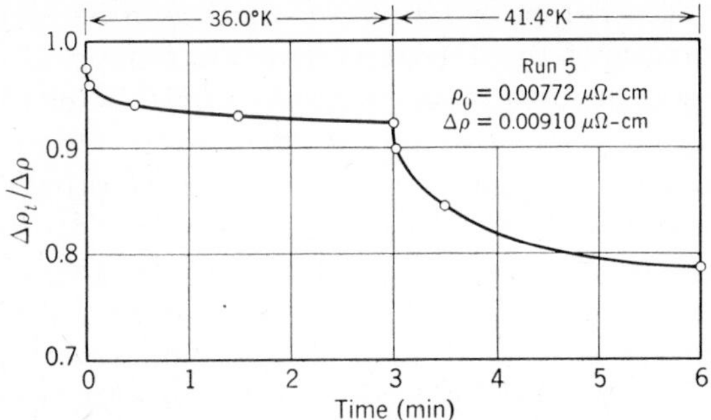

Fig. 15. The isothermal annealing at 36.0°K of zone refined copper (which was kindly furnished by W. G. Pfann of the Bell Telephone Laboratories) after bombardment in the ORNL Graphite Reactor at 17 ± 1°K for 8 × 10^{17} nvt. The sample was pulse-annealed with all measurements made at a reference temperature of 14°K. Following the anneal at 36.0°K the sample was isothermally annealed at 41.4°K. The first pulse of both anneals was made in a few seconds.

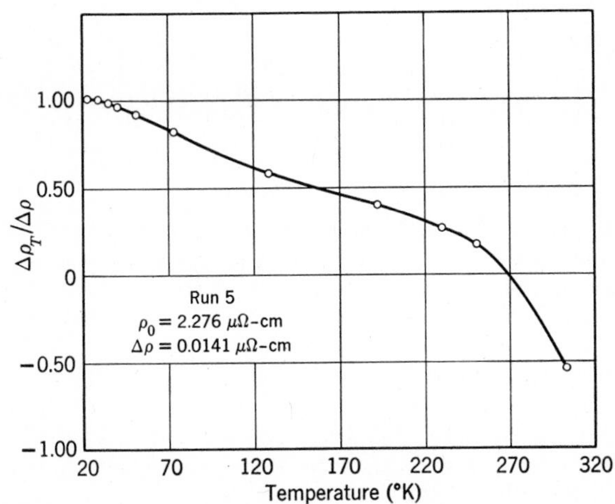

Fig. 16. Tempering curve for alpha-brass with 12.9 at. % zinc. The sample was bombarded in the hole #12 cryostat of the ORNL Graphite Reactor for 8 × 10^{17} nvt at 17 ± 1°K. The data were obtained by pulse-annealing with each pulse of 3-min duration. The measurements were made at a reference temperature of 14°K. The ordinate is the ratio of radiation-induced resistivity remaining after temperature T ($\Delta\rho_T$) to the radiation-induced resistivity ($\Delta\rho$).

ing peak * as they would then be free to wander about until they were captured by deeper traps or ran into a vacancy or an impurity atom. For bombardments of small nvt such as are encountered in hole #12, the ratio of vacancies to impurity atoms would be small so that in most cases impurity atoms would trap the defects. If the atom were of smaller size than the matrix atoms, then the resistivity would also decrease as the lattice strains would be reduced by the capture of a small atom. On the other hand, larger atoms would repulse the crowdion with only a slight, if any, reduction in resistivity. This scheme would satisfy most of the conditions required by experimental results, namely, a low ratio of energy to resistivity change and a spectrum of activation energies. Such a scheme would also explain why process I annealing did not occur in alpha-brass (see Fig. 16), as the density of impurities would be such that the crowdion would in the vast majority of cases be trapped by these defects immediately without the intermediate shallow traps. Whether or not this mechanism is the principal factor in process I will have to await further experimentation.

REFERENCES

1. E. Wigner, see F. Seitz, *Phys. Today,* **5,** No. 6, 6 (1952).
2. J. A. Brinkman, *J. Appl. Phys.,* **25,** 961 (1954).
3. G. H. Kinchin and R. S. Pease, *J. Nuclear Energy,* **1,** 200 (1955).
4. W. M. Lomer and A. H. Cottrell, *Phil. Mag.,* **46,** 711 (1955).
5. F. Seitz, *Discussion Faraday Soc.,* **5,** 271 (1949).
6. J. Neufeld and W. S. Snyder, *Phy. Rev.,* **99,** 1326 (1955).
7. W. Harrison and F. Seitz, *Phys. Rev.,* **98,** 1530 (1955).
8. F. Seitz and J. S. Koehler, *Solid State Physics,* II, Academic Press, New York (1956).
9. P. Jongenburger, *Phys. Rev.,* **90,** 710 (1953).
10. D. L. Dexter, *Phys. Rev.,* **87,** 768 (1954).
11. F. J. Blatt, *Phys. Rev.,* **99,** 1708 (1955).
12. A. W. Overhauser and R. L. Gorman, Technical Report 20, ONR, Contract N6-on-91, Cornell University, Ithaca.
13. H. G. Cooper, J. S. Koehler, and J. W. Marx, *Phys. Rev.,* **94,** 446 (1954).
14. J. W. Corbett, J. M. Denney, M. D. Fiske, and R. M. Walker, *Phys. Rev.,* **104,** 857 (1956).
15. C. J. Meechan and J. A. Brinkman, *Phys. Rev.,* **103,** 1193 (1956).
16. S. Siegel, *Phys. Rev.,* **75,** 1823 (1949).
17. R. S. Barnes and M. J. Makin, Atomic Energy Research Establishment M/R, 1626.
18. D. O. Thompson, D. K. Holmes, and T. H. Blewitt, to be published.
19. D. O. Thompson and D. K. Holmes, *J. Appl. Phys.,* **27,** 713 (1956).

* Since the crowdion is constrained to move in a line, raising the temperature will not permit combination of the crowdion and the other defect into a deeper trapping state.

20. H. Huntington, *Phys. Rev.*, **91,** 1092 (1955).
21. W. F. Giauque and P. R. Mead, *J. Amer. Chem. Soc.*, **63,** 1897 (1941).
22. T. H. Blewitt, R. R. Coltman, C. Klabunde, and T. S. Noggle, *J. Appl. Phys.*, **28,** 639 (1957).

ACKNOWLEDGMENTS

The authors wish to express thanks to D. S. Billington, whose encouragement and co-operation made this research possible. We should like to thank him, as well as R. H. Silsbee and H. C. Schweinler, for many valuable discussions. We are also indebted to J. K. Redman and C. Klabunde for their invaluable assistance in preparing this manuscript.

DISCUSSION

MOTT said that the conclusions seem to cast doubt on Koehler's proposal that there are no interstitials formed by cold work at low temperatures. KOEHLER remarked that there is a possibility that the purity of the sample may have an effect in that the interstitials may become trapped by the impurity atoms. MOTT wanted to know if there had been any controlled experiment of annealing with various amounts of impurities in the sample. KOEHLER replied that they had some isothermal annealing data which had not been analyzed as yet, but in which the amount of damage is quite a lot larger than the impurity content.

LOMER asked if it was clear that the low activation energy of 0.1 ev was a unique energy. For instance, if there were a spread of this energy by some kind of interaction with internal stresses, etc., then one might see something which is measurably not a single activation energy because of a 0.02-ev uncertainty. SEEGER reported that he and his co-workers were revising Huntington's calculations of the energy of formation and energy of migration for interstitials, and that the results indicated that the old values of the energy had to be changed. He no longer believes that 0.1 ev is a good value for the migration of interstitials in copper. LOMER replied that some calculations he had been making led to rather distressing conclusions. His calculations had shown that the forces at distances of two or three atomic separations were important in the calculation of point defect energies. On the other hand, the region of two to three atomic separations is precisely the region where one knows perfectly well that no adequate physical model is possible because there is no means available for the calculation of interaction energies and screening lengths, etc., to accuracies of 0.1 ev. Thus, in any calculation of this sort which Seeger reports, one should put in an uncertainty of at least 0.3 ev at the minimum.

SEITZ pointed out that the best available information indicates that the process observed in the annealing of radiation-damaged copper at low temperature is not monomolecular so that one is dealing either with a bimolecular recombination of Frenkel pairs, made somewhat complicated by the fact that the diffusing interstitial encounters trapping sites of varying depth, or with the rearrangement of a grosser imperfection. The recent work at the General Electric Research Laboratory by J. W. Corbett, J. M. Denney, M. D. Fiske, and R. M. Walker, using electron bombardment at helium temperatures, seems to make the first process most likely. Granting this, one faces the difficulty of explaining why the authors of the present paper observe so little stored energy during the annealing of electrical resistivity in neutron-irradiated specimens of copper. The easiest explanation is that the simple theory of displacements greatly overestimates the number of Frenkel pairs produced in copper, whereas the estimates of resistivity per Frenkel pair are much too low. This is the direction in which A. W. Overhauser has proposed modifications of the existing theory, although the corrections needed seem to be even larger than he has suggested. Measurements of changes in lattice dimensions during annealing which are now under way at the University of Illinois may add further important evidence to the present picture.

Index of Contributors*

Amelinckx, S., **3,** 51, 52, **55,** 352, 547
Ball, C. J., **353**
Barrett, C. S., **238,** 240, **419,** 491, 547
Blewitt, T. H., **179,** 422, 517, 547, 573, 574, 600, **603**
Boas, W., 240, **333,** 345, 346, **406,** 407, 490, 507, 600
Bredt, J. H., **587**
Chalmers, B., 115, **232,** 234, 477, 534
Coltman, R. R., **179, 603**
Cottrell, A. H., 207, 229, 230, 346, 404, 417, 418, 456, 457, 476, 478, 490, **509,** 514, 551, 573, 574, **577,** 579, 580, 586
Coulomb, P., **555**
Dash, W. C., **57**
Davis, R. S., **232**
Egli, P. H., 231
Eshelby, J. D., 91
Fisher, J. C., 162, 389, 417, 418, 477, **513,** 515
Frank, F. C., 51, 68, 163, **408,** 514, 515, 535
Friedel, J., **330,** 346, 405, 535, 536, **555,** 573, 574, 575, 576
Garstone, J., **391**
Gilman, J. J., **116,** 162, 163, 234, 357, 517, 543, 544, 574, 580
Granato, A., **425**
Hart, E. W., 346, 476, 477, 478
Henderson, J. W., **587**
Hirsch, P. B., 51, **92,** 113, 114, 163, **545,** 547
Hollomon, J. H., 516, 533
Holmes, D. K., **603**
Honeycombe, R. W. K., 234, 240, 346, **391,** 404, 405, 477, 490, 549
Horne, R. W., **92**
Ikeda, S., **548**
Johnston, W. G., 52, 91, **116,** 171, 357, 517
Koehler, J. S., 51, **208,** 230, 586, **587,** 601, 602, 623
Leibfried, G., 51, 52, 162, 230, 405, 456, 476, **495,** 501, 502, 507, 573
Lomer, W. M., 68, 162, 230, 237, 405, 455, 490, 502, 575, 580, 601, 623
Low, J. R., 114, 543
Lücke, K., 171, 230, 345, 403, 422, **425,** 455, 456, 500, 549, 573
Machlin, E. S., **164,** 171, 405
Maenhout-Van der Vorst, W., **55**
Mitchell, J. W., 68, **69,** 90, 91, 171, 515
Mott, N. F., 91, 162, 346, **350,** 351, 352, 455, **458,** 476, 477, 543, 574, 579, 602, 623
Nabarro, F. R. N., **235,** 237, 389, 476, 502, **521,** 523, 534
Noggle, T. S., **208, 603**
Pearson, G. L., **537**
Read, W. T., 68, 163, 233, 411, 412, 534, **537,** 543, 586
Redman, J. K., **179**
Seeger, A., 68, 90, 161, 162, 206, 207, 230, 239, **243,** 345, 346, **347,** 351, 352, 388, 389, 405, 456, 457, 489, 501, 503, **504,** 507, 534, 535, 579, 602, 623

* Boldface numbers refer to papers; other numbers refer to discussions.

Seitz, F., 162, 390, 412, 501, 601, 602, 624
Shockley, W., 114, 163, 233, 351, 352, 407, 478, 490, 501, 516, 533, 536, 551, 575, 576, **581,** 586
Suzuki, H., **172, 361,** 390, 405, **548,** 549, 551
Suzuki, T., **213,** 230, 231
Takeuchi, S., **548**
Thomson, R., 52, 91, 162, 575
Vreeland, T., 91, 544
Wadsworth, N. J., 477, **479,** 489, 490
Whelan, M. J., **92**
Wood, D. S., **413,** 417, 418, 543

Subject Index

Activation energy, to escape Cottrell locking, 365, 413
  to escape Suzuki pinning, 372
  for steady-state creep, 320
Aging, in silicon, 539
Alloy single crystals, 391–405
Alloying, effect on, cross slip, 318
  work hardening, 314
  work softening, 314
Alpha-band in alkali halides, 602
Alpha-brass, critical shear stress, 384
  deformation of thin crystals, 548–552
  short-range order, 385
  stored energy in cold work, 592
Aluminum, cyclic stressing, 459
  deformation substructure, 353
  direct observation of dislocations, 93
  evaporated films, 588–589
  fatigue testing, 481 ff.
  orientation dependence of flow, 266
  pressure effects on deformation, 238
  single crystal slip, 208
  stored energy during irradiation, 616
  substructure, 353
  surface sources, 232
  yield point, 419
Annealing, of neutron irradiation damage, 603–624
  of noble metals, 587–602
Annealing spectrum, 595–599, 609
Annihilation of dislocations, 39, 309
Arsenic in copper, 345
Atmospheres of impurities, 362, 364
  See also Cottrell atmosphere

Bardeen-Herring source, 41
Barriers, in radiation hardening, 573
Bauschinger effect, 279, 297, 463
Becker-Orowan theory, 396
Bend tests, lithium fluoride, 127
Binary alloys, 361–390, 391–405
Binding energy, in Cottrell effect, 413, 417
  interstitials at dislocations, 559
Birefringence, in KCl, 215 ff.
Bordoni peak, 428, 456, 502
Boundary junctions in Al, 99
Breakaway, 436
Breakaway stress, 438
Brittle-ductile transition in zinc, 279
Burgers vector, 546
Burgers vector of partial dislocations, 251

Cadmium, fatigue testing, 481
Calcium fluoride, decoration of dislocations, 5
Cavities, 555–576
  critical size, 564
  formed in quenching, 9
  growth, 564–566
  hardening by, 566–567, 573
  pinning by, 562
  shape, 562, 567–569
Chemical interaction (Suzuki hardening), 368–374, 380, 383, 386
Climb, in copper, 351
  of dislocations, 40, 51, 527, 535
  of extended dislocations, 352, 575
  and impurities, 350
  of networks, 44
  in silver, 166

Climb, of tilt boundaries, 44
Color change in metals, 406
Condensation, of Cottrell cloud, 559
of point defects, 560–562
Constriction of extended dislocations, 251
Copper, critical shear stress, 398
deformation at low temperature, 179
deformation of thin crystals, 548 ff.
deuteron bombardment, 589–590
easy glide, 397, 399
electron bombardment, 591
fatigue testing, 481
fracture at low temperature, 186, 195
internal friction, 427, 449
neutron irradiation, 196 ff., 590–591, 609
orientation dependence of stress-strain curve, 264
stored energy after irradiation, 616
temperature dependence of stress-strain curve, 264
twinning at low temperature, 179 ff.
Copper-germanium, 394
Copper-gold, critical shear stress, 394, 396
irradiation effects, 611, 612–616
Copper-nickel, critical shear stress, 378–382
Copper-silver, critical shear stress, 394, 397
easy glide, 396
Copper-zinc, critical shear stress, 384–387
Core of a dislocation, 504–508
Core energy, 406
Cottrell atmosphere, of impurities, 362, 364
of vacancies and interstitials, 556 ff.
Cottrell locking, 362–368, 378, 380, 382, 384, 390, 405, 413, 417, 450, 455, 461
Cottrell-Lomer dislocation (barrier), 258, 281 ff., 286, 287, 300, 355, 405, 464, 466, 469
Crack formation, 472–474
Creep, in close-packed metals, 319
of silver single crystals, 165
Critical shear stress, of alloy crystals, 361–390, 391–402
Critical shear stress, effect of impurities, 276
effect of surface polishing, 222
of lithium fluoride, 161
of pure metals and dilute alloys, 271
theory, 271
See also Flow stress
Cross slip, 308, 331, 467, 477
double, 308
effect of solutes, 318
of extended dislocations, 255
observed in Al, 107
over barriers, 300
Crowdions, 595, 611–612, 614, 620
Cyclic stressing, 469–475
Cyclotron bombardment of copper, 606
Cylinder, interaction with screw dislocation, 569–572

Decoration of dislocations, in calcium fluoride, 5
mechanism in sodium chloride, 13
observation techniques, 13, 57
in potassium chloride, 5
in silicon, 57–67
in silver halides, 74–91
in sodium chloride, 4
in transparent crystals, 3–56
Deformation twinning in copper at low temperatures, 179–207
Dekinking of whiskers, 521–536
Delayed yielding, 543
Dendritic growth of glide bands in lithium fluoride, 155
Density change in cold work, 333 ff., 345, 347
Deuteron irradiation, 589–590
Diffusion, of copper in germanium, 408–412
along dislocations, 408, 564
of oxygen in silicon, 539
of vacancies, 527, 583
Dilatation around a dislocation, 504–508
Dimensional changes in quenched gold, 601
Discontinuous slip in copper, 184
Dislocation bursts, 461–463
Dislocation climb, 40, 51, 350
See also Climb

Dislocation damping, *see* Internal friction
Dislocation density, 442
in aluminum, 97
after cold work, 337, 347
in gold, 109
in lithium fluoride, 119, 125
in palladium, 109
in silicon, 57
in silver, 109
Dislocation energy, examined at node points, 52
Dislocation helices, 41
Dislocation interactions, with boundaries, 108, 355, 357
with crossing dislocations, 48
with glide bands, 357
Dislocation loops, 41, 91, 115, 513–517, 525–526
formed in quenching, 139
intersection, 41
in lithium fluoride, 162
prismatic, 513–517
Dislocation movement, in aluminum, 95, 104, 107
by climb, 527
by glide, 524
in lithium fluoride, 117, 142
Dislocation multiplication, in LiF, 142, 146
Dislocation networks, *see* Networks of dislocations
Dislocation nodes, *see* Nodes of dislocations
Dislocation pile-up, *see* Pile-up of dislocations
Dislocation pinning, in nets, 38
by precipitates, 37
Dislocation pipes, 407, 412
Dislocation sources, *see* Sources of dislocations
Dislocation walls, 521–536
Dislocations in close-packed crystals, 247
Dislocations, resistivity of, 340, 348
Disordering by irradiation, 613
Displacements, 664
Divacancies, 596–597
Double cross slip, 308
Dynamic loss, 437
Dynamical hypothesis for critical shear stress, 275
Dynamical recovery, 263
face-centered cubic metals, 299

Easy glide, in alloys, 397–402
in face-centered cubic metals, 281
size dependence, 548–552
Elastic modulus, effect of irradiation, 613–614
in internal friction studies, 425–455
Electrical charge on a dislocation, 505
Electrical interaction with impurities, 368
Electron bombardment, of copper, 591, 610, 624
of surface, 585
Electron microscope study of dislocations, 93
Energy dissipation in fatigue, 479–491
Energy of jogs, 534, 535
Entropy of a dislocation, 501, 502
Etch pits, dislocation, in lithium fluoride, 116–163
in metals and alloys, 172
in silicon, 57
in silver, 164
in silver halide, 74
Evaporated films, 588–589
Extended dislocations, climb, 352
cross slip, 255, 331
description, 251
Extinction contours in Al, 97, 104
Extrusions in fatigue, 477

Face-centered cubic metals, glide and work hardening, 243–329
Face-centered cubic slip, 511–512
Fatigue, 471–475, 479–491
cracks, 485, 489
extrusions, 477, 490
hardening, 481–482
life, 485
role of cross slip, 477
softening, 482–488
stored energy, 472, 473
F-centers in decorated NaCl, 9
Fermi energy, 406
Fine slip, 209, 468

Flow stress, effect of impurities, 276
in pure metals and dilute alloys, 271
and substructure, 354
temperature dependence, 273
See also Critical shear stress
Forest of dislocations, 272, 330, 466, 468
effect on flow stress, 288
Fracture, 468–469, 477
of copper at low temperature, 186, 187, 195
of silicon, 537 ff.
Fragmentation of slip bands, 306
Frank-Read source, 114, 375, 376, 377, 404, 436, 459, 464, 513 ff.
in silicon, 63
theory for critical shear stress, 275
vacancy formation by, 470–471
Frenkel pair, recombination, 618, 624
scattering cross section, 604, 606

Gamma brass, fatigue testing, 491
Germanium, copper diffusion, 408–412
dislocation damping, 447
self-diffusion, 410
Glide, in aluminum, 208
in close-packed metals, 243–329
Glide band formation, during fatigue, 472
in lithium fluoride, 116–163
in metals, 303
from single dislocations, 145
Glide bands as obstacles, 357
Glide distance in hexagonal metals, 279
Glide markings, 465 ff.
Glissile dislocations, 261
Gold, quenching, 588
quenching and annealing, 601
stress-strain curve, 262
Goldschmidt atomic diameter, effect on alloy strength, 393–394
Gold-silver alloys, critical shear stress, 382–383, 389
Gold-silver-copper alloys, 406
Grain boundaries in silver halides, 81

Hardening, by cavities, 566–567
in fatigue, 481–482
of secondary systems, 297
Hardness change in cold work, 333 ff.
Helices of dislocations, 41
Hexagonal close-packed metals, glide and work hardening, 243
High pressure, effect on plastic deformation, 238

Image forces, 569–570, 571
Impurities, and critical shear stress, 276
at dislocations, 540
effect on annealing, 600
at stacking faults, 368, 372
and stored energy, 336
Interaction of crossing dislocations, 48
Internal friction, dislocation density effect, 442
dislocation theories of, 434–435
due to dislocations, 403, 405, 422, 425, 457
effect of impurities, 432, 441
effect of irradiation, 613–614
effect of plastic deformation, 430
frequency dependence, 447
loop length dependence, 449
orientation effect, 430, 443, 451
residual, 428, 435, 445
strain-amplitude dependent, 440–445
temperature dependence, 443, 450
time dependence, 445
Internal latent image, 74
Internal stress field, 272
Intersection of dislocation rings, 41
Intersection of dislocations, 39, 229, 509–512
Interstitial production, 469–471, 474
during glide, 509–512, 623
by localized radiation damage, 581–585
at low temperature, 602
by low-temperature cold work, 623
Interstitials, annealing, 595
interaction with dislocations, 559
Interstitialcy migration, 611–614
Ion bombardment, 582–584, 586
Iron-nickel alloy, thermal etching, 172

Joffé effect, 215, 225
Jogs, 321, 469, 528–530, 534, 538
energy, 321, 534, 535
in extended dislocations, 575
formation, 321, 575
glide resistance, 578, 579

Jogs, and impurities, 350
motion, 215, 225, 509
Johnson noise, 501
Junctions, of subboundaries, 44, 51
of tilt boundaries, 45

Kinetic energy of dislocations, 496
Kink bands, 399
Kinks in whiskers, 521–536, 545–547
Kirkendall effect, 556

Latent image, internal in silver halides, 74
Latent strain hardening, 279, 297
Lattice defects in deformed crystals, 333–346
Lattice parameter changes in cold work, 345
Lattice resistance to dislocation motion in lithium fluoride, 159
Lithium fluoride, dislocation density, 119, 125
dislocation movement, 117
dislocation multiplication, 142
etching of dislocations, 116–161
glide band formation, 145
mechanical tests, 126–132
neutron irradiation, 574
polishing chemically, 121
Localized radiation damage, 581–585
Low-angle X-ray scattering in cold-worked crystals, 506

Magnetoresistance in cold-worked metals, 598
Matthiessen's rule, 506
Mechanical testing of lithium fluoride, 126–132
Microcracks, 341, 346, 347
Microstrain, 413
Modulus change, 425–457
Mott-Nabarro theory, 362, 393, 435
Multiplication of dislocations in lithium fluoride, 142

Networks of dislocations, 14
in aluminum, 101
climb, 44
hexagonal, 15
parallel lines, 31
Networks of dislocations, in polygonized sodium chloride, 31
in silver halides, 76, 78
singularities, 17
square, 30
in transparent crystals, 3–50
Neutron irradiation, aluminum, 608, 616, 617
annealing, 603–624
cobalt, 618, 619
copper, 196 ff., 590–591
copper-gold, 611
dislocation mobility, 574
elastic constants, 612
internal friction, 612
iron, 607
low-temperature slip and twinning of copper, 196 ff.
metals, 603–624
nickel, 608, 620
numbers of defects, 604–609
resistivity change, 607
uranium, 556
zinc, 621
Nickel, density change, 334 ff.
pressure effect on deformation, 238
resistivity change, 334 ff.
stored energy, 334 ff.
yield point, 419
Nodes of dislocations, in aluminum, 99, 101
analysis, 52
in sodium chloride, 13
Nonconservative jog motion, 509
Nonlinearity of elastic laws, 504–508
Nonorthogonal glide systems, 511
Nuclear irradiation, annealing, 589–590
Nucleation of dislocations, 517
in lithium fluoride, 132, 139, 142, 155

Order-disorder, 407
Orientation dependence of work hardening, 283
Orthogonal slip, 510
Oxide film, interaction with dislocations, 107, 114
Oxygen in silicon, 537, 539–540

Partial dislocations, 251
Peierls force, 456

Peierls force, and critical sheer stress, 275
in lithium fluoride, 544
in silicon, 541, 543
Photolytic silver on dislocation lines, 88, 91
Pile-up of dislocations, 258, 293, 300, 301, 355, 401, 468, 476
against glide bands, 357
in silver, 165
at subboundaries, 357
Pinning of dislocations, 436
by cavities, 562
in networks, 38
by point defects, 573
by precipitates, 37
Pinning points, 495
Platelets, effect on climb, 562
Platelets of interstitials, 559
Point defects, by dislocation interactions, 229, 509–512
effect on hardness, 577–578
during irradiation, 604–608
in localized radiation damage, 584–586
Polishing, chemical, of lithium fluoride, 121
of silver halides, 73
Polishing, effect on plastic properties of KCl, 215
Polygonization, 535
of silver halides, 76
of sodium chloride, 31, 35
walls, 530
Potassium chloride, decoration of dislocations, 5, 55
dislocation source, 55
plastic deformation, 215 ff.
surface sources, 215
work hardening, 221 ff.
Potential energy of a dislocation, 496
Potential trough, 498
Precipitation, in decorated sodium chloride, 8
hardening, 376, 402
of vacancies, 513–520, 555–576
Pressure, effect on deformation, 243
Preyield microstrain, 413–418
Prismatic dislocation loops, 162, 513–517
Prismatic dislocations, 41

Quenching, 556
of gold, 588, 601
Quench hardening, 577–580

Radiation damage, anneal, 587–598, 603–624
hardening, 577–580
at surface, 516, 582
Radiation damping, 501
Radiation loss, 447
Recombination of Frenkel pairs, 618, 624
Recovery of hexagonal close-packed metals, 277
Recrystallization, 339, 597
Residual damping, 428, 435, 445
Resistance to dislocation motion, 368
See also Peierls force
Resistivity change, in cold work, 333 ff., 337, 347, 591–594, 598
upon irradiation, 604 ff.
Resistivity of dislocations, 505, 598
of point defects, 604–605
of stacking fault, 348, 506, 598
Reverse stressing, 458–478
Rings of dislocations, 41

Scattering of electrons, by dislocations, 505
by stacking faults, 506
Screw dislocation, interaction with hollow cylinder, 569–572
Segregation in alloys, 394
Sessile dislocations, 261
Short-range order hardening, 277, 368, 372–374, 376, 382, 385
Silicon, decoration of dislocations, 57–68
deformation, 58, 537–544
dislocation density, 57
dislocation etch pits, 57
fracture, 537–544
oxygen in, 189
whiskers, 537–544
yield point, 537 ff.
Silver, precipitates in NaCl, 9
thermal etch pits, 164–171
Silver halides, chemical polishing, 73
decoration of dislocations, 74
deformation, 81

Silver halides, pure material preparation, 71
single crystal growth, 72
Size effect, crystal deformation, 537–544, 548–552
easy glide, 548–552
stress-strain curve, 269
Slip, *see* Glide
Slip lines, 465 ff.
Sodium chloride, damage during cleavage, 162
decoration of dislocations, 4
deformation of single crystals, 235
Solutes, effect on cross slip, 318
Solution hardening, 361–405
Sources of dislocations, 375, 376, 513–517
in aluminum, 108
Bardeen-Herring, 41
in networks, 38
in potassium chloride, 55
in silicon, 63
See also Frank-Read source
Spiral whiskers, 547
Stacking faults, energy, 317, 343, 371, 380, 383, 386
f.c.c. metals, 247
impurity interaction, 368
nickel, 343
resistivity, 342, 348, 506, 598
surface tension, 255
Stages of deformation, 220, 261 ff., 270, 464
stage I, 280, 464
stage II, 287, 464
stage III, 298, 330, 466
Stages in magnetic behavior, 265
Static hysteresis loss, 438
Steady-state creep in metals, 319, 320
Stored energy, in cold work, 333 ff., 347, 592
in fatigue, 472, 490
in radiation damage, 616
release during anneal, 333 ff.
Strain aging, 421
Strain energy of impurities at a stacking fault, 372
Strain-rate dependence of yield stress, 128
Stress recovery, 114
Stress-strain curves of face-centered cubic metals, 261 ff.
Subboundaries, as obstacles, 354, 357
in silver halides, 78
spacing of dislocations, 94, 98
splitting at surface, 81, 91
Subboundary junctions, 44, 51
Subgrain size and flow stress, 354
Substructure, in aluminum, 97, 109, 353 ff.
in silver halides, 76
Surface perfection, effect on yield stress, 129
Surface radiation damage, 582
Surface as source of slip, 213–231, 232, 551
Surface sources, in aluminum, 232
and plastic flow in copper, 229
and plastic flow in KCl, 215 ff.
Suzuki hardening (chemical interaction), 368–372

Taylor hardening, 165, 275
Thermal etch pits, in metals and alloys, 172–178
in silver, 164–171
Thermal forces on obstacles, 498
Thermal motion of dislocations, 495–503
Thermal spike, 611
Thermal stresses in lithium fluoride, 141
Tilt boundaries, climb, 44
junctions, 45
in silver halides, 78
Tin whiskers, 545–546
Transient creep in metals, 323
Twinning of copper at low temperature, 179–207
Twist boundaries in silver halides, 78
Twisting, effect on tensile flow stress, 289 ff.
Twist of whiskers, 545

Uranium, neutron irradiation, 556

Vacancies, annealing, 595
clusters, 602
in cold-worked metals, 334
in deformed germanium, 411
formation, 469–471, 474

Vacancies, in glide, 509–512
at jogs, 529
at low temperature, 602
internal friction, 433
in localized radiation damage, 581–585
migration, 532
during climb, 527
platelets, 513
precipitation, 514–516, 555–576
resistivity of, 348
supersaturation, 556
Volume change due to a dislocation, 347, 504–508

Whisker, dekinking, 521–536
kinks, 546–547
in silicon, 537–544
twist in, 545
Work hardening, 458–478
close-packed metals, 243
effect of alloying, 314
face-centered cubic crystals, 281
Work hardening, orientation dependence, 281
potassium chloride, 221 ff.
temperature dependence, 330
Work-hardening coefficient, 268, 285
Work softening, effect of alloying, 314
face-centered cubic metals, 299

X-ray evidence of crystal perfection in LiF, 127
X-ray low-angle scattering, 506

Yield point, alloys, 389, 390
aluminum, 419
nickel, 419
steel, 413, 418
Yield strength of alloys, 361–390
Yield stress, 375, 377
lithium fluoride, 128
silicon, 539, 541
strain-rate dependence, 128

Zinc, reverse stressing, 460–461